ENCYCLOPEDIA OF TANKS

Other books by Duncan Crow

Non-fiction

The British Film Industry
Henry Wikoff, The American Chevalier
World in Action (Two Series)
The Man of Push and Go
Theresa, The Story of the Yelverton Case
How it Works
The Victorian Woman
British and Commonwealth Armoured Formations
    1919-1946
U.S. Armour – Cavalry 1919-1967
Panzer Divisions (with Brigadier H. B. C. Watkins)

Fiction
The First Summer
The Crimson Petal

Other books by Robert J. Icks

Non-fiction

Fighting Tanks since 1919 (with R. E. Hones and
    G. H. Rarey)
Heigl's Taschenbuch der Tanks (with O. H. Hacker,
    Otto Marker and G. P. von Sezschwitz)
Tanks and Armoured Vehicles
Modern U.S. Armoured Support Vehicles
Famous Tank Battles

Picture Credits

A.A.I. Corporation   49, 66
Enrique Garcia Albors   5
An Account of Our Stewardship, Vauxhall
    Motors   23
Armor   355
Austrian Official   116, 117
Author   444
Aviation Week   18
Baltimore Sun   382
Fabio Basilico   294
Bell Aerosystems Company   98
Bofors A-B.   83
Borg-Warner Corporation   447
Bristol Aircraft   12
British Army Film Unit   260
British Ministry of Supply   262, 263, 277
British War Office   33, 228, 229, 247, 323
Lt. Col. M. G. Burges-Short   219
Canadian Official   120, 121, 122
Peter Chamberlain   184, 251, 275
Chrysler Corporation   82, 97
A. J. Clemens   1, 52, 56, 57, 58, 67, 74, 78, 79
Michel Christesco   73
Comando de Arsenales, Argentine Army   110
Corazzotti Italiani, Pafi, Faletti & Fiore   298
D&PS Test Facilities and Capabilities, Aberdeen
    Proving Ground   20, 407
Daimler-Benz Archives   163, 164, 168
Deutsche Presse Agentur GmbH courtsey
    Herman Vogt   209
Dutch Defence Ministry   60
Etablissement Cinematographique des Armees
    15, 136, 138, 140, 144, 145, 146, 148, 149, 153,
    156, 157, 162, 329
Evolution of the Tank, Sueter   123
R. W. Faris   283
Ferranti Ltd.   85
Food Machinery Corporation   454
Ford-Sperry   435
French Embassy   128, 152
Major General Stephen O. Fuqua   347
General Motors Corporation   44, 434
German Official   17, 41, 92, 142, 166, 167, 175,
    179, 180, 185, 183, 186, 189, 193, 194, 201,
    335, 341
Christian Gurtner   63, 133, 135, 143, 160
O. H. Hacker   114, 139
Heeres Film und Lichtbild Stelle (Austria)
    116, 117
Herkenning   330

Histoire de l'Armee Motorisee, Duvignac
    129, 137
Lt. Gen. Tomio Hara   319, 320
R. P. Hunnicutt   251, 383, 384
Illustrated Record of German Weapons, British
    War Office   71, 192
Imperial War Museum   3, 4, 26, 28, 29, 32, 36,
    38, 46, 84, 99, 130, 154, 176, 182, 212, 215,
    217, 221, 222, 227, 230, 237, 238, 242, 244,
    245, 250, 253, 255, 256, 257, 258, 261, 263,
    265, 266, 267, 269, 271, 272, 278, 279, 316,
    459,
Ingersoll-Kalamazoo Division, Borg-Warner
    Corporation   450, 451
Colonel Shunzo Inoma   306, 309, 313, 317
Interavia   155
International News   314
Israeli Defence Department   292
Colonel G. B. Jarrett   13, 190, 191, 274, 296,
    311, 318, 345, 352, 390, 410, 412, 413
Captain E. Klima   287
Landsverk A-B.   353
R. G. Le Tourneau Inc.   40
Major J. W. Loop   21, 336, 443
John Loop   448
Marmon-Herrington Inc.   119, 372, 373
Military Review   346
F. Mitchell   8, 88, 216, 218
Mitsubishi Industries Ltd.   321
National Waterlift Company   87
Nephadsereguenk, Hungarian War Ministry
    26, 45
C. J. Nuttall Jr.   429
R. M. Ogorkiewicz   213, 243
Ordnance   19, 367
Oto-Melara   303
Ordnance Museum, Aberdeen Proving Ground
    35, 108, 177, 187, 195, 422, 423
Photographic Publications Ltd.   305
Y. Poelman de Brabandere   27, 132, 458
Colonel A. W. Portella F. Alves   118
Przeglad Wojsk Pancernych, Polish Defence
    Ministry   325
Sergeant Jackie Puckett, U.S. Armor School
    76
Rheinstahl Henschel A.G.   203
Rheinmetall GmbH   208
Colonel G. H. Rarey   361
Royal Armoured Corps Tank Museum Library
    10, 30, 105, 112, 171, 199, 222, 224, 226, 229,

230, 233, 236, 239, 240, 241, 246, 249, 252,
    276, 280
S.O.M.U.A.   151
A. L. T. Sassoon   268, 270
Scherl Bilderdienst   327
Dott. Umberto Signoriello   290, 298, 302, 334
Skoda   124, 127
Armin Sohns   126, 181, 307
W. J. Spielberger   141, 171, 188
Sir Albert Stern   284
Storia Della Motorizzazione, Pugnani   300,
    301
Nicholas Straussler   16, 248
Sturm-Artillerie, Turnau und Kurowski   328
Raymond Surlemont   134
Swiss Defence Ministry   357
Akira Takeuchi   308
Tank Museum Guide, Royal Armoured Corps
    Tank Museum   147
Tojhusmuseet, Copenhagen   197
Pierre Touzin   161
Sir William Tritton   89, 220
Garrett Underhill   342
Union Metal Manufacturing Company   37
UPI-Compix   169, 172, 286, 322, 334, 371
U.S. Army   7, 25, 31, 39, 53, 54, 62, 64, 72, 77,
    86, 95, 107, 315, 393, 398, 403, 405, 406, 416,
    417, 438, 439, 440, 441, 445, 446
U.S. Army Chemical Corps   392
U.S. Army Far East Headquarters   310
U.S. Army Ordnance Department   24, 43, 68,
    70, 93, 101, 102, 109, 131, 262, 358, 359, 360,
    363, 364, 365, 368, 369, 374, 375, 376, 377,
    379, 378, 380, 381, 385, 388, 389, 391, 395,
    397, 399, 402, 408, 409, 411, 414, 415, 418,
    419, 420, 421, 423, 424, 426, 427, 428, 430,
    431, 432, 433, 434, 449, 456, 457
U.S. Army Signal Corps   34, 198, 297, 425
U.S. Coast Guard   106
U.S. Information Agency   196
U.S. Marine Corps   22 (Mark Kaufman),
    312, 366, 452, 453, 455
B. H. Vanderveen   223, 252, 270, 281, 322, 354
Vickers-Armstrong Ltd.   231, 234, 235, 291
George N. Vulgaris   150
Warpics   9
B. T. White   100, 271
Dr. Fritz Wiener   174, 178
Wozy Bojowe, Magnuski   115
Brigadier General D. Willikens   204, 205, 206

Rare 1943 colour photograph of a
German PzKpfw VI Ausf E, Tiger I.
(Chris Ellis Collection)

Encyclopedia
of
Tanks

Duncan Crow
and
Robert J. Icks

Barrie & Jenkins
London

First published in 1975 by:
Barrie & Jenkins Limited,
24 Highbury Crescent,
London N5 1RX

ISBN 0 214 20080 9

Designed and produced by:
Carter Nash Cameron Limited,
25 Lloyd Baker Street,
London WC1X 9AT

Printed by:
Waterlow (Dunstable) Limited,
George Street,
Dunstable,
Bedfordshire LU6 1NR

Abbreviations

A/A   anti-aircraft gun.
A.P.C.   armoured personnel carrier.
A.R.V.   armoured recovery vehicle.
A/T   anti-tank gun.
A.V.R.E.   armoured vehicle, Royal Engineers.
D.B.   Daimler-Benz.
D.D.   duplex-drive.
F.R.G.   Federal Republic of Germany.
F.T.   Faible Tonnage, Light Weight (tank).
G.M.C.   General Motors Corporation.
HP   horsepower.
IR   infrared.
K-wagon   giant tank.

L   length of gun in relation to the diameter of the bore.
LaS   Landwirtschafthiher Schlepper, agricultural tractor.
LK   Leichte Kampfwagon, light tank.
MAN   Maschinenfabrik Augsburg Nurnburg.
M.B.T.   main battle tank.
mg   machine-gun
pdr   pounder.
SdKfz   Sonderkraftfahrzeug, special purpose vehicle.
sIG   schwere Infanteriegeschütz, heavy infantry gun.
Sfl   Selbstfahrlafette, self-propelled carriage.
StuH   Sturm Haubitze, assault howitzer.
StuK   Sturm Kanon, assault cannon.
StuM   Sturm Moerser, assault mortar.
T.U.F.   Tank und Fleiger.

Basic Gun Data

NOTE: Various discrepancies may be noted. This is because the length in calibres is given as ascribed by the country concerned and the bases used are not necessarily uniform. M/V is in feet per second.

Country	Gun	Calibre (inches)	Length	M/V	Year
USA	37mm	1.46	L/57	2900	1940
	75mm Pack	2.95	L/18	1270	1930
	75mm M1897	2.95	L/36	2000	1924
	75mm M2	2.95	L/31	1930	1941
	75mm M3	2.95	L/40	2030	1941
	75mm M6	2.95	L/39	2030	1942
	3" M7	3.0	L/53	3400	1942
	76mm	3.0	L/53	2600	1942
	76mm T91E3	3.0	L/55	3400	1943
	90mm	3.543	L/53	3350	1943
	90mm	3.543	L/73	3750	1943
	105mm How	4.134	L/25	1550	1942
	105mm Gun	4.134	L/67	3700	1943
	120mm	4.7	L/62	3800	1943
GB	6pdr	2.244	L/45.6	1765	1915
	6pdr	2.244	L/25.4	1350	1916
	3pdr I	1.85	L/35.8	1750	1923
	3pdr II	1.85	L/45.7	1850	1925
	3" How	3.0	L/28.5	600	1926
	2pdr	1.575	L/57	2800	1935
	6pdr III	2.244	L/49	2800	1941
	6pdr V	2.244	L/57	2965	1942
	3.7" Mortar	3.7	L/17	620	1939
	95mm How	3.7	L/23.7	1075	1942
	75mm V	2.953	L/41.6	2030	1942
	77mm	3.0	L/56	2600	1943
	17pdr	3.0	L/62.9	2900	1942
	17pdr VII	3.0	L/62.9	3950	1950
	20pdr	3.3	L/72.9	3300	1950
	120mm	4.7	L/63		1965
Germany	3.7cm	1.46	L/45	2500	1938
	5cm	1.97	L/42	3240	1938
	5cm	1.97	L/60	3700	1939
	7.5cm	2.95	L/24	1263	1938
	7.5cm	2.95	L/43	2428	1940
	7.5cm	2.95	L/48	2461	1940
	7.5cm	2.95	L/70	3068	1942
	8.8cm	3.46	L/56	2600	1936
	8.8cm	3.46	L/71	3720	1943
	10.5cm	4.134	L/28		
	10.5cm	4.134	L/68		
	12.8cm	5.039	L/55	3080	1944
	15cm	5.90	L/12	780	1933
	15cm	5.90	L/29.5		
France	3.7cm	1.46	L/21	1273	1917
	3.7cm	1.46	L/33	2300	1938
	4.7cm	1.85	L/34	2200	1935
	7.5cm	2.95	L/36	1788	1898
	7.5cm	2.95	L/17.1	1500	1932
	7.5cm	2.95	L/50	3280	1950
	7.5cm	2.95	L/61.5	3750	1955
	10.5cm	4.134		3800	1960
USSR	3.7cm	1.46	L/44	2500	1930
	3.7cm	1.46	L/71.8	2900	1935
	4.5cm	1.772	L/46	2700	1936
	7.62cm	3.0	L/18.8		1930
	7.62cm	3.0	L/34.7		1938
	7.62cm	3.0	L/47.3	2172	1939
	8.5cm	3.346	L/44		1942
	8.5cm	3.346	L/55.8	2600	1944
	10.0cm	3.937			1944
	12.2cm	4.803	L/49		1939
	15.2cm	5.98	L/31.9		1939

Contents

Foreword

This work is perhaps best described as a synthesis. It was prepared with the help of many people living in many countries–so many people indeed, that having thought anxiously about it, the authors decided not to risk the solecism of unintentionally omitting anyone from the list of well over a hundred who have helped us. We have therefore gone to the opposite and draconian extreme of not thanking anyone personally. To all our friends and colleagues in the field of armoured fighting vehicles whose names begin from A to Z–and you know who you are–we thank you for the help you have given us over the years and hope that this book will add something to that store of knowledge you already have.

It is, as you will see, a bringing together in one volume of all the information we have collected and collated over many years from all parts of the world. Importantly, we have brought into the main body of the tank canon the galaxy of experimental types which form the connective tissue in the progress of design. Thus, while not in any way ignoring the standard and well-known types of tank, we have, in selecting the illustrations, laid the emphasis on the lesser known vehicles.

Dimensions and similar data are included where known, based as far as possible on official information. Lesser known vehicles can be evaluated without difficulty from the data of the standard vehicle to which they are linked. Conversion tables between English and metric measurements are included in an appendix.

A note of warning about official data: identical track-laying vehicles off the same assembly line will invariably show some dimensional variations. Later in the tank's life, track wear, the working-in of the suspension components, and other settling that is the natural concomitant to use will also cause dimensional variations. In addition, for those whose enthusiasm outrides their collative prudence, we would remind them that a great deal of the unofficial data about tanks which has been published and re-published and then used again in one tank book after another has been found to have been based on guesswork. Need we say, therefore, that a certain amount of care should be exercised in citing them. One specific example of this is that some authors have overlooked the fact that English and metric horsepower are not the same and that, in the United States, there is a very definite difference between rated horsepower and brake horsepower.

Notwithstanding our decision not to list by name the plethora of people who have helped us in making this book possible we naturally, in accordance with civilized custom, give credit elsewhere in the book for the illustrations which we hope lend a wealth of examples to the fascinating mystique of THE TANK.

PART ONE

Armoured Vehicle
Types and Their Uses

1. Early Development

The armoured fighting vehicle of the twentieth century is a product of the internal combustion engine. But the idea behind such a vehicle is as old as warfare itself: to strike without being struck. From the war chariots of ancient civilizations through the mediaeval knights in armour to today's Chieftain, Leopard, AMX30, M60 and T62, the triple characteristics of such a weapons system have changed greatly in performance, but not at all in principle: offensive capability and protection allied to mobility.

The beginning of the automotive age in 1887, when Gottlieb Daimler produced the first petrol-driven motor car, opened the way for revolutionary changes in the degree of military and social mobility. Added to this were new inventions of processes for the production of steel; the making of the Paixhans gun with its explosive shell; the cast-steel rifled cannon; the machine-gun. All these, together with other inventions, ushered in revolutionary changes in the offensive and protective characteristics that could be given to armoured fighting vehicles.

The application of the automobile for military purposes was the result of the inventors' initiative rather than the military's acumen. When George V told the Canadian Motor Machine Gun Brigade at Aldershot in June 1915 that he thought they and their armoured cars would be 'very useful' on the Western Front he was far from

1
Schematic drawing of a Chieftain illustrating nomenclature.

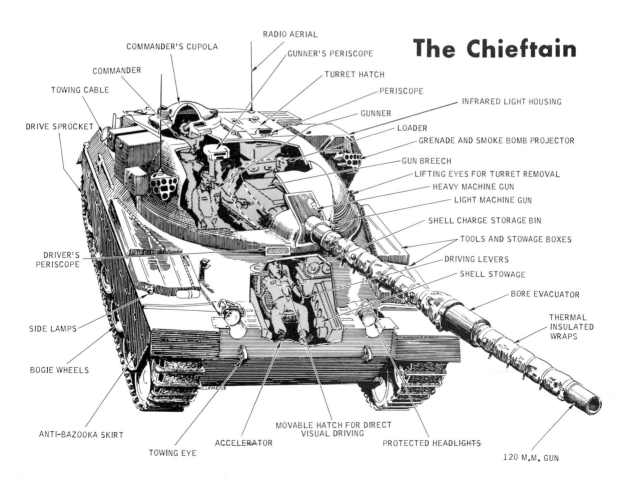

The Chieftain

RADIO AERIAL
COMMANDER'S CUPOLA
GUNNER'S PERISCOPE
COMMANDER
TURRET HATCH
TOWING CABLE
PERISCOPE
INFRARED LIGHT HOUSING
DRIVE SPROCKET
GUNNER
LOADER
GRENADE AND SMOKE BOMB PROJECTOR
GUN BREECH
LIFTING EYES FOR TURRET REMOVAL
HEAVY MACHINE GUN
LIGHT MACHINE GUN
SHELL CHARGE STORAGE BIN
DRIVER'S PERISCOPE
TOOLS AND STOWAGE BOXES
DRIVING LEVERS
SHELL STOWAGE
BORE EVACUATOR
SIDE LAMPS
THERMAL INSULATED WRAPS
BOGIE WHEELS
ANTI-BAZOOKA SKIRT
MOVABLE HATCH FOR DIRECT VISUAL DRIVING
TOWING EYE
ACCELERATOR
PROTECTED HEADLIGHTS
120 M.M. GUN

voicing current military thinking. Few in the higher echelons of any army at that time had the smallest enthusiasm for armoured cars or indeed for the idea of any other sort of armoured fighting vehicle.

Until 1915 an armoured fighting vehicle was exclusively a wheeled vehicle and was thought of primarily as a reconnaissance vehicle or a mobile anti-balloon gun and, to a lesser extent, as a machine-gun carrier. Types of wheeled fighting vehicles increased in variety early in World War I, thanks to the pertinacity of a handful of enthusiasts, but the use of the armour (to give it its modern term) did not begin on a large scale until the advent of the track-layer as an assault vehicle.

Many people in several countries claimed to have invented the tank. France, Britain, Russia and the United States can all produce evidence, conclusive or otherwise, to substantiate their claim. The Russians put forward V. D. Mendeleev, son of the famous chemist. The French can point to Captain Levavasseur who proposed the idea for a *canon autopropulseur* in 1903. The United States had Cleve Shaffer, E. M. Wheelock and Francis S. Lowe. There was the Australian L. A. de Mole who sent plans and specifications for a lozenge-shaped fully-tracked assault vehicle to the British War Office in 1912 and again in 1914. And in 1911 an Austrian army officer, Günther Burstyn, designed a *Motorgeschütz* which he submitted to the Austro-Hungarian War Office and which was subsequently seen by the German War Ministry. All these projected vehicles were track-layers, making use of the caterpillar track which was invented in 1801 by Thomas German. And in 1915 Italy produced the Pavesi-Cassali vehicle which had cleated wheels and twin turrets and which, even if it was not a track-layer, was certainly a tank.

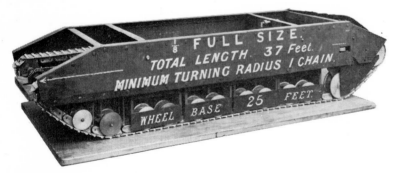

2
The model of the Australian De Mole tank that was submitted to the British War Office in 1912.

Despite all these, and other claims to have invented the tank, the undisputed fact remains that the British were the first to use tanks on the battlefield. The first British tank, Little Willie, was built in 1915. It was the direct predecessor of Mother (to give it the best-known of the several names by which it was called), the prototype of the British Mark I which ushered in tank warfare at the Battle of Flers-Courcelette on 15 September 1916 during the Somme Offensive.

Tanks were originally sponsored in Britain by the Admiralty through a 'Landships Committee'. This explains why, to this day, naval terms are still used to describe parts of tanks and similar vehicles.

Specialization of armour began with the first tanks. Starting with the Mark I, British heavy tanks were of two kinds: the male, armed with cannons and some machine-guns, and the female, armed only with machine-guns. The purpose of this differentiation was that the females should protect the males from infantry attack while the six-pounder guns of the males were engaging enemy guns, fortifications and defences. The females could also harass fleeing enemy infantry. After the first tank versus tank engagement, on 24 April 1918 when a Mark IV male, accompanied by two female tanks, met in action against a German A7V, the uselessness of the females' machine-guns against the enemy's armour plate resulted in the modification of a number of Mark IV and Mark V female tanks; one sponson carried a 6pdr and the other continued to mount machine-guns. Appropriately these modified tanks were called hermaphrodites.

3
Hermaphrodite tank with cannon in one sponson and machine-guns in the other.

All Marks of heavy tank were ponderous and slow moving, their maximum speed about 5 mph. For greater agility and speed medium tanks armed only with machine-guns were also designed and built. But only the first Mark, the Medium A or Whippet, was in action before the war ended, although the Medium B was used in the North Russian Expeditionary Force in 1919.

In order to expand the usefulness of the heavy tanks various devices were added, including towed supply sledges, grapnels on cables for tearing out barbed wire, brush bundles or fascines to drop into trenches to facilitate crossing, trench mortars on the rear deck and lengthened hulls to increase trench crossing ability and make the tanks roomy enough to carry stores or infantry. As successive models for combat were produced, older vehicles were frequently converted to become supply tanks. Field-guns and

4
The Second British Medium tank of World War I, the Medium B.

howitzers were mounted on gun-carrier tanks. These too eventually became supply vehicles for the carriage of ammunition for more orthodox artillery.

Because repairs were frequently needed and a heavy vehicle was needed to lift or move another heavy vehicle, salvage tanks or armoured recovery vehicles as they are called today, were improvised from combat vehicles. And some old Mark Is were converted to wireless tanks, unarmed but with an 'office' in one sponson and wireless equipment in the other.

The French were experimenting in the track-layer field simultaneously with the British, but for a time there was no liaison between them and neither knew what the other was about. It is notable, however, that in both countries some of the tank pioneers were inspired by the same vehicle. This was the American designed Holt tractor with caterpillar tracks that had originated as an agricultural vehicle but was also being used in the war as a heavy artillery tractor. Before the war the Holt had been manufactured in Antwerp and Budapest as well as in the United States, and it was the sight of one of these tractors that had started Günther Burstyn on the design of his *Motorgeschütz*. Furthermore, Leo Steiner, an early tank inventor, was one of Holt's agents in the Austro-Hungarian Empire. Although that design proved abortive, it is nevertheless fair to claim on behalf of the Holt that it was one of the greatest single stimulators of tank development. For example, the French Schneider and the St Chamond were both based on the Holt.

The first French tank, the Schneider C.A. (*Char d'Assaut,* Assault Car), weighed 14.6 tons–.6 ton heavier than the British Medium A. The second tank, the St Chamond, though considerably heavier at twenty-three tons, was five tons lighter than the Marks I–IV male tank and four tons lighter than the female. The Schneider was first in action on 16 April 1917; the St Chamond on 5 May 1917. As with the British, some of the early vehicles were converted to supply tanks (*Chars de Ravitaillement,* C.R.) after the third type of tank had come into service. This was the Renault F.T. (*Faible Tonnage,* Light Weight), for the French had decided to concentrate on the production of light tanks in sufficient quantity to attack 'in swarms' rather than to continue development in the medium field. Compared with 400 Schneiders and 400 St Chamonds, 3,177 Renault F.T.s were built.

Some of these Renaults were built as wireless tanks–*chars signals* –and some as self-propelled guns. The Renault F.T. was first in action on 31 May 1918. The French also turned to the design of super-heavy tanks. Two prototypes were built (Chars 1A and 1B), which served as development models for the sixty-eight ton Char 2C that was eventually produced in small numbers after the war.

Despite the proddings of enthusiasts the Germans got off to a late start and during World War I produced only some twenty tanks which were supplemented in action by captured British tanks. The Americans, though they had embarked on a large production programme, had only a few of their own tanks ready by the time the war ended. The American Tank Corps in France was equipped with French Renaults and British Mark V and Mark V Star tanks. The Canadian Tank Corps' two tank battalions in France were similarly equipped. The Italians, having experimented with the idea of tanks early in the war, ordered Schneiders from France after the Battle of Flers-Courcelette had shown what the future held in store. These could not be supplied. But on the basis of one Schneider and one Renault supplied by the French Government, the Italians designed their own heavy tank, the Fiat 2000, and their own light tank, the Fiat 3000. Only two of the former were built, and 100 of the latter–but these were not completed until 1919.

In the general reaction against war after 1918 there were only limited military appropriations. All armies had to be satisfied for the time being to use up existing stocks of equipment. Frequently some of the World War I vehicles were modernized and only small scale new experimentation took place. Self-propelled artillery was actively developed in the United States, but lack of agreement as to tactics made for shifting policies. In Britain, where no one except a few enthusiasts could make up their mind exactly what the tank was to do in the post-war army, and also in France, commercial tank designs were produced to meet the demands of smaller countries which lacked the industrial capacity or technical knowledge to build their own.

The first development change after World War I was caused by the short life of early tank tracks. During and after the war heavy tanks were moved by rail as close to the front as possible because track life seldom exceeded fifty miles. Light tanks were carried on trucks, trailers or track-laying tractors. Therefore, until tracks were improved, many varieties of convertible or wheel-cum-track tanks were devised in several different countries. As track life increased, most of these disappeared, although a new one was produced in prototype form as late as 1940 in New Zealand.

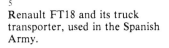
5
Renault FT18 and its truck transporter, used in the Spanish Army.

The next development was in the area of attempting to utilize commercially available components which would enable rapid expansion in production in the event of war. It was short-lived but led to many design changes and progress in the light tank field, particularly in Britain.

Apart from a few experimental vehicles to meet specialized military needs, until the outbreak of World War II, most countries concentrated on improving tanks as such. But during the war there was a tremendous mushrooming of both basic and specialized armour, much of the latter highly ingenious. Since then some of this specialization has disappeared, but there still remains a considerable variety of armour types.

Lines of demarcation between types of armour are not necessarily sharp, and overlapping obviously exists. There have, for example, been wheeled as well as track-laying tanks. Across classes there may be a common chassis for the purposes of simplifying maintenance and supplying spare parts. But in the main the broad classes which follow are satisfactory for covering the field of armour types.

2. Tanks, Tankettes and Carriers

Tanks are the basic armoured vehicles. For many years they were classified as light, medium and heavy. But in the course of time a weight that once might have been considered heavy came to be regarded as medium, and most modern light tanks would have been medium tanks in 1940. This, therefore, was a convenient but not a particularly accurate distinction because further subdivisions at either end of the scale led to additional categories from tankettes to super-heavy tanks. During and after World War II an effort was made to classify tanks as light gun, medium gun or heavy gun tanks. For example, the British Conqueror was classified as a heavy gun tank. But this classification, too, was unsatisfactory when one thinks of the little 2pdr gun on the big Churchill tank or the big 88mm gun on the little German 38(t) chassis.

6
Conqueror Mark I.

The general practice today is to group vehicles by function (as is done in this part of the Encyclopedia). Tanks can be classified as reconnaissance, airborne, main battle and heavy support–or in other ways. But vehicles intended for other than direct combat functions frequently are called tanks also, which makes for confusion. Thus one hears of flame-thrower tanks, anti-aircraft tanks, tank destroyers, command tanks and others. In addition the tactical views held in a given army may influence not only functions but definitions as well.

French practice will illustrate. Widely and favourably known as a light tank, the French AMX13 in reality was designed as a tank destroyer. It has been sold commercially and became a police vehicle in Peru and Venezuela, a reconnaissance vehicle in the Netherlands, and a light tank in Israel, while in Switzerland it continues to be a tank destroyer. On the other hand, the tiny French *Even* is considered in France to be a close support infantry

7

French Even with 90mm.

tank. Elsewhere it would probably be considered an airborne tank, a reconnaissance vehicle or a tank destroyer.

For reconnaissance the French and British tend to use scout cars and armoured cars (although within recent years the British have produced the Scorpion Reconnaissance Tank). The United States employ light tanks, and the Soviet Union scout cars or light amphibious tanks. Thus even the definitions of functions may vary by country, so naturally the vehicles designed to fill those functions will vary.

It is easy for the layman to recognize that there is a difference between a naval cruiser and a destroyer, and between a fighter plane and a bomber, because their functions are fairly obvious. Less easily recognized is the fact that while armoured vehicles may bear a superficial resemblance to one another, they may not at all be the same because they are not necessarily intended for the same tactical role. As already said, not all countries agree on the type of vehicle needed to perform a given function. There is general agreement only in that the word tank is used very loosely.

The word really should be limited to what is referred to today as a Main Battle Tank (M.B.T.) whose primary function is to strike an enemy from a distance and be able to close the gap rapidly between its gun and the target while being protected to a considerable degree. Although to some extent this may also be the measure of an assault gun, the latter is distinguished from the M.B.T. by the much smaller amount of armour carried and by the fact that it is not intended to close with an enemy in the same manner as the M.B.T. Instead, assault guns are intended to assist the advance of both tanks and infantry.

In World War I tanks were slow-moving and advanced ahead of, with or just behind the infantry. The faster medium tanks had more freedom of action and sometimes operated alone.

After the war, insofar as any clear-cut decisions were reached at all, tanks were generally regarded solely as a supporting arm for infantry. Tanks were feared and hated by the older arms, and there was great reluctance to allow them an independent existence. Only in Britain was a separate Tank Corps continued;

15

elsewhere it became part of the infantry arm. Despite strong opposition the idea of an independent force consisting entirely or largely of tanks and operating on its own instead of in support of infantry–an idea which had first been mooted by British Tank Corps staff in World War I–resulted in the formation of an Experimental Mechanized Force in Britain in 1927. This was the first armoured formation in the world. From the trials of this Experimental Force arose the concept that land warfare using tanks would become similar to naval warfare; light tanks, like destroyers, would guard the main battle fleet of medium tanks. This concept resulted in a new name for the medium tanks which, when the new models came to be designed in the years immediately before World War II, were called cruisers.

But the infantry support idea was far from dead in Britain. When the first post-war medium tank was being developed there was also a War Office requirement for a heavy tank to support infantry. This resulted in a single vehicle: the A1E1 Independent, produced in 1926. Eight years later the concept of two main classes of tank with a third for reconnaissance had taken firm root. There were to be cruiser tanks for mobile operations, slow-moving, heavily armoured infantry (or I) tanks to support the infantry assault and light tanks for reconnaissance.

During the inter-war period the United States considered tanks as weapons to assist cavalry and infantry in their traditional roles. Russia had fast tanks and slow tanks, and this was true also of Italy; France and Germany were exceptions. The French thought of tanks as infantry weapons to be parcelled out as needed, five to each attacking infantry battalion. Germany had been denied armour under the terms of the Versailles Treaty. Thus the Germans were not handicapped by a reservoir of older vehicles and could begin rearming from scratch, and, more important, thinking from scratch. British theories were studied and adopted. Tanks became a separate arm intended to spearhead advances, leaving to closely following motorized infantry the task of consolidating.

The early World War II successes of German armour forced a re-evaluation elsewhere. The word armour began to be used, as the Germans used it, to denote tanks as well as those vehicles which support tanks. The United States adopted the German approach, as did the Russians. The British retained their cruiser and infantry tank distinctions almost until the end of the war, with both lacking adequate fire-power until almost too late. The two distinctions were erased then with the adoption of the Centurion universal or all-purpose tank. Nevertheless, a few years after the war the British for a time added the heavy Conqueror as well, following German and Russian war-time practice. The Germans had ended the war with the Panther as a battle tank supported by the Tiger from greater ranges, in the same manner as the Russian T34 was supported by the Josef Stalin heavy tank.

The United States concentrated on a medium tank, the M4, and at the end of the war was just beginning to turn to the heavier Pershing which, after the war, was remodelled into the Patton. A heavy tank also was developed, but the Americans were not convinced of the value of a heavy tank, principally because American tanks had to be shipped by sea and a greater number of medium tanks could be shipped in the same space. When the special problem of attacking the Siegfried Line arose, the basic M4 tank was converted to an assault tank by welding on thick additional plates rather than turning to a heavy tank. The assault tanks were intended to move in close to the concrete

8
Morris-Martel tankette with single tailwheel which replaced the original dual wheels.

9
Praying Mantis, designed for upper storey street-fighting.

10
British Carden-Loyd Mark VII Light tank, with the first traversing turret.

dragon teeth and absorb punishment while pounding these obstacles to rubble with their guns. Since the war a heavy tank, the M103, has been built, but it is used only by the Marine Corps as a support to medium tanks and not by the army.

In the lighter vehicle field, the original French Renault tank was the prototype of all later light tanks in the world. It had been visualized as an infantry skirmisher. The continued emphasis on light tanks following World War I in France and elsewhere was largely a matter of economy. Smaller countries began to want them, and those which could not build their own bought surplus vehicles from France, thereby giving the French the funds and the encouragement to experiment with newer designs.

One school of thought in Britain visualized swarms of even lighter armoured vehicles. In 1925 Major (later Lieutenant-General Sir Giffard) Le Q. Martel introduced a one-man armoured vehicle that could be produced in quantity utilizing commercially available parts. Only a few were built, and these were a two-man version. Following the Martel vehicles came the Carden-Loyd tankettes: low, squat, one- or two-man vehicles also using many commercially available parts. These were taken over and developed further by Vickers-Armstrongs Ltd. who had already been building a new type of medium tank for the British Army. Many Carden-Loyd vehicles were sold to the British Army and to many other armies as tankettes or machine-gun carriers, as were the several varieties of light tanks which grew out of them.

From the Carden-Loyd also evolved the World War II vehicles known as carriers. First came the Bren Carrier mounting a Bren light machine-gun, then the Scout and Cavalry carriers, all three being superseded by the Universal Carrier which was produced for all purposes, any special requirement being met by minor modifications. Universal Carriers were used as mortar carriers, medium machine-gun carriers, observation posts, wire-reel or cable-layers, flame-throwers, self-propelled guns, ambulances, supply carriers and command posts. One experimental variation was the Praying Mantis. This was a carrier fitted with a scissors-like elevating platform intended for remote control machine-gun fire against upper storey windows in street fighting or for firing from a concealed position. It was, however, never used operationally.

Universal Carriers were built under licence in Australia, New Zealand, India and Canada, local designs appearing in Australia and New Zealand.

In addition to the development of light tanks (which continued to increase in weight) airborne tanks were proposed. The first of these was the American Christie, which was intended to be carried under the belly of a bomber, but it was never given a practical test. The idea was adopted in the Soviet Union, however, and early in World War II Russian light tanks were air-lifted into Bessarabia. The Czechs also built successful airborne tanks and sold them to Iran, Romania and Sweden. The British used their own Tetrarch airborne light tanks during the Normandy landings in June 1944 and then used them again together with American M22 Locusts for the crossing of the Rhine in March 1945.

As already stated, under the terms of the Versailles Treaty, Germany and the other Central Powers were denied the right to possess armour. Germany's chief designer, Joseph Vollmer, went to Sweden after World War I to supervise the building of a few light tanks from parts left over in Germany. He also designed the Czech KH50 wheel and track tank. Sweden too worked out wheel-and-track designs, as did the French, the British, the Hungarians, the Japanese and the New Zealanders. The Poles had a tank which was a convertible trailer.

In the United States, a different principle was applied. The other designs had provided both track frames and tracks and a separate wheeled chassis. By gears or hydraulics the change was made from one mode to the other. The American method, invented by J. Walter Christie, was to use large bogie wheels on coil sprung crank arms which permitted much more than the usual bogie motion. The bogie wheels were double, and the space between them served as recesses for the track guides. When the tracks were removed the vehicle could operate on the front and rear pairs of wheels, the others being raised slightly.

The Japanese also devised a few wheel-and-tank vehicles and eventually an interesting rail-and-track tank. This latter could be used as an armoured railway vehicle, or as part of a railway train to protect it or for strategic moves, and yet be able to go into action as a tank with only a brief delay.

11
Airborne M60 about to enter C–5A transport

12
Airborne AHIV tankette in Iran.

13
Japanese HO–GI rail-and-track tank in use in Manchuria.

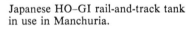

The combination vehicle began to disappear when track life improved, although examples still continued to appear up into World War II. Even in the case of the Christie design, although fundamentally still capable of operating on wheels, it was no longer so used by the Russians and the British who adopted it after the United States failed to develop it. The Poles also built a few experimental tanks with Christie suspensions.

Christie was also responsible for a series of amphibious tanks in the early 1920s, although he was not the originator of this type of vehicle. The first tanks to which flotation devices were attached, as well as the first amphibious tanks, were designed late in World War I in England by Lieutenant-Colonel Philip Johnson. They relied for motion in the water on the turning of the tracks. These tanks were capable of high land speeds. This direction of research was dropped, however, and amphibious tanks did not reappear in Britain until Vickers-Armstrongs produced small commercial amphibious tanks in the 1930s. These had screws and rudders. Some were purchased by Russia where development has continued up to the present time.

The French, and particularly the Japanese, were also active in this field. The Imperial Japanese Navy had amphibious tanks actually capable of being sealed and transported on the deck of their huge I-class submarines. In the United States commercial designer Donald Roebling built an amphibious vehicle not originally intended for military purposes but which later was developed by the navy. At first an unarmoured supply vehicle and personnel carrier, it finally became an armoured vehicle with turret. These were the well known L.V.T.s (Landing Vehicles, Tracked), sometimes called Amtracs. They had no screws but were propelled in the water by the turning of the tracks. These were a vast improvement over the Johnson tracks of twenty years earlier in that they were fitted with deep grousers which functioned as scoops.

14
Japanese tank on the deck of a submarine.

Similar vehicles, Neptune and Argosy, were built in small numbers in Britain but development did not continue after the war. The U.S. Navy, on the other hand, has continued L.V.T. development on an impressive scale, while the army has also entered the field of amphibious combat vehicles. These latter have had sufficient merit to be adopted in a number of other countries. One of their interesting features is that they utilize aluminium armour, which is becoming increasingly common in tank design.

Many types of flotation device have been devised in addition to amphibious vehicles since the first crude floats or 'camels' were applied to World War I British heavy tanks. Those developed in Japan, Britain and the United States during World

15
French Amphibie DP2 emerging from a river-crossing.

16
British Valentine tank showing its inflatable frame for canvas screen.

War II included sectional floats fitted together either fore and aft or completely around a tank. Screws and rudders were provided. These devices could be blown apart and discarded by small explosive bolts controlled from within the tank.

One of the best known flotation devices of a different type was the duplex drive (D.D.) invented by Nicholas Straussler and used by both the British and the Americans. It comprised a skeleton frame of flexible air-tight hose forming a collapsible framework covered with rubberized canvas and capable of being inflated, thus forming a boat around the upper part of the tank. This canvas boat could be dropped in an instant by bleeding the air from the framework. Twin screws with take-off were provided, giving the device its name.

Three American tank battalions, two Canadian armoured regiments and three British armoured regiments equipped with D.D. tanks (Shermans with D.D. equipment) were used in the Normandy landings.* For the first time in the history of armoured warfare, assaulting infantry could count on immediate armour support as or before they landed on hostile shores.

D.D. tanks were also used in Operation Dragoon (the invasion of Southern France in August 1944), in the clearing of the Scheldt estuary in October-November 1944, in the crossing of the Rhine in March 1945 and in the final stages of the Italian campaign in April 1945.

The Germans devised an interesting wading device for Operation Sea Lion, their proposed invasion of Great Britain in 1940. This was a buoyed snorkel on a hose connected to the tank turret. The tanks were completely sealed so that they could travel on the bottom of shallow rivers or approaching a beach. (A few were actually used in the crossing of the Bug River at the beginning of the German attack on Russia, on 22 June 1941. The equipment enabled the leading tanks of the 18th Panzer Division to move through thirteen feet of water.) Fixed snorkels or stacks were used on German Tiger tanks, permitting them to submerge up to twelve feet.

Fixed stacks were created for amphibious landings by the British and first used by the Canadians at Dieppe on 19 August 1942. Similar stacks were used on American tanks in the North African and later landings, the waterproofing devices for combat vehicles in the North African landings.

---

*As the performance of the D.D. tanks on that occasion is frequently under-estimated in latter-day accounts, it is worth giving their record in detail in order to correct this error. The record is as follows:

70th U.S. Tank Battalion–thirty tanks launched at 3,000 yards, one foundered;

741st U.S. Tank Battalion–twenty-nine launched at 6,000 yards, twenty-seven foundered, two swam in, three more beached from L.C.T.s (Landing Craft Tanks);

743rd U.S. Tank Battalion–not launched, all beached direct from L.C.T.s;

6th Canadian Armoured Regiment (1st Hussars)–A squadron launched ten tanks at 1,500–2,000 yards, seven touched down on beach, another six beached from L.C.T.s, B Squadron launched nineteen tanks at 4,000 yards, fourteen of which reached shore;

10th Canadian Armoured Regiment (Fort Garry Horse)–not launched, all beached from L.C.T.s;

Nottinghamshire Sherwood Rangers Yeomanry–not launched, all beached from L.C.T.s;

4th/7th Royal Dragoon Guards–not launched, all beached from L.C.T.s and

13th/18th Royal Hussars–forty embarked, six failed to launch, thirty-four launched at 5,000 yards, three sank during swim, thirty-one reached shore.

3. Self-Propelled Weapons

The original purpose of the self-propelled gun was to provide a better means of transporting a gun than drawing it by horses. One of the first methods was the portée gun, a regular field-piece carried on a truck. The advent of the military balloon led to the anti-balloon gun with a shield or in an armoured cab on a truck. There were many of these on both sides during World War I.

As track-laying vehicles came into military use guns and howitzers of various calibres were mounted on this type of chassis. The sea of mud on the Western Front–caused by rain falling on a countryside whose drainage system had been totally destroyed by shell-fire–meant that bringing up the guns to support a successful advance became almost insuperable. The British built gun-carrier tanks which used the same engine and transmission as their Mark I tanks. They carried either a six inch howitzer which could be fired from the tank or a 60pdr whose wheels were removed before it was hauled on to the tank and which, in transit, were carried on brackets on each side of the hull. These gun-carrier tanks were used on a few occasions. But after their arrival in France in 1917, despite their revelation of the way in which the tactical handling of artillery could be revolutionized, they failed to find favour in orthodox artillery circles and were relegated to ammunition and stores carriers.

The French, too, had self-propelled tracked mountings for heavy artillery; these, like the Schneider and St Chamond tanks, were based on the Holt tractor, that great stimulator of tracked vehicles. The Americans built their first track–laying self-propelled gun in 1916 and continued to produce a series of experimental caterpillar mounts until 1925.

The principal impetus after World War I was a continuation of self-propelled guns in the traditional artillery role. Perhaps impetus is too strong a word; the intermittent development pursued in several countries received little official support and even less enthusiasm. In the later 1920s the British produced a few samples of the 'Birch' gun (named after the Master-General of the Ordnance) which mounted an 18pdr, but further development perished in the sands of inter-arm suspicions. France, which lagged like other countries in this field, became interested in the years immediately before World War II and built a prototype of the *Char Automoteur* Somua SAU40 that mounted a 75mm gun in a modified Somua S35 hull. In general, there were a few sporadic attempts to devise and use close support artillery as isolated vehicles or, in the case of the British, to use tanks with low velocity mortars in place of the regular tank gun as close support tanks. The Germans originated the idea of the assault gun, *Sturmgeschütz,* for the close support of tanks or infantry– or at least they were the first to introduce them, which they did in 1940. The thinking behind these weapons was that what the infantry wanted for support was not the heavily armoured, lightly armed 'I' tank of the British, but an armoured vehicle mounting a weapon with 'punch'. Although they used guns of the same calibre as those in tanks the assault guns were not in revolving turrets. The guns were mounted low in front, producing vehicles with a very low silhouette. With high

17
German Geraet 040 24 inch mortar
in firing position.

velocity guns substituted these vehicles became tank destroyers, supporting medium tanks by destroying enemy tanks at long range, or forming part of an anti-tank defensive system. Such assault guns fired from a halt and leap-frogged as tanks advanced. The Russians used the same type of assault gun, and the Americans, British, Japanese and Italians all followed the same pattern during World War II. In configuration the modern Swedish S-tank resembles these World War II vehicles but is considered to be a tank.

Chassis common with tanks were frequently used for self-propelled guns. The advantages, of course, were in simplifying parts-supply and maintenance, as well as in reducing manufacturing costs. Not only were assault guns in use but self-propelled guns intended for use as conventional artillery were common. Tank chassis were employed, mobility decreasing directly with the calibre of gun mounted. This seldom exceeded 280mm, although Germany reached the ultimate after Hitler's approval of the gargantuan twenty-one and twenty-four inch mortars on track-laying chassis, so big and clumsy that for more than short moves special railroad cars had to be provided.

In spite of the emphasis placed on self-propelled artillery by the Germans, they also continued to use conventional artillery, both horse and tractor drawn. To some extent this was also true in other countries. The United States, on the other hand, was the first country to make its armoured divisional artillery completely self-propelled and to make all other artillery either self-propelled or tractor drawn.

The Russians had a ratio of two assault guns to every tank. They believed the mission of the assault gun was to destroy enemy tanks, and they were cheaper to build than tanks.

Another type of vehicle in this category is the light fast tank destroyer. Light tank chassis or vehicles expressly designed for speed are used for this purpose. They may look exactly like tanks, but their armour is thin and is intended only as protection against

small arms fire or shell fragments. Their weapons are high velocity guns from 20mm and up but usually from 75mm to 90mm. The British Striker, a vehicle of this light fast tank destroyer type, has Swingfire missiles.

The anti-aircraft guns likewise varied in calibre. Originally on wheeled mounts, they later utilized half-tracked and fully-tracked chassis. They can be single or multiple weapons of the same or of various calibres. During World War II all belligerents used single, dual, triple or quadruple automatic weapons up to 40mm or more, and also 37mm and two .50 calibre, 40mm and two 20mm, and other combinations. The United States found a use for such weapons in Korea and later in Vietnam as ground support weapons and as ambush thwarters and perimeter guards. An even greater future need is seen for defence against enemy attack planes, attack helicopters and mine-laying helicopters.

As an interesting sidelight on the attitudes of various nations regarding common problems, it may be pointed out that photographs will reveal that the tanks of most countries have an automatic weapon of one or another degree of sophistication mounted on tank turrets for anti-aircraft fire. The Germans today are an exception, their attitude being that such weapons are intended for the use of a tank commander and that he has enough to do without one. He should not have this responsibility. Other vehicles having no other responsibility than that of anti-aircraft protection can do it better, and a tank commander then is free to carry out his major responsibility.

Most anti-aircraft gun vehicles today are of the missile type, and many of them are provided with radar fire control. Missiles cannot always be relied upon. Because of this, although the Russians have a wide variety of missile vehicles, they continue to develop conventional multi-weapon mounts with radar fire control as well. The Russians stress night operations, and some of their missile vehicles may also be intended to function as high angle mortars firing illuminating shell.

Aside from anti-tank or anti-aircraft use, missiles or rockets were used on a large scale as conventional artillery during World War II. The Russians employed many truck-mounted multiple rocket launchers known as Katyushas. These were of various calibres. United States forces used multiple rocket launchers on a few wheeled chassis, on some L.V.T.s and a considerable number and variety on light and medium tank chassis. Some of these were

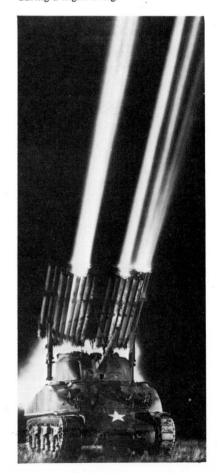

20
American M41 Light tank with
Shillelagh gun in experimental
turret.

nicknamed Calliopes from their resemblance to the pipes on a
circus steam organ, just as the Russian Katyushas were sometimes
called Stalin Organs.

Since World War II the Soviet Union has continued with multiple rocket launchers, but more and more these are being mounted
on track-layers rather than on wheeled vehicles. Their value was
demonstrated to Russian satisfaction since fire can be single round,
salvo (all together) or ripple (successive), and because volume fire
has a terrifying effect on the receiver. The Russians have also
shown a number of light-beam controlled missile cannon of
tremendous length mounted on Stalin tank chassis, several
varieties of large single missiles on modified Stalin and PT76 tank
chassis and others.

Other countries have developed missile and rocket projectors as
anti-tank as well as anti-aircraft weapons mounted singly or in
groups and on various chassis. They vary from recoilless rifles to
wire, light beam, infrared and radar controlled types. Up to six
recoilless rifles have been mounted on the track-layers in several
countries. Typical of this is the American Ontos. Clusters of SS11
missiles appear on the French AMX13 to augment the regular
armament.

One of the newest weapons is the combination missile and conventional projectile gun of the Shillelagh type used on the
American Sheridan light tank. Newer American medium tanks
are being equipped with it, and some of the older tanks are being
modified to accommodate it.

The American Lance missile system in 1973 was approaching
the capability of ejecting from nine to fifteen terminally guided
thermal-homing sub-missiles that would seek exhaust plumes or
engine radiation of enemy tanks. Each sub-missile weighed thirty
pounds and was about six by thirty inches with a shaped charge
war-head. Additionally, provision was being made to include a
discrimination device that would distinguish tanks from false
targets, probably an infrared seeker similar to that on the Redeye
missile. Whether the possibility exists of distinguishing between
differing heat signatures is not yet known.

Like missile and rocket projectors, flame-throwers have been
mounted in a variety of vehicles. The Russians and Germans used
obsolescent light tanks early in World War II, while the British
and Americans mounted them on a variety of vehicle chassis,
including Churchills (Crocodiles), Shermans, carriers and L.V.T.s.

Flame-throwers use a fuel made up of volatile as well as slow
burning petroleum products. These generally are unstable unless

21
American Chaparral anti-aircraft
missile-projector.

25

thickened with a product like silica gel or aluminium stearate. This fuel is fed into a tube from which it is projected under pressure from carbon dioxide or nitrogen gas and ignited as it is released. It is ejected in spurts, called rods or jets, of a few seconds duration. Being thick fuel, the flame and smoke are persistent, but ranges seldom exceed seventy-five yards. Therefore, the vehicles are vulnerable and require the protection of other combat vehicles.

The American experience in the Pacific was that the flame-thrower vehicle having a supplementary flame-thrower tube was quickly recognized by the Japanese and became a target. Thereafter there was a tendency to use old gun tubes or flame-thrower tubes simulating conventional guns. Most American flame-thrower vehicles were fitted with extension hoses so that flame could be used at some distance from the vehicle as well.

22
POA-CW5 75 H-I flame-thrower.

Flame-throwers lose much of their effect because of the pull of gravity on the rod or jet. Modernized versions use rocket-propelled shells which burst into flame on impact, giving greater range and greater accuracy.

As the Germans increasingly experienced shortages of labour and raw materials and began to go over to the defensive in the field late in the war, they resurrected the portée principle in their *Waffentraeger* (weapon carrier). The German version not only provided for transportation of a standard artillery piece but also for firing it from the vehicle.*

Basically the German weapon carrier, like the British gun-carrier tank of World War 1, was a tracked chassis which would accommodate a standard field piece from which the wheels were removed and carried elsewhere on the vehicle. By means of a small crane or by a sliding frame of a hinged lift, the piece could be removed and the wheels added and it could then be towed or placed in firing position, or the gun could be fired from the halted vehicle. Several types, some known as *Heuschrecke* (grasshopper), were built and many more were under construction at the end of the war.

Although customarily thought of and used as a ground weapon, the infantry mortar is often mounted on a light armoured vehicle for that role as well as to function in another role as a support weapon for tanks and other armoured vehicles. During daylight combat such weapons assist armoured infantry with high explosive or white phosphorus support fire. For night operations they can be used in a similar role as well as for firing parachute flares to light up an area in order to permit accurate fire from the flat trajectory weapons carried by the tanks they support.

---

*Early in World War II the British used the portée principle in Cyrenaica. The 2pdr anti-tank gun was mounted, complete, facing the rear, on the open back of a four-wheeled lorry and could be fired from the vehicle. The wheeled portée vehicle proved unsuccessful.

4. Mine-Defeating Vehicles

The land mine was the curse of tanks in World War I as it was of infantry, and it has remained so ever since with increasing intensity. In 1918 the British tested an anti-mine device consisting of two wooden beams projected in front of the tracks of a Mark IV tank; to each of the beams a roller was attached by a swivel. As the tank moved forward the rollers were supposed to detonate any mine in the path of the oncoming track, but the device was not really successful. An improvement on it was developed immediately after the war at the Experimental Establishment of the Royal Engineers at Christchurch, Hampshire. The commander of the Establishment was Major Martel, an engineer who had served in the Tank Corps during the war and who, as Lieutenant-General Sir Giffard Le Q. Martel, was to be Commander of the Royal Armoured Corps from 1940 to 1943.

The improved mine-sweeping device was attached to a Mark V Double Star tank that had been converted into an R.E. tank. This tank had a jib hinged to its front, and the jib could be raised and lowered by a hydraulic arm. By means of the jib the R.E. tank could carry out demolitions under fire, or lay a twenty-one foot bridge or detonate mines. In the latter role a heavy roller in two pieces, each weighing over one ton, was towed from the end of the jib and thus moved in front of the tank detonating any contact mine it encountered. Mines with nine pounds of high explosives were used in testing the roller and, reported Martel, their detonation was not found to be unduly unpleasant for the crew, though the blast usually lifted the front part of the tank a few inches. In practice the intention was that when a mine was detonated–destroying or damaging the roller as an area of five by ten yards was cleared–the tank would back out. Another would then move in and repeat the painfully slow process of clearing a path.

The problem of defeating the land mine appears to have been generally ignored after these experiments in 1919–20 until 1937 on the eve of World War II. Martel, who had spent the intervening years outside the tank field, had just been appointed Assistant Director of Mechanization at the War Office in direct charge of tank development. Among the new ideas put forward were two for mine-sweeping. The heavy roller idea was not suitable for the high speed cruiser tanks that were coming into production. Instead, it was proposed to use either a plough or a pair of light wheels in tandem in front of each track–that is, four wheels in all. Both ideas were translated into practice by the firm of Fowler and hence were known as the Fowler plough and the Fowler roller. Both had disadvantages that led to their rejection for general use. The plough was ineffective in hard ground, and the roller could only cope with two mines in front of each track because each detonation blew off a wheel.

When war broke out and the land mine became a virulent menace to the tank innumerable experiments were carried out with every conceivable type of roller device–plain, spiked and jagged. But all roller devices had one fundamental defect: they were liable to bridge the mine by consolidating the ground on either side of it thereby preventing the roller itself from making contact with the mine. To overcome this the Scorpion was invented on the suggestion of a South African engineer officer in the Middle East, Major A. S. du Toit. The Scorpion used the flail principle, in which the mine was exploded by beating the ground above it. Various forms of flail were developed for different tanks. The Scorpion itself was used mainly on Matildas, Grants and Valentines, and, to a limited extent and in Italy only, on Shermans. It was first used at the Second Battle of Alamein in October 1942. The Scorpion consisted of an axle carrying a number of heavy chains which was mounted on girder arms in front of the tank. The axle was driven by auxiliary engines mounted externally on the right hand side of the tank. When the axle revolved the chains beat the ground in a path about ten feet wide. If not buried too deeply, most or all of the mines would be detonated. It could also be used to beat down wire.

23

British Baron mine-flail using Matilda chassis.

Another flail device, fitted to the Matildas, was the Baron. It, like the Scorpion, had its rotor arm driven by auxiliary engines. But the flail tank design which proved most effective was the Crab. In this the rotor was driven by power take-off from the tank's main engine, which greatly simplified operation. Also the rotor arm could be lifted hydraulically until the flailing area was reached. The Crab was fitted to the Sherman, and the Sherman Crab became the standard British mine-clearing vehicle from the end of 1943 onwards during World War II. It was by far the simplest and best flail design of its period. The Sherman Crab retained its tank gun and was thus able, when it was not flailing, to act as a normal gun tank. Flailing speed was 1¼ mph. In dry conditions the dust that was raised made visibility extremely difficult for the flailing crew and furthermore made the hazardous task even more difficult by attracting hostile fire. Teller mines could be detonated at a depth of four or five inches, each mine destroying one chain. Provided that the angle of the lane swept coincided with the angle between mines, a Crab could explode up to fourteen mines before its roller had to be re-dressed with new chains.

Crabs were extensively used by the British in the Northwest Europe campaign 1944-45. The 30th Armoured Brigade in the 79th Armoured Division–the division that was equipped with specialized armour–was a wholly Crab brigade. Some Sherman Crabs were also used by American troops. But while it was effective the Crab was not foolproof. In his book on the 79th Armoured Division, *Hobo's Funnies,* Major-General N. W. Duncan, who commanded the 30th Armoured Brigade, summed it up thus:

Under normal circumstances any mine buried five inches below the surface would be set off by a flail tank. This figure was subject to considerable variations; if the ground was boggy the impact of the bob weight was deadened, or if the country was frozen hard the bob weight bounced off the surface without transmitting any blow to the mine detonator: under these circumstances the mines were likely to be inoperative as far as ordinary tracked or wheeled vehicles were concerned. The only thing that was certain was that their behaviour was completely unpredictable. There was one case of a lane which had been swept at Le Havre and had been used by dozens of vehicles going forward; a scout car coming back down the lane detonated a mine in the same lane and was destroyed. The mine must have been buried a little deeper than usual and subsequent tanks passing over had consolidated the ground in such a way as to shield the detonator which remained unexploded until the direction of thrust on it had been reversed.

Among the scores of devices that were invented and developed for defeating mines was the Brooks Walker Anti-Tank Mine Clearing Device. It was filed for patent in 1943 in the United States and patented in 1946, but it seems never to have been built. An auxiliary engine on the rear deck rotated a long arm pivoted to the top of the turret. Chains attached to the end terminated in either large concrete filled steel balls or a series of serrated roller dollies. Rotation of the arm would cause a circular path to be traced around a forward-moving vehicle.

In the United States and in Britain as well, various types of rollers, ploughs, dozers, forks and harrows were used to expose mines to view so that they could be made harmless in normal ways or to explode them. The Canadian Army invented the Canadian Indestructible Roller Device (C.I.R.D.) which had two heavy armoured rollers attached to projecting side arms in front of the vehicle, which was either a Sherman or Churchill tank. When a roller exploded a mine the blast caused it to jump up in an arc over the side arm so that the spade end of the roller arm dug into the ground. The forward motion of the tank and a mechanical arrangement brought the roller back to its travelling position.

One American device was the removal of the tracks from Sherman tanks, after which the tanks were mounted on large wheels, the whole forming a huge tricycle. The Americans also fitted a tank with a series of mechanized plungers on a framework extending from the bow of the tank. The plungers, on springs and mechanically actuated, stabbed into the ground to detonate mines. Still another American device was a tank with turret removed and fitted with nipples within the turret well and on the glacis. These held spigot grenades which could be ejected in a spread pattern. As the grenades exploded on striking the ground, the mines in turn were exploded.

Both the British and the Americans used explosives in other ways for this purpose. The British brought the old Bangalore torpedo up to date. Called the Snake, one variation of this was a series of pipes containing explosive charges. The pipes were screwed together, pushed by a Churchill or Sherman tank into a

24

American T10 mine-exploder on an M4 chassis.

minefield by means of a ratchet device under the belly of the tank, and exploded, thus clearing a path up to 400 feet long and twenty-one feet wide. Another variation was the Conger. A hose was fired by rocket into a minefield, one end remaining connected to a gutted Universal Carrier. The hose was then pumped full of explosive, the carrier was removed and the hose was fired, its blast creating a path through the mines. The carrier was towed into position by a Churchill or a Sherman tank.

Both the Germans and the Americans also experimented with mine-resistant vehicles. These were track-layers with extremely heavy tracks and suspensions and with greater than normal hull clearance. Such vehicles towing heavy rollers could themselves clear a path without breaking down.

The flail type has continued in favour in Britain while mine exploding rollers and mine ploughs seem to be the American choice–in so far as there has been any choice made at all. In Vietnam, in spite of constant Viet Cong mining of roads and the setting up of booby traps in the field, anti-mine devices were not introduced by the Americans until 1970, after nine years of war. However, there was some use made by the Marine Corps of the special engineering L.V.T. which is equipped not only with a minefork but also with a sort of Conger, a rocket-propelled line charge which can be thrown out some 350 feet. The British as well provide these on their latest A.V.R.E.s (Armoured Vehicles, Royal Engineers), and the Russians have added them to their M.B.T.s.

A related piece of equipment for mine-defeating vehicles was the Breach Marker developed by the British during World War II. This was a hopper or similar device attached to the rear quarters of a mine-sweeping tank to plant flags or markers or lay powdered chalk to outline the boundaries of a cleared minefield path. A similar device could drop small battery operated electric light markers for night operations. Usually detonating and marking were done by the same vehicles. The Russians have similar vehicles today, the purpose of which is to locate and mark the boundaries of a nuclear contaminated area. One is based on their PT76 amphibious tank chassis. Since World War II the Russians have developed both flails and rollers for minesweeping.

One of the latest developments in the United States is the use of fuel air explosives. Ethylene oxide liberated by means of an aerosol spray is detonated over the target by delayed action. A

25
American Snake being pushed from an M4 medium tank.

26
Russian mine-detecting equipment on the bow of a T54.

27
French mine-detectors on a Char 35R chassis.

28
British Lulu open for operation as a mine-detector and mine-exploder.

surface launched unit fuel air explosive system is mounted on an M548 tracked vehicle. The system includes a box rack for thirty navy Zuni missiles each containing seventy-four pounds of ethylene oxide. The missiles are fired singly or in ripple. Each dispenses a vapourized cloud about fifty feet in diameter and eight feet thick, which generates a blast more effective for clearing minefields than standard high explosives. The fuses are set so that the missiles are strung out in a trace for detonation, releasing parachutes which cause each war-head to descend vertically on the target area. The Soviet Union also began similar work in 1973.

Minefields normally are located through careless laying or sudden detonation. Several armies of the Soviet bloc have mechanical mine-layers, but one of their disadvantages is that such minefields can be detected from the air. Normally, engineers on foot and using electronic mine detectors attempt to determine the extent of the area mined. Since World War II a few such devices have been mounted on small dollies pushed ahead of jeeps. This type of approach is not new, however; the French before World War II mounted electronic mine detectors on a turretless light tank, and during the war the British developed Lulu (though it was not put into production) which detected mines by electrical detector coils carried in light wooden rollers arranged in tricycle fashion, two ahead and one behind, on a Sherman tank. The Russians today have equipped their latest medium tanks with such a device in the form of a row of eight sensors across the underside of the tank's bow. However, this would be useless against Asrolite, the liquid land mine developed by Explosives Corporation of America, which can be poured from containers or sprayed. It deactivates itself in four days, making mine clearance operations unnecessary. This interesting explosive could be sprayed over an area also to detonate mines or booby traps, by projecting it through a perforated plastic tube under pressure, by using it in a tube as a Snake, or by the projection by small rocket of an Astrolite-soaked nylon string.

The use of plastic mines has made their discovery impossible by electronic mine detectors. The Calspan Company of Buffalo, New York, has developed a radar which 'looks down' and is capable of discovering these mines and of distinguishing mines and other objects beneath the surface. The device can be mounted in a vehicle or used as a conventional mine locater.

5. Bridging and Engineering Vehicles

Trenches in World War I often were wide enough and deep enough to present serious obstacles even to the thirty foot long British heavy tank of the day. Barbed wire entanglements could break or tear off tank tracks. For the Battle of Cambrai in November 1917 the latter problem was solved by fitting grapnel hooks to a number of tanks so that they could engage enemy wire and destroy it or drag it out of the way. These tanks had the initials W.C. (for Wire Cutter) painted in large letters on their stern.

The former problem was solved for the same battle by compressing huge bundles of brush into chain-bound fascines and lodging them on the tanks' unditching beam rails. These fascines were dropped into German trenches to form a bridge for the tanks to cross. Late in the war skeleton steel cribs were used in the same way.

The idea was not lost. At the beginning of World War II, when the British were using small light tanks, a large towed drum was tested as a portable fascine for small tanks. But as the war progressed and tanks became larger, exactly the same types of fascines were used as in World War I, released by triggering mechanisms. Some use was also made of wooden cribs or wooden crib frames. Today the British still use steel cribs.

29
British wooden crib fascine on a Sherman.

30
British Dragon Mark I thirty-foot bridge carrier of the post-World War I period.

Royal Engineers under Major Martel were experimenting with a bridge-carrying tank at the end of World War I. This R.E. tank, by means of its jib, could lay and also pick up the bridge after use. A lighter bridge-layer was tested in the 1920s, but funds were not available for continuing the development. In the 1930s Nicholas Straussler, a Hungarian who emigrated to Britain and who was responsible for many important inventions and developments in the A.F.V. field, produced an actual working embodiment of a vaulting device which had been part of Günther Burstyn's proposed *Motorgeshütz* in 1911. Burstyn's drawing showed two arms projecting from each end of his 'tank' with a wheel in each arm. The arms could be raised or lowered as required, the rear wheels being driven as an aid to traction and the front pair, which could be pivoted, being used for steering. The arms, of course, as Straussler's embodiment showed, gave the vehicle a bridging capacity.

Another approach to crossing certain types of ground, and what is really another type of bridging vehicle, is the track-layer with ground pressure less than that of a man. The American Weasel of World War II was a small amphibious cargo carrier designed to cross soft ground, tundra or snow. Weasels were tried as tractors to tow small anti-mine rollers but lacked the power for the job. The British developed an offshoot of the Universal Carrier late in the war for the express purpose of crossing minefields or areas where normal track-layers might bog down because of mud or slipping shale. This was called the Tugboat Carrier.

31
Wire-laying B29 Weasel, used by the American army in Europe in 1945.

Another device for crossing larger gaps and slippery surfaces was the Bobbin or Carpet-layer used by the British on vehicles ranging from Loyd and Universal carriers up to and including Churchill heavy tanks. Some were employed at Dieppe and also in the desert and the Normandy landings. All were track-layers with an additional wide wool and canvas track or carpet carried in front on a bobbin or roller and unreeled as the vehicle advanced.

Of even greater value in World War II were the various bridge-laying devices, most of which were created out of obsolescent tanks. Some vehicles themselves became bridges. These were called ARKs (Armoured Ramp Karriers). They had hinged run-

ways fore and aft and, in some models, matching runways over the top of the tank which had its turret removed. In other models (the so-called Italian pattern) the crossing tank travelled over the tracks of the ARK tank. Other bridging expedients were tank chassis with mechanically or hydraulically-controlled scissor bridges which could be unfolded, laid and later picked up and refolded. These also towed girder bridges supported at one end by an orolo or tracked trailer; and some girder bridges were supported by two tanks, one a utility vehicle and the other a combat tank.

The British in particular built a considerable variety of bridging vehicles and furnished them to other Allies as needed. The Germans had a few assault ladder and bridging tanks. The Russians improvised a few vehicles of this type but concentrated for the most part on a different approach. One was the driving of stakes into a river bed. These would not be visible from the ground or the air but would serve as a treadway—albeit a precarious one. Another was the fabrication of a framework which would be pushed into a river where it would sink out of sight but still be available as a treadway.

Combat vehicles during World War II sometimes were used as carriers for assault boats together with a few connecting timbers. These could not only act as floats for the vehicle itself but could also serve as unit equipment for making up infantry assault boats or in fabricating pontoon bridges. The Germans use this method today.

The Japanese devised an interesting bridge-layer in addition to conventional types. This comprised a small bridge carried on a

34

framework. By means of a small explosive charge the bridge was literally shot through the air to close a small gap. They also had a cable-layer to shoot a line across a river for creating a raft ferry for crossing swift streams.

At the present time the Swedes have a bridge-layer which slides its bridge forward by telescopic beam during laying instead of raising it in the air as in the case of Scissor bridges, thus making the operation less conspicuous in action.

A field expedient used by American troops in overcoming the bocage country of Normandy in 1944 was the Rhino, or Culin Hedgerow device, invented by Sergeant Curtis Culin and Lieutenant Steve Litton. It consisted of sharpened steel angle irons welded to the bow of a tank and used as a fork to loosen and tear up ground and move it out of the way.

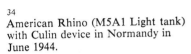

34

American Rhino (M5A1 Light tank) with Culin device in Normandy in June 1944.

In a way this was the same approach that the Japanese had in their ramming tank designed to crash through the forests of Manchuria when war with Russia was expected in the 1930s. Hitler asked for similar tanks during the siege of Stalingrad to break up houses used as strong points by the Russian defenders. A few of these Rammtigers were made but not in time to be used.

35

Japanese HO-K ramming-tank intended for use in breaking trees.

Bulldozers serve a similar purpose. The Americans and British found them of great value in building airfields even under fire. To protect the operator, both British and Americans built and still provide armoured cabs or complete armoured hulls designed to be lifted on to a commercial bulldozer and bolted into place. Tankdozers, that is dozer blades on the front of a tank, were used for the same purpose as well as for ripping open dugouts and foxholes or for covering the entrances to caves occupied by enemy troops.

The U.S. Marine Corps today uses dozers or ploughs having buoyancy tanks for beach work. The entire assembly can be released by means of explosive bolts.

During World War II the British developed the R.E. tank into the A.V.R.E. The need for this type of vehicle was made abundantly apparent during the Canadian raid on Dieppe on 19 August 1942. The A.V.R.E. was a converted Churchill Mark III or IV with the 6pdr replaced by a spigot mortar known as the Petard which was a large calibre low velocity howitzer for hurling heavy explosive charges nicknamed 'Flying Dustbins'. Brackets were fitted on the A.V.R.E. to take various devices such as dozers, anti-mine rollers and ploughs, mechanical charge placers, carpet layers, etc. For towing engineer stores (including fascines and explosives) a drop-side sledge with steel runners, called the A.V.R.E. sledge, was produced.

Prior to World War II it had been generally believed that various obstacles such as 'dragon's teeth' or railway rails set at angles in reinforced concrete would deny an area to tanks, forcing them to be channelled into a well-sited target area. But there is usually a defence against every weapon or tactic. It was found during World War II that systematic shell-fire from artillery and tanks would shatter reinforced concrete thus enabling tanks to move through the rubble. The A.V.R.E. could break up such obstacles. The British and American assault tanks were intended to function similarly by possessing sufficient armour to move in close to such concrete obstacles with weapons heavy enough to be effective. The A.V.R.E. is continued in Britain. The U.S. post-war combat engineer vehicle is its equivalent but is even more versatile in that it is also equipped with a crane.

For thick walls or concrete pillboxes which resisted even these weapons, others were devised. In the United States it was a

36
Churchill inspects a British N.L.E. trench digger and personnel carrier.
37
American M5 armoured cab on a commercial bulldozer, used for building airfields under fire.

British Goat demolition device, used for destroying walls and similar obstacles.

demolition tank carrying a large calibre rocket tube on either side of a massive turret with a flame-thrower in between. The British had the Carrot, the Onion, the Double Onion, the Kid and the Goat. Some of these explosive charge devices, most of which were carried by A.V.R.E.s were used in the Normandy landings. Essentially they comprised a framework from which a heavy explosive charge could be placed at the base of a wall or hooked to the top and detonated. The Double Onion was capable of dropping charges on both sides of a wall and detonating the charges. The Centurion Viper today has a rack on the dozer blade which can be used for placing explosives in somewhat the same way.

A new earth-moving method sponsored by the U.S. Army Research and Development Laboratory at Fort Belvoir is the Redsod, an acronym formed from Repetitive Explosive Device for Soil Displacement. The Redsod, an experimental device announced in January 1967, was described as comprising one or more large combustion chambers mounted between the vehicle and the bulldozer blade. A compressed air and petrol or diesel fuel mixture is pumped in and ignited by a spark plug. The dirt acts as a piston and is thrown upward and to the sides by the high pressure gases. At two miles per hour the Redsod with a single combustion chamber could move almost three times the dirt which could be moved by the normal dozer. It was expected that additional combustion chambers could be added which would increase the capacity to thirty times that of the normal bulldozer.

Allied to this is an American device known as the Rapid Excavation and Mining Concept (REAM). This is an inexpensive projectile that permits a tank or cannon to dig tunnels, trenches and road cuts. REAM employs concrete projectiles, plastic cases resembling beer cans, and shatters rock only in the impact area resulting in a tunnel without the supports necessary for the roof of a conventional drill and blast tunnel.

An American improvisation was made during the Korean War— a device which permitted the laying of the accordion wire which is used today in place of barbed wire. Accordion or coiled wire can get tangled in tank tracks today as effectively as barbed wire could in World War I. It is usually strung by hand but the American wire-layer on a medium tank was capable of laying a triple band of such wire while the crew was completely protected by armour.

The Soviet Union more recently has developed some highly
sophisticated equipment for mine-laying. Some of this equipment
was not even in the hands of their East European allied armies
when specimens were captured from the Egyptians by the Israelis
in 1967. One of these was a track-laying vehicle which launched
bundles of contact mines over a 160 foot area by means of compressed air. The mines, called 'deadly moles', were said to dig
themselves into the ground automatically. Another Soviet device
for laying mines which was captured by the Israelis was a track-
laying vehicle resembling a plough. It was said to be capable of
sowing an area 320 by 160 feet with 600 contact mines in a period
of ten minutes.

The British have a mechanical mine-layer using rectangular
mines. These not only expose more frontage per mine to an enemy
but also reduce the width of the trench needed for emplacement. And the U.S.A.F. in 1971 had under development the
Grasshopper anti-vehicle mine system which involved electronic
mines dropped from fighter aircraft. Equipped with sensors and
protruding antennae the mines are detonated by approaching
vehicles. Such mines are expensive and complex and perhaps
would find their best use in helping to stop a sudden enemy
armoured attack or when a situation permitted the use of aircraft
as rear guards in a withdrawal.

One of the problems of warfare in the jungles of Vietnam was
the ease with which guerrillas could disappear; defoliation was used
but was not too successful. In 1957, a device known as the Transphibian Tactical Crusher or Tree Eater was introduced, a product

of the Le Tourneau firm. It could crush trees up to twenty inches in diameter and break down a path many feet wide. Two huge star-shaped barrel-like wheels on the front and one in the rear formed a huge tricycle-like arrangement with an armoured cab. These wheels were hollow except for the motors which drove them. In spite of its weight of ninety-seven tons the vehicle was amphibious. For transportation, the vehicle broke down into twelve loads. Considerable use was also made of the Rome Plow, a bulldozer with a sharp prong on one side used to split trees of large diameter in order to simplify dozing.

Another type of engineering vehicle is the robot. The first robot tank was the Japanese Nagayama of the early 1930s. Other robot vehicles appeared in France and the United States but were used principally to provide target vehicles for gunnery practice. The British had both wheeled and tracked miniature robots as did the Japanese, but it remained for the Germans to develop the robot to a high degree.

As conceived in Germany, the robot was a demolition vehicle to be used against enemy tanks, pillboxes or strong points. One of the German vehicles was amphibious as was one British vehicle. The German vehicles were tiny track-layers which carried up to a quarter of a ton of explosive. They could be operated by one man to a point where he dismounted from the vehicle but could send it on either by wire or by wireless control to the point of demolition. There the explosive charge was dropped and detonated while the vehicle was returning to the operator.

Some of the German robots were fitted with remote-controlled rockets or anti-aircraft guns and controlled from the ground or from a larger command vehicle. These small vehicles were known as Goliaths to the Allied troops who encountered them, although this was the German name for only one model. In addition to the various models of these devices built by the Germans they also converted captured British Universal Carriers into robots–some as demolition vehicles and some as supply vehicles–during the siege of Stalingrad. Such vehicles would lend themselves to employment as remote-controlled mine seekers, mine sweepers and vehicles carrying Geiger counters for testing radioactive areas.

41

SdKfz301, a miniature demolition vehicle of World War II.

6. Armoured Personnel Carriers, Command & Miscellaneous Vehicles

How to cross a fire-swept zone to engage the enemy without too high a proportion of the attacking troops being killed or wounded in the process has been the preoccupying problem of soldiers and military inventors for centuries. The armoured personnel carrier provides the answer.

During World War I some of the later British heavy tanks were lengthened by inserting an extra six feet of armour plate midway along each side. The additional space inside was intended for carrying infantry who could be dropped off to consolidate and hold positions taken by the tanks. However, the troops carried in this fashion were so sick from the fumes and the motion of the tank that they were far from fit to fight when they disembarked and could only take part in the battle after they had had time to recover.

The British then built the Mark IX, known as the Pig, a heavy track-layer specifically intended as a supply and personnel carrier. The Mark IX could carry thirty fully equipped soldiers together with their personal weapons and equipment. The plans for 1919 contemplated also the use of some 22,000 small track-layers each capable of carrying a squad of men. Only a few hundred of these were actually completed in Britain and the United States. They were variously called the Newton tractor, the Fordson, the Overland, the Buick or the Studebaker tractor. An armoured hull was designed to be dropped into the last named causing it to be referred to as the Studebaker tank.

Between the wars the British had tracked personnel carriers, though none had overhead protection. Both the United States and Germany also recognized the need for armoured carriers for infantry before the outset of World War II. Both countries developed armoured half-track vehicles for carrying part of the infantry component of their armoured divisions–indeed, by the end of World War II all the infantry battalions in an American armoured division were carried in half-tracks, of which sixty-two were needed to lift one battalion. This created its own problems of route congestion and maintenance.

In the last year of World War II the British, Canadians and Poles fighting with the Allies removed the superstructures from medium tanks and self-propelled guns and thereby created armoured personnel carriers (A.P.C.s) which were called Kangaroos by the British and Canadians and Kaczka by the Poles. Fifty-three Kangaroos could lift a battalion of infantry.

The Germans devised troop-carrying sleds to be towed behind tanks, and the Americans and the British did likewise. Occasionally they were used successfully in the snows of Russia, but sand clouds produced in desert operations doomed the British experiment to failure. The Americans used them in the break-out at Anzio.

Since World War II the concept of the A.P.C. as a sort of

battle-taxi–a vehicle which would take troops to the edge of the battlefield where they would continue on foot–has given place to the view that the A.P.C. is an armoured *fighting* vehicle; complete with its passengers, it has an important battle-role to play in its own right. The early open-topped tank chassis and half-tracks have been replaced by specially built carriers that have overhead protection for their passengers, that are amphibious, that can be sealed against gas or bacteriological warfare and that can even give a substantial measure of protection against nuclear explosions and can safely cross irradiated ground. The modern A.P.C. is, in fact, a vehicle to fight from.

The Americans pioneered the use of rear doors to avoid the drawback of the passengers having to jump over the side which made them vulnerable to enemy fire.

The French AMX-VTT gave carriers a new look with front engine, double doors in the rear, and the passengers seated facing outwards so that they could use their own weapons through ports in the side armour to augment the fire of the machine-gun turret in front. In 1959 the West Germans built the HS30 (having previously built an unarmed carrier for export) which had a 20mm gun in a turret–the logical development in the change of role of the A.P.C. from battle-taxi to A.F.V. They have now replaced it with the Marder which also has a 20mm gun mounted in the turret as well as two 7.62mm machine-guns.

The British use the Saracen wheeled carrier as well as the FV432 tracked carrier. The Russians, like the British, use both multi-wheel A.P.C.s and track-laying A.P.C.s, the latter being an outgrowth of the PT76 amphibious tank. Some of the smaller countries like Austria and Switzerland have developed some excellent track-laying armoured personnel carriers which are also used in many other roles. Some of these, in turn, have been adopted by other countries including the HS30 by West Germany. The United States Army, after a great deal of experimentation, finally ended with the M113 type A.P.C. which has been adopted by many other countries and is being manufactured in Italy. Like those of other countries it is amphibious. The U.S. Marine Corps also has developed amphibious A.P.C.s out of its war-time experience with L.V.T.s.

The M113 has many roles in American service. One of these is for ground surveillance when equipped with highly sophisticated radar. Such radar can detect and identify vehicular targets up to 7,000 yards and personnel targets up to about 2,000 yards. In Vietnam the M113 was in considerable use as an amphibious tank.

Other developments in A.P.C.s have taken place in the United States, but a definite design has not been accepted because of conflicting views within the U.S. Army as to the proper role for A.P.C.s These are: as a carrier to take men to a fighting area after which the vehicles would be released to carry supplies; as an infantry-carrier to accompany tanks in battle with infantry dismounting only to support tanks or to hold ground taken and capable of engaging in A.P.C. to A.P.C. combat; as an infantry carrier used in the anti-aircraft role and not to accompany tanks in battle but for exploitation only; or that several types of carriers are needed, each specifically designed for one of the above roles.

Rear doors are not universal in A.P.C.s. HS30 has none. Overhead cover is not universal. Some Russian A.P.C.s have none–the wheeled variety in particular. What is, or is virtually, universal is armament and swim capability, as well, naturally, as armour protection. The future of the A.F.V. may well lie in the A.P.C. that carries its own infantry, has guided missile or other armament; and so we get back at last to a realization on a sophisticated scale of the swarms of skirmishers. There is one school of thought which feels that the tank is becoming too complex, and its individual unit-cost too high.

One of the first armoured command vehicles was the British Mark IV tank with wireless equipment employed in World War I. The French also had the Char T.S.F. (*télègraphie sans fils*) which was the Renault F.T. with a box superstructure instead of a gun turret. The British and Canadians also used a few Renault F.T. tanks as command tanks.

In the period between the two world wars, the French created a few light track-laying command vehicles. The British Box Tańk was built in 1928 to give a battalion commander better facilities for exercising command in the field than he normally had in a tank. It really came into its own with the Tank Brigade in 1931 when it was used by the Brigade Commander. In the United States there were some copies of the French Char T.S.F., and one was modernized by substituting an air-cooled engine during the period when the Americans had a counterpart of the British Mechanized Force.

Just before, and also during, World War II the British used armoured trucks as command vehicles completely fitted out with map-boards and wireless, together with armoured cars as radio link cars. The Americans used half-tracks and scout cars in the same way and various commanders in the field improvized command vehicles out of light tanks and M8 howitzer motor carriages.

The Germans made considerable use of half-tracks and armoured cars as observation posts, command vehicles and telephone and radio link vehicles. However, before the war the light tank PzKpfw I chassis had already been used as a command vehicle and, as the war progressed, command vehicles were converted from combat tanks in almost every weight category. Among other items of equipment in these vehicles (which had dummy guns) Leica cameras were fitted in the gun sight openings to take combat photos. 'Field-fix' in North Africa added a large artillery observation scope in the gun mantlet after it was found that observation from the turret hatch often subjected the vehicle to high burst artillery fire.

The Austrian Saurer RR7 wheel-and-track vehicle was also used as a command vehicle by the Germans but was fragile and not too well liked. Today, in most countries, few command vehicles appear to be in use. Exceptions are the British Army and the U.S. Marine Corps.

Among the miscellaneous vehicles one of the most interesting was the C.D.L. (canal defence light) also known by several other cover-names. It was evolved from an invention of British Navy Commander De Thoren in World War I, and although it went through several experimental modifications between the two world wars in both Britain and France, no large-scale action was taken until World War II. This device was a combat tank with a special turret containing a 154 million candle power arc light and a reflector and a narrow slot containing a shutter which produced a blinding flicker. A thirty degree angle of light made possible an advance of vehicles in line with the cones intersecting, producing deep triangular shadows between vehicles wherein infantry could advance. It was almost impossible for anyone to face this light even with dark glasses.

Although five British and six American tank battalions were trained in the use of C.D.L., it was one of the best kept secrets of World War II. So little was allowed to leak out about the C.D.L. tanks and their training areas were so restricted that in the end

British Grant C.D.L. (Canal defence light).

the secrecy defeated its own purpose because the tactical planners never seriously took them into consideration, and they were never fully used in action.

The first tanks to be used for C.D.L. purposes in Britain were Matildas. Thereafter the vehicles were M3 medium tanks in both countries although a few American improvements were made on an M4A1 chassis, and experimental models were made in Britain on M4A4 and Cromwell tanks.

The C.D.L. type of vehicle might still be of value as a weapon of opportunity, especially in view of the development in Britain in 1973 of an anti-riot weapon which could have military application as well. The weapon is a modification of the flashing strobe light used in night clubs. This light, when combined with ultrasonic waves, produces nausea and, it is said, also produces epileptic fits in some people.

Armoured vehicles require repairs and often may require towing or salvage after upset. As a rule armoured recovery vehicles were created out of older or obsolescent vehicles of the same weight class as the vehicle they were intended to handle. During World War II there was a considerable variety of vehicles in all armies produced as experience dictated needs. Winches, cables, cranes utilizing the tank turret, A-frames, welding equipment, tools and spare parts were provided. The Germans also provided a light-proof tent, and vehicles the British thought were derelict one day would be repaired during the night and back in action the next day through use of such equipment by the Germans.

Since World War II all major countries have designed A.R.V.s on standard tank chassis, building them on the same chassis as the tanks they are built to serve.

A variation on the A.R.V. is the B.A.R.V. (Beach Armoured Recovery Vehicle) used by the British. It is a vehicle designed to render aid to other vehicles in surf or during operations where they may drown. Built with high sides and well scuppered, they can operate satisfactorily in fairly deep water. The American counterpart is the L.V.T.-R., a recovery vehicle on an amphibious L.V.T. chassis.

Speciality vehicles as adjuncts to A.R.V.s were the British

starting and charging vehicles built on the Loyd Carrier chassis. British tanks did not have auxiliary electric generators and since there was considerable drainage on the storage battery, the starting and charging vehicles came in for considerable use. Welding equipment also was mounted on the ubiquitous Universal Carrier as an assistant to the larger A.R.V.s.

In addition to using older tank chassis for recovery vehicles, Kangaroos and in other such ways, the chassis were also utilized to improvise cargo, ammunition supply, tanker or 'milker' vehicles and tractors (or towers as they were called by the British). Of course, track-laying cargo and utility vehicles, tractors and prime movers designed as such have also been built in many weight classes in many countries.

Finally, there were the Nellies (N.L.E., Naval Landing Equipment), exceptionally large track-layers intended as transport for marines in a landing operation and then for digging a trench for them so they could be deposited safely on the beach. Only a few of these were built by the British Navy since it was seen that their disadvantages outweighed their advantages.

The United States Army has established a programme for 'biomechanics' to investigate nature with a view to improving the effectiveness of weapons. It is beginning to be thought that present system-designs have reached the ultimate in their capabilities and that investigation of living systems may be the only hope for continued improvement.

By now it should be apparent that a tank can be many things. Even an A.P.C. as used under conditions that were encountered in Vietnam can, under those conditions, be defined as a tank. Pershing tanks, often used in Korea although classed as tanks, actually were only artillery.

Many of the vehicles mentioned in this part, strictly speaking, are not tanks. But the word is so easy to use that their general appearance is likely to cause them to be called tanks even when they are not. If the vehicle has tracks people call it a tank, if it has wheels they call it an armoured car. Even that does not always hold true. Television commentators, for example, habitually refer to the six-wheeled Saracen armoured personnel carrier as a tank. The fact is, it would seem, that the word tank has by now its own minatory connotation that makes it applicable in the public mind to any armoured fighting vehicle.

PART TWO

Tank
Characteristics

7. Tank Design

Reduced to essentials, the combat effectiveness of a tank is measured primarily by its ability to bring effective fire to bear on an enemy and to make such fire-power mobile. Tremendous advances in design have occurred since the first crude and mechanically unreliable tanks appeared in World War I. The success of the tank in war has naturally caused the parallel development of many devices intended to destroy it. But this in turn has produced a forced evolution in tanks in order to maintain their position as effective combat weapons.

Design is thus based on a compromise between mobility, fire-power and protection. The proper ratio between these can be found only by determining the tank's mission. Three questions must be answered:

1. What is the function to be?
2. What armament is needed to carry out that function and how best can it be mounted?
3. What is the best type of chassis to make that fire-power mobile?

During World War II the United States criteria for tanks involved such additional matters as volume production, influence of ship-board loading on vehicle size, tactics, training, vehicle stamina, agility, crew comfort, armour thickness and shape, silhouette versus mechanical layout, and such logistical factors as maintainability, fuel capacity and kind, radius of operation, track-life, component life, land and sea transportability and bridge-crossing and fording. In other countries some of these factors were considered to be of no consequence or were ignored, while

43

Sketch of the original Christie tank.

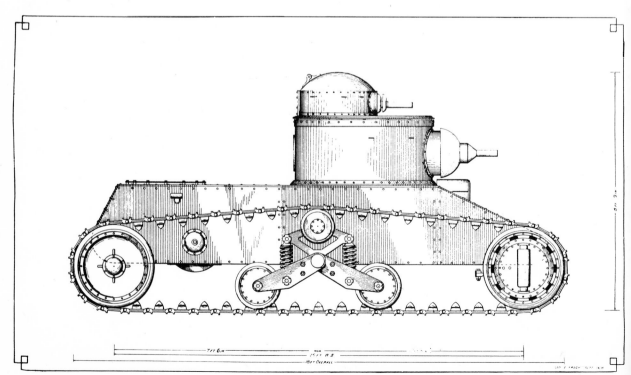

44
T26E3 Medium tanks on the assembly line in the United States.

others were added, such as rate of fire, calibre of weapon, sighting and fire control, foolproofness, vision and blind spots, ventilation, tunnel-clearance, railroad track gauge and others. But in all cases function was and is the first consideration.

After function is established and any limitations are spelt out by any of the many agencies usually involved, layouts are made. The next step is to make a wooden mock-up. Drawings are then made and checked, and one or more pilot or prototype vehicles are built. These are 'toolroom jobs' because they are in fact custom built. If the design is standardized, the manufacturer or arsenal then makes arrangements with hundreds of contractors who, in turn, contract with thousands of subcontractors, at the same time scheduling the flow of each product into the contractors' and prime contractors' assembly lines. During World War II, as an example, one large American prime tank contractor had 865 subcontractors, and they in turn had 5,432 sub-subs. And in actual fact the process of making and checking the 40,000 or so blueprints for the over 30,000 parts and 100,000 separate pieces often was not complete by the time the first production vehicle came off the line.*

For a long time the cost of producing a tank in the United States was reckoned at one dollar per pound weight, but that formula went out of the window when the cost of the MBT70 rose to over six times as much. A modern American battle tank is a much more complex vehicle than those built during World War II and costs well over £100,000 (app. $250,000), at least three times as much as, for example, an American medium tank cost in 1941-45. The U.S. M60A1 cost $257,000, the Improved M60A1 $320,000 and the M60A2 $458,000. If research and development costs are included this latter figure would be doubled. In the Russian economy, however, the same amount of money could probably produce five times as many vehicles.

In addition to the vehicles themselves, spare parts must be produced to keep them running. Spare parts needs are difficult to compute, depending as they do on campaign conditions. Desert warfare in World War II involved extremes of temperature but the khamsin, the hot south wind, caused the most serious problems. It whirled dust and sand into carburettors, radiator cores, air cleaners and engines and entered even tiny crevices, making it impossible to maintain vehicles or conduct almost any other activity, in addition to reducing visibility to a few yards. This and the flies produced human as well as mechanical problems. Vehicle tracks and bellies suffered from mine damage in all theatres and tracks especially suffered from African rocks and South Pacific coral.

---

*This entire process takes time but is a part of all industrial process and is known as 'lead time'. To illustrate with actual tank examples, the following are some representative lead times in months from the start of the design:

Vehicle	Prototype Built	Pilot Built	Production Start	Total Time
British Cromwell	10	6	3	19
Russian T34	—	$13\frac{1}{2}$	$4\frac{1}{2}$	18
*German Panther	$5\frac{1}{2}$	2	$4\frac{1}{2}$	12
*U.S. M3 Medium	$9\frac{1}{2}$	$3\frac{1}{2}$	$1\frac{1}{2}$	$14\frac{1}{2}$

*Several basic components previously designed

An idea of the materials involved in producing a tank can be obtained from the following official estimate of the materials and manpower needed in 1955 to produce an American M48 Medium tank: 90,000 lbs. of steel, 6,512 lbs. of bauxite, 1,800 lbs. of rubber, 950 lbs. of manganese, 1,484 lbs. of copper, 520 lbs. of nickel, 60 lbs. of cotton, 1,915 lbs. of chromium, 100 lbs. of tin and 75,000 man-hours or the equivalent of producing some 30 automobiles.

Soviet refuelling system in operation.

The handling and rehandling up to ninety times of storage batteries by native help in India and Burma, obsolescences, shipping losses, abandonment of bases for tactical or strategical reasons, ship shortages and rerouting resulting in cargo dumpings, capture by the enemy, bombing, troop fatigue, inadequate packing, lack of cross-identification numbers, the deliberate wastage in using full boxes of spare parts to corduroy roads and the overall filling of pipelines up to 12,000 miles long, all had a bearing on design and supply of vehicle maintenance parts. For each dollar spent by the United States on vehicles during World War II forty cents were allocated on spare parts.

Some two supply and maintenance vehicles are needed to keep one tank moving. The average civilian passenger car owner is dissatisfied if he fails to get a performance of at least fifteen miles per gallon of petrol from his car. The average battle tank in the best of going gets about one mile per gallon.

Transporting by rail and by ship requires special blocking and chocking as well as planning for tunnel clearances, passing tracks and crane loading facilities. Design must take such problems into consideration.

The complications of design can also be seen from the specifications under which combat vehicles are produced today in the United States. Among other things, they must be operable from 120°F. to −65°F., be completely water-proof, be completely fungus-proof, be capable of deep-water fording, possess low noise level, be air-portable if possible, possess the maximum in crew comfort, be capable of being maintained even though the crew members are wearing heavy mittens, have ease of control to reduce crew fatigue and possess a high degree of standardization and parts interchangeability.

Up to the time of World War II it was said that the philosophy of tank design demonstrated national characteristics. The French emphasized armour protection. The British, Italians and Japanese designed a hull and then found a place for the engine. The Americans, Czechs and Swedes designed a chassis and then found a place for the armament. The Germans and Russians designed a gun and then made a chassis for it.

This may be an over-simplification but even if true, World War II made everyone place the emphasis on armament. However, until this became inescapable, American love of gadgetry, the influence of politicians who meddled for merely political reasons, the unfortunate fact that military mental mobility often was less than

Ammunition stowage in the Soviet
T34 Medium tank.

military vehicle mobility, lack of organization and over-zealousness,
led to much waste.

The British too were far from being free from political
influences and panic news interpretation. In addition, it might be
posited that British tradition as the birthplace of the tank caused
much wasted design effort to prove for sentimental reasons that
British designs must lead the world. The Russians had the view
that a large percentage of tanks would become battle casualties
before being overtaken by mechanical failure. They relied on
quantity rather than quality, although quality continually improved
under the pressure of volume. The Russians also took into consideration their limited industrial capacity, kept their designs
simple and held down the number of type variations.

Of all the European tank producing countries before World
War II, Czechoslovakia perhaps best blended reliability and armament and showed imagination in vehicle design. Until overrun by
Germany in March 1939, great progress had been made in track
design, suspension systems, automatic transmissions, hydraulic and
compressed air booster steering, pre-selective gear shifting, use of
range-finders and hydraulic recoil arresters. The Germans benefited
from this engineering skill during World War II as the Russians
have benefited since 1948. Russia also has benefited from British
and American vehicles furnished under the Lend-Lease Agreement. American Pershing and Patton tanks captured or overrun
in Korea and later recovered often were found intact except for
their transmissions which had been removed. More recent Russian
vehicles reflect the additional knowledge gained.

Design of any device is always an engineering compromise.
Furthermore, designers reflect their own personality, ability or
interpretation of what is wanted for carrying out the tactical and
strategical doctrines of their respective countries.

It would seem generally sound that nothing should be incorporated in any weapon unless it contributes directly to the purpose
for which it was created. Still, there seem to be designers who have
a passion for complexity rather than for need and reliability.
Over-complexity can result in failure of a mission because of
mechanical inadequacy or breakdown more than from enemy
action. Weapons have continued to become more complex as time
goes on, so training requirements necessarily must keep pace. The
skilled designer always will be able to produce designs approaching
perfection, but an armoured vehicle must remain within the
capacity of average soldiers to use it properly.

There is another point which has great significance but which is overlooked in western countries in particular: automobile manufacturers have long known that the civilian public finds far more faults in automobiles than are uncovered even in the severe testing done by manufacturers. The reason is that such tests are conducted by highly skilled test course technicians who are interested in their work. This is true also of military testing. But the soldier who dislikes army life may care little about careful use of equipment or about proper maintenance. In combat conditions soldiers may be too tired to perform as efficiently as they might when rested and will drive their vehicles accordingly. Or the tactical situation may be such that there is little time to spare for optimum care. These are situations difficult to simulate in a test situation.

A typical example of wartime needs overriding vehicle limitations is that of transport vehicles. It was recognized during World War II that a two and a half ton truck was being tested with a two and a half ton load but that in action the load would often be up to ten tons, making breakdowns frequent. Despite this recognition of the facts little has been done since to make testing more realistic. As a result deficiencies show up after issue, necessitating major design changes. Similar problems arise with armoured vehicles with their greater complexity.

It would be desirable to create a yardstick by which overall design adequacy could be measured, especially if it could be applied while a tank was still on the drawing board where they all look perfect. Several formulae for this purpose have been suggested but have not been generally accepted. There may be no one formula which would be acceptable even within one country. For several years the systems research group at Ohio State University in the United States has been attempting to develop a theory relating tank performance to crew and vehicle characteristics. But even if they succeeded in finding one acceptable in the United States it probably would not be acceptable elsewhere.

The study group which, by the use of electronic computers, worked out the formulae under which the U.S./F.R.G. (Federal Republic of Germany) MBT70 tank was built was not able to reconcile certain viewpoints between American and German design policies, and this is probably as it should be. Both countries had adequate combat experience on which to draw, but American commitments around the world are far broader than German commitments which are confined to Europe.

Computer graphics grew largely out of the doctoral thesis of Ivan E. Sutherland of the Massachusetts Institute of Technology and was later carried on by Evans and Sutherland Computer Corporation in Salt Lake City, Utah. The new tool, which is already in use, comprises a T.V.-like screen linked to a computer, on which sketches can be made using beams of light produced by pointing a light pen at the screen from a short distance. A keyboard straightens lines, proportions circles, enables the sketch to be enlarged, engages moving parts, shows top, front, side and angled perspectives, and even rotates the new design in a complete circle on the screen or deletes it entirely. The sketches can be stored on tape at any stage or recorded on microfilm.

The system is already used by several aircraft and automobile manufacturers and by the U.S. Defense Department research agencies; many computer manufacturers are working to develop graphics systems.

The increasing complexity of fighting vehicles requires that more than ordinary attention be paid to adopting those improvements genuinely felt to be necessary but in as simple a form as is compatible with the improvements. The more duties a crew member has, the lower will be his efficiency, and as fatigue sets in the ability of a crew to function as a crew may make impossible the carrying out of a mission. No matter how well trained a crew may be, combat fatigue and stress reduce the ability to perform. There could well be a return to the system used by Bolivia during the Gran Chaco War in the mid-1930s when spare crews were used because the heat and humidity were so great. In peace-time, professionals may perform well but quality deteriorates with war-time conscription.

In peacetime, professionals may be able to perform not only their own duties but those of other crew members as well. This also should be true in war in the event of casualties, but it remains an ideal. In the case of the United States during World War II, thousands of trained tankers were used as infantry replacements while tank units received casuals as replacements, often necessitating combat with some crew members having had no more than a few hours training.

The requirements of maintenance of highly technical vehicles necessitates skilled maintenance personnel as well–another argument for simplicity.

The size of the crew in an armoured vehicle is dependent on the mission for which it is intended and on its mechanical layout. Basic duties in the case of a combat vehicle are those of the driver, the commander and the gunner. Non-fighting armoured vehicles have the first two and whatever others are needed for carrying out the mission assigned. And vehicles with light weapons

47
View of the American M60A1
M.B.T. undergoing maintenance.

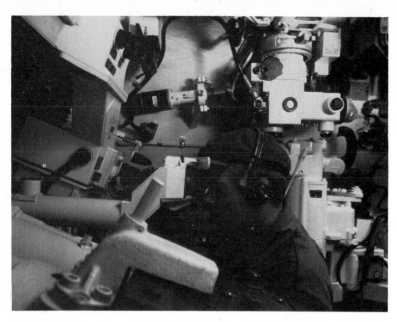

Gunner's position in the German Leopard 1.

may differ in crew make-up from those mounting heavier weapons.

The development of automatic loaders and other refinements have changed crew composition and duties. And today a tank commander is seldom required also to function as the main armament gunner. It has long been believed that the poor showing made by French tanks against the Germans in 1940 was due to French design combining the two functions. On the other hand Russian T34/76 tank commanders appear to have done well in this respect, although even in this case the subsequent T34/85 separated the functions. Current practice recognizes that a tank commander can operate best with only that basic responsibility. For the few occasions when the situation would suggest that he act as gunner, the modern vehicle has override devices enabling him to do so. What has not been universally accepted is that a tank commander should not have to keep scanning the sky for enemy aircraft or man a weapon to combat them. His responsibility should be the terrain, the enemy on the ground and other vehicles of his unit, thus leaving sky-watching for the gunners of special A/A vehicles.

The modern Swedish S-tank (Strv103) makes the driver also the gunner for the main armament but limits his driving to the forward direction only. Another driver, who is also the wireless operator, faces rearward and is responsible for driving the tank backward. In some tanks the driver may also control the firing of fixed or remote-controlled secondary weapons up to cannon size, as in the World War II French Char B. In other tanks secondary armament may be operated by machine-gunners or by a wireless operator.

Tank radios are interconnected with the intra-vehicle crew communicating system. And most post-World War II vehicles have an outside telephone with extension cable so that close contact can be maintained with accompanying infantry or with the tank commander outside the tank when he is directing fire from a dug-in position or similar situation.

One of the problems facing the combined armies of the NATO countries is the diversity of language. Considerable progress has been made toward a more general use of codes and of English, but this is a difficult problem to solve and one which has been made worse by the increasing use of radio.

8. Armament, Fire Control and Vision

The weapons in a tank must be mounted so as to permit the elevation and traverse needed without allowing hostile fire to enter. In the case of hull or glacis mounts, a so-called ball mount is used. In the case of a turret mounted machine-gun a ball mount may be used with or without a shield or there may be a double acting mantlet. When a cannon is the main armament its trunnions form a vertical pivot behind a curved armour mantlet or a double bulb or cone of armour. These usually are external but internal mantlets have become more common in recent years. Lateral movement depends on traversing the turret.

Tank armament has come a long way since World War I. The French 37mm L/21 tank gun of that period had a muzzle velocity of 1,270 F/S (feet per second) while the British 57mm L/23 gun was only slightly better at 1,350 F/S. Even the famous French 75mm L/36 gun of that period only reached 1,790 F/S.

After World War I, machine-gun armament became the common main gun although there were a few .50 cal. and .60 cal. or 20mm guns and some 37mm and 39mm L/30–40 guns with muzzle velocities up to 2,800 F/S. The Germans up-gunned before the start of World War II with a 75mm L/24 gun with relatively low muzzle velocity. But as the war progressed this gun lengthened to L/33, L/44, L/48 and finally to L/70. The Russian 76.2mm L/16.5 gun lengthened successively to L/26, L/30.5 and L/41.5.

The muzzle velocity (M/V) of a cannon is in part dependent on the length of time the powder gases can continue to expand and act on the projectile, imparting increasing speed and rotation momentum.* The higher the M/V, the flatter the trajectory, but this is gained at the expense of chamber and tube erosion due to the increased amount of propellant. Nevertheless, this price has been and is being paid so that the main armament of a battle tank today probably is capable of penetrating up to fifteen inches of armour at normal or ninety degree angle of impact at 500 yards.

Even this amount of penetration may be increased. During trials, velocities in the neighbourhood of 20,000 F/S have been achieved with five pound projectiles using a variation of the shaped charge as a propellant. Chamber erosion, however, probably is extremely severe.

Tank guns firing fixed ammunition use vertical or horizontal sliding wedge semi-automatic breech blocks which close automatically when the round is pushed home. In a few instances automatic loading devices are employed. Either separate loading or fixed ammunition is in use, and a rate of fire of about eight rounds per minute is possible with either method but, with automatic loading, there is less crew fatigue. However, it must be remembered that fire rarely goes on indefinitely at such a rate. After all, the number of rounds carried seldom exceeds 100 and usually is less. A 90mm round of fixed ammunition is about the limit in length and weight that a man can handle in the crowded

---

*Work has been done on a paper-epoxy rotating band for cannon projectiles to replace the iron bands now used. Results indicate that accuracy is improved and gun tube life is increased.

49
Experimental modern automatic
loader for tank gun.

turret of a moving tank and the space required for an automatic
loader sets about the same limit.

Ammunition quantity decreases with weapon calibre. With
separate loading ammunition as in the British Chieftain, more
rounds can be carried, a smaller turret and turret ring are possible,
loading is easier and often is supplemented with a power rammer.
A disadvantage is a somewhat greater danger of fire. But fire is
a danger even with fixed ammunition. Late in World War II
American tanks were equipped with 'wet stowage' in which the
ammunition stowage tubes were surrounded with a mixture of
glycerine and water. But tank crews often loaded extra ammunition in the turret and the ready rack, which increased the hazard
of fire and negated the value of the wet stowage. (The wet stowage
in the British Chieftain is under pressure.)

Fixed rounds create an additional problem over the disposal of
spent cases unless they can be ejected outside the tank. The
loader, if he must handle them, has to wear asbestos gloves because
the cases are almost at white heat when ejected.

Combustible plastic ammunition cases would eliminate the
problem of handling white hot empty cases but as yet they have
not come into general use. Shillelagh ammunition for the
American Sheridan and M60 and caseless machine-gun ammunition are the only examples thus far known to be successful and
then only moderately so. The cases are made of the same substance
as the propellant but have a different molecular structure. Burning
residues make mandatory the use of carbon dioxide, air or nitrogen
jets to clean out the chamber in the case of the Shillelagh. In
the case of machine-gun ammunition, 'cook-off' rounds in the
chamber and erosion of firing pin and bolt face remain serious
and unsolved problems.

In manual loading of either fixed or separate rounds, the rounds must be accessible and arranged so that proper selection can be made quickly. These are the so-called 'ready rounds'. Additional rounds are stowed in the floor. Proponents of automatic loading claim it permits easier and faster round selection. With automatic loading, the mechanical system can fail. If it does, and the loader cannot be manually operated, the vehicle of course loses its combat effectiveness. On the other hand, the same can be said of most of the mechanical devices making up the modern combat tank. Automatic loaders are of two main types, the selective magazine type and the revolver type. The former is used in most countries, the latter is used in the French AMX13. In Sweden and in France crews have been reduced to three through their use. This in itself can be a disadvantage, paradoxical as that may seem, because with smaller crews tank units may be short of adequate man-power to meet the needs of security, maintenance and fatigues, to say nothing of casualties.

The automatic loader developed for the MBT70 by the Allison Division of General Motors Corporation comprises a belt-like magazine of canisters holding the various types of ammunition, both conventional and Shillelagh missiles. Loading can be in any sequence, but the desired type of round can be loaded selectively. At the end of each load cycle the magazine automatically positions the next available round. A chain-driven rammer pushes the round into the gun through a telescoping chute that extends to the breech for the loading operation and then retracts. The entire device is driven by a combination electrical and hydraulic mechanism. If either fails, the loader can be operated manually.

There is a rule of thumb that a cannon weighs roughly 100 times

50

Allison MBT70 automatic loader.

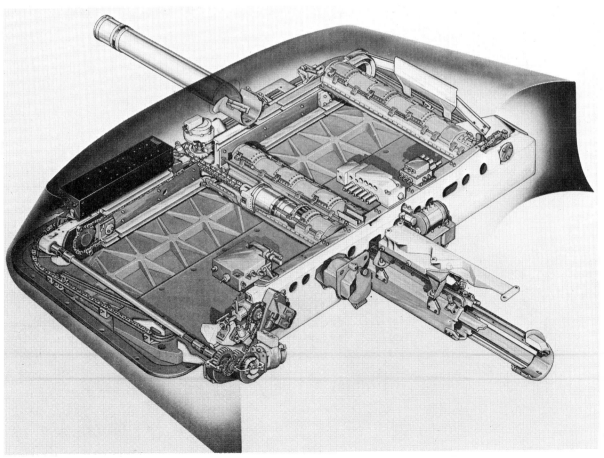

the weight of the projectile. Another rule of thumb states that the weight of a projectile in pounds is equal to one half the cube of the calibre in inches. At one time these were handy rules but today they are no longer accurate because ammunition varies considerably in both type and weight. In the 1920s most tank gun ammunition consisted of solid shot; modern weaponry has produced a variety.* Many are fired by electric primer, a German development of World War II, either by foot pedal or thumb trigger on the elevating hand-wheel or on the weapon itself.

It has long been recognized that the shaped or hollow charge is much less effective in a rifled gun than in a smoothbore. This is one of the reasons for the tremendous development which has taken place in light beam or wire-controlled missiles in recent years.

The French have overcome this limitation inherent in the shaped charge by devising their Obus G or OCC 105F1 for their AMX30 tank. This is a shell within a shell. The outer shell rotates on ball bearings, leaving the inner shell almost immobile through inertia. It thus arrives on target without rotation except for the outer shell which has had the advantage of the accuracy given it by the rifling. The British, on the other hand, have not exploited the shaped charge and prefer the big hole of the AP shell or the use of HESH to the much smaller hole of the HEAT.

After being obsolete for many years, the need for a canister shell led to its manufacture for use in Vietnam. Canister acts like the shot in a shotgun shell by spewing a large number of small balls, tiny steel arrows called flechettes, or other projectiles.

Muzzle blast is a serious problem on dry ground or loose snow. The dust or snow raised by firing obscures vision and slows the

Armour Piercing Capped (APC) (obsolete)

Armour Piercing carbide core

Armour Piercing Discarding Sabot (APDS)

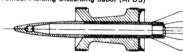

Sub-calibre fin-stabilized overlong APDS.

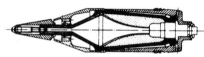

HEAT (French Obus G round)

High Explosive Squash Head (HESH)

51
Types of tank gun shells.

---

*AP–Armour piercing, uncapped.
AP (SE)–Armour piercing special effect, delayed action fuse.
APBC–Armour piercing, ballistic capped.
APC–Armour piercing, armour piercing capped.
APCBC–Armour piercing, armour piercing capped with ballistic cap.
APCR–Armour piercing composite rigid.
   or HVAPC–High velocity armour piercing capped.
APDS–Armour piercing discarding sabot, AP core with split shell body which drops away.
APSVDS–Armour piercing super velocity discarding sabot.
BH–Beehive round filled with 5000 flechettes ($1\frac{1}{2}$in long steel arrows) in compartments similar to a honeycomb.
CP–Concrete piercing.
HE–High explosive.
HEAT–High explosive anti-tank hollow charge.
HEI–High explosive incendiary.
HESH–High explosive squash head.
   or HEP–High explosive plastic.
HVAPDS(FS)–Hyper velocity armour piercing discarding shot (fin stabilized)
HVRAP–High velocity rocket assisted projectile.
ILL–Illuminating.
T–Tracer.
WP–White phosphorus.
The APBC is a solid shot with a plastic windscreen to reduce wind resistance while permitting the projectile nose to have the best shape for armour piercing. The APCR is a tungsten carbide core of small calibre within an aluminium jacket. The APDS is similar except that the jacket strips off after firing, leaving the smaller inner projectile with its much smaller air resistance to travel alone. The HESH tends to spread out on hitting the target before exploding, and its shock action is such as to cause armour plate to spall or break off in fragments on the inside, each fragment in turn becoming another projectile. WP is a smoke and incendiary shell. HEAT is the so-called shaped charge which liquifies its thin metal jacket and drives it as a molten jet through very thick armour. It produces less spalling and may be less lethal than a smashing blow from AP or SH. The HVRAP projectile maintains its initial velocity over a longer period of time.

56

rate of fire. Dust also settles on periscopes and lenses of the optical systems. Muzzle brakes act as blast deflectors and also tend to reduce recoil distance. But hydro-pneumatic or other recoil cylinder mechanisms usually are required to control recoil distance which of necessity is limited by the diameter of the turret. Where recoil in a field piece might reach twenty-seven inches, the same gun in a tank might have to be limited to half that distance. Therefore, tank recoil mechanisms must permit fast recoil, buffering and a slower return to battery. If the gun may have to fire at higher elevations, spring, hydro-pneumatic or torsion bar equilibrators may also be required.

Some models of the PzKpfwIII used a transverse torsion bar mounted under the turret roof and connected by a hinged link to the gun to compensate for muzzle heaviness. In others, a coil spring in compression served the same purpose. A spring expanding with elevation and connected by a link below the cradle and anchored to the floor of the turret was used with the long guns on the later PzKpfwIV tanks.

Gun trunnions must be so placed that the recoiling breech will just clear the floor at maximum elevation. The entire assembly may be controlled by means of hydraulics. Some depression as well as elevation is desirable, but the Russians are satisfied with a minimum of this in order to keep their turrets lower.

Late in World War II the Germans experimented with heavy guns mounted without recoil mechanisms on extremely heavy trunnions. In recent years the British, the Germans and the Russians have returned to experiments such as those, but no production vehicles have appeared using this system except in France, where AMX13 is designed in this manner, and in Germany on an experimental *Jagd Kanone*.

Efforts to reduce piston rod pull and increase firing mount stability have produced a method called 'firing out of battery'. The gun is latched at its rear-most position in recoil. Releasing the latch causes firing. The recoiling parts then accelerate forward, counterbalancing the recoil which again places the gun out of battery.

Because powder fumes are toxic and because there is danger of fire from incompletely burned powder, the Germans made use of an air jet. Today the bore evacuator is in general use. This is a cylinder around the gun tube and connected to it by ports in the tube. As a projectile is fired, pressure is built up in the cylinder. Following firing, the pressure escapes and sucks the fumes toward the muzzle. With pressurized and filtered interiors to protect

52
Schematic drawing of a typical bore evacuator.

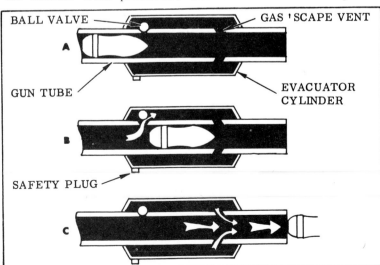

BALL VALVE — GAS 'SCAPE VENT

A

GUN TUBE — EVACUATOR CYLINDER

B

SAFETY PLUG —

C

against A.B.C. weapons (atomic, bacteriological and chemical) or C.B.R. as it is called in the United States (chemical, bacteriological and radiological), a bore evacuator is not needed. But if the blower fails, the bore evacuator, while it would prevent toxic powder fumes from entering the crew compartment, would not be able to prevent other toxic material from entering other openings. And even a bore evacuator cannot cope with the residual fumes from spent cases. Unless these are ejected directly to the outside, some kind of internal pressurization is desirable.

The Russians were the first to pressurize tanks as early as the middle 1920s. But later, when it appeared that the use of poison gas would be generally abandoned, they seem to have dropped this feature. The Germans began to design gas-proofing into vehicles in 1944 and today most tanks have some type of pressurization. The American M60A1 and later tanks are fitted with a central collective protector system providing filtered air from a central filter to each crew member through individual masks having large clear plastic face pads. A similar system in the French AMX30 is said to be effective even against napalm. The Leopard is equipped with an ingenious exhaust system for both the coaxial machine-gun and the main armament. Although fitted with a bore excavator, an air exhaust pump also operates in conjunction with the recoil of either the machine-gun or the 105mm cannon. The pump is so shaped as to seat and seal in the mantlet if necessary in order to hold out C.B.R. and for deep-water fording.

A tank cannon of any size is usually provided with a travelling lock. The long gun tubes in use today could injure their own trunnions very easily as well as other mechanisms during non-combat travel. Therefore, for such driving, the turret is usually reversed and the gun tube is locked in a hinged clamp that lies flat on the deck when not in use. There may also be examples of such locks both front and rear and capable of engaging or releasing by remote control. A device of recent origin is the thermal jacket intended to prevent distortion and loss of accuracy from rain, cold or overheating. First introduced on the Chieftain, it also appears on the AMX30 and later models of the AMX13. The French version is of magnesium and is heated electrically.

Tank machine-guns are used against personnel and soft-skinned vehicles. Air-cooled guns are used as a rule, because of complications in liquid cooling, but barrels require changing more often with air cooling–as is also true of recoil operated guns. Gas operated and blow back type machine-guns are not usually used because of the toxic fumes from the extraction of cases. But some

53

Remote-controlled machine-gun on an American T41 Light tank.

American T42 Medium tank showing remote-controlled mudguard kit and range-finder 'ears'.

fumes are also created by recoil operated machine-guns. Often a collector tube is used which sucks the gas toward the muzzle.

Coaxial machine-guns for ranging or for anti-personnel use are common, but not all vehicles have auxiliary anti-aircraft machine-guns. In Germany, for example, World War II experience dictated that a combat vehicle commander should not be distracted from his primary responsibility of being alert for ground targets by firing at hostile planes. This latter job should be handled by special A/A vehicles which are specifically charged with this responsibility.*

Other machine-guns are placed elsewhere in the turret or in the hull. Those which once were mounted in the front plate or glacis have been eliminated in most countries. They do not justify the space occupied and the openings represent weak spots in the armour. At one time or another fixed sponson machine-guns controlled by the driver were used, as in early models of the American M3 Light tank. Remote controlled machine-guns operated by one or another crew member were used on the M41 Light tank turret or in the form of 'Fender Kits' mounted experimentally on the front fenders of several American vehicle types after World War II. The later models of German self-propelled guns in World War

---

*The following description of a method needed to hit a fast-moving aerial target by such an A/A vehicle points out how ridiculous it is to attempt hits by the method available to a tank commander.

Aerial targets require a much greater lead angle than any ground target. Lead angle computation requires the inclusion of such factors as range, target speed, the angular relationship of target path to line of fire, and the time of flight of the projectile from the gun to the future position of the target. Radar systems are in common use but are complicated, and any system-error affects hit probability at all ranges.

There are simpler systems which are perhaps just as effective. One of these is that used on the British Falcon twin 30mm. In this system the lead angle is figured on the basis of a selectable fixed range. Firing begins before the target is within range and stops when the target is closer than the selected range. During this time the lead angle must at some time be correct and with high density of fire provided by the dual guns there is a high hit probability. The gunner uses a two motion joystick to keep the target within a moving circle electronically produced on a cathode ray tube for the range selected and set as a computer.

One of the new French A/A vehicles with similar fire control equipment includes also a two axis wind force measuring device mounted outside the turret which feeds data to the computer. During World War II self-destructive mechanisms were a part of anti-aircraft gun shells even down to 20mm because of the danger to friendly troops when these projectiles returned to earth.

II commonly were equipped with remote controlled machine-guns as are some of the present armoured personnel carriers.

Machine-gun feed can vary from the trays used in the original Hotchkiss guns of World War I or the drum magazines of the Lewis gun to the commonly used web belt and finally to the dis-integrating link belt in ammunition chutes and an electric booster motor. Regardless of the type of magazine, once it is used it must be moved out of the way and the empty cases disposed of. In peacetime, empty cases usually are collected and often in a bag attached for the purpose. In wartime, the spent cases more often are ejected to the outside, as are disintegrating links when they are used.

Those who believe that the development of high velocity guns as well as missiles spell the doom of the tank are wrong. The tank has always been vulnerable just as the human being is vulnerable. Using the same reasoning in the latter case would mean that no weapon more sophisticated than the stone axe would ever have been needed to stop unprotected human beings and would have put an end to war thousands of years ago. It is just not so.

Missiles are beginning to be used to supplement conventional armament and in a few cases to supplant it. Early missiles were lighter than conventional projectiles, but slower in rate of fire. They were vulnerable and less accurate because sighting was by simple line of sight. However, second generation missiles are much more accurate and have much more sophisticated fire control. The gunner still aims through an optical sight as before, but the rear of the missile now has an infra-red or similar device which registers on a precision goniometer referenced parallel to the optical line of sight. Angular deviation voltages are forwarded from a small computer to the missile by means of wire or radio impulses.

The armour piercing versions of some missiles like the SS11 B1 used in the French Harpon can penetrate up to twenty-four inches of armour. Other versions are H.E. fragmentation or smoke types. These missiles are powered by a one or two stage solid propellant motor, and most have fins which are folded flat and are spring actuated to pop out for stabilization in flight when the missile is fired. Steering is accomplished by jet deflection of the gas exhaust from the rocket motor.

The French Pluton, another Nord-Aviation product being developed in 1968, was one of the first automotive tactical nuclear weapons. It is mounted on the AMX30 chassis as a standard self-propelled weapon for the 1970s.

Another weapon now in being is the combination type. The American Shillelagh can fire either a missile or a conventional projectile. Such weapons could well become the main tank weapon of the future. However, an anti-tank missile requires concentration by a gunner for as long as twenty seconds. If he is under fire his accuracy may be less than perfect especially since the target must be kept in his sights throughout that period. If such a weapon is in a tank, the vehicle must be stationary during that time and itself becomes a target. Dust and snow not only obscure the target but may also stop transmission of guidance signals. In firing at night the glare from the missile motor may be brighter than the target and so the target may easily be lost. Finally, a missile lacks flexi-bility while a gun can fire various kinds of shell by night or by day.

'Smart' weapons employ a technology known as 'terminal homing'. This in turn uses electronic sensors which read target 'signatures' such as engine heat, electro-magnetic energy or the degree of light reflection. Placing such sensors in the nose of a

55
American M60E2 had a special turret
with Shillelagh gun and auxiliary
weapons and a position for the driver
in the turret.

projectile to control a guidance mechanism leads it to the target.
A poorly defined signature target may be given a stronger one by
'painting' it with laser energy which reflects off the target enabling it to be 'seen' by the sensor. The projectile launcher can
even leave a firing point immediately after launching, leaving the
projectile to home in on the target.

Enthusiasts believe that, although these rounds are expensive,
many fewer would accomplish the same result as a larger number
of the conventional types. Calculations have shown that the 200
rounds per casualty in World War II increased to 340 in Vietnam
and, if only the killed are considered, the sixteen to twenty tons of
ammunition per casualty would be tripled. Thus, with 'Smart' projectiles the cost could actually be less.

However, at the present time these rounds are not infallible.
Target searching, moving targets, release of numerous rounds,
would all be confusing to the sensors. Smoke, decoys, fog, snow-
storms, rain, all break the continuous line of sight needed from
weapon to target by anti-tank weapons, whether dumb or Smart.
Enemy Smart projectiles could also follow beams back to friendly
launchers, especially if these were centralized or under centralized
control. Enemy tanks equipped with sensors which tell their crews
they are being 'painted' so that jamming, smoke or 'spooking'
with decoy signatures can be brought into play would circumvent
friendly Smart weapons, especially if the enemy tanks attacked in
waves in close succession.

Considerable effort is being expended on the development of
what has been referred to for years as a 'death ray'. The advantages of such a weapon would be that it would not be affected
by time, wind, temperature, gravity or range. The high energy
laser systems: gas dynamic, electric discharge and chemical, show
some promise of producing such a weapon.

The old axiom that for every weapon there is a counter-
weapon still tends to hold true, but because the tank is a moving
weapon counter-weapons have still not caught up. Regardless of
what they must face the survival formula for tanks is still what it

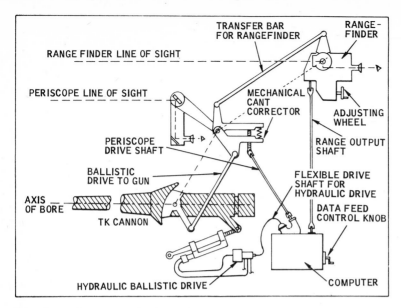

Schematic drawing of a fire control system.

has always been: survival equals rapid target pick-up, identification, engagement and hit.

There are several types of fire control system which, as they increase in complexity and accuracy, decrease in reliability. They are: ranging by optical sight reticules or by ranging machine-gun, permitting firing from a halt or on the move; ranging by range-finders of several types, no firing on the move; ranging by range-finders coupled with computers and ballistic drive without stabilization, no firing on the move; and ranging by range-finders coupled with computer and ballistic drive and with stabilization in elevation and/or azimuth, permitting firing from a halt or on the move.

Gunners face several problems in using any system, all involving the time element. These are: picking up the target; selecting the proper type of ammunition from the several types available, especially if discarding sabot is indicated and friendly troops are nearby; loading, and ranging, laying and firing. These times are increased in the event that the wrong kind of round for a given target is already in the chamber.

Although telescopic and periscopic sights are still in use with tank armament, many other devices have been developed to improve gunnery from tanks. Among these is stabilization.

Stabilization is of two kinds, the stabilized sight and the stabilized gun. The former is a German and Russian development, the latter is American. The stabilizer was used for naval gunnery for many years but was not applied to tank gunnery–where the problems are similar–until about 1938 when a crude model was tried on an American light tank.

With the stabilized sight, the sight remains on target with the eyepiece stationary. The gun is fired electrically when the moving gun tube reaches a point parallel to the line of sight, taking into consideration pre-ignition time lag. It has the advantage of not having to control a mass of weight. Limits of elevation and depression automatically disconnect it if a violent pitch exceeds those limits.

In the stabilized gun, the gun tube remains on target vertically regardless of the pitching motion of the vehicle. It operates only in elevation like the stabilized sight. Stabilization in both elevation and azimuth since World War II has appeared in several countries and in some cases the gunner is reported to be stabilized with the gun.

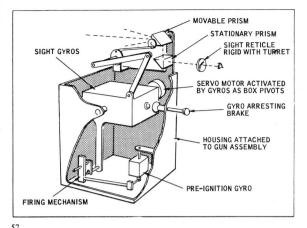

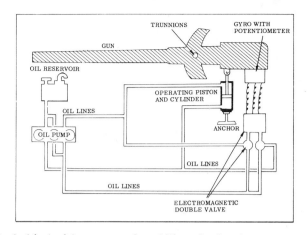

57
Schematic diagram of a German
stabilized gun sight.

58
Schematic drawing of a typical gun
stabilizer.

The principle behind either type of stabilizer is simply that of the gyroscope which tends to maintain a definite position with respect to the earth's axis. By a set of electrical contacts or silver-stats in the form of a rheostat, hydraulic devices connected to the gun keep it in the position toward which it is pointed, regardless of the motion of the vehicle carrying it. Or, in the case of the stabilized sight, a comparable mechanism controls the sight.

American tank crews during World War II as often as not disconnected the apparatus and the latest American tanks are not so equipped. It is believed that, even with complete stabilization, fire can never be as accurate as halting to fire. Nevertheless, by 1968, consideration was being given to the General Electric Optimum Ratio Stabilized Drive for the M60A1E2 tank.

Société d'Application des Machines Motrices in France have developed an electro-hydraulic stabilization system for a tank turret which enables it to be traversed and elevated at speed. The gun remains laid on the target initially selected, but if the target also is moving, allowances can be made by the gunner.

Experience with stabilizers is matched to some extent by experience with range-finders. Stereo range-finders require a certain optical ability not possessed by all individuals. American designers therefore changed from the stereo to the coincidence type. A relatively new technique called flicker-ranging replaces the beam splitter by a flicker device comprising motor driven sliding mirrors. It alternately interrupts the light entering each side of

59
The commander's ranging unit assembly
is mounted on the right hand side of the
T95 turret.

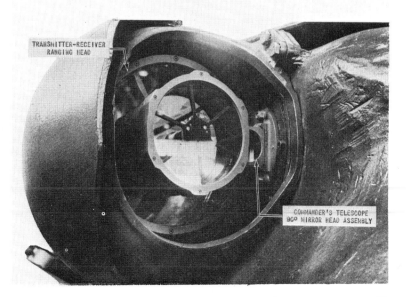

the range-finder, giving a dynamic viewing effect permitting easier and faster ranging especially on obscure or poorly illuminated targets. Range-finders can be found on modern tanks where their 'ears' protrude from the sides of the turret. These are relatively long base range-finders and therefore quite accurate. In some European vehicles much shorter base finders are found as, for example, in the Russian T55. It has a base only the width of the turret hatch to which it is attached. Range-finders are sensitive devices and require frequent re-boresighting to ensure their continued accuracy.

Britain and Sweden used a heavy machine-gun for ranging instead of a range-finder. This method is used also in other countries with some types of self-propelled guns, particularly those of the recoilless rifle type. Range-finders are vulnerable but ranging machine-guns lack the range of the weapon they are intended to help unless they are of large calibre like the 20mm gun used in addition to a range-finder on the Swiss Pz61.

But, both British and Swedish practice is changing. Bofors Elektronic A.B. have developed a laser range-finder compensated for snow for the Strv103 (the S-tank). It is claimed that it possesses an accuracy of better than two minutes at ten miles. The British also have introduced a laser range-finder on the Chieftain tank as have the Germans for the Leopard. The Hughes Aircraft Company of Culver City, California, has built laser range-finders for the United States and for Japan, West Germany, Sweden and Switzerland. R.C.A. (Radio Corporation of America) developed an intermittent beam laser range-finder for test in the MBT70. Although similar to radar a laser beam is less detectable by an enemy and it reduces background clutter. Should this type of range-finder come into common use it is likely that tank crews will have to be equipped with protective eye-glasses and other protective equipment to guard against eye damage from opposing laser range-finders.

Every country today engaged in the development of military hardware is working with lasers, not only as directional signals and range-finders but as weapons also. All such activity is highly classified, but since lasers are in industrial use certain facts have come to light which bear on their military value. One is that laser beams behave similarly to ordinary light rays. For this reason they are affected by clouds, bad weather, fog and smoke. In addition, they can be defeated by shinning surfaces or mirrors. Future armoured vehicle painted surfaces may thus return to glossy rather than the present matte finishes.

Obviously, the whole matter of fire control is extremely complex. Even if laid on exactly the same spot, successive shots may vary at point of impact due to changes in initial velocity, projectile motion, atmospheric conditions, tube wear or erosion, drift and type of ammunition. To take matters of this kind into consideration, the United States for some years has combined the range-finder with the electronic computer. According to a description in *Armor* magazine, the M16 ballistic computer as used in the M60 series of tanks is 'an electro-mechanical analog computer using potentiometers as functional generators, parallel resistors as summing networks and transistorized servo amplifiers driving A.C. servomotors as outputs'.

The range-finder is connected mechanically by a synchro-transmitter system to transmit range data to the computer. Computer stored ammunition data and any required ballistic correction introduced manually are then converted and conveyed through a differential ballistic drive to the periscope sight cant corrector and the gun trunnions. The cant corrector is an optical mechanical device which projects an illuminated reticule image into the field of view of a periscopic sight correcting the sight pattern by compensating for deflection errors caused by a canted position of the vehicle.

The complete apparatus corrects not only for wind, drift, lead, humidity, cant and type of projectile but even for gun tube wear and tube droop from over-heating. Colour and haze filters are used but must be introduced manually. A recent addition to the ballistic computer is an ultrasonic wind sensor. According to an announcement in *Ordnance* it enhances first-hit probability in correcting for ambient wind conditions 'by measuring the transmit time of ultrasonic pulses through the moving air mass, determining range-wind and cross-wind velocities'.

The German Leopard can use either coincidence or stereoscopic range-finder mode. The range-finder is operated by a foot pedal so that the gunner can keep his hands on the traverse and elevation controls. The tank commander's 360 degree periscope angle has a zoom lens from 4 to 20× for observation and target acquisition. This can also be locked into line with main armament. A gun stabilization system has now been introduced in the Leopard.

The Cobelda fire control system developed by *S.A. Belge de Constructions Aeronautiques* and Hughes Aircraft in the United States comprises a laser range-finder, sensors and a computer which operates through a mirror system so that when the cross hairs are brought on to the target all corrections have been made. The sensors cover ambient temperatures, atmospheric pressure, powder temperature, tube erosion, cross-wind, cant and tube jump with a lead angle derived from the rate of turret traverse during tracking measured by a tachometer.

In spite of the apparent sophistication of such equipment, studies aiming at improvement continue. Some of the areas being investigated include adaptation of fighter plane target lock-on tracking systems combining stabilization, electronic scanning and contrast, continued development of sensors, and also making use of captive ducted fan or captive balloon viewing devices or submarine type periscopes. The Chieftain has an umbrella-type periscope which can be raised or lowered in submarine fashion.

About 1966 the stabilized gun-sight again began to receive attention. For all the sophisticated equipment being provided today, visual sighting must still be used. And for high accuracy the target image must be stationary and the eye itself must be steady. Stopping to fire, of course, allows for greater accuracy but is dangerous. The image of any target is collected first by an objective lens. In motion this image is unsteady and naturally will continue to be so throughout the remainder of the optical system.

Some success in steadying the image is being achieved. One way is to stabilize the entire device on gimbal axes as was done in a German wartime sight. It requires precise balancing and is practical only for a simple sight and not when range-finders and other devices must be involved. Another way is to use a prism cluster behind the objective. If this is pivoted so that the effects of motion on image transmission are cancelled it becomes practical, but still not over the angles encountered by the motion of a moving vehicle. A third method which is capable of handling such greater amplitudes is similar to the second method but the line of sight goes through right-angled prisms which act as rotary joints. Such a method permits the use of range-finders and other optical equipment and, in addition, permits a broader field of view. Fast-acting servos maintain excellent stabilization.

These are inertial systems. There are also non-inertial systems, but they require more power, generally are more complicated, and are suitable only for relatively small amplitudes.

For steadying the eye of the gunner, the head-rest must be soft enough to prevent injury, hard enough to prevent blurring through rapid movement, and also give eye relief. Telescopic magnification is needed for high accuracy. It can be high in a stationary weapon but much less high in a moving weapon. But these new developments in sight stabilization are beginning also to show possibilities of increasing magnification with resultant increased accuracy in firing from a moving vehicle.

Post-World War I headlights on combat vehicles were of the automotive type. Such lights were a far cry from the cupped cigarettes of walking guides in the tank approach marches of World War I, but a return to the earlier principle became mandatory again soon after the start of World War II. During World War II the slitted blue 'black-out lights' were adopted. Today's Chieftain has a tiny electric light low down in the rear with painted reflecting strips for convoy control.

For peacetime road use, the automotive type of light has again come into use in combination with the black-out light. Since night combat is contemplated to a greater degree than ever before, Xenon and infrared lights coaxial with main armament are provided on tank guns on both sides of the Iron Curtain. These too represent a tremendous advance over the double searchlights mounted on the guns of Russian T26 Light tanks during the 1930s and into World War II, and over the crude infrared sighting and driving devices of World War II itself. Although such equipment is highly desirable it is also highly vulnerable to hostile fire. A further liability in the case of I.R. is that it requires considerable electrical power.

The rectangular searchlight box resembling a small portable T.V. set is easily recognizable on American, French, British and German tanks. The Russians use separate infra-red systems each resembling a conventional searchlight. The main one on the turret is for the weapon, one on the top of the turret hatch is for the use of the commander, while a separate system on the front plate is for the driver. In 1973 the Leopard II was experimentally fitted with a retractable television device which included I.R. for night viewing.

Xenon light is useful even in daylight to blind opposing gunners. There are several ways of using it. On-off lighting is most effective against stationary targets. Continuous lighting is used against moving targets, alternating between vehicles. Like the C.D.L. of World War II, use is made of the 'cloak of darkness' from a flank. Peak beam candlepower of the Xenon light is over 120 million. The several settings are: visible, infrared, wide beam, fixed focus beam and black-out. An interesting German patent modifies the usual coaxial arrangement for lights of this kind. This is the *Schimmelpfennig* elevating periscope mirror which has the Xenon light pointing upward into it, permitting use of the light in firing from a defilade position.

Rain, snow, fog, dust and smoke reduce the effectiveness of both white and I.R. light and a tank's own muzzle blast or that of a nearby tank will momentarily blank out vision.

A new device which already has passed the experimental stage is the starlight sight which gathers and amplifies dim light in order to make a target visible. Faint light collected by the objective lens passes through a system of optical fibres, electric fields and phosphor screens and is intensified about 40,000 times before

60

Xenon light on an AMX13 Light tank.

reaching the observer's eye. But these image intensifiers are tiring to operate and, in addition, too much white light blinds them. Recent developments combine I.R. or thermal 'pointers' to locate a need to use image intensifiers. Still more recent is the development of subdued tracer ammunition visible only with a starlight scope. The reason for these supplementary developments is that a man using a light intensifying device requires several minutes to readjust to darkness after use. In addition, the light produced from firing a major weapon may make it impossible to use the light intensifier for an appreciable interval. This would appear to be a major handicap in the use of the 1970 French development of a starlight periscope for a tank driver.

Experience with starlight scopes has brought out a hazard for the user. Night vision devices of this kind use thorium glass which emits a low-level radiation which can be harmful to the eyes unless the eyepiece is covered with a lens of plain glass; this appears to absorb the harmful radiation.

The limitations of starlight scopes have caused another approach toward achieving vision under adverse conditions. This involves thermal imagers which can present images white on black or black on white, whichever contrast is better under the circumstances. The imagers are based on infrared equipment which measures heat contrasts and intensities. Not only can they show up targets and the progress of tracer rounds, but they can even detect buried mines.

A viewing device called 'Totem', which was offered commercially by Canadian Westinghouse Company Ltd., comprised a closed-circuit television system operating a camera at the top of a retractable mast with the receiving screen inside the turret for the use of the tank commander. Elsewhere, experiments are taking place using television for driving, viewing and sighting. Another interesting development was announced early in 1968 by the Kollsman Instrument Corporation. It was a device called a 'night window' which could see in darkness. It projected, on a foot square screen, images which appeared to the eye as real objects in their true positions. The system was so designed that the eyes had to focus on the image as they would on a distant object. Unlike radar or I.R. the device was completely passive and emitted no waves by which an enemy could either detect or jam it. The company also was working on an improved model which showed promise of seeing through fog and rain as well.

Unattended ground sensors which can be fired by artillery behind enemy lines to give warning of unusual activity are another development being pushed. In Vietnam such electronic sensors were 'seeded' from U.S. aircraft along Viet Cong supply routes. Some of these sensors were self-burying up to their antennae which were shaped to resemble a jungle plant. These sensors transmitted vehicle sounds and even voices to U.S. aircraft operating overhead. These, in turn, relayed signals to a computer at a rear base. Some were I.R. sensors which registered heat from vehicle engines. At first glance these devices would appear to be significant, but their overall value did not seem to justify their cost. Leonard Sullivan, Deputy Director of Defense Research and Engineering for Southeast Asia in the Pentagon, described in *Army Times* the equipment available to the army in 1970: 'One can now perceive an evolving capability to locate and track anything that moves, perspires, broadcasts, makes a noise, shakes the ground, runs an engine, shoots a weapon, or is hotter or colder than its surroundings'–but there is not yet a computer digester which can link all such information.

9. Turret and Hull

61
Welded plate turret and 183mm
Mark 1A tank gun intended for
mounting on a Centurion III chassis.

62
T95E3 Medium tank with turret
reversed.

The main armament in a conventional tank is generally carried in
a rotating turret. The turret rolls on a ball-bearing race which is
protected by lips in the hull as well as by the planes being in
general continuation of the planes of the hull. A turret is
vulnerable to being immobilized by an enemy round between hull
and turret, especially in the rear if there is an overhang or bustle.
Sometimes a rear opening for ejecting spent ammunition cases is
provided. The German Tiger turret ring was sealed by an inflatable
rubber tube and all hatches had rubber seals for complete vehicle
immersion. All modern tanks now have this feature. The size of
the turret and the diameter of the turret ring are dictated by the
calibre of the main armament; this in turn dictates the minimum
width of the vehicle. And, steering being a function of vehicle
width and length, length also is affected. In this way, a large tank
can actually have lower ground pressure than a smaller one and
be more agile.

As mentioned in the previous chapter, the gun is mounted on
trunnions forming part of the turret so that it can be elevated for
range. For lateral or azimuth adjustment the entire turret rotates
and may be controlled by hand gear in a light turret or by hand
or foot controlled electric or hydraulic means at about 4 rpm.*

---

*A device which appeared on some German tanks during World War II was
provided for the driver, consisting of left and right blue indicator lamps
which signalled when the turret gun projected to either side of the hull thus
warning him so that he could avoid running into obstacles by not driving
too close to them.

Positive power and control are necessary not only to overcome inertia due to turret weight but also to stop momentum; and both must be done with a minimum of backlash or overrun.

Many turrets have cupolas for observation or for A/A purposes or both. They increase target silhouette and are liabilities going under bridges or in railroad tunnels and have little value for A/A purposes.

In both turret and hull, vision devices, episcopes or periscopes, are necessary. Vision from within a tank is curtailed at best, and over rough ground vision devices are far from perfect. During World War II tank crews tended to fight with hatches open for better vision and communication with friendly infantry, thereby courting casualties in order to see better.

The vision cupola used by the Germans and later considerably improved by the Americans and still in use today gives all-round vision. The Zeiss porro prism rotating periscope used on various European tanks is an excellent device, but it has been outdated by the vision cupola. In both cases the solid shatter-proof glass or plastic exposed to fire or dust can be replaced easily or removed for cleaning.

The vision cupolas on most German tanks were fitted with a circular scale just above the vision blocks. This served as a target position indicator. When the turret rotated, the scale was driven at the same speed but in the opposite direction and so remained stationary in relation to the tank. The commander could read the bearing of any target observed through the windows or vision blocks. A blue lighted position indicator with corresponding numbers enabling him to determine the bearing of the turret in relation to the hull was available to the gunner so that he could lay on any bearing ordered by the commander. The contra-rotating cupola on the Chieftain tank functions in similar manner. Periscopes or episcopes which can be rotated are provided for both turret and hull. At one time the French experimented with the geoscope which had a small objective lens but a large exit lens which was not critical for viewing; but in motion the view was annoying because the motion was exaggerated.

When periscopes are used as gun sights they have magnification and sight reticules. The sight reticules are etched in various ways from simple crosshairs to range indications containing corrections for various types of ammunition, or with separate scales for the same purpose. Filters of various colours are provided and provision is usually made for varying the magnification power. The modern German sight has a flash-shutter which closes automatically for a quarter of a second to protect the gunner from being blinded momentarily by the flash of the gun, particularly at night.

The Russian T54 tank sight is probably the simplest. It is of the so-called stadiametric type in which range scales are provided for targets of several given heights. The commander (or gunner) estimates target height and selects the reticule applicable; he then reads off the range from the size of the image on the range scale.

The Leopard sight also has this feature but is more complicated in that the user must know both the height and the width of a target.

The Helio Mirror Company in Britain has developed a cupola containing non-reflecting periscopes. An external light source such as the sun, a searchlight or I.R. tends to reflect off conventional periscopes. The faces of the Helio periscopes slope downward to avoid these reflections. The eight periscopes used on the Chieftain are also each fitted with double electric wipers.

French Char FAMH equipped with stroboscope.

After World War I the French, on the heavy Char 2C and other tanks, and the Americans, on the heavy Mark VIII, used a stroboscope. This was a double rotating cupola, the outer one having vertical slits in nine groups of five each, converging on the point of observation. When rotating, there was all round vision on the principle of the Zoëtrope, the precursor of the motion picture. Some experimenting was done in Italy a few years later with a vertical stroboscope, but today it is no longer used.

64

Comparative silhouettes: American M4A3E8 and Russian T34/85 Medium tanks by a roadside in Korea.

65

American T54 with oscillating turret.

Since it is desirable to keep a low vehicle silhouette, various means are used to keep turret height low. The French improved on the gimbal or oscillating turret first used in the German *Kugelblitz*. The top portion of such a turret is free to oscillate on the rotating base. It was copied by the Americans in a few experimental tanks but was never standardized. The French use it on the AMX13, and it also has appeared on various of their experimental vehicles. Its major fault is difficulty in sealing.

The American T92 Light tank was provided with a split or cleft turret which permitted a low silhouette. In this, the main weapon is exposed and operated in the open centre of the two sides of the turret. A later variation has appeared on the M60A1E1 armed with the Shillelagh. The Russians have employed dome-like turrets of excellent ballistic shape. These have the disadvantages of being crowded inside and limit gun depression, but the Russians accept these drawbacks as against the benefits of this design.

The use of smoke developed greatly during World War I and various devices to produce smoke were tried on tanks. One of these dripped sulphonic acid into the hot exhaust pipe. But this method was never standardized and smoke mortars were adopted instead. These are located on the outside of the turret, usually arranged in clusters so that a protective pattern of smoke grenades can be used to envelop or screen the vehicle when quick concealment is needed. One such device is a six unit British instalment which can project smoke grenades about thirty feet by pressing a single button, forming an instant smoke-screen 1,000

66
Rear view of cleft turret on American T92 Light tank.

TURRET ROTATION, ELEVATING MECHANISM, COMMANDER'S CUPOLA AND GUN BORE SCAVENGING MECHANISM

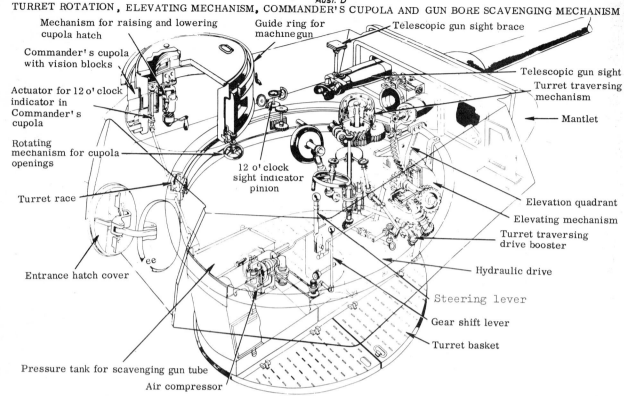

Mechanism for raising and lowering cupola hatch

Commander's cupola with vision blocks

Actuator for 12 o'clock indicator in Commander's cupola

Rotating mechanism for cupola openings

Turret race

Entrance hatch cover

Pressure tank for scavenging gun tube

Air compressor

Guide ring for machine gun

12 o'clock sight indicator pinion

Telescopic gun sight brace

Telescopic gun sight

Turret traversing mechanism

Mantlet

Elevation quadrant

Elevating mechanism

Turret traversing drive booster

Hydraulic drive

Steering lever

Gear shift lever

Turret basket

feet in length. Late during World War II the Germans used a *Nahverteidigungswaffe* to replace the earlier smoke mortars. This was a small breech-loading mortar able to fire H.E. as well as smoke shells from a small opening in the roof. It was found on most of the self-propelled guns. The modern Soviet tanks have returned to an even simpler version of the earliest smoke-producing method. A simple drip device introduces diesel fuel into the engine exhaust pipe.

A turret usually is fitted with a basket which rotates with it so that the commander and gun crew are relieved of foot travel and the dangers of foot injury. The turret's many electrical devices are connected to the hull and its electrical system by means of a slip ring comprising concentric metal bands and brushes. Radio and interphones are standard equipment. An outside tank-infantry phone box is provided so that friendly troops or tank guides can communicate with the crew from a distance or be connected by means of the tank's radio to a headquarters. When using tanks as artillery or in order to keep radio silence wire may be used to maintain communication by attaching a wire line to the phone box. On modern American tanks this has about forty feet of extension cord.

Because of the very considerable current drain in a modern combat vehicle, storage battery capacity increased from the original six volt system to twelve volts during World War II and to twenty-four volts today. British tanks until recently had one battery for all electrical needs while American tanks were equipped with an auxiliary generator. This also served in the winter to heat the interior. But, curiously, frost-bite and trench foot were more common among American tankers than among American infantry or British tankers.

67

Schematic drawing of a Panther turret.

68
Barbette hull on American M1
Medium tank.

69
Swedish S-tank.

70
Heavily armoured American M6.

Before going from the turret to the hull, it would be well to point out that there was a period in the 1930s in the United States when turreted tanks were in favour with the cavalry, while the infantry insisted on the so-called barbette type of hull which made the vehicle more of a pillbox than a tank. This was dropped when a new chief of infantry was appointed and illustrates how politics or personal preferences may enter into design. The modern Swedish S-tank has no turret and resembles the German and Russian assault guns. However, its very flexible suspension and steering mechanism permit elevation and traverse of the fixed cannon to a degree, it is claimed, equal to a turret mounted gun. The tank of the future could well be of this type but having a remote-controlled cannon with automatic loader mounted on a flat rotating turntable.

The extent of armour protection and its thickness will vary considerably according to the intended function of the vehicle. Some may lack it almost completely. Others may be over-protected. The tendency to utilize basic vehicle chassis for various functions for logistical reasons will also create vehicles where armour exists but is not needed for the particular function. The extent of armour thickness also depends on the tactical views of the nation concerned. Protection is not absolute. The vehicle could not move if it were. As it is, armour represents about one-third of the total weight of a tank.

It is impossible to build a combat vehicle that some kind of projectile cannot penetrate. Modern weapons are capable of a high degree of armour penetration; thus anything more than a

compromise is out of the question. Ballistic shape is of more importance than thickness. An angle of impact presented to an oncoming projectile permits the use of thinner armour to achieve the same protective effect. The term 'armour basis' is used to represent the equivalent of the given thickness through combining a lesser thickness with angle of impact. An angle of impact of twenty to forty-five degrees will allow less penetration than normal or ninety degree impact. An angle of less than forty-five degrees very seldom can be penetrated except by a shaped charge or an ultra high velocity projectile.

The hulls and turrets of tanks generally are shaped ballistically by themselves and in conjunction with one another. In addition, any possible hull weaknesses are carefully considered. German experience on the Eastern Front during World War II showed that a hatch or machine-gun mount on the front or glacis plate was easily sprung by even a small calibre weapon and represented a weak spot for a larger projectile. Manufacturing difficulties also are eased by the use of a clean surface.

Armour must be hard in order to defeat a projectile. It must be tough to resist cracking or shattering on impact, and ductile enough to resist back spalling, yet strong enough to withstand the pressures of fabrication without distortion. Advances in metallurgy have made this possible in addition to producing hundreds of types of steel alone, each with individual characteristics. Whereas years ago one referred simply to iron, steel, brass or bronze, now each is coupled with an identifying specification number. It is because of this kind of research that modern armour plate or cast armour can continue to exhibit desirable characteristics even at extremely low temperatures.

Homogeneous armour is armour of the same density throughout. It may be either rolled plate or cast. Cast armour in the large size needed for hulls has the disadvantage of varying in thickness due to uneven shrinkage during quenching. Tank hulls may be made up either of rolled plates welded together or cast in one or several pieces. Turrets today are generally cast in one piece. Before the development of welded and cast armour, plates were riveted. Riveting had the serious disadvantage of the rivets shearing off under impact to become secondary projectiles inside the tank.

Aluminium armour has been used in some modern American vehicles since 1959. The original type 5083 is an alloy of aluminium, magnesium and manganese with small quantities of copper, iron, silicon, chromium, titanium, zirconium and other metals. This aluminium armour, to provide the same protection as steel, must be thicker by as much as three times. That is to say, its areal density, or its weight per unit of area protected, is virtually the same as that of steel. On the other hand it has the advantage over steel that plates made of it are inevitably thicker and therefore stiffer and in consequence have structural properties that allow designers to do without many of the struts and stiffeners necessary to maintain rigidity in light vehicles armoured with steel. For given outer dimensions, however, the interior is necessarily smaller. Later, laminated plates with alternating layers of polypropylene and steel provided the same protection as steel alone, which weighs three times as much.

But the more recently developed 7039-type alloy of aluminium-zinc-magnesium, while retaining the structural advantages of the earlier 5083-type, is superior to it ballistically. This means that for a given level of protection it has a better areal density than either the 5083-type or conventional steel armour. This 7039-type alloy has been used on the American M551 Sheridan (hull only) and on the British Scorpion reconnaissance tank (hull and turret).

Boron carbide and titanium alloys as well as ceramic armour show promise of further reducing weight and thickness; but they are very difficult to fabricate and machine. However, a composite material comprising layers of resin-bonded glass cloth sandwiched between sheets of boron carbide ceramic appears very promising. This is Noroc armour made by Protective Products Division at the Norton Company.

Armour is not applied in the same thickness throughout a vehicle. Frontal turret armour is the thickest and the rest of the turret is usually thicker than the hull. Frontal hull armour is the thickest part of the hull, sides are next, and the top is the thinnest. Frontal armour generally is proof against the tank's own weapon at 500 yards, side armour at 1,000 yards. Belly armour varies in thickness, being heaviest in front because of the danger of land mines.

Since World War II several American patents by V. V. Pagano, Harry Spiro and Z. J. Fabrykowski have represented interesting approaches to lightening armour and increasing protection. One of these was to use appliqued detachable panels having angled separators between the outer plates of the sandwich making up the panel. The interstices could be filled with fire retardant or buoyant plastic sealed for use on amphibious vehicles. Another patent was for similar supplementary armour. In this, a high hardness ribbed steel plate was bolted to an aluminium plate. The ribbed plate was made up of a series of short vertical or inclined plates welded to a steel plate of lower hardness, the entire sandwich to be fastened to a vehicle made of aluminium armour. Both types were reported as very effective.

The MBT70 tank, developed jointly by West Germany and the United States between 1963 and 1970, was reported as saving on armour weight through the use of nylon armour in the rear where hostile fire is seldom received. The design requirements of this tank were based on use over European terrain. It would not necessarily be ideal elsewhere in the world. The Swedish S-tank has ribbed armour which gives added strength with less weight.

Sometimes supplementary plates are used to add thickness, or they may be added in the form of separated plates. In the latter application, heavy mesh also has been used. Spaced in this way, such supplementary armour causes premature detonation of

71

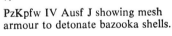
PzKpfw IV Ausf J showing mesh armour to detonate bazooka shells.

delayed time fuses or shaped charges, thereby negating their effectiveness. The French AMX30 tank employs spaced or laminated armour which accomplishes the same thing, and also adds to buoyancy in water. It has been found in Sweden that the penetrating power of HEAT rounds is much reduced by a layer of liquid in front of armour plate, but the practical application of this discovery is' not yet clear. U.S. troops in Vietnam using M113 armoured personnel carriers as light tanks usually carried fifty feet of eight foot chain link fencing and eight fence stakes. In laager at night the fence was set up to provide a screen which would cause premature detonation of enemy HEAT rounds.

Armour has another property which is important under modern conditions. Not only is there the necessity of withstanding enemy projectiles or shell fragments, but thermal and ionizing radiation must be kept out as well. Nuclear radiation could be a battlefield hazard but armour provides considerable protection, keeping out about three-fourths of any radiation to which it is exposed. Under development are systems which will permit tanks to operate for substantial periods of time in radioactive contaminated areas. Generally these systems are based on the use of sensors to detect contamination whereupon the crew compartment is sealed off to protect the crew. A further refinement would provide for decontaminating the entire tank after it had left the area without the crew leaving the vehicle.

Drain valves and bilge pumps are not uncommon and most modern tanks provide fire protection in the form of carbon dioxide with automatic and manual pull valves which can be actuated both from within and without the tank.

Tank hulls are fitted with towing shackles, towing pintles and lifting eyes for towing by means of the towing cables which tanks carry and for use in loading on to ships or tying down in rail shipments. These were separately fabricated, then welded to the hull. Experience in World War II showed the desirability for dozer blade attachment to combat tanks, and these needs are met in American tanks by a modification of the same appendages. Late in World War II the Germans adopted an ingenious method of providing towing eyes. The side plates of the hull were extended forward beyond the bow, and holes were cut in them to provide the eyes.

Hatches are provided in various places. The usual spring-loaded

72
American M24 Light tank showing escape hatches.

hatches are provided for normal ingress or egress in the top of the hull and turret. The Germans also provided escape hatches in the sides of the hull below the upper track line in some of their tanks. American tanks had escape hatches in the belly which were used for escape as well as for waste elimination. The covers had to be lifted out for use and often were covered with dirt, grease and oil and therefore hard to get out. In addition, knowledgeable infantrymen sometimes stole them for use as foxhole covers.

Drivers' cowls have taken many forms. The tendency today is to keep the glacis clear and to provide driver cowls above the glacis line. An interesting cowl is that found on the Sheridan. It is rounded and can be rotated out of the way. It eliminates the common problem of the rotating gun tube hitting the driver's head. The Sheridan driver can operate without changing position and can see his instruments and the terrain in either cowl position over a radius of 145 degrees with three periscopes, the centre one of which can be replaced with an I.R. periscope.

Explosive charges were built into World War II American tanks at vital points. These had fifteen second delay pull fuses so that, if it had to be abandoned, the tank would prohibit easy use by an enemy. At the time it was adopted it was believed to be a new idea, but the British had such a device in 1916. In it, the explosive charge was detonated by a cartridge fired by a lanyard-actuated trigger.

During World War II various items of equipment were designed to be jettisoned after use. Jettison fuel tanks and other devices were used after World War II also. These were released by means of explosive bolts, which were unreliable and dangerous. The Francis Silent Explosive Bolt made by Francis Associates Ordnance Company of Denver has refined these to the point where they can be held in the hand and exploded without harm.

One of the design problems learned, forgotten and relearned has been that of the distance the front of the hull protrudes from the tracks. Another, a variation of the same problem but one difficult of solution, is that of today's long gun tubes when a vehicle in combat dips suddenly into a fold in the ground.

No matter how well designed tank armour may be, there will always be blind spots for the crew for observation purposes as well as for bringing fire to bear close in to the tank. Good design minimizes these problems but cannot eliminate them completely.

73

French AMX13 showing the problem of crossing obstacle with long gun barrel.

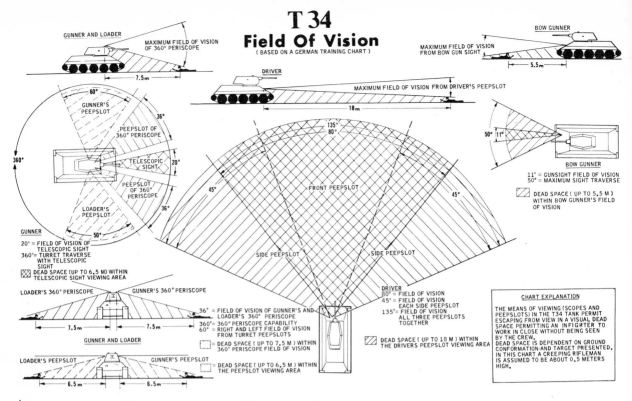

T 34
Field Of Vision
(BASED ON A GERMAN TRAINING CHART)

GUNNER AND LOADER

MAXIMUM FIELD OF VISION OF 360° PERISCOPE

7.5 m

DRIVER

MAXIMUM FIELD OF VISION FROM DRIVER'S PEEPSLOT

18 m

BOW GUNNER

MAXIMUM FIELD OF VISION FROM BOW GUN SIGHT

5.5 m

60°

GUNNER'S PEEPSLOT

36°

PEEPSLOT OF 360° PERISCOPE

TELESCOPIC SIGHT

20°

360°

PEEPSLOT OF 360° PERISCOPE

36°

LOADER'S PEEPSLOT

50°

135°
80°

FRONT PEEPSLOT

45°

45°

50°

11°

BOW GUNNER

11° = GUNSIGHT FIELD OF VISION
50° = MAXIMUM SIGHT TRAVERSE

DEAD SPACE (UP TO 5.5 M) WITHIN BOW GUNNER'S FIELD OF VISION

GUNNER

20° = FIELD OF VISION OF TELESCOPIC SIGHT
360° = TURRET TRAVERSE WITH TELESCOPIC SIGHT
DEAD SPACE (UP TO 6.5 M) WITHIN TELESCOPIC SIGHT VIEWING AREA

SIDE PEEPSLOT

SIDE PEEPSLOT

LOADER'S 360° PERISCOPE   GUNNER'S 360° PERISCOPE

7.5 m   7.5 m

GUNNER AND LOADER

LOADER'S PEEPSLOT   GUNNER'S PEEPSLOT

6.5 m   6.5 m

36° = FIELD OF VISION OF GUNNER'S AND LOADER'S 360° PERISCOPE
360° = 360° PERISCOPE CAPABILITY
60° = RIGHT AND LEFT FIELD OF VISION FROM TURRET PEEPSLOTS
□ = DEAD SPACE (UP TO 7.5 M) WITHIN 360° PERISCOPE FIELD OF VISION
□ = DEAD SPACE (UP TO 6.5 M) WITHIN THE PEEPSLOT VIEWING AREA

DRIVER
80° = FIELD OF VISION
45° = FIELD OF VISION EACH SIDE PEEPSLOT
135° = FIELD OF VISION ALL THREE PEEPSLOTS TOGETHER

DEAD SPACE (UP TO 18 M) WITHIN THE DRIVERS PEEPSLOT VIEWING AREA

CHART EXPLANATION

THE MEANS OF VIEWING (SCOPES AND PEEPSLOTS) IN THE T34 TANK PERMIT ESCAPING FROM VIEW IN A VISUAL DEAD SPACE PERMITTING AN INFIGHTER TO WORK IN CLOSE WITHOUT BEING SEEN BY THE CREW.
DEAD SPACE IS DEPENDENT ON GROUND CONFORMATION AND TARGET PRESENTED. IN THIS CHART A CREEPING RIFLEMAN IS ASSUMED TO BE ABOUT 0.5 METERS HIGH.

Therefore, any vehicle may be vulnerable to a single courageous infantryman able to get in close with a satchel charge or other explosive. This is one of the major reasons for saying 'infantry need tanks but tanks also need infantry'.

The number of members of a tank crew varies but on average it is four: commander, gunner, loader and driver. In the S-tank, as already mentioned, the driver is the gunner, the commander is solely that, while the third crew member observes to the rear and can operate the vehicle rearward at full speed. This is a radical rearrangement and assignment of duties which gives the gunner-driver tremendous responsibility. It would seem to require a great deal of personnel selection and training not always possible in wartime. A better arrangement is that of the MBT70. In its three-man crew an automatic loader separates the responsibilities of commander, gunner and driver. The driver is in the turret in a

74

Schematic drawing of the blind spots on a Russian T34 Medium tank.

75

The gunner's position in a German Tiger I shows the increase in the complexity of instrumentation.

M47 tank crew with stowage.

pod which rotates counter to the direction of turret traverse. Both methods of locating the driver are in great part due to a desire to lower vehicle silhouette. Both increase mechanical complexity.

In the Chieftain the driver is supine when closed down and operates the vehicle in that position. Although provision is made for driving from a conventional sitting position in non-combat situations, this arrangement permits a very low silhouette in a large tank without adding to design complexity.

Various pieces of additional equipment are required to make a tank crew more or less self-sustaining and to carry out their normal duties. Tanks are subject to wear and tear and breakdown, some types of which can be fixed by the crew without calling on repair crews. In the American service this is known as first echelon maintenance, in British service as crew maintenance, and tools for this purpose are provided.

In addition other items are carried, including picks, shovels, tarpaulin, camouflage net, track adjusting bar, spare track plates or shoes, tow cables, crew packs and bedding rolls and similar equipment. These are fastened to the outside of the turret and hull by means of brackets, loops, baskets or boxes. The loops also serve to tie down camouflage nets or tarpaulins.

Inside the vehicle brackets are affixed to hold other items of equipment such as spare parts, artificial lungs, binoculars, a gunner's quadrant for indirect fire, signal flares, radios and radio and inter-phone accessories, asbestos mittens, dust respirators, submachine guns, spare vision blocks and periscopes, extra oil, goggles, handbooks, vehicle log, machine-gun tripods, small cookers, canteens, gas masks and more. The brackets are mounted on springs because it was learned that rigid mountings, like rivets, become projectiles under impact of an enemy shell on the outside. And such stowage, as it is called, must be adequate, small, compact, well-placed and must not obstruct movement or injure a crew member through vehicle motion.

A tank crew is subject to rough motion, noise, heat, cold, poor ventilation, limitations of clothing and equipment, poor vision and the inevitable strain of combat as well as being required to service their vehicles after combat before being able themselves to rest. Designers try to mitigate these pressures as much as possible and have succeeded fairly well. At least there is a vast improvement over the conditions in World War I. At that time, common ailments were breathlessness, collapse, giddiness, convulsions, headaches, high body temperature, confusion, vomiting and unconsciousness from the combination of tension, motion, powder fumes and carbon monoxide.

Fatigue clothing and special helmets of leather formed the uniforms and protective clothing of early tank crews. Over the years, clothing has been refined so that today it is light, all-season and fire-resistant. In the case of the United States, a built-in integral retrieval strap on the crew member's clothing permits the removal of an injured or wounded crewman through a hatch. Helmets now have built-in interphone equipment.

What is called an 'environmental control life support' is used on the MBT70 to provide temperature and humidity control. This vehicle also was reported in the press as being equipped with a friend-enemy radar recognition or transponder devices similar to those used on military aircraft.

Another American experiment to improve crew conditions was an 'ear defender' mounted inside the machine-gun cupola on the M60 tank and wired to the tank communication system. It worked by alerting the ears to oncoming noises by creating a 150 millisecond pause before a round was actually fired. During this period three clicks were transmitted to the ear. These activated the ear muscles and prepared them for the forthcoming sound, reducing the possibility of damage to the inner ear.

77
American M60A1E2 crew member pulling associate from turret by means of a built-in lifting hook.

10. Power Plants

Two of the most important vehicle characteristics are H.P./weight ratio which should not be under 10:1, and ground pressure/square inches which should not be over 8 lbs./sq. in. Tanks can operate on many types of terrain, but these ratios are difficult to meet since the tendency today is toward increasing armament without increasing size. The basis for both characteristics lies in the power plant provided.

Tank engines have developed through the years as have other components. The biggest problem to overcome in an armoured vehicle is that of engine cooling. And engine cooling may be complicated by engine location. Normally the engine is located at the rear, but in smaller vehicles like the British Light Mark VI, the U.S. T92 and the French AMX13, it may be beside the driver. In some tanks the engine has been in front but while this presents no problem in an automobile in a tank it blinds the driver. Because of the cramped space available and the need for armour protection, relatively little air for cooling is available through louvers. Whether air or liquid cooled engines are used, fans are needed. These take power to operate. There are also power losses from air cleaners, silencers, accessories, friction, the power train and from inertia. Therefore, sometimes as little as half the rated H.P. of an engine may actually be delivered to the tracks, and there may be additional loss there as well.

General Heinz Guderian once said: 'The engine of a tank is no less a weapon than its guns'. Unless a tank has a *delivered* H.P./weight ratio of at least the 10:1 mentioned above, it is likely to lack the agility needed for combat. Not much H.P. is needed to keep an automobile moving at a constant speed on a level road, but if there is little reserve power there will be insufficient power for extra effort such as acceleration or cross country driving, and this is even more true of a track-laying vehicle.

Petrol and diesel engines are in common use. Diesel engines use about forty per cent less fuel than petrol engines. High compression is needed to start a diesel in cold weather, gradually

78

Schematic drawing of tank engine types.

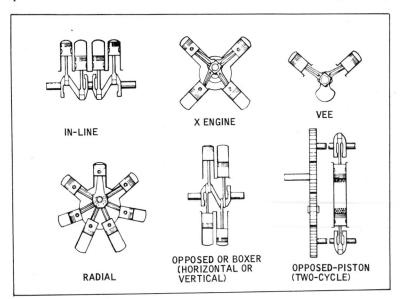

IN-LINE

X ENGINE

VEE

RADIAL

OPPOSED OR BOXER (HORIZONTAL OR VERTICAL)

OPPOSED-PISTON (TWO-CYCLE)

lowering it as the load increases. This is done by automatically adjusting a hydraulic control increasing the depth of the piston so that pressure is higher only until started. Multi-fuel engines vary compression in the same way. Modern practice in tank design is toward the fuel injection multi-fuel type.

Engines originally were gravity fed, later vacuum fed, and finally the mechanical fuel pump came into use. The higher the compression the more power is developed per pound of fuel used. Horsepower and torque (or twisting persistence) increase with the rpm until mid-range and then, while H.P. continues to increase, torque falls off.

The Russians and the Japanese consistently used diesel engines in tanks, the Japanese changing from liquid cooling to air cooling in the mid-1930s. Lack of anti-freeze caused Russian tank crews to use diesel fuel as a coolant in winter with apparently few difficulties. Both diesel and petrol engines were used by the British and Americans in World War II, but this was more a matter of engine availability than of specific planning. But even during World War II, American designers knew they wanted an air-cooled multi-fuel engine; yet satisfactory types were not achieved in any country until about 1960.

After World War II efforts were made in the United States to achieve a multiplicity of engine types for various needs by the use of common cylinder barrels, pistons and other parts. This was accomplished, but in more recent years there has been a lessening of pressure to retain this logistically desirable arrangement.

The use of diesel fuel reduces fire hazard, but since volatile fuels can be used in a multi-fuel engine fire hazard can be present at any time they are used. Engine fires are relatively rare except from enemy action and then a tank is immobilized anyway. Fire, of course, can ruin an engine, all rubber parts and lubricants, to say nothing of igniting the fuel supply and ammunition as well as endangering the crew. Some designers consider fire protection .devices unnecessary. But in American tanks flame detectors are used in various locations to warn of fires and, in addition, all tanks are fitted with carbon dioxide fire-control devices thermostatically controlled.

The little French Even has anti-flame shutters fitted to the air intakes which bypass flames to the exhaust grill. Carburettor air passes through a fire-proof oil bath filter but if flame should reach the carburettor a celluloid sleeve burns to create a bypass. The U.S. L.V.T. P5 has a unique fire suppression arrangement in the fuel system. Fuel is carried in fuel cells in the floor. These cells · are filled with a porous polyurethane plastic foam forming a baffle which reduces sloshing as well as vaporizing caused by fuel cell rupture. Sensor grids between the fuel cells and the hull detect any physical penetration of the hull and these trigger the release of freon gas faster than the fuel can ignite.

Jettison fuel tanks, mono-trailers and fuel cans carried on the outside all have been used to provide extra fuel but all, and particularly the last named, greatly increase the fire hazard. Fire hazard is also increased when hydraulic systems such as turret traversing devices are used. Many designers therefore prefer electrical to hydraulic systems wherever possible.

The type and shape of the engines used in tanks were for a long time dependent on commercial automotive practice, but with the development resulting from hot and cold wars and the special needs of tank engines, specialized types have been developing. In-line engines in the higher horsepowers become too long so the V-type has proved more satisfactory. The radial type was a makeshift to begin with because it was the only commercial engine of considerable power likely to be available in any quantity in an emergency even though it is and was too high and too wide. The opposed or boxer type is an excellent form for keeping vehicle silhouette low, but it is difficult to cool. The Leyland engine used in the Chieftain is a most interesting engine of this type. Most modern engines with exhaust driven turbochargers eliminate the need for silencers and the power losses they cause. The American M60 uses no silencers. Although quietness is still considered desirable, characteristic tank sounds divulge tank presence anyway. And with modern tactical radar it helps little to suppress noise.

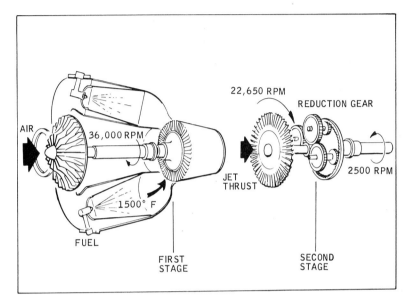

79

Schematic drawing of a typical tank turbine.

There has been come experimental work performed with turbines in various countries. The Germans were first; the French tried a Turbomeca in 1951; the British and Americans later tried gas turbines for tank motive power. A gas turbine is multi-fueled and has the advantage of easy starting in cold weather. It has the disadvantage of requiring a large volume of filtered air, much fuel and considerably more reduction gearing. The Swedish S-tank combines a conventional engine with a hydrostatic transmission and a gas turbine through a planetary transmission. Either or both engines may be employed but normally this is done only for surges of power, for emergencies or to use the gas turbine to start the conventional engine in extremely cold weather.

Electric drive was first used in the World War I French St Chamond tank. It has appeared occasionally since, but in the case of the World War II American T23 Medium tank, in spite of remarkable performance, the Armored Command was afraid it would be vulnerable in combat. (Since electric drive is a combination of engine and power train, more will be said about it in the next chapter.)

One of the more interesting design refinements which grew out of the American T7 Light tank series was the installation of tank engines and final drive mechanisms on guide rails so that the disconnecting of a few bolts permitted the sliding out of the complete unit. This has been a great boon for maintenance and repair.

The use of liquefied petroleum gas (L.P.G.) for fuel could triple the radius of operation, but it would also increase fire hazard considerably. As a result it has not been seriously considered for combat vehicles except in Germany where it was used for factory break-in running late in World War II in order to save petrol. In 1973 there were experiments in the United States in the use of water vapour and hydrogen injection for complete petrol consumption. Such engines use a fuel atomizer instead of a carburettor. Steam power would be quiet, quick-starting and could multiply the radius of action many times over as well as simplifying and reducing the number of parts of a power train. But no tanks so powered in World War I and since have ever seen combat. Henschel designed a steam-powered tank during World War II, but the High Command was not interested so the project was dropped. An American officer proposed an experimental installation in an M4 in 1942 but the proposal was ridiculed. A similar proposal by a prominent American automotive engineer in 1954 met a similar response. Ten years later, the Convair Division of General Dynamics Corporation proposed a steam powered tank and built a three foot scale model to illustrate the proposal. It called for a pair of turbines each delivering 250 H.P. at 24,000 rpm, including a three to one reduction gear. The turbines were expected to be no more than nine by eighteen inches in size. However, the U.S. Army was not interested.

Modern heat exchangers that power steam engines have not been exploited except to a limited extent. This involves mostly civilian long haul operations in the U.S. Pacific Northwest and in buses and passenger automobiles in several parts of America and Australia. But with the recent attention being given to air pollution, more emphasis is being placed on the subject. Steam engines have good speed control over a wide range and have good torque characteristics even when starting. The engines are small, simple and have low weight per horsepower. The transmission is eliminated, thus actually increasing available horsepower. The dangers of working pressure of 3,000 psi and operating temperatures of 1,000 degrees F. are sometimes used as arguments against steam, but these hazards exist with internal combustion engines as well. However, their elimination would be possible through another type of vapour engine. Freon has been applied by Kinetics, Inc., of Sarasota, Florida, and others. It is cheap, non-toxic, has a low freezing temperature and is a good lubricant for steel.

A new closed-circuit steam automotive system appeared in Australia in 1972, invented by Gene Van Grechen. In this, the boiler or steam generator has a burner whose output adjusts to meet power demands by means of flame settings. A photoelectric cell monitors the flame size and, by means of a solid state computer with two memory banks, controls the output of the generator.

In 1950 studies were made in all seriousness in the United States on a medium tank powered by an atomic engine. However, some very serious problems in design soon came to light. Bulkiness and the problems of shielding were not easy to solve and the weight of the tank grew to seventy tons. In addition, it was believed that the battlefield hazards were too great to justify possible exposure to dangerous radiation.

Study of the clean and quiet gas turbine has continued in several countries. A Parsons turbine installation was made in Britain and a Solar turbine was installed in one of the American T95 series. In 1967, the U.S. Defense Department announced the development of the AGT1500 gas turbine weighing 1,600 pounds, just half the weight of a comparable diesel engine. It delivered 1,500 H.P. and occupied a space only sixty inches long and forty inches wide. This included a fuel saving regulator and a hydrostatic transmission controlled by an electronic computer which senses

80

Model of an American atomic-powered tank.

Cutaway view of a modern Stirling engine.

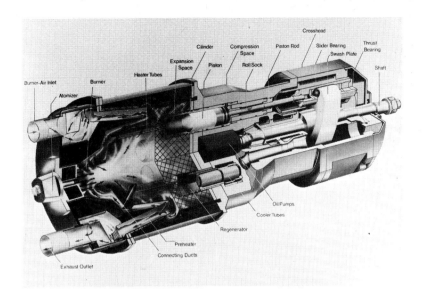

vehicle speed and adjusts throttle position to load and automatic relight in case of flameout.

Extensive development work on the Stirling Thermal engine has been conducted by the N.V. Phillip Laboratories in Holland since World War II. General Motors Research Laboratories in the United States have also been experimenting with a series of engines based on the Stirling principle devised by the Reverend Robert Stirling, a Scottish clergyman of the early part of the nineteenth century. In this hot air engine, combustion takes place outside the engine cylinder in a hot walled chamber having an unlimited supply of air. Fuel is alternately heated and cooled to deliver power to a sort of closed-circuit engine with double pistons in each cylinder, separated by a regenerator which accepted and rejected the heat which provides the moving force. Gas combustion is continuous. Expansion takes place at high temperature while compression takes place at low temperature. The hot gases leave part of their heat in the outside regenerator. This heat is picked up by the cold gas when passing through. One of the big advantages of this type of engine is its extreme silence.

General Motors appear to have dropped the Stirling engine in favour of the Wankel, but the Ford Motor Company has taken up the Stirling as being superior.

Another and even more experimental approach is the use of chemicals to produce electricity for an electric drive. Instead of batteries, a fuel cell device using hydrazine-monohydrate (sixty-four per cent hydrazine and thirty-six per cent water) is treated so as to extract relatively pure hydrogen and then to oxidize it in a hydrogen-air reformer cell. In simple terms, chemical treatment breaks the mixture into hydrogen, oxygen and carbon. The hydrogen and oxygen combine to form water. In the process, electric current is generated. A static stepless controller matches the constant voltage of the fuel cell to the variable voltage required by the load demand. It is quiet, efficient and uses little fuel. It is less hazardous than petrol, and experimentation is tending toward eventual utilization of whatever carbon fuel is available at a given time. However, it will be a long time before the power needed for combat vehicles can be developed within the weight limitations imposed. Nevertheless, its use for developing power for electrical auxiliaries would reduce power drain on the tank engine.

Another engine considered by some to be the automotive power plant of the future may some day also be applied to combat vehicles. This is the rotary engine of the Toric, Wankel, Mercer or Tschudi type. In the Wankel engine of 1967 each side of a triangular eccentric rotor forms a piston surface. With a modified oval-shaped cylinder the four cycles of the normal spark ignition engine take place as in a conventional engine but without normal pistons or valves and with turbine smoothness because the rotor movement is never interrupted. There are problems, but they are being worked out in West Germany, Japan and the United States.

In some respects the Wankel engine is similar to the French Toric engine that was patented in 1882 but which had not been developed further until recent years. In this engine the piston looks like four pivoted spokes. One cross-piece on a rotating shaft continues to rotate while the other is free to swing back and forth on crank arms geared to the rotating shaft. This action alternately draws in the maximum fuel mixture and compresses it by the squeezing action of the oscillating cross-piece in the conventional four-stroke cycle. The Traugott Tschudi rotary engine (U.S. patent 3,381,669) functions in somewhat the same way, but uses a toroidal space with curved pistons varying their positions through a cam. Such engines have an almost flat torque curve, giving power directly proportional to speed. All have a high power to weight ratio, few parts, and almost no vibration.

A late development is the Wishart Split Cycle Engine (British patent 1,190,948) registered by John Wishart, an Australian. The processes in the normal four-stroke cycle spark ignition engine are carried out in one cylinder. In the split cycle engine air is compressed and cooled in a four stage compressor having successively smaller cylinders. This air is distributed to the firing cylinders on their down-stroke with a jet of petrol introduced by a fuel pump just before the air reaches the intake valve. When the up-stroke is completed the charge is ignited.

The big advantage this engine appears to have is that half the number of firing cylinders are required for the same power and these cylinders are smaller, although the compressor is an added item. A corollary, equally advantageous, appears to be that fuel is more completely burned, thus not only conserving fuel but also releasing fewer pollutants.

The Sarich orbital engine, an Australian development, was being considered in 1973 for use in the Swedish Strv 103. This is a two stroke cycle type which combines the conventional reciprocating and the Wankel rotary principles. It is cheaper, more compact and has a high output to weight ratio compared with conventional engines. A great deal of development work will be required before any of these power plants will prove practical for tank use. Of much more immediate interest is the development of a power plant for the U.S. version of the MBT70. Its Continental AVCR1100 engine represented a major innovation in existing design. By the use of unique outer pistons which are free to slide on the inner pistons, the compression ratio automatically varies, increasing with load. By this means, the power produced is almost doubled for a given weight.

The need for increased safety against fire regardless of the type of power plant has led to experiments in the use of jellied or viscostatic emulsified fuels. Not only would the hazard of fire in combat conditions be reduced by such a fuel, but vehicles could be air-transported with filled tanks, a practice not normally indulged in. Additionally, the storage and shipment of fuel itself would possess greater protection against fire and explosion as well as the fact that, should a fire occur, it could be extinguished with water.

11. Power Trains, Steering and Vehicle Navigation

The cross country ability of the tank derives from spreading the weight over a larger area than is the case with a wheeled vehicle. As weight increases, protection may increase; but not all added weight is for protection. A good part of it can be added weight

Driver's position in an American M48 Medium tank.

necessary to support the other added weight. Ground pressure decreases for any given weight as more track surface comes in contact with the ground.

In steering, one track is slowed, stopped or even reversed. Especially in the second case, dirt sometimes piles up causing a track to be thrown, although this is less true today than it has been in the past. But a designer is limited in the amount of track area which can be in contact with the ground in trying to reach the ideal ground pressure referred to at the beginning of the previous chapter. Experience has taught that the ratio of track length in contact with the ground to the distance between track centres should not exceed 1.5 to 2.0.

The process of steering has been greatly simplified over the years. Early World War I British heavy tanks required four men to steer them. The first British medium tank, the Medium A Whippet, was steered by one engine for each track, the speeds of the two engines being varied through a steering wheel. Although the two engines could be clutched together for straight running, there was not sufficient power for one engine to drive the tank satisfactorily if the other broke down. Stalling of one engine or the other by inexpert drivers was not uncommon. A variation of this system was tried in the U.S. T6 Light tank of the late 1930s. In this the two engines could be used for steering, or either engine or both in tandem permitted steering in the conventional manner.

Today some tanks use steering levers, others a T-bar or steering wheel. The Swedish S-tank provides all controls, including driving, selection of round, elevation, traverse and firing all in one device. Override controls for a tank commander are common but the Swedish tank is the only one where any crew member can take over complete control. This system grew out of the so-called

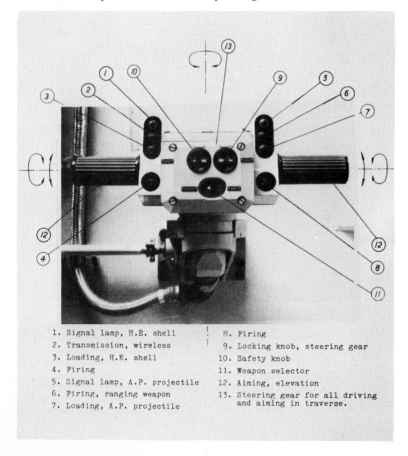

1. Signal lamp, H.E. shell
2. Transmission, wireless
3. Loading, H.E. shell
4. Firing
5. Signal lamp, A.P. projectile
6. Firing, ranging weapon
7. Loading, A.P. projectile
8. Firing
9. Locking knob, steering gear
10. Safety knob
11. Weapon selector
12. Aiming, elevation
13. Steering gear for all driving and aiming in traverse.

83
Swedish Strv 103 controls provided for the driver-gunner.

'crow-bar steering' experiments devised for fine traversing by inching the hull slightly on the tracks for accurate fire when stationary. It comprised hydraulic controls rigidly attached to the hull and shoes which held the track in contact with the ground as the hull was moved. One of the American M60 tanks placed the driver in the turret rather than in the hull as was also the case with the West German-American MBT70.

Tank steering is a most intricate problem because the forces required to deflect the tank from its predisposition to continue in a straight line are very large in comparison with the forces required to propel it. In the same way that the inner wheels of a turning automobile turn more slowly than the outer, in steering a track-layer the inner track moves more slowly than the outer. Therefore, the usual method of steering involves the use of some means of interrupting the transmission of power between the engine and the tracks.

Among these are the following:

1. Flexible track frames were used on some of the British Medium D tanks and involved movement of the horns in the direction of turn causing the tracks to follow. Later the British Universal Carrier used this method for slight changes in direction. For sharper turns, the clutch-brake system came into play.*

2. Clutch-brake steering requires a clutch to disconnect power to each track and a brake to hold the inner track. Pivot turns are possible but the system is suitable only for slow vehicles because the power to the inner track is completely wasted.

3. Geared steering is similar except that disengaging one clutch engages another having a different speed ratio. It also needs a brake to assist in holding the inner track.

4. Multi-geared steering also is similar but instead of one alternative speed ratio, each track has a gear-box having several speeds.

5. Simple differential steering utilizes a differential as in an automobile but with a brake for each track. It is suitable only for light vehicles.

6. Geared controlled differential steering adds supplementary gears to the simple differential so that the speed not used by the inner track is added to the outer track when braking is applied to the former. However, the same gear ratio is not suitable for all speeds and straight ahead driving can be erratic during engine deceleration. In addition, there is a tendency to lose power on turns, requiring shifting of the transmission to a lower gear. This system is sometimes called the Cletrac from the Cleveland Tractor Company which patented it.

7. Geared differential with clutches method of steering operates on the same principle, but steering is accomplished by clutches rather than brakes.

An improvement on the controlled-differential method is the double differential in which two differentials are arranged in parallel with their output shafts geared together. The double differential steering mechanism was first built in France in the early 1920s and was used in the Char B. A similar but simpler variation was used in the SOMUA S35 medium. In this the en-

---

*The British Mark VII Light tank, the Tetrarch, had a new type of steering whereby the bogie wheels were tilted and turned in such a manner as to make the tracks take a path of concentric circles. The diameter of the turning circle at full lock was eighty feet. A steering wheel was provided for normal purposes, but provision was also made for skid steering by means of brakes and a differential control operated by a lever and selector gate mechanism, see 5 and 6.

gagement of the steering differential was controlled by dry plate clutches, operated by cables from the driver's steering wheel. This had the effect of slowing down, through epicyclic gears, the drive to the inner track and simultaneously increasing the speed of the outer track with a minimum loss of power and speed. It was a mechanical, regenerative system. The original method, as used in the Char B, was not mechanical. In it the mechanical drive with clutches was replaced by a hydrostatic unit set in the steering drive from the input of the propulsion gear-box.

In a sense the petrol-electric transmission system operated in much the same way as the double differential. The World War I St Chamond had a petrol-electric system, and a trial was made in Britain in 1917 of two such systems, one made by the Daimler Company, the other by British Westinghouse. Control in the Daimler system was effected by shifting the brush position on the generator and motors. The generator, which was coupled direct with the six-cylinder Daimler engine, supplied current to the two motors in series. Each motor drove through a two-speed gear-box to a worm reduction gear and from thence through a further gear reduction to the sprocket wheels and thence to the driving wheels. The independent control of each motor was achieved by shifting the brushes, and this carried out the steering. A differential lock was obtained by connecting the two worm wheel shafts by a dog clutch. In the British Westinghouse system two separate sets of generator and motor were used, the two generators being driven in tandem. Steering was carried out by operating the motors independently.

Developments of the double differential system in Britain led first to Dr. H. E. Merritt's design which had two two-speed epicyclic gear-boxes instead of the steering clutches and was used in conjunction with a propulsion gear-box of Maybach design, as a result of which the whole system was known as the Merritt-Maybach transmission. Merritt then developed a triple differential system and this went into general use in British tanks from the beginning of World War II in the Merritt-Brown transmission.

The latest version of the triple differential is the so-called 'hot shift' used in the Chieftain. It combines the triple differential with a planetary transmission operated by hydraulically actuated brake-bands. This arrangement was dictated by the fact that the driver is supine. An electrical foot-operated ratchet switch actuates solenoids one at a time, which permits shifting to be done without loss of speed or power.

As is apparent from some of the above descriptions, steering of a track-layer in modern practice has become combined mechanically with the transmission. Shifting gears is distracting and co-ordination is required to do it in conjunction with steering, especially when double de-clutching is involved, so that gunnery will not be unduly affected. Synchromesh transmissions to eliminate noisy clashing shifts and double de-clutching made some improvement. Later, automatic transmissions were adopted to eliminate the attention-distracting job of shifting gears. Among these was the hydramatic, a fluid coupling or clutch with a set of planetary gears. A control system balances the speed of the vehicle against the position of the accelerator pedal to determine when the transmission will shift either upward or downward.

In the torque converter the operation is similar. This is a multi-stage oil turbine with nearly constant engine speed where the fluid coupling also acts as a transmission, helping the planetary gears exert more torque (or twist) on the drive shaft when needed. The torqmatic was a combination of the two devices which provided

Churchill ARV showing skid turn effect.

torque multiplication in the various speed ranges of the hydra-matic.

Out of these various steering mechanisms and transmissions emerged systems which combined a smooth combination of steering and speed change. One which grew out of the torqmatic was the cross-drive which is half hydraulic and half mechanical at low speeds, the hydraulic ratio increasing with speed, and which is self-adjusting to load and speed. It permits one-hand driving and pivot turns with one track turning forward while the other turns backward. The single control is a small lever like the one-time airplane 'joystick'. The vehicle moves in the direction the lever is pushed or pulled, increasing speed the farther the lever is pushed in any direction.

By the mid-1950s the cross-drive transmission with its 4,000 odd parts was recognized as a military liability because of its complexity. Experience with it led to development of a transmission which is a form of geared steering in that it acts at one speed ratio at high speeds and as a clutch brake system at low speeds. Automatic transmissions are not as economical but are smoother in operation and easier to handle than manual transmissions.

One of the interesting devices which first appeared on the post-World War I Delaunay-Belleville tank was a mechanical fore-runner of the 'lock-on' electronic system of today. This later appeared in more refined form as the Naeder device for the bow gun in the French Char B. In this, once the target was in the sights, driving was relinquished by the driver with the vehicle steering stabilized to sighting. Today the same thing is accomplished by stabilization in azimuth completely separated from the transmission or steering mechanism.

Final drive reduction gears are needed to transmit power from the final drive shafts to the sprockets. These are in housings which not only have to carry their own weight but also the strain of track tension and, in the case of the modern regenerative forms of steering just described, must stand up to power greater than that delivered by the engine.

For the purpose of vehicle navigation early tank compasses were of the magnetic type. These had grave shortcomings in such a highly magnetic field as a tank hull as well as suffering from the aberrations resulting from the gun mass changes as the turret is rotated.

One of the first gyroscopic compasses used in a tank was the

Sperry. First tested in a U.S. Mark VIII tank in 1925, it had vacuum drive. An electric drive model was tried later on a U.S. T2 Medium tank, but it was not dust free. About the same time came the Vickers-Schilovsky compressed air driven gyrocompass in the British A6 tank. The French Char B had a gyrocompass, but it also had a magnetic compass so that one could act as a check on the other.

Because the space required was considerable, no further development took place and most tanks that did have compasses used the time-honoured magnetic compass in spite of its deficiencies. The needs of World War II brought the gyrocompass back into prominence, but it was not until after World War II that a really effective one was designed. The modern Sperry vehicle compass is small (about eleven by fifteen inches) and is a completely sealed unit with the internal gimbals immersed in oil to provide neutral buoyancy and shock protection as well as to ensure a low drift rate.

Today, along with the gyrocompass, navigation devices are available. One of these is the Decca roller map. This device utilizes a ten-inch wide strip map made up as required and running between two electrically operated rollers. The vehicle's position appears as an index on a transparent belt. Pre-determined routes can be followed even in darkness or bad visibility or in order to avoid hazardous areas such as known minefields. The Decca roller map is used in conjunction with navigational equipment such as the Chobham Navigator also made by Sperry.

The Chobham Navigator is a dead reckoning device operating on the continuous resolution of distance (derived from the speedometer cable) into map grid co-ordinates. The starting point reference is set on the counters before moving, and thereafter the plotting is continuous and automatic. The counters define the position of the vehicle by a six or eight digit map reference and also the compass heading as it refers to grid north. These are operated by a small computer. Adjusting knobs are provided for data correction.

A somewhat more sophisticated unit which combines the roller map idea with a computer is the Ferranti pictorial vehicle navigator. This also operates with a gyrocompass. In the Ferranti device the maps are microfilmed on 35mm colour film. A film strip which can contain a large number of indexed maps is constructed and cassette-loaded into the navigator. The film is projected as a moving map onto a screen at the correct rate. The internal computer receives 'distance travelled' from the vehicle transmission together with directional information from the gyrocompass.

The computer resolves the input data into outputs of eight digit grid co-ordinates which are used to drive the film carriage and co-ordinate read-out counters. A heading pointer is also driven from the compass. Lens changes permit map scale changes for a 'broad view of the terrain'. Controls are also provided for 'updating' at recognizable points on the route as well as for changing maps.

85
Ferranti tank navigation device.

A late development in this general area is the Northrop Omega Navigation System developed for the U.S. Navy. In this, eight permanent very low frequency transmitters cover the globe. Using what is called a differential technique (the day to night shift of the ionosphere which affects the phase or bounce of low frequency radio transmissions), a moving vehicle can use signal corrections from a fixed receiving position located within 200 miles to correct its own readings. High accuracy within a tenth of a mile under any weather conditions day or night is expected.

12. Suspension and Tracks

The force which a bump exerts to raise a bogie wheel varies inversely with the square of the time available. The time available in turn is inversely proportional to the speed of a vehicle. Thus a vehicle travelling at 60 mph experiences 25 times as much force from a bump as does one travelling at 12 mph.

Running gear may be of many types. The original British tanks had small rigid track rollers, while the original French tanks used wheel pairs sprung partly by leaf and partly by coil springs. Running gear may comprise large bogie wheels which eliminate track return rollers, or the bogie wheels may be smaller and the gear will then include return rollers. Large over-lapping bogie wheels were used on some German World War II vehicles. They produced a more even load distribution but were heavier and had a tendency to clog with snow and mud resulting in increased track tension. Crank arms or similar arrangements connect the bogie wheels to the springs. Ball joint arrangements also are possible but must have protection against the entry of dust.

One form of springless suspension was the link type used on the American T1 Light tanks of the 1930s. In this, link arc motions were absorbed by a series of links connected to other bogies. The Straussler cross-articulating system was related to this although sprung. Here, the upward motion of a bogie on one side of the vehicle caused a downward motion of the corresponding bogie on the other side, tending to keep the vehicle level.

The French Char B1 had a link between adjoining bogie pairs which caused the next pair to take an opposite move. A similar device in part was used on the American M18 tank destroyer but for the purpose of keeping track tension constant. The Johnson cable suspension shortly after World War I comprised bogie wheels having connecting pulley wheels which alternated over and under a cable anchored at one end and connected to a volute or coil spring at the other.

Originally made entirely of steel, bogie wheels later were rubber-tyred. In the United States bogie wheels were standardized on those sizes commonly used in industry for industrial shop wagons and tractors. The Russians made some use of steel rims over rubber. The Germans tended toward use of rubber insulated hubs instead of tyres. They caused less trouble with winter icing and saved rubber. For a time the Russians used all steel wheels, as did the British Churchill. The French tried pneumatic-tyred bogie wheels experimentally for a time after World War II. Today, aluminium or magnesium, sometimes slotted for weight saving and cooling, are used instead of steel in bogie wheels and return rollers to save weight. In the United States epoxy-bonded fibreglass bogie wheels were tried; they were very light but were found to be insufficiently sturdy.

Bogie wheels may be in pairs, in double pairs, in threes or separately sprung on a bogie-rail. One early Spanish vehicle, the Trubia, had rigid rollers but a sprung track frame. The long coil springs used in the Christie suspension occupied space at the sides of the hull and therefore permitted less room inside. On the other hand the amplitude of bogie motion was some eighteen inches, while the amplitude of most other types often is only a third of that. But, if damaged, such a vehicle may be crippled and replacement is difficult. The multi-wheeled type of suspension is held by many to be much more easily removed and repaired. All modern tanks provide some form of bumper spring to limit bogie travel.

When bogie wheels are mentioned it must be understood that they are single when the track has double track guides and that double wheels are used when the tracks have single guides.

Springs may be coil, leaf, half leaf, volute, belleville washer (stacked cones), torsion bar, rubber cylinder (torsilastic, used on amphibious vehicles because it eliminates salt water corrosion), single or compounded, with or without snubbers and shock-absorbing action in accordance with the severity of the shock sustained and applicable to the front and rear bogie on each side. Either coil springs or torsion bars provide good riding qualities because of amplitude, but just as coil springs limit lateral space, torsion bars limit vertical space or cause the vehicle to be higher. They are also vulnerable to land mines. Late U.S. practice is to enclose the bars in tubes.

Hydraulic suspensions have been tried, as on the American TE13 Light tank, and in recent years rubber-nylon air bellows have been tried. Still more recent is the hydro-pneumatic suspension used on the original little French VP90, on the Swedish S-tank, on one of the American T95 Medium tank series and on the MBT70 vehicles. In all four cases the suspension is controllable as part of the fire control system. In the Swedish tank, gun elevation and depression are accomplished by raising or lowering the suspension to raise or lower the bow of the tank, the main armament being fixed. In the American and Swedish vehicles the two tracks additionally are separately controllable to correct for gun cant. The system is also used for firing from defilade.

Such systems are vulnerable. Although battle statistics show that hits seldom are lower than three feet above the ground, British designers continue to protect tank suspensions with armour skirts. In point of fact such skirts do serve as an extra skin to protect against shaped charge projectiles entering the lower part of the hull, but they also increase weight and maintenance problems.

86

American M46E1 tank showing torsion bar anchors.

87

Suspension flexibility of the T95 tank.

In an experiment in the United States in the early 1960s, an effort was made to smooth out a tank ride by means of an electronic computer which anticipated and corrected the motion needed by the bogie or road wheels to meet ground conformation. In effect, this was a translation of gyro ship control to a tank. Ships use bow fins which swivel to match the character of the pitch and dampen it. A vertical gyro gives the pitching angle and a rate gyro gives the angular acceleration and velocity. This is fed into a computer which calls for compensating movements of the pistons controlling the fins. In a tank, instead of fins, the leading bogie wheels act to match the character of the pitch.

An improved version appeared in 1968. This involved hydraulic suspension and laser speed and motion sensors. By means of a sensor warning of a six inch bump eight feet ahead, the bogie begins rising thirty inches before reaching the bump, reversing the direction of force and thus stabilizing the hull. A remote sensor at 100 feet would also be involved but that one could be overridden by the driver because of a change of direction.

Rolamite, the invention of Donald F. Wilkes at Sandia Laboratories in New Mexico, may have possibilities in the future for new types of vehicle suspensions. This invention comprises two parallel guide surfaces, a flexible metal band held in an S-shape between the guides and two rollers held in the loops of the band.

Two variations on a new type of suspension are being tested in the United States to smooth out the ride in high speed vehicles. Called 'in-arm' suspension, its chief advantage, in addition to withstanding higher speeds, is that it is utilized and applied to the exterior of the hull. This makes it very accessible for maintenance and repair and of course allows additional room inside the hull.

One type comprises hydro-pneumatic springing or hydraulically activated air-spring with hydraulic damping. The other type utilizes compressible liquid as the spring medium with hydraulic damping. Although successful on an experimental basis, it has not yet been adopted for production vehicles.

Sprockets may be either at the bow or the stern. The front sprocket is supposed to let the track clean itsef before it brings debris to the sprocket, but this is not a universal dogma. Sprockets wear and so does the track. Both are influenced by driving, braking, climbing or ascending a slope and coasting. Sprocket drive may be internal or external off the track pin, the track wedge or the track body, or it may be off a wheel having rollers instead of teeth. The Russian BT tanks had this type.

The idler wheel serves to contain the end of the track opposite the drive sprocket. It too may be in the form of a sprocket or it may be a single or double guide wheel. The Germans, late in World War II, saved on weight and materials by making idler wheels out of steel tubing.

The height of an obstacle that can be surmounted is the same today as it was in 1916. It is governed by the height of the front sprocket or idler from the ground and by the length of the track in contact with the ground. The British Medium D track frames copied in the American M1922 Medium tank provided a novel solution by having track frames higher in rear than in front. This permitted extreme obstacles to be negotiated in reverse should it become necessary.

No tanks have ever duplicated the cross-country ability of the original British heavy tanks. But even these sometimes had difficulty in negotiating heavily-shelled terrain such as was found around Ypres, for example. To overcome this problem British

tanks were initially equipped with the so-called 'torpedo spar
unditching gear'. These were wooden rods about four feet long
attached by a chain to each track and used to extricate the
vehicle. They proved unequal to the job and were replaced by a
square wooden beam wider than the tank which was chained to
the tracks and passed completely around the tank thus moving
it forward. These unditching beams finally became standard equipment and were carried on rails above the tank. They could be
fastened to the tracks from the inside with a minimum of exposure
for the crew. An automatic coupler and decoupler was devised,
but it was fragile and no further development took place.

In 1916 the British also built a 100-ton heavy tank known as
the Flying Elephant, which had armour thick enough to resist
field gun-fire. It had two sets of tracks, the main tracks two feet
wide, the others set inboard under the belly and slightly higher
than the main ones. The auxiliary tracks could be clutched in to
provide extra traction if required by the nature of the ground.
It would have been impossible for the tank to be bellied on a stump
or rock but questionable whether even it could have surmounted
Ypres mud. However, the world was never to know because it
was broken up for scrap immediately after its trial run, mobility,
it was thought, being a surer defence than heavy armour.

Mention should also be made of the numerous attempts to
create combination wheel and track vehicles. In these there were
usually two separate suspension systems, one as a track-layer and
one as a wheeled vehicle. The results were not good since neither
type of vehicle operation could achieve its full capabilities, because
of greater weight, complexity, and more moving parts. The
Christie vehicles used the same running gear for operating on
tracks or on wheels and therefore avoided this complication. But,
even here, the centre wheels were raised for operating on wheels,
placing the full tank weight on the front and rear wheel pairs.
The Russians initially made use of the convertible in the BT

88
World War I special unditching
beam.

89
Flying Elephant of World War I
provided with inner anti-bellying
tracks.

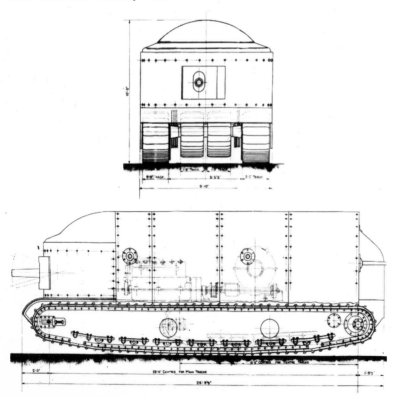

90
M60A1E1 Medium tank showing the double road wheels for retaining to Centre Guide Track.

91
'Leaping' is a result of sudden engine acceleration.

series, as did the Poles, but later dropped it. The British never used the convertible feature in their cruiser tanks.

The track is the foundation of the tank chassis both literally and figuratively. Both the width of the track and the length of track in contact with the ground have a bearing on supporting the vehicle as well as the ability of the vehicle to change direction. The ideal ground pressure would be that of a man, but the best that is reached usually is ten to twelve pounds per square inch. This and high ground clearance made Russian tanks basically superior when operating in snow or mud. The Germans later adopted wider tracks but had to remove them for rail travel.

Because the track is flexible and because of the way power is transmitted to it and because it supports a heavy vehicle, inertia and momentum can cause some unique reactions. A tank may squat when started or when accelerated due to inertia; it may leap or dive when braked due to momentum, or it may sway, roll, yaw or pitch on turns and sometimes on the straight due to unequal braking or overspringing or both. These reactions have a bearing on crew comfort, on gunnery and on track and roller life. Above all, the suspension and tracks have a great bearing on accuracy of fire in motion or in halting momentarily to fire because of the slowness or quickness with which a tank settles upon halting.

Originally tank tracks were more or less flat plates of long pitch or distance between joints and with provision for dry pins retained by cotter pins to connect them, or by pins retained by castellated nuts. Sometimes the pins had no retainer at all, in which case they were held in by a Skoda wiper plate or wiper wheel which pushed them back in as they passed if they had worked themselves out beyond a given amount. The use of track guides, both single and double, was mentioned earlier in connection with bogie wheels.

Early British experimental tracks following World War I were so-called 'snake tracks'. These were ball-jointed tracks with cigar shaped cross-pieces. The joints were lubricated and picked up soil which quickly formed an abrasive paste causing track failure. Usually, but not always, the front horns of the vehicle were hinged which helped in making slight turns. This principle as mentioned in the previous chapter, was used many years later with the short pitch tracks of the Bren and Universal carriers and Alecto vehicles.

Endless band tracks were used experimentally in Britain and the United States and by the French during the Riff campaign in the early 1920s. These tracks were usually steel cables covered with rubber. Some of the later French vehicles also used such tracks with bolted-on rubber grousers or cross-pieces.

Over the years track pitch has been reduced considerably and frequently tracks are of skeleton or self-cleaning face. The shortest pitch tracks were those on vehicles like the Bren Carrier. The open or skeleton type was common to many countries and used on medium and heavier tanks and most were of the dry pin type.

In spite of dry pins this type of track has a good life–up to 1,000 miles. The United States developed the rubber-bushed pin, using two to a track block joined on both sides by steel end connectors. The rubber bushings or 'doughnuts' cushion blows and keep out dust and dirt. Some European tracks today and most light armoured vehicles use rubber-bushed single pins. In both cases either integral or detachable rubber pads or track faces are used which are either flat or chevron faced.

Track life probably is no greater for this type of track than for all-steel tracks in a heavy vehicle, but in a medium tank or lighter vehicle the rubber bushed rubber-faced track life may reach 10,000 miles or more. The rubber face reduces road damage and skidding on wet surface or ice but tends to break up on rocky or frozen ground or to blow up in hot desert use. Noise reduction favours their use generally. Steel tracks skate on hard surfaces and on soft ground tend to tear up the soil. Recent practice, in the Chieftain for example, tends toward steel tracks with detachable rather than integral rubber pads.

Like so many features in tank design the choice of grouser or track face must be a compromise because the tank may be called upon to operate anywhere.*

Natural obstacles like streams, swamps, snow, deep mud, woods, steep and wooded slopes, boulders and shale are difficult and sometimes impossible to negotiate. Artificial obstacles such as canals, ditches, walls, cut trees, tank obstacles and mines also have their hazards as do accordion wire or barbed wire which can mat tracks so that they snap or throw.

Some problems can be met by what the Americans called 'extended end connectors' which were supplementary tracks making the total track width up to thirty-six inches. Detachable clamp-on grousers also were used. The width of some of the German heavy tanks would not permit their transport on railway cars so special narrow tracks were substituted for getting vehicles loaded and transported and the wide combat tracks would be reinstalled after unloading from trains. The American T28 Heavy tank had double tracks, the outer set being detachable and able to be towed behind the tank in parallel like a tender.

Track tension must be watched carefully. Not only can it cause tremendous waste of power if too tight, but it can also cause the track to break. The PzKpfw III had an interesting shear-in-tension adjusting device. This caused a ring to shear off if tension became

92
German snow tracks (*Ost Ketten*) on a self-propelled gun.

---

*The surfaces likely to be encountered are as follows:
  Clay: characteristics change with the moisture content; Ice: presents problems of adhesion; Laterite: a decomposed rock; Loam: hardens when dry or frozen to form ruts; Sand: better when moist but like quicksand when dry; Shingle: rocky surface tending to flow beneath the surface; Snow: characteristics change with the time elapsed after falling; Volcanic soil and Windblown sand: a drag on tracks.
  Any of these may be mixed or have one or the other as a top or under layer.

93
American Combat Car M1E3 with endless band track.

94
American M29 cargo carrier mounting 106mm recoilless rifle in Norwegian service in 1973.

excessive, causing the adjustment to slacken. On the other hand tank tracks stretch in use and can become a drag or can be more easily thrown at higher speeds or in turning. In either case track tension is adjustable by one means or another, most often by a spring compensating idler wheel.

A special type of track face or grouser was developed for L.V.T.s or Amtracs. In this type of track the face serves not only as a grouser but also as a scoop or paddle to give the vehicle motion when in water. Such tracks have the disadvantage of tending to wear out rapidly on land. Detachable grousers or rubber pads are furnished, but under landing operation conditions there is seldom an opportunity to attach them even if crews remember to do so. For these reasons some countries prefer to use single or dual screws or jet pumps for propulsion in water rather than scoop type tracks.

Various types of propulsion are possible. Paddle wheels have been tried but to be efficient they must be large and, therefore, are vulnerable. Hinged screws with and without rudders, shrouded screws and screws with pivoted shrouds for steering all have been used. Jet pumps are not completely efficient, and vertical axis propellers, while they can be used to control a vehicle in any direction, are bulky and vulnerable and add to vehicle weight.

The Soviet BTR50, for example, has one water jet unit on each side. Steering is accomplished by closing a gate in the direction to be turned which then redirects the water jet to discharge from the side, forward at an angle of twenty degrees, causing the vehicle to turn within its own length. Closing both gates causes the vehicle to reverse. The engine must be reduced to idle in order to make a steering adjustment because of jet pressure on the gates, and this affects momentum. The Indian Army during the war in East Pakistan (now Bangladesh) found that these vehicles were immobilized after about eight minutes at full power and had poor control in a river flowing at four miles per hour or more.

13. Water Crossing

The whole problem of designing an amphibious vehicle is that such a vehicle should represent a compromise between desired performance needs on land and in water. Thus a hull designed for superior performance in water may lack good ballistic qualities. Amphibious vehicles often end up with rectangular box hulls with flat bottoms. But considerable work has been done with both V-bottoms as well as inverted V-bottoms and bows of various shapes. Bow or trim vanes often are used to overcome the tendency to flood the bow, as well as to add buoyancy at low speeds. Buoyant bogie wheels were also used in early Sheridan vehicles and in the Soviet PT76. In the Sheridan these were later eliminated when a collapsible screen, such as is used in the Scorpion, the FV432 A.P.C. and the S-tank, was adopted. The possibility of applying the hydrofoil principle is desirable but somewhat remote because greater speed is required to rise to the hydrofoils than has yet been possible to achieve except in a lightweight track-laying vehicle.

The built-in collapsible flotation screens on the Sheridan, the Scorpion, the S-tank and other vehicles are an outgrowth of the Straussler duplex drive device. American practice normally is to provide kits only for wading and not for flotation, which is a change from the policy in effect during World War II. The wading kits of World War II involved sealing the hull and the turret race and using sheet metal stacks for air intake. These were applied to both light and medium tanks for landing operations. After the war the kits were refined so that large stacks were no longer necessary. Instead, pipes were used with elbows reducing the possibility of taking in water.

German Tiger tanks were fitted with snorkels or breathing tubes for river crossings, and the vehicles were sealed well enough so that they could be completely submerged. Since the war this method has been developed in several countries to a point where a high cylinder permits the tank commander to sit at the top controlling the tank by interphone when it is submerged to a

95

M60 snorkel-equipped Medium tank crossing a stream.

PT76 Model 2s in the water.

depth of eighteen to twenty feet. For this type of auxiliary equipment and in amphibious vehicles it is desirable to add a bilge pump or pumps to the tank's special equipment.

The Russians have used great numbers of amphibious tanks since the 1930s. In order to prevent track rusting after submerging, their tank tracks are treated with petrol-softened bitumen varnish applied under pressure. Some other countries have devised amphibious tanks but on a cyclical basis rather than consistently. Vehicles designed as amphibious vehicles in the United States in recent years have been, for the most part, those of the armoured personnel carrier type rather than of the tank type. The exception has been the M551 or Sheridan. Most such vehicles are fitted with a trim vane on the bow for stability when in the water.

Some experimentation has taken place in the design of vehicle hulls in accordance with shapes developed for submarine hulls. These are the so-called 'Coke bottle' or dolphin shapes which permit higher speed through reduced water resistance. These and other hull shapes were tested in model form in the United States after World War II in connection with submersible L.V.T.s. Such vehicles, it was felt, would have the military advantage of concealment in landing on a hostile beach. Early shapes were found to be sufficiently stable underwater but much less so on the surface. The later 'Coke bottle' shape snorkel equipped model vehicles were found to be practical and had higher speeds under water than conventional L.V.T.s on the surface. However, no full-sized vehicles were ever built and the project seems to have been dropped. In conjunction with this is the advance in the use of foils or water stilts. The hydrofoil rides on one of three types of foils: surface piercing, base-ventilated or tandem. The vehicle becomes foil-borne at about 18 mph in a distance of about 500 feet. Foils produce a smooth ride under practically all weather conditions. The limiting problem thus far in the case of track-laying vehicles, as mentioned above, is the attainment of sufficient launching speed.

In 1966 the Chrysler Corporation presented a version of a snowmobile dating back to 1928 in principle. This was the Chrysler Marsh Screw Amphibian, equally at home in water, land, muck and snow. Two Archimedes screw pontoons filled with styrofoam give flotation even if the hollow screws should be punctured. Top speed in muck is about 14 mph, in water almost 10 and in snow, 20 mph. Such a vehicle should have definite possibilities under

Chrysler Marsh screw armoured
amphibian vehicle.

special conditions. It has been copied in the U.S.S.R. according
to photos seen in the military press.

A new vehicle known by various names is being studied in
several countries. This is the Hovercraft or Air Cushion Vehicle
(A.C.V.) which floats on a cushion of air created by a large horizontal fan. The height of its hover depends on its engine power,
the fan and the shape of the air chamber inflated by the engine
which also drives the forward thrust propeller. Over flat ground,
smooth water, swamps, snow or ice it can operate well. But its top
speed over water is limited by wave height and wind direction and
speed. Over land it cannot at present climb hills with a grade of
over seventeen degrees or negotiate obstacles higher than four feet.
Driving it is more difficult than driving a tank but easier than
flying a plane or helicopter. These vehicles are expensive, noisy,
produce water and dirt spray and use a great deal of fuel. They
are clumsy and have a huge turning radius but could be used in
action as personnel carriers and for supply. Most importantly, they
operate below radar height. Designers are considering the use of
wheels, tracks and screws with conventional power trains for forward propulsion to replace the present forward thrust propeller
while the air cushion would reduce their normal ground friction.
In the future more will undoubtedly be heard of this type of
combat vehicle.

98
Sketch of an air-cushioned vehicle.
The tank of the future?

14. Concealment, Camouflage and Markings

Concealment and surprise are not new to warfare and World War I with its introduction of tank warfare did not break the pattern. The mechanical characteristics and appearance of track-laying vehicles involved concealment of two types. The characteristic clacking sound of track-layers, the spring squeaks or chirps and engine noises may disclose their presence. The need to cover up or reduce these sounds, especially at night, caused behind-the-lines movement during World War I to be at a snail's pace or to be co-ordinated with low flying planes which in itself soon became a giveaway. The higher speeds of tanks in recent years can cause track sounds to reach almost a scream and the use of torque converters and turbines with their characteristic whine also raise new problems of concealment.

The second type of concealment involved the use of natural or artificial means to change or cover up the appearance of armour. Camouflage is as old as warfare, but the use of painting for this purpose began in 1914 with a small group of artists in a French artillery battery. In order to conceal their guns from air or land observation they broke their outlines by painting uneven stripes and splashes of colour on them. The idea caught on and by 1915 the French had set up a camouflage section and were quickly followed by the British.

In June 1916 the British, under Lieutenant-Colonel Solomon J. Solomon, a Royal Academician temporarily in the Royal Engineers, began research into the camouflage best suited to tanks. Their efforts were directed primarily to the colour tones best calculated to blend with the variety of backgrounds tanks were likely to encounter. A matt grey-green was selected but was found un-

99
Camouflaged British Light tank Mark VIc.

suitable for France, so a harlequin system of breaking up outlines was adopted. White, cream and straw dazzle painting was found to produce the lowest visibility and black the highest, with other colours in between.

The British camouflage patterns varied from permanent zigzag stripes in contrasting black, white, grey and blue to a patchwork of red, brown, green, blue and grey. Eventually this was dropped in favour of one colour, usually brown, green or dark grey depending on the unit commander's whim or on what paint could be obtained–a factor that in war is often the overriding one. This was coupled with stationary camouflage developed around colour, texture, light, shade and position. Cloth covers were used at first, followed by fishnets with canvas strips or raffia nets. To eliminate the remaining shadows, bamboo poles were spread out to create the impression of ground undulation. Collapsible canvas screens to simulate huts or sheds were devised, and dummy tanks of wood and cloth or inflatable rubber were used. Such methods were sufficiently successful at Ypres in 1917 that 180 tanks were concealed in Oesthoek Wood for fifteen days.

The French also used this type of concealment. French tanks were painted blue-grey or mixed green, with brown and maroon splashes or broken shapes. The Germans used a broad zigzag in grey or black and white on a few tanks but plain brown for most and also made use of camouflage nets. The few American tank units that saw action in World War I used either British or French vehicles.

Between the end of the war and 1938, French tanks were painted dark green, but with the approach of war a camouflage pattern of green, brown and maroon was adopted. The British continued the solid dark colours of World War I until the period of the Experimental Mechanized Force (1927–28). Then, after a number of experiments, a uniform system of painting vehicles was adopted. The top half was painted battleship grey and the bottom half khaki, the two colours being separated by a two-inch horizontal black line. A solid sand colour was used in India.

With the rearmament period in Britain came a change to a glossy dark green. In 1940 the British Expeditionary Force vehicles were painted a matt dark green with dark brown patches.

In the United States the standard colour between the two world wars was a dark olive-drab which, however, was subject to fading. Considerable research produced one which resisted fading, but post commanders of the 'spit and polish' variety often were quick to have vehicles varnished, which destroyed the concealment of the dull olive-drab colour. Russian olive-drab was similar to, but somewhat more yellow than, the American variety. In Egypt before World War II, British tanks were painted in a broad camouflage pattern of yellow resembling sand and pale blue. During World War II, in the Desert and in Italy, British vehicles were painted a light yellow, sometimes with elongated black patches. In Burma and the Far East, olive-green was used, sometimes with a superimposed yellow pattern. Elsewhere, beginning in 1942, British vehicles were painted olive-drab but often with dark brown and black patches. Sometimes 'Malta camouflage' was seen which simulated field stones set in mortar.

Between the two world wars up until 1935 the Germans used camouflage patterns of green, brown and yellow. After that they adopted a dark grey and dark brown combination, changing to an overall matt dark blue-grey in 1940. Some mixed colour combinations also were used such as dark green, muddy brown or dark yellow stippled over the grey. In 1942, a sandy yellow, sometimes mottled with green and brown was in use, and early in 1943 all previous paint was replaced by a dark yellow. The yellow cast soon weathered away and by the end of the war grey was again in use.

During the Ethiopian and Spanish campaigns, Italian L3/35 tanks were painted a ruby red or red brown with patches of dark green and the M11/39 had dark green vertical stripes or Zebra pattern. Later Italian tanks were painted a dark grey-green camouflage scheme except that after 1941 in the *Afrika Panzerarmee* they were painted sand yellow the same as the German tanks.

The *Afrika Panzerarmee* used yellow/brown in 1941, grey/green and later brown and grey in 1942. In 1943 the universal dark yellow came into use. Camouflage paste in olive-drab, red-brown and dark yellow, to be diluted with water or petrol, was furnished to all German tank crews to fit local conditions. In winter a water base removable white paint was used. Whitewash or white paint was used in winter by other armies as well, sometimes with irregular black lines to simulate shadows of tree branches.

The Japanese used green, yellow and black in irregular blotches and also used an olive-green. The American L.V.T.s in the Pacific were painted an ocean blue. The U.S. Marine Corps today employs a dull blue-grey colour.

After World War II most armies adopted olive-green in varying shades, but in the 1960s a camouflage pattern again was seen on British and American vehicles in sand colour with dark green patches. Egyptian and Israeli tanks used a light buff in 1967, while Jordanian tanks were painted with a mottled camouflage pattern and Syrian tanks were painted a medium green. Later, Israeli tanks were painted a colour resembling German *feldgrau* (field grey).

Just as armour can be made to appear as something else, something else can be made to appear as armour. That the former is possible was proved by the Russians on at least one occasion in January 1944 near Smierinka when the entire Russian First Tank Army concealed itself so well that it was lost to German air reconnaissance for over a week. The latter was demonstrated in both world wars by both sides by the use of dummy tanks.

Dummy or camouflage brigades whose task it was to confuse enemy intelligence were also used. For example, when 4th Armoured Brigade of 2nd New Zealand Division left Castelfrentano on the Sangro Front in Italy to take part in the opening Cassino battle in January 1944, the exact positions it had vacated

100
Disguised Churchill tank.

were occupied by 101st Royal Tank Regiment to conceal the fact that it had moved. The 101st R.T.R. was in fact a camouflage unit, its tanks made of lathes and canvas. Camouflage units were also widely used in the Desert, especially during the build-up for the second Battle of Alamein.

In the Libyan desert campaign, tanks were camouflaged as trucks by adding bows and canvas tops known as 'sun shields'. This disguise was used for approach marches or during the build-up for a battle when the camouflaged tanks were moved at night into truck parks to replace trucks. Tracks were carefully brushed away so that aerial photography would apparently show no change day after day. Dummy supply dumps and dummy pipelines were created and phoney wireless traffic was set up to deceive the Germans into believing an attack with armour would be elsewhere than it appeared. In addition, the progress of visual build-up was at a pace which would deceive them as to the probable time of attack.

Just prior to the Arab-Israeli War in 1967 an Israeli armoured brigade was moved opposite El Kuntilla. Then, dummy tanks under camouflage netting were added gradually to represent two more brigades.

The use of colour photography in aerial reconnaissance requires much attention because dry or dead foliage in camouflage nets is easily spotted. Today, infrared detection devices, lasers, radar and similar equipment help to detect the presence of concealed armour. Infrared paint once was of value to prevent detection, but newer developments have made it useless.

In 1969 the U.S. Army was experimenting with a soil colourant comprising an inexpensive water emulsion coating with a latex base. It dried in a few minutes to provide a durable coating that also prevented dust. It could be sprayed from the ground or the air and was devised in various camouflage colours to use in areas where it was desired to have the soil blend with the surrounding terrain when it may have been scarred for various reasons. And a camouflage system commercially available from Sweden produces a three-dimensional effect and is not detectable even with colour photography. It comprises camouflage nets of various kinds and colours of specially-treated materials.

During World War I the French identified vehicles by platoons within a squadron by painting on a heart, diamond, club or spade, and numbers were sometimes stencilled on vehicle hulls. The British used twelve-inch wide white and red vertical stripes on the tank horns, on front of the hull above the driver and on top of the cupola. Vehicles were identified with the letter of the alphabet corresponding to the Tank Corps battalion letter as well as with the number of the tank within the battalion. In the case of medium tanks the number was painted on the side of the turret. Early in 1918 when lettered titles were replaced by numerical ones–'A' Battalion becoming the 1st Battalion and so on–tank names continued to be given according to the original letter. War Department numbers in white were painted on each side at the rear, later in the war preceded by a capital 'T'.

German tanks usually were identified by the Maltese iron cross painted in black and edged with white on all sides of the hull. In the case of captured British tanks used by the Germans, the cross was painted on the sides of the track frames of heavy tanks and on the sides of the turret on medium tanks. Continental style numerals represented the tank number. A few vehicles had names painted on the sides in white.

American tanks followed either French or British marking

systems, depending on whether they were in light or heavy tank battalions. The three coloured triangular tank corps insignia was not painted on vehicles as a rule until after World War I. After the Tank Corps was abolished in 1919, this insignia was supposed to be eliminated as soon as it had become unsightly, but units carefully continued to brighten up the paint until World War II. The official insignia between the wars was either the infantry or cavalry insignia painted on vehicle sides together with the War Department vehicle number in white.

The Italian Army before World War II adopted a definite colour code: company 1 red, company 2 blue, company 3 yellow, company 4 green, battalion headquarters black and regimental headquarters white. The signs were rectangular with the company commander in solid colour, the first platoon divided into two blocks, the second into three, the third into four, the blocks separated by white stripes. Individual tank numbers appeared in Arabic numerals in the company colour above the rectangle. The battalion commanders had the colours of their companies evenly divided, with Roman numerals in white above the rectangle. Until 1940 only rear number plates were used. In 1941 a front plate was added.

In Britain between the wars the unit name was shown in abbreviated form in small letters on the sides, sometimes with a regimental badge. After 1940, the white and red vertical stripes were sometimes seen, but ordinarily the divisional or brigade sign appeared on the left front and the twelve-inch square arm of the service in appropriate colour or colours together with the serial number within the unit appeared on the right front. This was repeated on the same sides in the rear. A yellow disc showing the vehicle weight for bridge classification was painted in front. Some-

101
Sherman with identification markings.

times the R.A.F. red, white and blue roundel was used. Beginning in 1944, the Allies in Europe adopted a white star, sometimes in a circle, painted on the sides and top deck.

British tanks also used a squadron marking on the turret sides. Triangle, square, circle and diamond were used for A, B and C squadrons and headquarters respectively. In many units vehicles also carried names.

Japanese tanks used by naval units were identified by a golden anchor or small Japanese flag stencilled on the hull or both. Army vehicles were identified by a golden and later a white star, and often had the red sunburst of the Japanese flag as well.

The German iron cross identification changed from the World War I Maltese cross to a symbolic white cross in the 1939 Polish campaign. In the 1940 French campaign and later, it became a symbolic black cross with white edging. The crosses were painted on the turret sides and often on the back of a turret. Frequently the red Nazi flag with black swastika was stretched over the top deck for identification from the air. Identity numbers were in white or in red/black and edged in white. Virtually all panzer divisions had individual divisional signs.

The Russians used identity numbers in Cyrillic numerals in white or yellow with a unit designation expressed as a fraction in a small diamond on the turret or a fender. The red star was seldom used in combat except on captured vehicles used by the Russians. Sometimes the red star was on a white disc or in a yellow circle. Today the red star is usually white edged.*

At present Russian tanks are identified by large white numerals on the turret. For night operations, coloured insert lenses are used over the rear lights, each company in a battalion using a different colour.

Chinese tanks use a large red star on either side of the turret.

The U.S. identification was the Allied white star alone or in a circle facing in all directions. Sometimes a white band was painted around the middle of the turret. The War Department vehicle serial number also appeared in white on the sides of the tank hulls. Today, distinctive markings are little changed from World War II. British NATO vehicles have a Union Jack painted on them with the unit insignia. The U.S. vehicles have abbreviated numerical unit designations stencilled in white on the bow.

Identification signs are of great significance today when tanks of all countries bear such a close resemblance to one another. Even the markings used on the top decks of tanks in World War II were not always effective because there were frequent examples on both sides of friendly aircraft bombing or otherwise attacking friendly armour.

What happens in wartime, however, is not always according to the textbook. Tank crews, of whatever nationality, are not over-enthusiastic about prominent vehicle markings arranged in a regular pattern. They may well identify a tank to one's friends, but they also provide aiming points for one's enemies.

---

*The Warsaw Pact countries use the following:
  Bulgaria: Red star with white, green and red roundel.
  Czechoslovakia: Trisected circle with red in top segment, blue in the left and white in the right.
  East Germany: A square set diagonally and trisected, the left triangle black, the right triangle gold and the centre section red with a superimposed golden compass and hammer enclosed in a wreath.
  Hungary: Red star with a white and green cockade.
  Poland: White eagle.
  Romania: Red star with yellow and blue cockade.

15. Communications

Colonel Swinton's original 'Notes on the Employment of Tanks' were written in February 1916. As a result of one recommendation in these notes, special wireless telegraph sets for use in tanks were constructed by the British and tank personnel received training in their use. These early spark type wirelesses were not too satisfactory, and visual signals of several types were still relied upon.

Within tanks, because voice communication was virtually impossible, reliance had to be placed on touch signals or touch and hand signals. There was little communication between tanks and infantry without exposing commanders to enemy fire. As a result, practice between tanks and infantry was undertaken behind the lines before combat, and units worked out systems of signals which were simple and easily understood. This system was fairly effective, but as replacement troops who had not practised beforehand with the same tanks entered action the liaison between tanks and infantry naturally suffered.

The signal systems which evolved were prearranged arm signals, coloured flags, lights, semaphores mounted on tanks, smoke, pyrotechnic signals or, for communication with friendly planes, ground panels. Some of these had the disadvantage of being misunderstood as well as being visible to the enemy who quickly learned to decode them.

Carrier pigeons were sometimes used for distant communication, but this involved the establishment of pigeon lofts several weeks in advance of an operation. Messengers, aircraft, motorcycles and armoured cars also were used in this way.

In April 1917 the British formed tank signal companies. These were equipped with visual and telephonic communication as well as older Mark IV tanks fitted with wireless telegraph equipment for which several types of antennae were tested.

These tanks were used as relay points for information to higher headquarters regarding battle progress. The French, and later the Americans, used a modified Renault F.T. as a wireless telegraph tank. Its characteristic appearance had the disadvantage of advertising its purpose to the enemy. Both British and French eventually assigned one of these tanks to each tank company where they functioned on the axis of signal communications. As a rule they were no closer than 600 yards from the front, and they were signal tanks rather than command tanks.

After World War I, in an endeavour to overcome the problem of communication between a tank commander and his crew an instrument called the Laryngaphone was developed. The first model was in the form of a double speaking tube which enabled the driver and tank commander in Belgian Renault F.T. tanks to converse. By the end of 1927 some fifty tanks in the British Royal Tank Corps were equipped with improved Laryngaphones, and the number was soon increased.

In the U.S. the same disadvantages and limitations of the available methods of communication were also felt. Light tanks and combat cars were the accepted combat vehicles with three or four man crews. Signals to the driver were managed by taps on his helmet or by the commander placing his feet on the driver's shoulders. Pressure on one side or the other signalled a desire for a turn while pressure with both ordered a stop. Likewise a loader might indicate to his commander by a tap on the helmet that loading had been completed and the main weapon was ready to fire.

The formation of the British Mechanized Force in 1927 accentuated the need for improved communications between tanks and tank units. This was made possible by the development of the tank wireless. The invention of the radio valve led to continuous wave transmission as early as 1918 and later to radio telephony on a large scale commercially. British Marconi, with a great deal of expertise in this field, developed the first tank wireless. This was a fifty watt tank set, type SB1a. It gave communication between two moving tanks for distances up to one and a half miles, and up to five miles when both tanks were stationary. A twelve foot jointed steel rod was used for the antenna; wave length was in the five to seven metre band. By 1928 radio telephony had been installed in sufficient tanks in Britain to allow experiments to take place on the control of tank units by wireless in field conditions. Allied to this was the development of a battle drill for which a code of signals was evolved. Learning to communicate by wireless between tanks on the move was a key step in the efficient handling of armoured units and armoured formations.

Until tank wireless was fully developed the older methods of communication continued to be used. As late as 1940 recruits to the British Royal Tank Regiment were still being taught signalling by flag and lamp, and carrier pigeons had not been entirely banished as a reserve means of communication in case of emergency.

Some British tanks of early World War II had a periscope-like tube topped by an electric lamp which could be raised from the turret and used for signalling by the tank commander.

One of the features of the Marconi wireless was that a cheek transmitter was used and later a throat transmitter which permitted the collection of voice vibrations but excluded outside noises. With constant improvement continuous wave wireless telegraphy was added.

Other countries quickly began developing similar equipment. In the United States antennae assumed the so-called 'buggy-whip' form which mounted the antenna on a spring base so that it would bend when passing a low object and then spring back into place. On the Continent wireless antennae were in the form of rails, sometimes around the hull and sometimes around the turret.

In addition to functioning as a wireless, the Marconi set also permitted internal communication. This feature was also copied in other countries. The first combat test to which the Marconi equipment was subjected was in the Gran Chaco War in South America in the mid-1930s. There, heat and humidity made it ineffective and siren signals were used for communicating between tanks and with accompanying infantry.

Most radio circuits were amplitude modulated systems (A.M.) which are subject to interference by static. The Armstrong frequency modulation system (F.M.) eliminated most static and had come into commercial and home use in America. Although F.M. radio requires line-of-sight transmission, its superior clarity led to the decision to put all but a few U.S. military channels on the F.M. principle. This meant that hills, depressions, large buildings and similar obstacles could blot out signals because they interfered with line-of-sight transmission. Nevertheless the decision was made and U.S. forces entered World War II with F.M. radio equipment. The few sets which were amplitude modulated were specifically for continuous wave (C.W.) telegraphic communication and only incidentally for telephonic communication. In installing

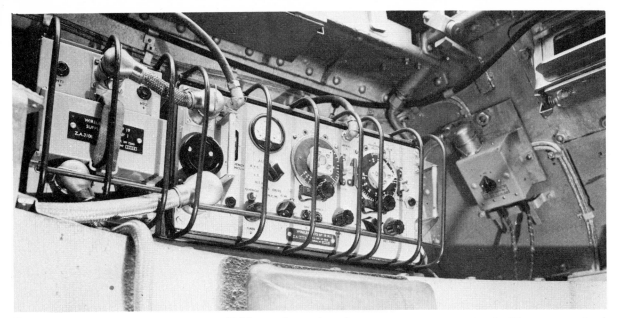

102
A 19 set in a British Crusader.

F.M. equipment noise suppressors were used. These comprised resistor-suppressors between spark plugs and distributors and between distributors and ignition coils with capacitors or filters also used to eliminate interference.

Despite the handicap of line-of-sight transmission, U.S. military wireless functioned satisfactorily during World War II. There were instances in other armies where A.M. radios had great difficulty. One of these occurred during Canadian operations in the lower Rhine area in February 1945.

Tank radios today have transmitters capable of switching frequencies and two receivers so that two frequencies can be monitored at the same time. Provision also is made for automatic re-transmission so that any tank can act as a re-transmission station, thus eliminating the need for rear link vehicles such as the British used in World War II. The radios are part of an internal telephone or intraphone system among crew members. Also provided is an interphone device comprising a tank-infantry telephone in a box at the rear which includes a long extension cord. This permits infantry to hook up their radio network as well as permitting wire tie-in. Wire communication sometimes is used during static periods, or when the need for silence prevents recharging of the tank batteries or when wireless silence is mandatory.

The use of wireless communication is limited by the range of the equipment used, the adaptability of the particular equipment to tie into related equipment, the number of transmitters operating in a net and the tactical restrictions on use, atmospheric conditions, geographic conditions and the possibilities of breakdown and interference.

Enemy jamming may also cause problems, but enemy imitative traffic for deception and enemy monitoring may prove to be even greater problems. The German *Afrika Korps* was adept at monitoring British wireless traffic and often anticipated British tactical moves as a result. American radio use was often undisciplined, not only permitting German monitoring but cluttering the air so that necessary liaison and control could not penetrate.

Organization of communications requires liaison with attached units, supporting units and adjacent units as well as internally in a given unit down to company and platoon. Thus many networks are needed, making radio call signs, frequencies to be used and, if tied into wire lines, telephone directory names essential. Networks also involve tactical air request, air reconnaissance and artillery and infantry support.

An interesting radio transmitter called a Digital Message Entry Device (D.M.E.D.) was designed by Litton Industries in 1966. It was a microminiature radio transmitter not much bigger than a soldier's canteen. It allowed forward observers on reconnaissance vehicles to communicate vital information with less chance of jamming, interception or garbling. Each of twenty-two numeric thumb-wheel switches represented a single piece of information agreed to in advance which, when properly set, created a sequence of digits communicated in a burst over a standard wireless transmitter. Messages were received on a standard receiver and unscrambler and receipt was acknowledged by an audible tone.

Of even greater significance is the development in several European countries of a radio scrambler to be used on tank radios. Although such a device adds to the growing list of complications in equipment, it would be valuable in preventing an enemy from intercepting instructions and acting to counter the move of an opposing force as happened so frequently during World War II.

Experiments continue with some success in several countries toward the development of automatic antennae matching and tuning for additional security against communications eavesdropping.

The U.S. Defense Department took a step forward in communications early in 1973 in deciding thenceforth to purchase only voice communications equipment which contained scramble devices. This included all radios from 'handy-talkies' up. Critics of previous open communications had pointed out that the Viet Cong and North Vietnamese Army had usually known what the army was doing by monitoring U.S. radio traffic.

103
A tank computer panel in 1960 and an electronic module performing the same function shows the advance made in ten years.

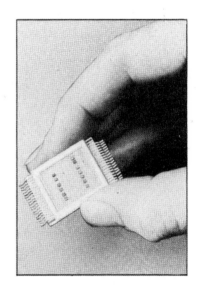

16. Defence Against Armour

The success of the tank in war has naturally caused the parallel development of many devices intended to destroy it. Indeed a school of thought has grown up since World War II which assumes that, because of improvements in weapons, defensive fire power has gained the ascendency and that hence the tank is obsolete. Such a belief is not new. It was evident on occasions after World War I as well. In a mathematical sense such a view may be correct, but ever since the introduction of gunpowder the volume of fire power has increased while relative destruction has decreased. In other words, the weight of projected metal has increased tremendously, but the volume which never reaches the intended target has likewise increased a great deal.

It has long been demonstrated that under peacetime conditions firing of any weapon may be seventy-five per cent or more accurate, but under the stress of battle it may drop to as low as two or three per cent. As new and more powerful weapons capable of projecting an increasingly greater quantity of metal or explosive are developed, war will produce even more strain and greater terror. The dispersion necessary to avoid being hit adds to these and in turn will cause an enemy to return that fire with less and less accuracy. The whole process becomes a vicious circle and, one which must be considered both in offence and defence.

Tank vulnerability is based on:

1. Armour penetration;
2. a) Flame introduced or induced into engine louvers or ventilators;

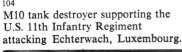

104
M10 tank destroyer supporting the U.S. 11th Infantry Regiment attacking Echterwach, Luxembourg.

b) Engine castings of magnesium alloy;
c) Fuel;
3. Track breakage, and
4. Blinding vision devices.

The characteristics of armour influence its tactics as well as the tactics of an opponent facing armour. Some terrain is better than others for the employment of armour, and a defender must use his knowledge of the offensive capabilities of armour in preparing any defence against it. Natural obstacles such as streams, ponds, lakes, swamps, deep mud, woods, steep slopes and boulders are difficult and often impossible for armour to negotiate. Artificial obstacles such as canals, trenches, walls, inundations, cuts and sunken roads, abattis, wire entanglements, anti-tank ditches and houses in cities and towns, likewise are used in defence against armour by channeling it into lanes covered by fire or by causing it to break down.

Natural defences have the advantage of not requiring labour or material, which may not be available, but they suffer from the defects that they preclude surprise, are easily recognizable and may prevent the movement of friendly troops as well. The creation of artificial obstacles on the other hand may require a great deal of labour. Neither form may be completely effective. Aggressive and intelligent use of armour in the past has overcome situations considered impossible. The famous reinforced concrete dragon teeth defences of the Siegfried Line and West Wall were impossible for armour to negotiate. A tank will belly or tip over in attempting to cross such an obstacle. However, reinforced concrete is not impervious to aerial bombing or to fire from tanks and artillery. By reducing it to rubble it then became relatively simple for armour to overcome this type of obstacle. Sometimes it was also possible to push the dragon teeth out of the way by the use of tank dozers.

The virtues of utilizing both natural and artificial obstacles are that an attacker is slowed down, his time-table is dislocated and, for this reason and because his attack may be canalized, he becomes a better target for the defender's anti-armour weapons. Since defence in depth is basic, anti-armour weapons must be disposed in depth as determined by their characteristics, principally of range.

Anti-armour defence came into being during World War I with the advent of the tank. The Germans, facing armour for the first time, were forced to extemporize but quickly built up techniques. Their system of anti-armour defence passed through three phases. The first phase was the period of surprise at facing a new weapon during which the principal measures were local and on a trial-and-error basis. The morale effect of armour initially was so great that the German High Command officially down-graded its value. The second phase was a conflict between the official doctrine and a dawning recognition that armour was presenting a real threat. During these first two phases, although the local commanders were developing their own doctrines and techniques there was only half-hearted interest in the rear areas.

Local measures included both direct and indirect artillery fire with air spotting of tank concentrations prior to an Allied attack as well as during an attack. The careful plotting of defensive artillery fire was already a well-established technique on both sides, and it was not long before the Germans utilized variations on this technique in their defence against armour. The 'triple box' barrage, originally thrown against Allied infantry, was now used against Allied tanks. But the result was that while it succeeded in concentrating on enemy armour it left Allied infantry relatively free to advance.

114

Some aerial bombing was tried. For close-in fighting, German machine-gun and rifle fire was directed against vision slots in order to blind tank crews. Trench mortars and gas were used on occasion, and armour-piercing rifle ammunition was developed and issued to troops for use in both rifles and machine-guns. Production was also begun on a .51 calibre 'T' rifle, a single shot rifle resembling the infantry Mauser but larger and weighing 35.5 pounds. It fired a 1.66 ounce bullet at 2,500 F/S. In tests it would penetrate $\frac{3}{4}$-inch armour at 600 yards, but German armour plate lacked certain essentials of a good alloy, so test conditions were not reproduced in the field. German troops found that this rifle would not even penetrate the $\frac{5}{8}$-inch armour on the side of the little French Renault F.T.

The third phase began in July 1918 when the Germans went into their own use of armour offensively and had accumulated and analyzed a mass of front-line reports. After that the emphasis was placed on an anti-armour defence which would circumvent surprise. A complete course of instruction outlining the principles of tank tactics and defences against them was prepared and released to troops. Captured Allied tanks were used for training purposes, and company officers attended special classes which taught the use of natural obstacles together with practice in preparing barricades, tank traps, proper use of mines, camouflage, concrete blocks with protruding girders, the use of flame-throwers, clusters of hand grenades, searchlights and the proper use of communication systems in giving warning of approaching armour.

Early sound trumpets and ground detectors were adapted from anti-aircraft warning equipment. Aircraft and artillery flares were used to illuminate the front during a night attack. A new *Tank und Flieger* (T.U.F.) .51 calibre machine-gun was put into production but did not become available before the end of the war. A special carriage was designed and issued so that the normal trench mortar could be used for direct fire. Field guns were mounted on heavy trucks and held in reserve to be thrown in as needed; harnessed up horse-drawn field-gun battalions were also held in reserve as emergency guns. Anti-tank rifle grenades were developed but never became available at the front.

Defence in depth had been developed in World War I from the time opposing artillery began drawing away from one another. In the same way, German anti-tank defences were arranged in depth. Artillery was charged with the primary responsibility for anti-tank defence. For close-in defence the infantry used its own weapons. Should these fail, then the truck-mounted and horse-drawn reserve batteries were thrown in. This process might be repeated several times.

All the Germans' skill applied to anti-tank defence was too late to change the course of the war in 1918. After the war the lessons of defeat were studied in detail and one basic conclusion was reached before the minutiae of German rearmament were worked out. This was that both armour and anti-armour defence must keep abreast of each other and of the techniques of offence and defence. Anti-aircraft defence was made a responsibility of the *Luftwaffe,* and anti-armour defence was made a responsibility of the *Panzerwaffe.*

The Germans had another advantage after World War I. Being denied the possession of armour under the terms of the Versailles Treaty, they were free to study without prejudice the results of Allied offensive use of armour during World War I. Where the Allies were handicapped in the matter of development because of the existence of large stocks of World War I tanks, the Germans were free to theorize without hindrance. They followed the limited developments in other countries and studied the ideas of armour pioneers like Fuller, Liddell Hart and Martel.

During the period following World War I, speed and mobility became the keynotes in the use of tanks. Armour thickness was considered of less significance than speed. Thus, in most of the former Allied countries and even in Germany, the largest anti-tank gun was from 37mm to 42mm. Tank armament likewise seldom exceeded those calibres, and many of the post-war tanks were armed with nothing larger than weapons of 20mm or even only heavy or light machine-guns.

The emphasis on mobility and on the offensive by Germany was in the direction of a quick overwhelming war of only a few months –a *Blitzkreig* (lightning war) as it came to be called. Yet, in spite of the emphasis on offence, the Germans had a well-developed anti-tank arm. The anti-tank regiments were organized into battalions of three companies of twelve guns each, two of the companies intended for anti-tank duties and one a dual purpose anti-aircraft/anti-tank company.

In addition to the anti-tank units each infantry regiment had six 75mm and two 150mm weapons which later were self-propelled. Each infantry division had seventy-five anti-tank guns. The principal weapons were the 37mm wheeled carriage gun and a Gerlich tapered bore 2.8cm high velocity gun. The dual purpose companies used self-propelled 37mm to 88mm anti-aircraft guns. Infantry companies also had a 7.92mm anti-tank rifle, one to a platoon. Rifles of this kind were common in European armies during the late 1930s. The British, for example, had the .5 inch Boys anti-tank rifle which had been designed with the dual purpose of being suitable for colonial-type warfare and of costing considerably less than a thorough-going anti-tank weapon.

After World War II began, weapon development was accelerated. The Germans began up-gunning both tank and anti-tank weapons. The Allies were obliged to increase armour thickness and in turn to increase weapon calibres, whereupon the Germans likewise had to thicken armour plate on their vehicles. This seesaw situation continued throughout World War II with the Germans always in the lead.

The land mine was another weapon used in World War I which continued to be developed in Germany and elsewhere. Increased armour thickness of necessity required a constant increase in the explosive power of these anti-tank devices. Before the end of World War II the Germans had at least forty different kinds of anti-tank mines. Since buried mines could be detected by an electrical device because of the metal they contained, the wooden and plastic mine came into use, as did a magnetic mine which could be attached by hand to an enemy tank.

Land mines, both anti-personnel and anti-tank, are made up in various shapes, the most common of which was the round thick saucer-like shape about a foot in diameter and weighing about eighteen pounds, its explosive charge accounting for some ten to twelve pounds of its weight. Such mines were fitted with a bail or handle for carrying. A pressure of about 20–60 pounds for anti-personnel, and from 175 to 600 pounds for anti-tank use, would cause them to detonate.

Newer developments include land mines filled with napalm; but the most startling change has been a reduction in weight, with the same power, to about a twentieth of World War II weights. Shapes, as mentioned in an earlier chapter, may now be rectangular as well as round. Today most mines are fitted with little anchors to detonate them if they are tampered with or lifted.

Although land mines are effective for canalizing enemy armour or causing it to advance with caution and are thus of tremendous advantage in a retreat, as masterfully demonstrated by the Germans on many occasions, they increase tremendously for the defender the logistical problem of his own defence or retirement and may endanger friendly troops.

The hollow or shaped charge principle was one that was developed by both sides during World War II. This principle is known by several names and was discovered many years before that war. Simply stated it involves the shaping of a cone in an explosive which focuses on a secondary small projectile. On detonation the face of the explosive drives the small projectile forward at a speed of up to 40,000 F/S. A variation comprises a metal liner over the core which disintegrates and, with the gas, forms at the apex of the core into a jet about a tenth of an inch in diameter. This jet is extremely hot and literally melts a hole in armour. Although the jet is small the entrance hole may be large, and the exit hole much larger. Such a jet can kill or can start a fire almost instantly; it can pass through a tank and penetrate, sometimes completely, the armour on the opposite side.

This principle was used by the United States in the rocket weapon called the bazooka and by the British in the PIAT (Projectile Infantry Anti-Tank). The Germans quickly followed with the similar *Panzerfaust,* and continued development resulted in calibres up to 88mm with the weapon mounted on a small wheeled carriage.

There was much public criticism of the 2.36 inch World War II bazooka which was used initially in Korea because it failed to stop the Russian T34/85 tanks used by the North Koreans. This fault, however, was less a defect of the weapon itself (which was perfectly capable of penetrating the armour on that tank) than it was the defect that weapons of this kind generally possess. They must be used at close ranges and soldiers must have the training and the nerve to wait until they are near enough not to miss.

The shaped charge rifle grenade, hand grenade, or land mine, work on this same principle, but the first two have the disadvantage of also requiring to be fired at close range.

The Germans were the first to develop recoilless weapons of various calibres mounted on small field-gun type carriages. Originally these were intended as airborne artillery, but the Germans grew less enthusiastic about this type of weapon and turned to the so-called 'high-low' pressure gun.

The high-low gun had a nozzle plate interposed between the case and the projectile. The high pressure from the igniting powder was thus not directly communicated to the base of the projectile as in the normal gun but was reduced by passing through orifices in the nozzle plate. This resulted in the elimination of a high pressure peak in the base and in a much steadier and more uniform pressure on the projectile as it moved forward through the tube. Lower stresses were imposed on the gun tube and recoil mechanism and erosion was reduced. But although maximum pressure values in the gun tube were lower, the mean effective pressure was higher and greater muzzle velocities were achieved for the same quantity of powder.

The recoilless weapon, in effect, deliberately wastes some of the energy of the powder charge by channelling some of the gases rearward, sufficient to offset the recoil. These guns have a definite advantage, but the back blast is a serious disadvantage. The high-low gun, on the other hand, did not have this disadvantage.

The Germans also experimented with a variation of the channel-

105

Canadian PIAT battery on Universal Carrier.

ling of powder gases by venting them at intervals in the gun tube so that, as the gases expanded, they were vented forward to give the projectile continually increasing boosts to raise its final muzzle velocity to the greatest possible figure.

Another interesting German device–already mentioned–was the remote-controlled demolition vehicle, originally controlled by an electric cable which the vehicle paid out as it left the control point. These demolition vehicles were the Goliath or Beetle miniature tanks. They carried heavy explosive charges which could be detonated when the tiny vehicle arrived near an enemy tank. Other models were radio-controlled and had a greater range of action. Some were expendable, others could drop their charge and return.

Such devices were not new. The French had experimented with some early in World War I for the purpose of breaking up barbed-wire. The Japanese experimented with similar devices, beginning in 1929. The French had a few such devices, which were radio-controlled, in 1940; and the United States Navy's radio-controlled Salamander was a related device intended for the destruction of beach obstacles and mines.

There is a great deal of difference of opinion as to the effectiveness of such devices. They were used principally on the Eastern Front by the Germans against the Russians who claimed they were useless; but some German officers since then have insisted that they were highly effective and that their development should have been continued.

In spite of all these devices the main German reliance was on

106
Goliath.

107

Japanese M2597 Medium tank in tropical conditions.

high velocity artillery, usually towed, although as many guns were self-propelled as German industry was capable of producing. The famous German 88 was originally an anti-aircraft weapon which was used also in the anti-tank role. All the later German anti-tank guns, or Pak (*Panzerabwehrkanonen*), were distinguished by their long tubes, high velocity, and their accuracy. Sighting and fire control equipment were superb. In the use of the combination Flak (*Fliegerabwehrkanone*) and Pak, the fire control system could be used against ground as well as aerial targets.

These weapons were used in conjunction with in-depth elastic defences and strong points, or *Pakfronts,* which controlled centrally all anti-tank weapons. Weapons usually were sited in defilade so that they were concealed from the front and fired crosswise with arrangements for intersecting fields of fire. Forward observers in touch with the *Luftwaffe* directed fighter-bombers on to targets. As an attack progressed, enemy tanks were hit by anti-tank gun concentrations and isolated by smoke shells thrown behind them, while at the same time they were also hit by fire from self-propelled guns moving from position to position. Should an enemy armoured force succeed in running such a gauntlet it would still have the hazard of counterattack from friendly armour held in reserve for just such a contingency.

The types of anti-tank defence used by the Japanese were less involved and due to their need to defend small islands, took a somewhat different form. Horned mines and buried aerial bombs, concrete and steel tetrahedrons, piles of coral rock, fences of coconut logs chained together and aprons of defensive wire, were all used as underwater defences against personnel, armour and landing craft. These underwater defences were integrated with pillboxes of coconut logs emplacing light weapons and with larger pillboxes farther inland mounting larger guns, all with defilade fields of fire.

In some instances petrol drums on the beaches, to be set off by remote control, were used. Once a landing succeeded, tank-fighter teams of two or three men would attempt to set off satchel charges, clusters of grenades or mines tied to grenades, magnetized mines or mines fastened to the ends of poles, in order to cripple a tank after artillery inland had isolated it from its infantry team by the use of smoke shell. Another method was to attempt to kill the Allied infantry team by mortar, machine-gun or artillery fire, and then turn all available anti-tank fire on the isolated tank.

The German defences on the Normandy beaches were based on similar tactics, added to anti-tank ditches and permanent fortifications.

The Russian scheme of anti-tank defence was similar to that of the German, and the Russians quickly copied the *Pakfront*. The primary target of the Red air force in combat was enemy armour. The Russian Stormovik rocket-firing plane was the first of its kind and was designed with this in mind–although it was equally useful as a general purpose ground attack plane. Such use requires air supremacy to be completely effective. Massed artillery fire centrally controlled also had as its primary mission the destruction of German armour, and such artillery included the truck-mounted multiple rocket launchers known as Katyasha.

Anti-tank regiments were pooled in a given area and attached to other units as needed. Dug-in tanks having alternative firing positions and sacrifice field-guns and anti-tank guns were located in front lines. Radar-controlled minefields and booby traps were also quite common. Engineer flame-throwers were attached to infantry units both for offence and defence. Russian troops were also taught to use smoke pots to blind German tank crews and on

occasion even threw tarpaulins over the turret or driver's periscopes of German tanks.

The Russians preceded the development of the German Beetle
by a scheme of training dogs to hide under an approaching tank.
A satchel charge with a contact spindle was carried on a small
pack-saddle. When the spindle touched the belly of the enemy
tank, the explosive charge was detonated. The Germans soon
learned to disperse these demolition dogs which, often as not, took
refuge under Soviet tanks, destroying them instead.

As in most armies, the Russians in their close-in tactics
attempted to separate supporting infantry from its armour. When
armour was used against armour, they often resorted to ramming
as a means of immobilizing an enemy tank. Many awards for
valour were made to Red tank commanders who were successful
in this manoeuvre.

Lastly, the Russians produced and used great quantities of self-
propelled artillery, much of it earmarked as support for friendly
armour and with an anti-armour role. By the end of World War
II the ratio of self-propelled artillery to tanks was at least three to
one.

The Americans and the British developed the napalm bomb of
jellied petrol, the use of white phosphorus shells, and the V.T. or
proximity fuse. The napalm bomb and white phosphorus are a
terrific expansion of the Molotov cocktail or flame-thrower
principle.

108
American T31 demolition tank
combining flame-thrower and
rocket-projectors.

Armour fears fire. Napalm bombs used against vehicles or in
forests where tanks may be concentrated and concealed are very
effective as are white phosphorus shells. Fire can ruin a tank's
engine and rubber parts and can ignite grease, oil and fuel, as well
as ammunition. Crews invariably bale out and become targets for
small arms fire. White phosphorus rifle grenades or hand grenades
can blind a tank, or set it on fire when particles are drawn into
the ventilating system or carburettor air intake. But these weapons,
like the Molotov cocktail, the bazooka, or any hand weapon,
demand that the user gets in close enough to obtain a hit; to be
used effectively troops must stand their ground.

The V.T. fuse is a tiny radar device in the nose of a shell which
causes detonation in the proximity of a target. Its main use is
with high explosive, which is more effective against personnel than
against armour; but because of that characteristic it is a potent

weapon against enemy infantry supporting armour.

With the normal fuse it is necessary either to pre-set for time or to leave it to explode the shell on contact; with the V.T. fuse it is not. The V.T., however, has the disadvantage that it cannot distinguish between friend and foe. The most effective fuse is the delayed action type used with armour-piercing shell. The fuse begins to function on impact, and a fifth of a second later it detonates the shell. Thus detonation occurs after penetration of the armour plate when the shell has reached the interior of the vehicle. Its disadvantage is that against thin armour it usually detonates after passing completely through the target. But against thicker armour it is extremely effective.

Poison gas was used by both sides during World War I. Gas was not used during World War II, but towards the end of the war the Germans had begun to introduce gas-proofing into tank designs. Although filters were not issued, they were stocked for the various types of gas likely to be encountered, in case the Allies started using gas.

Since World War II there has been a great upsurge in the development of the guided missile. Fantastic claims are made to the effect that the tank is now obsolete. It is true that demonstrations can be given which make it appear that the missile unerringly reaches its target. Controlled by a thin wire which is paid out as the missile flies, or controlled by radio or by a light beam or by laser, the fact remains that the gunner must keep the target constantly in his sights. As was said at the beginning of this chapter, the stress of battle may reduce potential accuracy to a small percentage. Add to this, smoke, dust, fire and other distractions; remote-controlled missiles are not the perfect anti-tank weapon.

Anti-tank defence of the future may well encompass not only the co-ordinated use of mines pre-laid by vehicles or by air, anti-tank missiles from ground and air, tank destroyers and mobile tank reserves, but also scatterable mines and self-burying mines laid by vehicles or by air to meet emergency situations.

A new development with design of land mines has been taking place in what are called scatterable mines. These can be emplaced by hand, by ground vehicle, by aircraft or by artillery fire. They include an anti-handling mechanism preventing enemy attempts to disarm them and can be timed to self-destruct.

Such mines can be used to deny an area to armour very quickly. Normally minefields when no longer needed create a problem because they may deny friendly forward movement such as a counter-attack. By the self-destruct feature, this problem can be minimized. Mines of this new type could be used to interdict supply lines and encircle enemy forces and areas out of which enemy armour can be expected to debouch.

The British have developed a bar minelayer which can lay plastic mines with laying depths and spacing controlled at a rate of 600–700 mines per hour. The device is wheeled and is towed behind a FV 432 A.P.C. Another British device announced in 1972 is a Rapid Cratering Kit which, by means of explosives, digs a deep crater instantly to obstruct an enemy tank. It is used in conjunction with Ranger anti-personnel mines.

The West Germans have developed a minelayer called the Pandora which is similar to the British Ranger. The mines ejected from the Pandora remain effective for twenty-four hours and then automatically self-destruct.

The U.S. Army Materiel Command began working on an underwater mine in 1972. It is presumed that such a weapon would be used against armour and other forces attempting river crossings.

The U.S. Air Force developed an aerial bomb called F.A.E. which was used in Vietnam. It comprised a parachute bomb which released an explosive ethylene mixture which when triggered produced a tremendous shock wave. These bombs are capable of denuding trees and of detonating minefields.

The Hughes Aircraft Company developed a plastic spray in 1972 which hardens quickly to enable a man to walk safely through a minefield by distributing his weight. It is perhaps only a question of time before a vehicle projector is developed which will do the same thing for armoured vehicles, depending on the density of the mine pattern.

The laser beam bathing of a target in order to guide a projectile to that target would appear to be almost infallible. Such a round is known as C.L.G.P. (Cannon Launched Guided Projectile). However, a tank-mounted threat-sensor could alert a crew that it was being marked and result in their firing a round destroying the designator and its observers.

High electro-magnetic and radar bursts released against an enemy ship have very effectively blacked out all its electronic equipment. This type of defence may also be very useful in tank warfare.

Nevertheless actual battle experience indicates that anti-tank defences are not completely successful in spite of the fact that tanks are most vulnerable on the sides, back and belly. Many factors, of course, enter into the situation. Not the least of these is the fact that armour is normally a moving target and combat vehicles continually change direction to disconcert an enemy. Even when travelling in a straight line speed may make the target hard to hit.

Defence against armour is not absolute; nor is attack by armour. Complete teamwork and co-ordination are as important in defence as in attack. The one factor, aside from a well co-ordinated defence, which tips the balance in favour of the defender, is the tendency in all armies to use armour piecemeal and always in the same offensive pattern. When armour is used with skill and imagination, the balance inclines to the side of the offence.

PART THREE

Vehicle
Identification

Introduction

This part of the Encyclopedia contains what is believed to be the first attempt to record the myriad designs that have been created in the track-laying branch of the military art. The vehicles included are those built in a given country as well as modifications made in that country of vehicles built elsewhere. Each country's list of vehicles (with a few exceptions) is introduced by an account of the salient points in the tank history of that country. There are many sources which cover different aspects of those histories in far greater detail than can be given here. Our object has been to summarize a great deal of that material and thus make it available in a single source.

This vehicle identification list is unquestionably incomplete. Nevertheless, it is the most complete list ever made and, we hope it will be valuable as a reference source for vehicles which otherwise would have been forever lost to posterity in unrecorded history.

The arrangement followed in the list is chronological. Within each period, because the various systems of nomenclature are not uniform, no single uniform plan could be followed. In addition, there has not always been consistent application of its own system within a given country, and sometimes systems were changed with more than one remaining in use for a time.

Therfore the official numbering system is used so far as it is known; but vehicles not assigned an official number or name, or which are on the same chassis as a vehicle carrying an official number or name, follow such vehicles in the listings.

Among the nations listed, the main AFV-producing countries which have the greatest influence on tank production and development are France, Germany, Great Britain, the Soviet Union and the United States. Four others have played a near-major role: Czechoslovakia, Italy, Japan and Sweden.

Most of the smaller countries of the world which use or have used armoured vehicles, purchased them from foreign manufacturers or bought them from or were given them by foreign governments. Some obtained used vehicles by purchase from scrap dealers or have improvised vehicles locally. Still other countries have modified foreign vehicles or have designed and built their own on a small scale.

Foreign sales of armoured vehicles are not only important to the purchasing countries to meet their defence requirements, but they are also important in advancing tank design. This is a factor which is often overlooked. Not only do foreign sales make possible more or less continuous production in the producing country, but they have the advantage from the designers' point of view of providing user comments under many different operating conditions.

Vehicle dimensions, even official, are not absolute. Manufacturing differences by the same manufacturer, manufacturing differences by different manufacturers, track wear, track sag, spring sag, measurements taken without ammunition load or stowage, measurements taken to turret top, cupola top, machine-gun mount, mud guards, track skirts and others, all have bearing on the published figures.

Where drawings were available, they were used over printed figures from other official sources. When it appeared desirable, compromises were made. Conversions from metric figures in most official cases were considered accurate; but in some cases it was obvious that where English measurements were converted to metric and then reconverted, discrepancies from the original English had taken place.

In any case, and in view of the above, all dimensions are to the nearest one-half inch. The arrangement in every case is length, width, height. Nameless tanks are indicated by (- - - - - -). Entries follow pictures.

CONVERSION TABLES

The bold figures in the central columns may be read as either metric or imperial measures. 1 inch is equivalent to 2.54 centimetres, or 1 centimetre to 0.394 inches.

Feet		Metres
3.281	1	0.305
6.562	2	0.610
9.842	3	0.914
13.123	4	1.219
16.404	5	1.524
19.685	6	1.829
22.966	7	2.134
26.247	8	2.438
29.527	9	2.743

Inches		Centimetres
0.394	1	2.54
0.787	2	5.08
1.181	3	7.62
1.575	4	10.16
1.969	5	12.70
2.362	6	15.24
2.756	7	17.78
3.150	8	20.32
3.543	9	22.86

Miles		Kilometres
0.621	1	1.609
1.213	2	3.219
1.864	3	4.828
2.486	4	6.437
3.107	5	8.047
3.728	6	9.656
4.350	7	11.265
4.971	8	12.875
5.592	9	14.484

Pounds		Kilograms
2.205	1	0.454
4.409	2	0.907
6.614	3	1.361
8.818	4	1.814
11.023	5	2.268
13.228	6	2.722
15.432	7	3.175
17.637	8	3.629
19.842	9	4.082

1 imperial ton = 2240 pounds
1 short (U.S.) ton = 2000 pounds
1 metric tonne = 2205 pounds

ARGENTINA

Argentina's armoured force began both with Vickers Light tanks bought from Britain and with Crossley armoured cars. In 1943 local production began with twelve Nahuel (an Aracaucano Indian word meaning Tiger) Medium tanks which appeared in a military parade in Buenos Aires that same year. The Nahuel closely resembled the American M4 Medium tank, the Sherman. Another locally produced vehicle that appeared some years later was an anti-tank vehicle resembling the American Ontos.

After World War II Argentina obtained Crusader IIs, T16 carriers and standard and Firefly Shermans from Britain. The Crusaders were re-built into self-propelled guns. American M41 Light tanks and M113 armoured personnel carriers were bought, but shipments were stopped after the coup d'état of June 1966. Subsequently French AMX13s were built in Argentina under licence. Later AMX30s were built from parts imported from France, and in 1971 complete AMX30 tanks began to be built, also under licence. The hulls for the French originating vehicles are built by Astarsa shipyards, the engines by Fiat-Argentina, and the power trains by IKA (Kaiser-Renault).

Argentina produced vehicles include:

▼ 110
Nahuel marca DL43, 1943, similar to Sherman, Krupp, 7.5cm L/30 later 7.5cm Bofors and 3mm coaxial mg plus 3 mgs, built at Estréban de Luca arsenal, name officially changed to Tanque Nahuel Modelo Baisi in 1943 to honour Colonel A. A. Baisi, the designer.

▼ 111
Crusader, British cruiser modified, box hull w/raised superstructure, forward mounting Schneider 105mm L/30 M1928 howitzer and 3 Madsen mgs, alternatively 75mm L/60 M1935 gun and 3 mgs.

(------), 1959, 6 barrelled recoilless rifles w/laterally deflected blast, resembled Ontos.

Tanque AMX13, 105mm French vehicle, partly built in Argentina.

Tanque AMX30, French main battle tank, partly then almost wholly, built in Argentina.

AUSTRALIA

In 1933 Australia built a copy of the American Disston tank, which was its first excursion into tank production. During World War II the country made a tremendous effort; one out of every two men between the ages of eighteen and forty-five was in uniform, and Australian war production was prodigious. This included the production of British Universal Carriers in considerable numbers, sufficient to meet the Australian Army's own needs as well as 1,500 for China. Several experimental self-propelled guns were also devised.

In 1941-43 the Australians designed and built the Australian Cruiser (A.C.) tank. There were four Marks, but only the first went into production. It was taken into use for training by the Australian Army. Despite the fact that it was never tested in action the Sentinel, of which sixty-five were built, was a note-worthy tank. Its hull was cast as one unit, something that had never before been attempted anywhere with a tank of this size, and it was so designed that it could be up-gunned without radical alteration. The Sentinel's very existence was a remarkable achievement for a limited engineering industry. The Australians also developed specialized equipment for the Matilda which were used in the South-west Pacific campaigns.

Australia's armed forces in World War II included three armoured divisions and one independent tank brigade raised for home defence. When the Japanese threat of invasion receded these were disbanded leaving one armoured brigade which fought in New Guinea, Bougainville and Borneo. A.F.V.s were also used by the divisional cavalry regiments of the Australian infantry divisions in the Middle East campaigns.

De Mole, see Great Britain.

Experimental Tank, 1933, a copy of the Disston on a commercial tractor.

Carrier MG LP No. 1, local pattern, riveted armour, headlights close together, stowage box right side, rear sloping armour, ball mounted mg left side, lever steering, Mark IVb Light tank tracks.

Carrier MG LP No. 2 welded armour, stowage boxes rear, Universal Carrier type hull, Ford 1938-39 heavy duty truck type rear axle,

Mark VIb Light tank tracks, 12' × 6' × 5' 2½".

Carrier MG LP No. 2A, same as No. 2 but Ford 1940 heavy duty type truck rear axle, brackets fitted for flotation device.

Carrier No. 2 with 3" Mortar, unaltered LP carrier, mortar above engine.

Carrier 3" Mortar (LP), longer track, rounded rear, mortar on turntable, engine left of driver.

Carrier LP No. 2 with 2pdr A/T Gun (Carrier 2pdr Attack-Hydraulic), longer track, 2pdr on hydraulic hoist, engine left of driver, 12' 4" × 6' 4" × 4' 9½" to 6' 2".

Carrier 2pdr Attack, longer track, engine left of driver, gun mounted on turntable, 13' 3" × 6' 7" × 6' 2".

Carrier, Starting and Charging (The Slave), same as British model but LP chassis.

Tracked Truck (Australian), carrier type vehicle, 3 single bogie wheels, front 1 reversed, open hull.

Sentinel Prototype (ACI), 1942, 30 tons, cast hull and turret w/2pdr and coaxial mg, bow gun in large ball mount, hull overhung for ventilation, horizontal volute spring scissors suspension resembling that on French 35R w/support roller offset to the rear, 54" turret ring.

AC I Pilot, support rollers above bogie brackets, 2pdr.

AC Cruiser Mark Ia, same for 6pdr but never installed.

AC Cruiser Mark II, designed but not built.

AC Cruiser Mark III, same as Mark I but w/25pdr and coaxial mg but no bow mg, long glacis, 64" turret ring, 20' 9" × 9' 1" × 8' 5".

▼ 112
AC Cruiser Mark IIIa, same as Mark III but w/British 17pdr and bow mg.

AC Cruiser Mark IV, similar to Mark IIIa but slightly longer, 70" turret ring and 25pdr, 21' 3" long.

AC Cruiser with Alternate Suspension, 5 road wheels on bell cranks w/volute springs.

Matilda, British tank modified w/thick plates welded to hull to protect turret race.

Matilda Frog, see Great Britain.

Matilda Hedgehog, rear mounted 7 spigot type flat rocket projector elevatable and rotatable to firing position.

Matilda Murray, see Great Britain.

Matilda Dozers No. 1 and No. 2, improvised box-like dozers on Matilda, operated by glacis-mounted winch and cable.

Matilda Tankdozer (Australia No. 3 Mark I Matilda), massive dozer assembly fitted to Matilda could be jettisoned.

ARV Mark I, simple Caterpillar D8 tractor w/various changes including addition of large rear winch.

Grant with Snorkel, 1949, commander's cylindrical mount on turret and high engine air vent tube.

ARV (Australian) Mark II, modified Grant w/forked rear trail spade.

M113 (T50), US APC w/M706 Commando armoured car turret, twin mg or 1 light and 1 heavy mg.

M113 Fire Support Vehicle, US APC w/modified British Saladin armoured car turret.

Centurion Modified, Vietnam modification, F/T w/100 gallon fuel tank mounted left rear.

AUSTRIA

Dr. Leo Steiner, a Hungarian engineer and farmer, read about the Holt tractor in an agricultural magazine in 1912 and immediately requested that Holt appoint him as one of their agents. His request was granted. He demonstrated a tractor to the Austro-Hungarian military authorities who were enthusiastic about it. German army observers, on the other hand, not only were disinterested but antagonistic. It was not until 1916 that Steiner was brought from Austria to Germany with a tractor and, with engineer Joseph Vollmer, began the design of the A7V tank.

Austria, like Germany, was forbidden the use of armoured vehicles after World War I. However, Major Fritz Heigl became recognized internationally as one of the foremost authorities on the subject, and in the early 1930s, as Germany secretly began to rearm, the firm of Austro-Daimler (later merged into the Austro-Daimler-Puch combine), under their Chief Engineer Oscar Hacker, began producing armoured vehicles for the Bundeswehr and for export. Among these was the small A.D.M.K. wheel and track machine-gun carrier. After the 1938 *Anschluss* with Germany, equipment from the Third Reich was used except for the *Ost Traktor* and the small Saurer wheel and track tank.

After World War II when Austria was permitted a small military force, one of the vehicles adopted was a Saurer armoured personnel carrier in several versions. Oscar Hacker, who had been a member of the three man top level German Tank Committee during World War II, had intended building for export a series of small and agile armoured vehicles, but his death in 1964 prevented any further development.

Burstyn, 1912, box hull on tracks, outriggers fore and aft, 11' 6" × 6' 2½" × 6' 2½" w/o outriggers, project only.

ADMK (Motorkarette) (Mulus), 1935, small wheel and track carrier, several successive models w/minor changes, 9' 1" × 3' 11" × 3' 10½" on tracks, 11' 6½" × 4' 11" × 4' 3" on wheels.

Ladungstraeger RK4, remote-controlled demolition vehicle, project only.

le gp Beob Kw auf RK7, 1941, armoured 7-ton command or reconnaissance vehicle on RK7 wheel and track personnel carrier chassis, 14' 10" × 7' 4" × 7' 3".

le gp Beob Kw auf RK8 (PzSpWgRK Ausf A), improved model w/rotating turret, 17' 1" × 9' 8" × 8' 2½".

RSO (Ost), see Germany, Miscellaneous.

Saurer 4K, 1958, low open top track-layer, 5 road wheels, 2 support rollers, original design study, 16' 4" × 8'2½" × 5' 1".

Saurer 4K Flakfahrzeug, A/A vehicle design study, 16' 4" × 8' 2½" × 7' 8½".

Saurer 4K 2cm, reconnaissance vehicle w/gun in low turret, design study, 17' 6½" × 8' 2½" × 6' 7½".

Saurer 4K Kraftfahrzeug, basic vehicle as cargo carrier, design study, 16' 7" × 8' 2½" × 6' 2½".

Saurer 4K mit Rueckstossfrei Gewehr, 6 recoilless rifles parallel, design study, 16' 4½" × 8' 2½" × 5' 1" w/o weapons.

Saurer 4K3H, 1956, armoured track-laying vehicle, high hull, long sloping bow, V-type diesel engine, 12 tons, 5 road wheels, no support rollers, 17' 6½" × 8' 5½" × 6'.

Saurer 4K3F, same but lower, in-line supercharged diesel engine, 5 road wheels, 2 support rollers, 18' ½" × 8' 2½" × 5' 5".

Saurer 4K3FA (4K2P), similar to 4K3H but short sloping bow, undercut rear, louvers in sponsons in front, pedestal mounted heavy mg.

Saurer 4K3FA-FU, command vehicle.

Saurer 4K3FA-FU/A, artillery control vehicle.

Saurer 4K3FA-FU/FIA, A/A control vehicle.

Saurer 4K3FA-FS2, radio. variation, light instead of heavy mg in cupola.

Saurer 4K4F, similar w/remote-controlled 12.7 Browning mg.

Saurer 4K4FA, similar, 17' 8½" × 8' 2½" × 5' 5" (w/o turret).

Saurer 4KFA-G, similar w/remote-controlled 2cm gun.

Saurer SPz 4K mit Turm AMX13, 1966, French light tank turret experimentally mounted as prototype SP gun, 17' 2" × 8' 2½" × 6' 9".

Schildkroete 7.5cm Pak, small Graef und Stift Christie type vehicle, 4 road wheels, rear-mounted articulated turret w/7.5cm recoilless rifle, design study dropped after death of designer O. H. Hacker, 11' 7½" × 8' 2½" × 5" 2'.

Schildkroete 10.6cm Pak, similar, design study, 11' 9½" × 8' 2½" × 5' 2".

Gr Wr 16cm, basic chassis w/centre mounted 16cm mortar in centre well, dozer equipped to dig hole for base plate dropped from vehicle, design study only, 16' 3½" × 8' 6½" ×11' 9½".

10.6cm R Pak Vierling, 4 parallel recoilless rifles in front-mounted articulated turret, design study, 14' 9" × 8' 2½" × 5' 2".

Schwimmfahrzeug, basic chassis as amphibious vehicle, design study, 16' 7" × 8' × 10'.

Splittersichermannschaftfahrzeug, (shell fragment secure personnel carrier), basic vehicle as 14-man APC, design study, 13' 1½" × 8' 2½" × 4' 11".

Pak Sfl, A/T gun in articulated rear turret, design study, 15' 1" × 8' 6½" × 5' 3".

Saurer SPz mit Turm AMX13, 1966, French light tank turret experimentally mounted as prototype SP gun.

▼ 117
Panzerjaeger K (4KH6-FA-FL/12) (Kuerassier), special Saurer chassis w/105mm AMX13 turret, 17' 8" (25' 6") × 8' 2½" × 7' 8½".

Bergepanzer K, Greif 1970, recovery vehicle on Saurer 4KH6FA-B, box hull forward w/folding crane pivoted at top right front, low rear deck, 20' 7" × 8' 2½" × 7' 9½".

M47 (Diesel), M60A1 diesel engine installed in US M47, rear deck raised, 23' 8" × 11' 6" × 8' 11½".

BELGIUM

Beginning in 1937 *Fabrique Nationale* built light tanks and SPs for the Belgian Army under licence from Vickers-Armstrongs Ltd. Purchases were also made direct from Britain. Since World War II a few SPs have been built, but most Belgian armour has been imported.

In October 1970 it was announced that Britain and Belgium had signed an agreement to collaborate in the production of the British-designed Scorpion reconnaissance tank. Belgian production lines would be set up for the production of important components as part of the deal. In June 1971 British Leyland, the parent organization of Alvis Ltd., which built the Scorpion, announced that it was to supply 130 Scorpions to Belgium. This was to be the first of a series of contracts totalling some 700 vehicles (including others of the Scorpion family) valued at about £30 million including spare parts.

Utility B Tractor, British Carden-Loyd light tractor built in Belgium under licence as an APC for 6 men and driver.

T13, 1934, built under British Carden-Loyd licence, light tank w/very large bevel-front turret open at the rear, 47mm gun in hooded mantlet, 4 road wheel leaf spring suspension, 2 support rollers w/triangular track retainers, later w/modifications.

T14, French ACG 1 w/left side turret cut for episcope, left side hull episcope moved rearward and original episcope opening plated over.

T15, 1937, Carden-Loyd M1934 chassis w/4 wheel coil spring suspension, 2 support rollers, high slope sided turret w/heavy mg or 37mm gun, 4 tons.

(- - - - -), 1934, close support 47mm w/hinged top armour and shield on Carden-Loyd carrier chassis having one support roller, gun fired front.

(- - - - -), 1938, close support 47mm in half turret offset to left and firing to the rear, on T13 chassis, 12' 3½" × 6' 1½" × 6' 1".

CAT I (Canon Antitank d'Infanterie), Caty (Cat 1), 1955, 90mm Mecar A/T gun on British-Loyd carrier chassis, gun fired front, 11' 7" (13' 7") × 6' 11" × 5' 2".

Chenilette Ravitailleuse, accompanying ammunition carrier.

(- - - - -), 1955, US M4A4 Medium tank w/124mm.

(- - - - -), 1969, US M24 Light tank w/electric transmission.

AMX13 VC1, standard French APC w/ or w/o 2 pedestal mounted Entac missile units, made in Belgium under licence.

BRAZIL

The only track-laying vehicle known to be of Brazilian origin is the small Cutia reconnaissance carrier which was announced in 1966. It was named after the guinea pig-like Brazilian

agouti. Other Brazilian vehicles were of French, Italian and American origin.

Fiat, Italian CV3/35 w/ribbed barrel 13.2mm.

▼ 118
Vete T1A1 (Cutia), 1966, 3-ton 4-man reconnaissance vehicle and personnel carrier, 1 mg in front plate, 5 road wheels, 2 support rollers, narrow (12") tracks, 11' 9½" × 6' 1" × 4' 2".

M3, 1972, US Medium tank w/US 57mm replacing original 37mm in turret.

Viatura Blindada Transporte Pessoal, US M113 APC.

Viatura Socorro, US M578 ARV.

Carro de Combato Leve, US M41A3 Light tank.

Obus 105 Autopropulsada, US M108 SP.

CANADA

During World War I Canada had a Motor Machine-gun Brigade in American-built armoured cars and a small Tank Corps of two tank battalions. The tank battalions were equipped with British Mark V and French Renault F.T. tanks. The corps was formed in 1918 and demobilized after the war. Not until after 1930 were armoured tracked vehicles again in service with the Canadian Army. These were a dozen Carden-Loyds brought from Britain to equip machine-gun platoons. In 1936 six militia regiments were designated as tank regiments and a Fighting Vehicles School was started. Apart from the carriers the only tracked vehicles available were two British Mark IV Light tanks. In 1939 Britain supplied fourteen Mark VI Light tanks.

After World War II began, 265 American Six-ton tanks as well as a few Mark VIII tanks from the World War I era were purchased as scrap iron at $20 a ton for use as training vehicles. In 1940 work began on the production of British Valentine tanks at the Canadian Pacific Railroad's Angus Shops in Montreal. The Canadians, who followed American industrial practice, had difficulty with British drawings, but they eventually fulfilled the entire contract of 1,420 Valentines, most of which were shipped to the Soviet Union.

A medium tank called the Ram, based in part on the American M3 Medium tank, was produced in several variations by the Montreal Locomotive Company; fifty were designated Ram I, the remaining 1,899 Ram II. Many of the components were interchangeable with those of the American M4 Medium. Canada also produced British Universal and Windsor Carriers, SPs, artillery observation post vehicles and flame-thrower vehicles. The American M4A1 Medium tank was produced as the Grizzly.

Canada produced an enormous amount of material during World War II, both naval and military. Some idea of the volume can be appreciated from the number of vehicles produced: trucks–815,729, wheeled armoured cars–10,054, and tanks and other tracked vehicles–40,609.

Canada's armed forces in World War II included two armoured divisions and two independent armoured brigades. These fought in Sicily, Italy and in North-west Europe. In addition, Canadian manned Churchill tanks took part in the raid on Dieppe on 19 August 1942.

After the war several types of high flotation vehicles were developed in Canada. In addition, several armoured vehicle projects were undertaken jointly with the United States.

Carrier With Piat Battery, frame w/14 Piat projectors at rear,

Carrier With Piat Gun, Piat mounted in mg sponson.

Carrier, Universal, 2pdr Equipped (Canadian Tank Hunter), 2pdr gun w/6pdr field carriage shield, 12′ 4″ long × 6′ 11″ wide.

Windsor Carrier Mark I* (Malcolm Campbell Armed Tractor), lengthened Canadian carrier using Loyd-Carrier components, 14′ 4½″ × 6′ 11″ × ′4 9½″.

Windsor Carrier, 4′ 2″ Mortar.

Windsor Carrier, Command.

Windsor Carrier, 6pdr A/T Towing.

Windsor Carrier, 6pdr Ammunition Carrier.

Tracked Jeep Mark I, 1943, five made by Marmon-Herrington in the US to Canadian specifications, resembled Windsor Carrier but 5 road wheels w/simulated spokes, suspension similar to that on Japanese light tanks, 7′ 8″ × 5′ 9″ × 4′ 1″.

Tracked Jeep Mark II, 1944, six made, suspension same as Mark I but solid disc road wheels and

w/hull and other changes, 9′ 8″ × 5′ 9″ × 4′ 1″.

Covenanter With Spigot Mortar, 1942, predecessor of British AVRE.

Churchill Bobbin, experimental carpet-layer used at Dieppe.

Valentine VI, 1942, standard British Valentine built in Canada but nose-plate cast not bolted, 2-man turret w/2pdr and Besa or Browning .30 (after the first 15 vehicles) mg, GMC diesel engine, most of production given to Soviet Union.

Valentine VII, 1942, same but minor changes including wireless change, most of production given to Soviet Union, 17′ 9″ × 8′ 7½″ × 7′ 5½″.

Valentine VIIa, same but modified cast turret, welded hull, nose and engine louvers and jettison fuel tanks.

Ram I, 1941, cast hull w/side doors having protectoscope, cast turret w/cast front plate and later w/bolted mantlet frame, mg cupola left of hull opposite driver, US M3 Medium tank suspension, 2pdr w/coaxial mg, 29½ tons, name derived from family crest of General F. F. Worthington, creator of the Canadian Armoured Corps, 19′ × 9′ 5″ × 8′ 9″.

Ram II (M3 Cnd), 1942, resembled US M4A1 Medium, 32½ tons, early vehicle had short 6pdr gun, later vehicles had longer 6pdr gun w/muzzle counterweight, first 300 produced continued to have Ram I hull w/side doors but w/ventilator replacing protectoscope, after first 1,207 bow mg cupola eliminated and escape hatch in floor provided, 19′ × 9′ 10″ × 8′ 9″ originally, w/ventilators in doors 19′ × 9′ 6″ ×8′ 9″, final production w/smooth hull sides and no doors and ventilators under sponsons, 19′× 9′ 1″ × 8′ 9″.

Sexton (25pdr SP Mount), Ram chassis w/superstructure resembling US M7 Howitzer Motor Carriage w/o pulpit, 20′ 1 ″ × 8′ 11″ × 8′.

Sexton GPO, Sexton converted to artillery command vehicle.

Sexton Kangaroo, armament removed to form an APC.

Ram OP I, early Ram converted to command vehicle, dummy gun in

limited traverse turret, wire reels on rear deck.

Ram OP II, similar conversion of Ram II adding storage boxes on turret and rear deck, 19′ 5″ × 9′ × 9′.

Searchlight Ram I, turret removed and A/A searchlight mounted.

Badger Ram, Wasp flame gun in turretless Ram chassis, F/T in ball mount in front plate.

3″ SP Tracked, open Ram I chassis w/3″ A/A gun.

QF 3.7″ A/A SP Mount, resembled above, gun shield added later.

Ram I ARV I, 1944, conversion to armoured recovery vehicle, dummy gun in smaller turret, rear crane.

Ram ARV II, early Ram II converted, dummy gun, A-frame added later.

Ram AVRE, experimental prototype for Churchill AVRE.

Ram II Armoured Gun Tower, (17pdr), turret removed, used as tractor for 17pdr wheeled mount.

Kangaroo Ram, Ram II w/turret removed and converted to APC, 19′ × 9′ 1″ × 6′ 4″.

Wallaby, ammunition carrier, 25pdr SP, Ram conversion.

Ram GPO Tracked, Ram converted to artillery command vehicle for gun position officer.

Ram/25pdr, Ram experimentally fitted w/25pdr.

Ram A/A (Skink), quadruple 20mm Polsten guns in special cast turret

on Grizzly chassis, 19′ 1″ (20′ 4″ w/sand-shields) × 8′ 9″ × 9′ 4″.

Grizzly, 1943, Canadian produced US M4A1 Medium tank, 20′ 1″ (w/sand-shields) × 8′ 8″ × 9′ 10″.

Tank OP Sherman, command tank conversion from US M4A2 and M4A4 Mediums.

Tank Command Sherman, conversions of US M4A2 and M4A4 Mediums.

Tank Control Sherman, conversions of US M4A2 and M4A4 Mediums.

Priest Kangaroo, conversion of US M7 Howitzer Motor Carriage to APC.

Badger Sherman, Wasp F/T on turretless US M4A2 HVSS.

Kangaroo Sherman, turretless US M4A4 and M4A2E8 converted to APC.

Wolverine, US M10 Gun Motor Carriage.

Churchill with 16″ CIRD, Canadian Indestructible Roller Device, anti-mine roller.

AVRCE, 1942, prototype Churchill AVRE later adopted by British.

Stuart OP, US light tank converted to command vehicle.

Armoured Bombardier Tank, 1946, large version of Windsor Carrier w/very wide tracks.

Bobcat, 1958, amphibious APC w/two small domed cupolas, 15′ 9″ × 8′ 2″ × 6′ 4″.

Mauler, 1965, radar controlled A/A missile projector on US M113 APC developed jointly w/US.

Lynx, US M113 C+R, 20mm mg cupola forward, mg top rear, 15′ 1″ × 7′ 11″ × 6′ 8″.

Dynatrac Close Support Vehicle, small cargo carrier, 5 slotted road wheels, 3 support rollers, rear mounted 105mm recoilless rifle.

CHINA

(People's Republic of)

(- - - - -), 1946, Japan's Chi-Ha w/long barrelled Russian gun. LVT 4, US Amtrac modified by addition of Russian A/T gun.

T59, Russian T54 Medium tank made in China.

T60, 1971, light tank based on Russian PT76 but longer gun in moulded turret, driver offset to left, some sources refer to this as PT63.

T62, 1971, light medium 21 ton tank w/85mm and 2 mg, resembling Russian T55, 2 types of suspension,

one w/5 large road wheels, one w/5 small road wheels and 4 support rollers, 18′ 5″ × 9′ 4″ × 7′ 5″.

K63, APC resembling Russian BMP-76PB.

CZECHOSLOVAKIA

Czechoslovakia became a nation in 1919 as a result of the break up of the Austro-Hungarian Empire at the end of World War I. The high command of the new Czechoslovak Army preferred armoured cars and armoured trains to tanks, and the Czechoslovak tank force until 1931 consisted only of seven Renault F.T.s bought from France.

Apart from a tank improvised from a farm tractor, early Czech AFV production concentrated on armoured cars and wheel-and-track vehicles. Not only did poor track life make the wheeled mode desirable (the cause of much wheel-and-track experimentation in several countries) but in the case of Czechoslovakia it was essential because of the cobbled roads along which tanks would have to move from a central reserve area to the fighting zone. Cobblestones were the ruination of tracks.

Vollmer, who had designed the German tanks in the war and who moved from Germany to Sweden after World War I, went to Czechoslovakia and joined the firm of Adamov for whom he designed wheel-and-track vehicles. No satisfactory vehicle of this dual nature was produced, however, and in due course attention was directed to normal tank design.

Ceskomoravska Kolben Danek (C.K.D.), a Prague-based machine-tool factory, bought the manufacturing rights of the Carden-Loyd carrier from Vickers-Armstrongs and in modified form it was taken into service but was far from popular with its crews who christened it 'Black Peter', a Czech nickname for bad luck. In 1933 C.K.D. began constructing a series of light tanks. The first was variously known as PII (*pancer*), or, when it was taken into service in 1934, as LT vz.34 or LT34. After the LT34 from C.K.D. came the LT38, the factory designation of its prototype being TNH. This tank was produced for export to over half dozen countries with particular modifications to meet the customer's specification.

C.K.D.'s industrial rivals, the world-famous Skoda works, came somewhat later into the tank field, its capacity being fully employed in building the guns and steam locomotives on which its prosperity was founded. But it could not ignore indefinitely its customers' enquiries for tanks. In 1936 it offered five prototypes of the SII tank to the Czech Army for trials. After modifications the tank was taken into service as the LT35. Both the LT35

and the LT38 was taken into German service after the occupation of Czechoslovakia in 1939. At this time the Czechs had 418 tanks and tankettes in service, but they had also sold a considerable number to other countries.

Czech Corps were formed of Czechs captured by the Russians in World War II, but they were never trusted with armour. The Free Czech forces armed by Britain had one armoured brigade which was in 21st Army Group in the Northwest Europe campaign of 1944–45.

After World War II the two Czech forces failed to amalgamate until after the Communist coup d'état in 1948. The Czechs built some Russian vehicles under slightly different numbers to distinguish them from the Russian versions.

M18, French Renault F.T. in mg. cannon and wireless versions.

Praga, 1925, improvised tank on farm tractor.

BD2 (Adamov), 1925, wheel and track vehicle, 8′ 2½″ × 3′ 3½″ × 5′ 3″ (7′ 4″ on wheels).

KH50 (Kolo Housenka, track-wheel), 1926, Renault FT type hull w/2 hemispheric headlight covers, cylindrical turret w/cupola, convertible wheel and track, 8.3 tons, the 50 in its title referred to its HP, later w/larger engines became KH60 and KH70, 14′ 8″ × 7′ 6″ × 7′ 5″ (8′ 4″ on wheels).

PI (P-I) (S-I) (LT33) (MU4) (MV4) (CKD vz 33) (Tancik vz 33) (Cerny Petr, Black Peter), Carden-Loyd type w/horizontal louvers in hull front, mg in rotor mantlet, 1.7 tons.

MU6 (MUV6) (R3) (S-Ib), Carden-Loyd type w/twin turrets, rail suspension, sold to Romania.

(- - - - -) (SIc), almost identical to S-Id but shorter and minus final road wheel.

S-Id (T1) (T32), see Yugoslavia.

▼ 123

P-II (P-2) (YNH) (AH43) (LT34) (Lehky Tank vz 34), 5 tons, 4 pairs of road wheels on rail, 4 upper rollers, mg front of hull, first 44 made w/long 37mm in turret having bustle and cupola, last 6 w/mg only, 13′ 1½″ × 6′ 8″ × 5′ 11″.

P-III (P-3) (CK3), similar to P-II but wheel and track, 8′ 6½″ × 7′ 2½″ × 7′ 4″ on wheels.

S-II, TNH prototype built by Skoda, see T11.

S-IIa (S2a) (S35) (Tancik 35) (LT35) (R2) (35(t)), 1932, similar to but larger than P-II, 8 small road wheels, 4 support rollers, unique dished-in sprockets and idlers, 15′ 1½″ × 7′ ½″ × 7′ 4½″.

▼ 124

S-IIb (SPIIb) CKDV8H) (V8H), 1938, suspension similar to P-II, turret w/small round cupola w/overlapping cover on right, flat turret front and sloping downward in rear, mg centre of front plate,

S-IIc, suspension similar to S-IIa, 6 sided turret, 5 sided cupola.

S-IId, similar to S-IIb, see T22.

SIIs (T23), similar to SIIb but differing suspension.

LKMVP (Lehky Kanonovy Motorovy Vuz Pasovy, light cannon motorized tracked vehicle), 1935, resembled Russian Komsolometz, 4 road wheels, 3 support rollers, open front-mounted portee 47mm A/T gun.

▼ 125

SIII (S3), modified LT35 suspension, resembled Carden-Loyd, air-cooled mg in centre front plate, drop sides, 3 versions: w/37mm and 2 mgs considered as SP; w/66mm and 2 mgs; w/37.2mm and 2 mgs in open top cylindrical turret.

F IV H (F IV HE), 1938, light amphibious tank, side metal sponsons enclosed balsa wood, small turret w/cupola, 2 screws, 4 slotted road wheels, 6¼ tons, 16′ 7″ × 8′ ½″ × 6′ 9½″.

R-1, AH43 type w/thinner armour, cylindrical turret w/o cupola, large glacis maintenance cover, sold to Romania.

R-1 (Command Type), almost identical but slightly roomier right sponson, dome top cupola on turret, normally no armament.

AH-IV, 1934, small tankette w/high box hull, mg in right hull bevel and in turret, turret cupola, 4 large road wheels, 1 support roller, sold to Iran, 11′ 2″ × 4′ 4″ × 6′ 2″.

AH-IVJ, similar, sold to Portugal, 10′ 6″ × 5′ 10½″ × 5′ 6½″.

AH-IV Sv, similar but semi-round turret w/dual mg, knob cupola, no glacis hatch, no side bevels, Volvo engine, called Model 61 in Sweden, 11′ 2″ × 4′ 4″ × 6′ 2″.

TNH, 1935, conical turret, right hand dome cupola, flush mantlet, right hand mg blister, Skoda 37mm L/40 gun, long recoil cylinder above gun, left and right visors in front plate, centre mg in curved out centre section of front plate, left side muffler, 4 large dished out bogie wheels, 2 support rollers, TN100 engine, sold to Iran.

TNHP (LT38), same but armoured silencer, flat sided turret with built out turret front, disc bogie wheels, 125 HP engine, tested by British.

TNHSv, 1938, same but Bofors 37mm gun and Volvo engine, sold to Sweden, 14′ 9½″ × 6′ 9″ × 6′ 9½″.

TNH Model A, 1938, same as TNHP but 70 HP engine, low left-hand cupola w/fixed periscopes, recoil cylinder below gun, flat front hull plate, mg mount centre, sometimes plated over by Germans, 14′ 9½″ × 6′ 9″ × 7′ 9″.

TNH Model B, conical turret built out front, left-hand cupola w/removable periscopes, flat front plate, left visor lower than right, mg mount sometimes plated over by Germans.

TNH Model C, short recoil cylinder above gun, rectangular turret mg mount, ball mounted bow mg in jutting out box.

TNH Model D, same but German 37mm L/45 gun.

TNH Model E, curving mantlet, wireless antenna left front of hull top, long stowage boxes added over tracks, some vehicles w/flat pyramidal ventilators in turret sides.

TNH Model F, integral cupola across turret top, longer turret bustle, curved gun shield, short glacis, built out front plate eliminating mg bulge.

TNH Model G, Model D built after German takeover, last production became SPs.

TNH Model H, same as Model D but

150 HP engine, all used as SPs by Germany, none as tanks.

TNH Model M, same as Model D but hull as in Model F.

TNH Model S, same as Model F but much heavier armour, some furnished to Sweden.

▼ 126

T11, similar to TNH but conical turret, flat front w/bevelled corners, left-hand dome cupola, flush mantlet, right-hand mg blister, recoil cylinder above Skoda 37mm L/40, visor on left of front plate, ball mounted mg in front plate, 3 support rollers, wireless antenna left front of turret.

LTL, 1937, prototype, conical turret, flat front, low flat right-hand cupola, right-hand mg blister, Skoda 37mm L/40 in flush mantlet w/recoil cylinder above, visors left and right of front plate, mg left centre front plate, 4 large dished out bogie wheels, 2 support rollers.

LTL, 1938, same as prototype but dome cupola, some furnished w/20mm gun in a box on left mudguard, remote controlled by driver, production as sold to Lithuania.

LTP, 1938, similar but rectangular mantlet, bullet-nosed recoil cylinder above gun, visor right-hand front plate, ball mounted mg left front plate, 3 support rollers, sold to Peru.

LTH (LTL-H), 1937, turret flat front and rear, right-hand dome cupola, rectangular flush mantlet, right-hand mg blister, 25mm Oerlikon w/concentric recoil cylinder, long visor right of front plate, ball mounted mg left side of front plate, 3 support rollers, Saurer engine, sold to Switzerland, 14′ 7½″ × 6′ 6½″ × 6′ 10½″.

Tatra VTLU, 1934, experimental wheel and track tank.

Tatra T807, 1955, amphibious tractor resembling US LVT1 but rounded bow.

T15, larger LT38 (TNHP) w/heavy outside mantlet and larger gun.

T21, 1936, design study.

T22, similar to S-II, see Turan under Hungary.

127

T25, 1939, streamlined Christie type, 20 tons, conical turret w/75mm gun. 6 large bogie wheels, project only, 20' 3½" × 9' ½" × 9' 2".

G13, 1946, commercially produced German Hetzer made for Switzerland, 15' 11" (20' 6") × 8' 8" × 7' 2".

T36, 1935, Czech produced Russian T34/85 tank.

SU101, 1955, Czech produced Russian SU100SP.

BTR50, with long tube 106mm recoilless rifle mounted amidships.

K61 Tractor Modified, 1960, Russian amphibious tractor w/rocket projector.

OT62 (Obrnene Transportery, Armoured Carrier) (Topas), Czech version of Russian BTR50P, cupola left and right front w/added mg turret above right side cupola, two small rectangular top hatches, some vehicles w/recoilless rifle on right cupola.

DENMARK

(- - - - - -) British Green Archer radar on US M113 APC.

EGYPT

Before being armed by the Soviet Union, the Egyptians obtained several varieties of British and American vehicles from continental European scrap dealers, together with a few vehicles purchased from France. In order to up-gun the Sherman, the Egyptians experimentally mounted at least one with the turret and 90mm gun from a French AMX13. One was captured by the Iraelis in the second Arab-Israeli War.

Sherman/AMX13, US M4 Medium tank w/AMX13 oscillating turret.

D30, Russian T34/85 w/turret removed and 122mm A/T gun in a similar but larger plate turret.

EIRE

(- - - - - -), 1974, 90mm gun on turret race of British Comet, project dropped.

FINLAND

Vickers-Armstrongs 6 Ton Type E (Viku), modified in Finland for Swedish Landsverk turret and Bofors 37mm.

Vickers-Armstrongs 6 Ton Type E (Viku), same turret type but single or dual mg.

Vickers-Armstrongs 6 Ton Type E (Viku), same turret type but 37mm Puteaux gun from original Renault FT17 tanks.

Vickers-Armstrongs Type E (Viku), Russian T26S turret substituted.

T26A (Viku), Russian T26A w/2 mgs in turret instead of 47mm gun.

Sotka, Russian T34/76.

Pitkäpotkinan Sotka, Russian T34/85.

Klimi, Russian KV.

Postivaunu, Russian T28.

BT42, Russian BT rebuilt to mount a Spanish 114mm howitzer in a massive turret.

Sturmi (Stu40), German SdKfz142/1 Ausf G.

Nelonen, German SdKfz161/1.

10IT PSV40, Swedish LVKV40.

SU57-2, title of Russian A/A vehicle apparently applied also to Swedish LVKV41.

T26K, command tank, Vickers 6 ton tank w/turret removed, hull covered and centre hatch added.

FRANCE

In the early months of World War I many of the French hierarchy regarded the main problem on the stabilized Western Front to be that of finding a way to defeat barbed wire. This resulted in a number of experimental devices being produced under the sponsorship of J. L. Breton, Under-Secretary of State for Inventions, but none was adopted for use. Artillery fire continued to be the chief means employed to destroy wire.

There were other people, however, who recognized that the main problem was how to overcome the machine-gun. Chief among these was Colonel (later General) J. B. E. Estienne, an artillery officer. Like Colonel Swinton with the British Expeditionary Force, Estienne had seen a Holt tractor in operation. The thought occurred to him that it would make a good basis for his land ironclads which were to travel across country carrying guns and infantry. Unknown to him, Eugene Brillié, chief engineer of the Schneider armament firm, was experimenting with two Holt tractors with something of the same idea in mind. Estienne had worked out the broad ideas for the tactical employment of his projected armoured vehicles. He put these to

General Joffre, the French Commander-in-Chief, who gave him permission to contact a manufacturer. Renault felt unable to help because his firm lacked experience with tracklayers. So Estienne went to Schneider and came in contact with Brillié. From this collaboration came the Schneider *Char d'Assaut* (Assault Car), or C.A.

Estienne's direct approach to Joffre put a few noses out of joint, especially in the department of the French Army responsible for automotive development. Jealous of its rights, the department ordered an 'official' tank from the F.A.M.H. company at Saint Chamond. This tank was designed by Colonel Rimailho, and once again the Holt tractor formed the basis of the vehicle.

The first French tank action took place with Schneiders in an attack on Chemin des Dames on 16 April 1917. On 5 May, St Chamonds were first used to support an infantry attack on Laffaux Mill. On both occasions the shortcomings of these medium-heavy tanks became only too obvious. The St Chamond was known as 'the elephant with the legs of a gazelle'. It broke down constantly and sufficient spare parts had not been provided. Spare parts for the Schneiders were likewise in short supply, and cannibalization became the order of the day. Nevertheless the St Chamond was a highly advanced tank in one particular: it had petrol-electric transmission. Indeed it was this advanced type of transmission that increased its weight to the point where its suspension proved inadequate. Design changes were ordered in both tanks, but it took time to get these into production.

Furthermore, by this time interest in the medium-heavy type was waning in France. Colonel Estienne had been back to Renault and had succeeded in persuading him to change his mind. Estienne was now convinced that what was needed were light tanks attacking 'in swarms' in support of infantry. Renault agreed to build such a light tank. Work on it began at the end of 1916, and by October 1917 it was in mass production with other firms as well as Renault. The new Renault light tanks first went into action on 31 May 1918, during the battle for the Forest of Retz.

As well as the Schneider, St Chamond, and the Renault F.T. (*Faible Taille*, light weight), the French also built a few heavy tanks. These were the *Chars 1A* and *1B*, and the *Char 2C*. The first two were not continued with, but ten 2Cs were built and taken into service in 1921. They were ultimately destroyed on their railway flats by the *Luftwaffe* in 1940, after being used only once. In all, France built 3,870 tanks during World War I, of which more than 3,000 were Renault F.T.s.

During the war the tanks had originally been considered as assault artillery; then they came to be re-

France

garded as an accompanying weapon for infantry. This became the official French doctrine, and in 1920 tanks became part of the infantry arm by law. Nonetheless, the terrible slaughter that had destroyed the manhood of France from 1914 to 1918 had created a climate in which defence, not attack, was to be the military doctrine of the future. Tanks were basically a weapon of attack. Tanks were therefore a weapon to be shunned. The Maginot Line mentality was dominant–not unnaturally–and began to assume physical form when the line began to be constructed in the early 1930s.

Meanwhile the plethora of Renault F.T.s which were lying about at the end of 1918 were gradually sold off to many countries. Indeed this remarkable little tank found its way all over the world, and many a nation that today boasts an armoured force founded that force on one or two dozen, or even a couple of Renaults bought from France in the 1920s and 30s. But France did not reject the tank: 534 Renault F.T.s were still deployed with the French Army in 1940.

The French attitude towards tanks was not unusual in those days. It obtained in most armies except Germany's. There were, however, cells of armour enthusiasts in all military establishments. This certainly was the case in France where developments of the Renault F.T. took place and resulted in a new series of Renault tanks culminating in the R35 and R40. General Estienne, too, was still a sufficiently powerful figure to sponsor the development of the *Char B,* one of the most remarkable tanks ever to be built.

As well as these infantry tanks, there were other tanks built for the French Cavalry–though these had to be designated as armoured cars in order to get round the law which allowed only the infantry to have tanks. (A similar situation occurred in the United States where the cavalry had to call their tanks combat cars in order to avoid breaking the law.) Regardless of whether the particular vehicle was a tank or an armoured car they were called *Auto-Mitrailleuses* by the cavalry. Thus: A.M.C., A.M.D. or A.M.R. (*Auto-Mitrailleuse de Combat, Auto-Mitrailleuse de Découverte* and *Auto-Mitrailleuse de Reconnaissance*), designated according to function.

When Germany began openly rearming there were instincts of alarm in France despite the Maginot Line–which, as it turned out, was not only psychologically destructive but geographically inadequate. De Gaulle published his *Vers L'Armée de Métier,* but it received little attention until Paul Reynaud championed its ideas in the *Chambre des Députés;* even then they were shrugged off as a political ploy. Indeed, had Reynaud refrained from favourable comment it is possible that De Gaulle's book would have been better received. It

is sometimes claimed that the Germans learned the theory, if not the art, of *blitzkrieg* from De Gaulle's book; the truth is that the Germans were committed to their strategy long before his book appeared.

A writer who had a more positive influence on French military thinking at this period was General Narcisse Chauvineau, who began writing articles in 1930 and in 1939 published a book which was widely read because it was endorsed by Marshal Pétain. Its title was *Une Invasion,* and it received considerable publicity, both civilian and military. Today he is a forgotten author because World War II proved him to be so wrong.

Chauvineau's views on armour can be expressed in a few main points, which are not without their proponents today: (1) defence was supreme; (2) it was the loss of German manpower by Allied artillery and infantry rather than by armour which defeated Germany in the Great War; (3) armour could be defeated by strong nerves, discipline, high explosives and mines, and because the ability to command armour could be achieved by very few officers; and (4) the only possible value for tanks might be a certain limited use as a defensive weapon in counter-attacks.

As in the United States and Great Britain the cavalry reluctantly began to give up their horses–or some of them–and falter into the modern world of mechanization. The first French mechanized cavalry division, *Division Légère Mécanique* (D.L.M.), was permanently formed in 1934. (This, interestingly enough, was one year before the formation of the first German *panzer* division and four years before the formation of what was to become the first British armoured division. But in this particular instance it must be noted that the British had inaugurated armoured formations in 1927 with their Experimental Mechanized Force which was

not fully developed into a permanent armoured division until nine years later.) A second D.L.M. was formed in 1938, a third in August 1939, and a fourth was being assembled in May 1940, but was never completed.

Another type of cavalry formation with tanks was hastily formed in the winter of 1939-40 when five horsed brigades were released from cavalry divisions to join five new partially mechanized *Divisions Légères de Cavalerie* (D.L.C.), which were in fact only smaller and weaker versions of the D.L.M.s.

The third sort of French armoured formation was the only one which approximated to the armoured division as it came to be thought of in World War II. This was the *Division Cuirassée de Réserve* (D.C.R.). Though authorized in 1937 the first D.C.R. was not formed until September 1939. A second was formed in January 1940 by breaking the first into two, a third came into being in March 1940, and a fourth, under De Gaulle's command, was being hastily put together in the face of the German assault.

French mobilization in 1939 was indiscriminate in the calling up of reserves. At a time when production of weapons was most needed, factories lost much of their skilled labour. For example, the Renault plant was reduced from 30,000 to 7,000 workers. But by September 1939, 3,000 modern tanks had been built, causing certain official bombast and self-congratulation. So sure were the French of adequacy that they had been shipping new tanks to Belgium, Poland and Romania.

As a matter of fact, the French had more tanks than Germany at the time of the latter's attack in May 1940, but they were deployed piecemeal over the entire French front in keeping with official French tank doctrine.* Neither the D.L.M., the D.L.C. nor the D.C.R. had been in

*The following table shows the deployment of French tanks during the campaign against the Germans in 1940. R35/40 = Renault 35 or 40; H35/39 = Hotchkiss 35 or 39 (basically tanks built for the cavalry); F.C.M.–Forges et Chantiers de la Méditerranée (infantry tanks); D = Chars D1 and D2 (Renault built infantry tanks); 2C = the post-World War I super-heavy tanks; F.T. = Renault F.T.; S35 = Somua 35, rated by some to be the best tank in the world in its day—fast, reliable, heavily armoured and with a powerful punch; it was developed from the D1 and D2. A.M.R. and A.M.D. have been explained in the text.

DEPLOYMENT OF FRENCH AFVs IN EUROPEAN OPERATIONS MAY-JUNE 1940

Unit or Formation	R35/40	H35/39	FCM	D	Tanks B	2C	FT	S35	Autos-mitrailleuses AMD (Whl)	AMR (Track)
Tank battalions organic to Armies										
Eighteen	810									
Two		90								
Two			90							
One						6				
Eight							504			
Independent Companies		30		40	57		30			
1 DCR		90			66					
2 DCR		90			66					
3 DCR		90			66					
4 DCR	135			45	66					
1 DLM		87						87	45	60
2 DLM		87						87	45	60
3 DLM		147						87	45	
1 to 5 DLC		110							70	110
Reconnaissance groups of seven motorized infantry divisions									154	154
	945	821	90	85	321	6	534	261	359	384

NOTE: The numbers are based on the organization of formed units deployed in this period, and on the equipments available within the respective formations.

132

existence long enough to function properly. They were not completely equipped and were no match for the German *panzer* divisions although General De Gaulle's 4th D.C.R. gave a brief but commendable account of itself.

In May 1940, Louis Renault went to the United States and Canada in the hope of having tanks produced outside France, but it was a futile mission because while he was in Canada France surrendered.

During the remaining years of World War II, Free French armour was organized along American lines into *Divisions Blindées*. After the war the French organized an experimental *Division Mobile* and finally the *Division Mécanique Rapide* (D.M.R.) which was composed of self-sufficient battalion-strength battle groups.

After World War II, one French tank battalion was equipped with German Panther tanks which later were replaced with French ARL44 medium tanks. From then on, a great deal of interesting tank design took place. The French have long been able to build light tanks with heavy armour. Equally important contributions have taken place over the past decades through an integrated programme combining government laboratories and arsenals with industry. This programme is controlled by *Direction Technique des Armements Terrestre* (D.T.A.T.) under the *Delegation Ministerielle pour l'Armement,* formerly the *Ministre des Armes* and prior to that *Direction des Etudes et Fabrications d'Armament* (D.E.F.A.) including the commercial *Societé des Forges et Ateliers des Creusot* (S.F.A.C.), the whole comprising *Groupement Industriel des Armements Terrestres* (G.I.A.T.).

French commitments in Indochina and Algeria led to the development of lighter armoured vehicles possessing airborne capability. Following the elimination of these overseas responsibilities, a new concept based on nuclear warfare began to develop late in 1964. With their AMX13 family and AMX30 (firing the Obus-G), the French are well to the fore in modern armour–much of which is available for export.

Industrial, departmental and arsenal initials were, and are, used in French tank nomenclature, as follows:

ABX now EFAB—Bourges Arsenal
ALM—Le Mans
ALS--Limoges Arsenal
ALX—Lyon Arsenal
AMX—Moulineaux Arsenal
APX—Puteaux Arsenal
ARL—Reuil Arsenal
ARS—Rennes Arsenal
ARX now ARE—Roanne Arsenal
ASS—Sallieres
ATE—Toulouse Arsenal
ATS—Tarbes Arsenal
FCM—Mediterranean
MAS—St Etienne
MAT—Tulle
RNUR—Renault Light vehicles
SAVIEM—Renault Heavy vehicles

SOFAM—Armament and Motors
SOMUA—*Société d'Outillage Mécanique et d'Usinage d'Artillere.*

WORLD WAR I VEHICLES AND MODIFICATIONS

Breton Destructeur des Barbieres des Fils, 1914, circular saw at end of hinged steel tube power driven through electric cable, mounted on small 4 wheel carriage, intended as a wire-cutting device.

128

Diplodocus Militaris (Appareil Boirault), 1915, rhomboid-shaped skeleton tank w/o armour, w/single overhead track.

Gabet Blockhaus Blindé, 1915, armoured hull, large dome turret w/cannon on 2 large wheels and small rear steering roller, powered through electric cable.

Rouleau Frot-Laffly, 1915, 4 wheel w/armour shell resembling early vehicle British heavy tanks but w/o sponsons, 23′ × 6′ 7″ × 7′ 6½″.

Aubriot-Gabet Destructeur des Réseaux, 1915, small track-layer w/tracked rudder, open platform chassis w/electrically powered wire-cutter operated through electric cable.

Schneider Crocodile, 1915, skeleton track frames, continuous band tracks w/large block grousers, shielded wire-cutter in front, intended as remote-controlled explosives carrier.

Tracteur Breton-Prétot, 1916, Bajac tractor, 2 large wheels w/serrated tread, front shield to depress barbed wire, small trailing steering wheel w/large vertical power driven shear saw.

129

Tracteur Filtz, armoured hull, large grousered front wheels, 2 small rear wheels, 1 mg.

Delaunay-Belleville, 1916, 4 wheel auto chassis w/girders to be laid down and picked up in breaching barbed wire or crossing trenches.

Schneider-Holt Type A (Breton-Boissin), 1916, small unarmoured track-laying tractor.

Schneider-Holt Type B (Tracteur Lieut. Fouché), 1916, Schneider track frames, driver front, boat-shaped armour hull.

Schneider Char d'Assault (CA), prototype, 1916, box hull, short 75mm gun in right front, ball mounted mg left and right sides, single projecting wire-cutter, pointed nose, twin tailpiece, limited rear fuel tanks.

Schneider CA, 1916, fuel tanks enlarged, ventilation improved, 19′ 8″ × 6′ 7″ × 7′ 10″.

Schneider Char de Ravitaillement, 1918, armament removed and door installed where 75mm had been, front of hull cut down, used as supply tank.

Schneider CA2, 1917, similar to original vehicle but small turret w/47mm gun added, 1 prototype used as training vehicle.

Schneider CA3, 1917, 2 dome cupolas, shorter nose, bigger rear overhang, mg added centre front, project only, 18′ 4½″ × 7′ 10½″ × 8′ ½″.

130

Char St Chamond, prototype, 1916, box hull, faceted bow overhanging tracks, St Chamond 75mm gun in nose skirted suspension, flat top hull w/2 cupolas top front for driver and commander.

Char St Chamond, 1916, first production, skirts removed, armoured cylinder for searchlight between front cupolas, cupola added in rear, 4mgs, 1 in nose.

Char St Chamond, 1917, top beveled to both sides, hatches only in top, front end of hull increased in height, with St Chamond 75mm, 25′ 10″ (28′) × 8′ 9″ × 7′ 8″, 75mm M1897 gun for later production, 25′ 10″ (28′ 10″) × 8′ 9″ × 7′ 8″.

St Chamond Expérience, a first production vehicle w/tracked orolo assembly suspended from nose as anti-bellying device.

Char St Chamond, 1917, 75mm M1897 gun, 4mgs, wider tracks,

front end of hull higher, commander's box cupola w/hinged sides on left front.

St Chamond Char de Ravitaillement, 1918, armament removed and nose armoured-over for use as a supply tank.

La Seyne (Char Lourd FCM 1a) (Char 1a), 1917, improved Renault-type tank projected at 55 tons, 75mm howitzer in turret having cupola, 5 mgs, not completed, 30′ × approx. 9′ 6″ × 11′.

Char 1B, similar with 75mm or 105mm gun and 2 mgs, petrol-electric transmission, forerunner of Char 2C, 27′ 4″ × 9′ 4″ × 6′ 6″.

Char 2C, 1919-1923, 75 tons, 75mm gun in forward turret, mg in smaller rear turret, stroboscope on each turret, mg in each side forward, high centre superstructure, 33′ 7″ (39′ 4″) × 9′ 7″ × 13′ 3″.

Char 2C, 1923-27, various improvements made in suspension, insulation, communication and engines, tailpieces added to some vehicles, weight raised to 81 tons, special low bed railway cars built for strategic moves.

Char 2C bis (FCM), 1926, dome-like Saut du Tarn turret w/short 155mm howitzer substituted for forward turret.

Char Renault, 1916, intended as command vehicle, no armament, no tailpiece, artillery-type idler wheel, rounded sloping front turret w/small knob cupola.

Char Mitrailleur FT17, same w/mg in ball mount added later, as well as tailpiece and horizontal louvers rear of hull, coil and leaf spring suspension, 6 tons, 13′ 5″ (16′ 5″) × 5′ 8″ × 7′6½″.

Char Renault FT (Char Mitrailleur FT17), 1916, hinged cupola cover added, one vehicle w/large cap instead of cupola over, split doors centre rear of turret, rear louvers, laminate wood steel-rimmed idler, 1 mg, 16′ 5″ × 5′ 8″ × 7′ 6½″.

Char Renault FT (Char Mitrailleur FT17), 1917, 8-sided turret w/cupola replaced rounded turret due to manufacturing difficulties, doors in rear of turret first offset to right, later offset to left, Hotchkiss mg, in trunnion mount.

Char Canon FT17, same w/37mm Puteaux L/21 gun.

Char Renault FT, 1918, moulded turret w/cupola, normally transported on truck or tracked transporter, also known as Char FT17 (Berliot turret), turret doors in rear centre.

Char Renault TSF (Télégraphie sans Fil) (Char Signal FT17), 1918, square front hull, square box cupola w/dome cover, wireless tank, 16′ 5″ × 5′ 8½″ × 8′ 2½″.

Char Renault FT Amphibie, 1919, turretless, new boat-shaped hull, intended as APC.

Renault Char de Ravitaillement, turret and tailpiece removed for use as supply vehicle.

Char Renault BS (Batterie de Support), large 10-sided turret beveled front and rear w/short 75mm in ball mount, 16′ 5″ × 5′ 8″ × 7′ 6½″.

Char de Forteresse, high built-up hull w/small cupola, short 75mm low in front.

Char Peugeot, 1918, resembled Renault but fixed rounded cab w/37mm gun and mg at rear w/engine front.

Char Delaunay-Belleville, 1918, 14 tons, resembled Renault but considerably larger, small bogies, coil and leaf spring suspension, Renault FT 1918 turret, crude gun and steering stabilizer, 16′ 5″ × 6′ 10½″ × 6′ 5″.

Matériel de 105 long sur Char Renault, 1918, stripped-down Renault FT w/105mm gun firing to the rear, early light SP.

Canon de 75 Modèle 1897 sur Char Renault, 1918, open hull built up in rear, gun in centre fired to rear, caisson behind driver.

Canon de 75 Modèle 1897 sur Char Renault Projet STA, 1918, hull reversed, gun fired forward, caisson rear.

Canon de 155 GPF (Grande Puissance Filloux, high powered Filloux gun) sur Char Renault, 1918, gun on Renault FT chassis.

Canon de 120 sur Char St Chamond, 1916, 120mm on St Chamond chassis.

Canon de 220 court sur Chenilles St Chamond, 1917, 220mm on St Chamond open chassis.

Matériel de 105 long M1913 sur Affut-Auto Propulseur Schneider, 1917.

Canon de 220 long Schneider sur Affut-Chenilles, 1917, tricycle-tracked carriage w/electric motor, remote-controlled.

Canon de 220 long Schneider sur Chenilles, 1917, gun on open-tracked chassis.

Caterpillar Schneider portant 155 long M1917, Chassis of Char CA w/framework mounting portée field-gun.

Obusier de 280 sur Chenilles, 1917, 280mm on open-tracked carriage.

Canon de 194 Mle GPF sur Chenilles, open carriage, gun lowered and retracted for travel, still in use in 1940, 21' (31') × 8' 6" × 8' 8".

Canon de 220 Schneider M1917 sur Chenilles, similar.

Obusier de 370 sur Chenilles, long low carriage.

Renault FT Modifié, short pitch tracks, modified entrance doors and driver's hatch, AMR turret.

Renault Prototype avec Chenilles Souples, 1924, original M1916 w/Kégresse suspension, 8 road wheels, continuous band rubber tracks, large double rollers in front and small double rollers rear for anti-bellying, metal front idler, spoked rear sprocket.

Char Renault FT 18 avec Chenilles Souples, 1925, similar but small rear rollers eliminated, used in Riff campaign, 18' × 6' 5" × 7' 9".

138

▼ Renault Kégresse-Hinstin, improved model, rear top deck modified, rear sprocket strengthened w/very thick rim and hub.

Renault FT31 (Char Mitrailleur FT31), renovated FT18, improved ventilation, new engine, Reibel mg replaced Hotchkiss on mg model, new fuel pump substituted in 1940.

Char Renault Portée de Pont, 1925, w/ and w/o turret, light bridge carried on raised rails and rollers.

Charrue-Mines de Char Renault (Char Demineur), mine plough on FT.

Char Renault avec Fascine (Char Poseur de Fascine), FT w/fascine carrier.

Char Renault Dozer, bulldozer on FT.

Char Projecteur Renault, searchlights mounted on a high skeleton framework on combat tank.

Char Renault avec Projecteur Brillant, 1934, early de Thoren CDL on FT.

Char de Transport Renault, built-up box hull w/square cab in rear.

VP38 (Vehicule Pommelet), 1936, small track-laying remote-controlled demolition vehicle, 2 cylinder air-cooled engine.

FT Telecommande par Radio, 1940, remote-controlled vehicle.

FT Telecommande par Fil et par Radio, remote-controlled vehicle, cable and wireless.

POST-WORLD WAR I LIGHT TANKS AND RELATED VEHICLES

Chenilette St Chamond, 1921, prototype wheel and track vehicle, 3½ tons, rigid tankette suspension, leaf spring wheel suspension, box hull, wheel tread narrower than track treads, change from wheels to tracks from inside not vice versa, front wheels removable and placed on rear brackets, mg added to production vehicle and small refinements made, 11' 10" × 6' 10" × 6' 4" on wheels (5' 7" on tracks).

Chenilette St Chamond M24, turret w/45mm gun added, 11' 10" × 6' 10" × 7' on wheels.

St Chamond, unarmoured version as 155mm howitzer SP chassis, also used as experimental artillery tractor.

Chenilette St Chamond M26, similar to M24 but higher hull w/mg, no turret, changeover either way controlled from inside, 11' 10" × 6' 10" × 6' 6" (on tracks).

Chenilette St Chamond M28, wheels now on sides, raised or lowered on crank arms, 37mm gun front of hull, cupola rear of hull, 12' 7½" × 7' 10½" × 6' 7" (on tracks).

Schneider-Laurent Amphibie, 1928, resembled Chenilette St Chamond M28 but larger, 7.7 tons, symmetrical boat-shaped hull, centre turret w/37mm gun and 1 mg, 19' 8" × 7' 2½" × 8' ¼".

AM Amphibie Type DP2 (ARL Batignolles), 12 tons, low tracks, 8 bogie wheels, high floats over tracks, boat-shaped bow, pyramidal turret w/20mm gun.

Renault M26/27 Char de Combat Muni du Propulseur Kégresse-Hinstin, 4 bogie wheel pairs, 1 support roller, spoked rear sprocket, small tail rollers, hull and turret almost identical to FT18, 15' 9" × 5' 11½" × 8' 5½".

Char Renault NC27 (NC1), 1927, hull similar to FT18, Kégresse half metal tracks, 3 double bogie wheel pairs w/exposed vertical triple concentric coil springs, could be steered w/foot pedal brakes, 14' 5" (17' 5") × 5' 7" × 7'.

Char Renault NC31 (NC2), 1931, improved NC27, new radiator, new hull but same basic design, first tank w/Cleveland (Cletrac) differential, steel tracks w/heavy rounded edge grousers, 14' 5½" × 6' × 7'.

Char NC31 Modifié, coffin bow widened, Renault AMC35 type turret w/medium long 47mm.

Char NC31 Modifié, modified original FT tailpiece added as well as suspension skirting, prototype of Char D-1.

Char Renault NC3, same chassis and hull as NC2 but conical turret truncated and w/slope front, dual mg, design study only, leading to Char D-1.

Char D-1, Première Modèle, 1930, FT17 turret w/coaxial 47mm gun and Reibel mg, 1 Reibel mg in hull, wood shoes instead of support rollers for silence, rigid triangular wireless telegraph antenna on right rear of hull, episcope in turret cupola, 14 tons, 17' 5" (w/o antenna) × 7' 2" × 7' 10½".

Char D-1 (Car D-1A), 1933, type ST2 turret w/dome cupola, 47mm gun and Reibel mg separated by sight in turret, recoil cylinder above gun tube, vision block in turret step above mantlet, 1 fixed mg in front plate, large and small parallel triangular wireless antennae, 18' 7" × 7' 2" × 7' 7½".

Char D1B, same but cast experimental turret somewhat lower because of absence of vision block above mantlet.

Chenilette Renault, 1926, small 1-man tankette, 1 mg, Kégresse half metal tracks.

Chenilette Sabathé, 1929, small 2 ton 1-man tankette, driver erect but prone in action, engine rear, mg in nose, 4 road wheels on rail, trailing idler, 8' 6½" (10' 6") × 4' 7" × 3' 7½".

Tracteur d'Infanterie Renault UE, 1931, Carden-Loyd type, covered rail suspension, 2 support rollers, 2 small double half dome cupolas, rear stowage box added later, usually used w/tracked trailer, rubber block track, later w/beveled downward mud cover above road wheels and no support rollers, 8' 10" × 6' 2" × 3' 10".

Tracteur d'Infanterie Renault UE, 1939, improved and strengthened suspension w/narrow suspension support rail and reversion to 2 support rollers, 8' 10" × 5' 7" × 3' 10".

▼ 139
Chenilette Renault (DAF1), 1933, UE w/raised cab on right w/heavy mg in ball mount, 2 tons, 8' 10½" × 5' 7" × 4' 1".

AMR Renault M1933, resembled British Mark II Light tank but pyramidal turret toward rear, 2 leaf spring bogie wheels pairs, 3 support rollers.

AMR Renault HC, similar but larger box hull and larger pyramidal turret.

AMR Renault M1933 Type VM (VM33), prototype, low turret more forward, 1 bogie pair pivoting at end of vertical coil spring, 2 single spoked road wheels on bell crank w/horizontal hydraulic cylinder, 4 support rollers, 5 made, 11' 6" × 5' 3" × 5' 10".

AMR 33VM (AMR Renault VM 2éme Mle), production of 117 vehicles, higher turret than prototype, later some w/13.2mm gun, 14' 5" × 5' 5" × 5' 1".

AMR Renault M1934 (Renault Type YR), prototype w/Char FT18 turret and 37mm gun, silencer on right front mudguard.

AMR Renault M1934 (Type YR), resembled Char 35R but riveted hull w/angle strips at edges, 25mm gun and 1 mg in cast turret w/cupola, 1 bogie pair, 2 single road wheels, 4 support rollers as on 33VM, first 3-man tank, 12 made.

AMR Renault M1934 (Type YB), AMR w/35R turret.

▼ 140
Renault YR Poste de Commandement, box hull, engine front, command vehicle, 13' 1½" × 6' 9½" × 7' 6½".

AMR Renault M1935 (ACG1) (AMC35), similar to YR but 2 bogie pairs and 1 lead road wheel, all scissors rubber washer suspension, 5 support rollers, 25mm gun and 1 mg or 37mm gun and 2 mgs, 14' 11½" × 7' 2½" × 7' 6½".

Renault YS Poste de Commandement, ZT chassis, hull similar to YR command vehicle, 12' 5½" × 5' 4½" × 5' 11".

Tracteur Renault YS, similar but only partially armoured.

▼ 141
AMR Renault Mle 1935 (ZT-1) (Type ZT), (ZT35), improved, riveted faceted slope front turret, 13.2mm and 7.5mm mg or 25mm gun,

4 road wheel rubber washer single scissors suspension, 13' 11" × 5' 9" × 5' 11".

▼ 142
Canon de 25 sur AMR (Char ZT-II), same chassis but box hull w/25mm gun low right, small cupola, 13' 11½" × 5' 9" × 5' 11".

AMC Renault 1935, same chassis as AMR Renault 35 (ACG1) but 20mm gun and 1 mg in larger cast turret, 14' 11" × 7' 2½" × 6' 7".

Obusier Court de 135 sur Chassis d'AMR 33VM, 135mm howitzer SP.

Obusier Court de 135 sur Chassis d'AMR 1935 (135 Automoteur), similar.

Char Hotchkiss 35H, 1935, cast hull, driver right, sloped rear deck, cast turret w/37mm gun and pivoted cast insert diascopes, dome on turret, 3 paired bogie wheel coil spring scissors suspension, 2 support rollers, bulging front sprocket, 5 hole rear idler, 13' 10" × 6' 1" × 5' 10".

Char Hotchkiss 35H 2e Type (1938 Modèle H Serie D), similar but almost flat rear deck, lipped peep slots substituted in turret, disc idler, more powerful engine, some w/tailpiece.

Char Hotchkiss 38H, similar to 35H 2e type but w/longer SA/38 gun, more powerful engine, some w/tailpiece, 13' 10" (w/o tailpiece) × 7' ½" × 6' 1".

Tracteur Blindé Hotchkiss, 35H chassis, long glacis, short flat-sided cab,

▼ 143
Char Citroën P103, 1935, resembled Renault Kégresse-Hinstin but riveted faceted turret, higher cast and riveted hull w/protruding oscillating driver visor on right, 3 double road wheels, hydraulic suspension, 2 support rollers, trailing idler, continuous band rubber block tracks.

Char Leger FCM Pilot, 1936, bevel-sided welded hull, beveled skirted suspension w/flared front mudguard extending over front sprockets and suspension, tracks like NC2, overhanging cast turret w/37mm gun and mg.

Char Leger FCM, 1936, faceted welded hull and pyramidal turret w/cut to form set-back cupola, front mudguard flare eliminated, 4 small road wheels in pairs, short 37 SA/18 gun, later w/37 SA/38, 14' 8" × 7' × 7' 8".

Char Leger Renault, similar to Hotchkiss 35H but smaller cast hull w/driver centre and silencer across rear, rubber washer scissors suspension, 2 bogie pairs and 1 single road wheel, 3 upper rollers, solid sprocket, solid idler, cylindrical cast turret having slight forward slope, 2 Reibel mgs.

Char d'Accompagnement Renault (35R), similar but 37 SA/18 gun in same turret as 35H, silencer left, trailing idler, some w/tailpiece, 13' 8" × 6' ½" × 6' 11".

Renault Char ZM, 35R variation w/5 small 4 wheeled bogies, skirted w/mud chutes, 3 return rollers, 13' 1½" × 6' 1½" × 6' 10½".

35R avec Tourelle FCM 36, experimental installation of FCM welded turret.

▼ 144
35R avec Tourelle Nouveau, 1938, similar but cast FCM-type turret, modified 35R spoked trailing idler.

39R (R40), similar to 35R but turret changed as on 38H, later production had 37 SA/38 gun, some w/driver left, some w/tailpiece.

Char AMX38, 37 SA/38 in pilot, 47mm gun in limited production, 8 double wheeled bogies, 4 return rollers, skirts w/mud chutes, 17' 5" × 6' 9" × 7' 4".

Char AMX40, 1938, larger version of 35R, rear drive, skirted, 12 small road wheels w/vertical coil spring suspension, 4 support rollers, raised idler, diesel engine, Wilson-Talbot transmission, some w/37 SA/38 gun.

35R Detecteur-Mines, open chassis w/3 mine detector arms on pivots w/headphone detection.

AMX/R35, 1938, 35R w/new skirted
suspension, 3 support rollers,
17' 5" × 6' 9" × 7' 4".

AMX/R40 (Renault ZM), 35R
w/AMX40 skirted suspension
permitting 10 per cent weight
increase w/same engine, reduced
vehicle pitching, originally
w/tailpiece, 4 support rollers.

Chasseur de Char AMX 47mm, 1940,
47mm APX M37 gun on 35R
chassis.

Chasseur de Char AMX 75 sur
Chassis 35R, Mle 1897, 75mm gun
on 35R chassis.

35R Poseur de Fascine, skeleton
framework to support brush
fascine.

35R Telecommande par Radio,
remote-controlled vehicle.

*POST-WORLD WAR I MEDIUM
TANKS AND RELATED
VEHICLES*

Schneider-Renault SRA, Char de
Bataille, 1923, track frames
resembled British Medium D,
75mm gun in front plate, 1 mg in
low domed turret, 14 tons, 18' 10"
× 8' 5" × 6' 10".

Schneider-Renault SRB, Char de
Bataille, 1924, two 75mm guns,
6 mgs, petrol-electric transmission,
20 tons.

Char FAMH, 1924, miniature Char
2C in appearance but short 75mm
gun in front plate, cylindrical
turret topped by dome capped
cylindrical stroboscope, high rear
superstructure, enclosed suspension,
tracks like NC2.

Char NC3, similar to NC2 but
additional supplementary armour
plate outside tops of tracks
w/chutes for 2 of the 4 support
rollers under the plates, cast APX
sharply sloping pyramidal turret
w/long 47mm gun and spare mg
mounts.

Char D2, prototype, 1930, similar but
w/o double plates but skirted
suspension, 4 support rollers,
driver's head room juts forward on
left, originally w/FT18 turret,
17' 9" × 8' 9" × 7' 3"..

Char D2, similar but front armour
flush w/driver head room, bevelled
sponsons, 3 double pair bogie
assemblies, 2 single bogie wheels,
NC2-type track, 22 tons, 47mm
gun in APX1 turret as on Char B1,
16' 7" × 7' 2" × 8' 8½".

Char Renault ACK1, 1936,
experimental, cast hull, skirted
suspension, large low cast turret
w/20mm gun and cupola w/dual
mg, double tracks, 20 tons, 18' ½"
× 8' 4½" × 8' 1".

Char B1, prototype, 1929, original
turret had 2 mg, 75mm gun and
2 fixed mgs in front plate, high
track frames almost concealing
hull, turret like Somua, louvered
grill left side, entrance door right,
heavy single grouser tracks, 27 tons,
hinged episcopes in turret, 3 built,
20' 11" × 8' 2" × 9' 4½".

Char B1 (Char de Manoeuvre), 1930,
cast APX1 turret, w/1 mg and
short 47mm gun in turret w/recoil
cylinder showing above gun tube,
Naeder steering-targeting unit
recalling similar device in the 1918
Delaunay-Belleville tank, single
fixed hull mg fired by cable by
driver, 34 tons, 25mm armour,
20' 11" × 8' 2" × 9' 3".

Char B2, 35-ton tank, project only,
40mm armour intended.

Char B3, 45-ton tank, project only.

Char BB, 50-60-ton tank, project
only.

Char B1 bis, 1935, lips on turret peep
slots, in 1936 changed to APX4
turret w/longer nose and longer
47 54/35 gun, welded and riveted
hull, some w/rail antenna over rear
deck, HP increased from 250 to
300, track and suspension later
copied for Churchill tank, episcopes
eliminated for turret peep slots
w/lips, 75mm hull gun.

Char B1 ter, 1940, larger track
frames, more room inside, hull gun
given 10 degrees traverse, bevelled
out skirting, 20' 10" × 8' 11" ×
9' 6".

Char G1, 1939, gun similar to later
Sherman 75 in Char B turret, not
completed due to German invasion.

Char de Forteresse 90mm long
(FCM), massive cast two part
barbette-type hull w/heavy bolt
seat fluting across bow, on
strengthened 35R type suspension,
mg right front, main armament
centre front recessed slightly from
mg.

Char de Forteresse 160mm long
(ARC), similar but gun in a turret.

Char SEAM (Poniatowski Petroleo-
Electrique), cast hull, dome turret,
6 bogie wheels partly exposed by
skirting having hinged maintenance
plate.

Char Somua Type AC2 (1935-S),
prototype of Somua, cast hull and
turret, two section skirting, slope-
sided hull, sloping back turret like
Char B, short pitch track, short
47mm gun and mg, 1 vehicle
w/welded hull and turret and
slightly different skirting, 17' 7" ×
6' 11" × 8' 7½".

Char Mle, 1935-S (Somua) (Char
Moyen) (AC3 in cavalry, S35 in
infantry), improved production
model, louvers in rear portion of
hull, louvers later w/panelled
covers, long 47SA/35 in APX4
turret as on Char B1 bis.

Char de Transition, 1939, welded
hull, cast turret similar to 35S,
17' 4½" × 6' 11½" × 8' 10".

Char 35S, improved tracks, improved
hull w/lipped driver vision slots,
new engine and suspension, 17' 8"
× 6' 11½" × 8' 7½".

▼ 151
Canon 75 Auto Propulseur (Somua
SAU40), long barreled 75mm gun
centre front of cast hull, Char B
turret left centre ,buggy whip
antenna right front, strengthened
Somua suspension, 19' 5" × 6' 11"
× 8' 10".

Canon 75 Auto Propulseur (Somua
40S), ARL turret, modified Somua
tank hull welded and cast, similar
to above.

▼ 152
Automoteur ARL 75mm APX,
resembled SAU40 but lower and
track frames sloped downward
sharply from turret to sprockets,
turret centred instead of offset to
left.

ARL40, project only, produced
w/modifications after WWII as
ARL44.

POST-WORLD WAR I
MISCELLANEOUS VEHICLES

Ford 3 Tonnes, U.S. Ford 2-man
w/new mg and mount and cylinder
cupola replacing original cupola.

M29 ST Type A, 1929, 75mm gun and
2 mgs in barbette hull, reported to
be wheel and track, 16' 4½" ×
6' 6½" × 6' 10½" (on tracks).

M29 ST Type B, 1929, 75mm gun
and 2/37mm guns in barbette hull,
reported to be wheel and track.

Renault M29 AT, wheel and track,
75mm gun and 1 mg in turret,
20mm A/A gun.

Renault M29 BT, similar but 105mm.

Chaise-Affut Auto Propulseur à
Quatre Chenilles pour Canon
82CA, 1927, 82mm A/A gun on
4 track chassis.

370 Automoteur, 1940, portée
howitzer on AMX Alsthom petrol-
electric chassis, not completed.

Saute-mines du Charrue, mine plough.

Saute-mines à Pression du Liquide,
mine roller liquid filled.

Latil Tracteur N, Carden-Loyd
Mark VI w/1 large support roller,
built under licence.

Tracteur Lorraine (Tracteur Blindé
38L), 1939, low welded hull cargo
carrier used w/tracked trailer,
3 bogie pairs on leaf springs,
4 support rollers, driver later
moved forward, 13' 9½" × 5' 2"
× 4'.

Porte-Armes Lorraine, original 38L
w/raised rear cab, resembled WW!
British Medium A tank, intended
as weapons carrier, 1 example
w/hull reversed and 1 mg in bow.

Chenilette Leger, Lorraine w/2 bogie
pairs instead of 3.

Tracteur Leger, very small armoured
tractor resembling British Vickers
Utility Tractor GS.

Véhicule Leger K Telecommande par
Fil, remote-controlled robot
through cable.

Véhicule Spéciaux Rapide P Telecommande par Radio, similar but
wireless-controlled.

▼ 153
Char Leger Schneider, 1932, box hull
w/over track sponsons, small bevel
front, well forward turret w/mg,
closed track frames, track grousers
like NC2.

WORLD WAR II (FREE FRENCH)

Lorraine Tractor, with British 17pdr
fitted with Galliot muzzle brake.

UE with British 6pdr with Galliot
muzzle brake.

▼ 154
UE with shield and 47mm Polish
A/T gun.

Universal Carrier (Carrier Anti-Char),
with Hotchkiss 25mm, French gun
on British carrier, armour
heightened for driver.

US M8 Howitzer Carriage with 40mm
Bofors.

POST-WORLD WAR II
LIGHT TYPES

Char AMX13 (2A) 1948, prototype
tank destroyer, oscillating (gimbal)
turret w/ cupola bulging out from
right side of turret, long 75mm gun
w/muzzle brake and high double
rod travel lock, 4 bogie wheels plus
trailing idler, 1 support roller, short
pitch open track, 12 rounded bow.

Char AMX13 (2B), 1949, similar but
5 bogie wheels, raised idler, 1
support roller, turret w/bustle,
cupola on left side of FL10 gimbal
turret, 75mm gun, 13 tons, 16'
(20' 9") × 8' 2" × 7' 3".

Char AMX13 avec Canon 57 L/100,
same w/special gun.

Char AMX13 (2C) (Turenne), 5 bogie
wheels, 2 support rollers, higher
cupola dome w/vision blocks, FL11
turret w/75mm gun w/single
muzzle brake or 105mm w/double
muzzle brake, 16' (21' 2") × 8' 3"
× 7' 8½".

Char AMX13 (2D), 1959, 5 bogie
wheels, 4 support rollers, flat
auxiliary bow plate, 75mm gun
w/single muzzle brake or 105mm
w/double muzzle brake, 16'
(20' 10½") × 8' 3" × 7' 2".

Char AMX13 (2E), 1966, 5 bogie
wheels, 3 support rollers, flat
auxiliary bow plate, 90mm smooth
bore w/bore evacuator and muzzle
brake, 16' (20' 10") × 8' 2" ×
7' 7".

Char AMX13 (2F), 1968, similar but
2 support rollers, permanent 2 part
thermal shield on gun tube, later
production w/laser range-finder in
small 4 sided truncated pyramidal
cupola on top of turret.

DCA de 40 Bofors (Char 13T DCA
à 40mm Bofors), 40mm L/70 gun in
large faceted A/A turret on
AMX13 chassis, 16' 10" × 8' 8"
× 7' 10".

AMX de DCA, 1960, twin 30mm guns
in cast dome front A/A turret on
AMX13 chassis, 16' 11" × 8' 8"
× 9' (w/radar screen folded).

Oeil Noir (Black Eye), 1965, improved model w/radar.

Automoteur de 105 du AMX13 (en casemate) (105mm MK61), 1949, 105mm howitzer rear mounted in large fixed turret 17′ 5″ (21′ 4″) × 8′ 8″ × 8′ 9″.

Obusier Automoteur de 105 ABS Mle 50, 1950, 105mm gun and 2 mgs w/shield on above vehicle, later w/mg cupola added, minor faceting changes.

Automoteur AMX de 105 B (en tourelle) (105mm CT) (Obusier Automoteur de 105 à Casemate Tournante), improved model of above w/rotating turret, 17′ 5″ (21′ 4″) × 8′ 8″ × 8′ 9″.

Automoteur de 155 sur Pneus, 1949, slope-sided superstructure housing centre mounted 155mm gun, 5 pneumatic tyred bogie wheels, 4 support rollers.

AMX de 155, (Obusier de 155 Automoteur) (Automouvant de 155), open chassis AMX13 w/155mm howitzer.

AMX13 avec Tourelle A14, German HS30 APC turret substituted.

AMX avec Obusier de 155 (AMX155 Automouvant), (155mm MKF3), improved open carriage SP, 20′ 5″ × 8′ 10″ × 6′ 10″.

AMX13 avec SS11 (AMX13 T75) (Char Lance SS11), (Harpon), 1959, standard AMX13 w/4 SS11 missiles in frame parallel to 75mm gun, several arrangements.

AMX13 avec Lance-Missile Hot

(AMX13/HOT), box missile mount either side of turret.

AMX13 Canon Bitube de 30mm, Anti-Aerien Automoteur (AMX13/S530), 1963, twin 30mm guns in cast turret, 4 support rollers.

AMX13 Canon Bitube de 20mm, 1970, twin 20mm in welded turret w/o bustle.

AMX13 VTP (Véhicule de Combat par Infanterie), sometimes called AMX12, successively called VTP, ETT and finally VCI, APC w/2 rear doors, right and left topside hatches, small faceted commander's cab in front of passenger compartment, later small turret added on right, in 1967 SS11 missile projectors were added at the rear, 12.7 or 20mm gun, 18′ 8″ × 8′ 10″ × 7′ 10″.

AMX13 VCI, lower hull, smaller cupola, hinged firing slots in hull sides.

AMX13 VTT/Roland, dual A/A rocket projector w/radar on hull similar to 105mm MK61.

AMX13 VTT avec Tourelle NA2, missile turret.

AMX-VCG (Véhicule de Combat du Genie), APC w/engineer equipment including dozer blade.

Char de Depannage AMX13 (AMX55) (AMX-D), armoured recovery vehicle, box cab, winches, A-frame, dozer, also used as a fascine carrier, variations exist, 18′ 4″ × 8′ 6″ × 8′ 4″.

Char AMX Poseur de Pont, 1962, hydraulically lifted folding scissors bridge, 40′ gap, variations exist.

AMX Dozer, turretless dozer.

(- - - - -), self-propelled mine-layer, resembled AMX-VTT.

AMX13 avec Rapace 14, box-type missile projector.

AMX13 avec Tourelle EER (Char 13T Fl 11), improved design EBR armoured car turret, reduced weight 1.5 tons, latest design of vehicle has louvered hull, some vehicles w/2 Breguet searchlights, some w/Reibel mg coupled to cowled IR light and equipped to fire SS11 missiles.

AMX13 Poste de Commandement (Véhicule Blindé de Commande-ment), 1957, APC type w/or w/o cupola, also appears as engineer and ambulance vehicles.

AMX-PM (Porte-Mortier), 81 or 120mm mortar on VTT chassis.

AMX13/M24, 1960, US M24 Light tank turret on AMX13 chassis.

Véhicule Chenille Transport de Blessés, AMX13 VTT equipped as an ambulance.

M24/90, M24 Light tank w/90mm smoothbore w/muzzle brake.

M24/AMX13, 1960, AMX13 turret on M24.

(- - - - -), self-propelled mine clearing unit.

Char 48FCM (Char 12T FCM) (DCA de Quatre Canons de 20mm), 1948, original AMX13, 4 bogie wheel chassis w/four 20mm guns in Fl 4 turret, 14′ 8½″ × 7′ 10½″ × 7′.

HS-C30, Hispano Suiza 5 bogie wheel 3 support roller chassis, faceted hull, low turret w/twin 30mm HS A/A guns, 12 tons, 17′ 6″ × 8′ ″ × 5′ 1½″.

Hotchkiss Ic, 1960, Hotchkiss APC w/90mm gun in turret.

Hotchkiss TT6, 1951, small 6 man APC, 4 bogie wheels, 2 support rollers, several hull variations, 12′ 11½″ × 7′ 5½″ × 6′ 1″.

Hotchkiss Airborne Carrier, similar, lower hull, 11′ 2″ × 7′ 2½″ × 5′ 3″.

Véhicule de Transport Hotchkiss, 1951, same but for 12 men.

Véhicule Transport de Matériel M1952, Hotchkiss-Delahaye, very similar.

Hotchkiss-Delahaye Transport de Matériel CC2, 1955, larger, rear ramp, petrol cans carried in racks over tracks, 11′ 6½″ × 7′ 4″ × 4′ 6½″.

Chenilette Hotchkiss TT6-55, 7 tons, double rear doors, small front turret, some w/open mg and shield, long sloping glacis, later models continued to appear, 12′ 5½″ × 7′ 6″ × 6′ 1″.

ERAC (Engine de reconnaissance amphibie à chenilles), 1967, low hull, long glacis, plastic windowed trim vane, 105mm gun in turret resembling that on US M41 Light tank, small idler, raised sprocket, 5 road wheels.

VCAI (Véhicule de combat amphibié d'Infanterie), 1968, above basic chassis as APC.

VCAI, 1969, similar but roomier, prototype for AMX10A.

158

AMX10A (VCAI, Véhicule de Combat Amphibié d'Infanterie), 1969, prototype, resembled US M114 but equipped w/hydrojets, later models were 10P as APC, 10M w/HOT or Roland missile, 10C as tank destroyer w/long 90mm front-mounted missile gun, AMX10P fitted w/twin A/A mg, as well as AMX10PC as command version, AMX10D as ARV and AMX10TM as mortar carrier versions, basic vehicle 19′ 7½″ × 9′ 3½″ × 8′ 4½″.

Automoteur 105, 1960, 105mm howitzer in low sloped back turret on HS30 chassis.

Automoteur CC–6, Hotchkiss carrier resembling Carden-Loyd Mark VI, w/75mm recoilless rifle.

Automoteur CC–2–55 avec Nord SS11, Hotchkiss carrier w/missile.

Chenilette Fouga, 2 man prone crew, open chassis, 1 large, 2 intermediate and 2 small bogie wheels, recoilless rifle, 6 bazookas or as demolition carrier.

VP46 Teleguide, 1946, remote-controlled demolition vehicle, television control by green, violet and red beams, 9′ 10″ × 3′ 11″ × 2′ 3½″ (4′ overall).

VP90 (Voltiguer Patrouiller), 1956, similar but controllable suspension for weapon elevation, 2 tons, armament varied, 11′ 6″ × 5′ 2″ × 3′ 2″.

159

Chenilette Rexim, 1968 version of VP90, made by Hotchkiss-Brandt.

Le Crabe, US Weasel w/mg and shield.

Chenilette Studebaker, US Weasel w/ring mount and 30 cal mg.

(- - - - -), cargo carrier, 4 bogie wheel Christie type suspension, faceted front, cargo box rear.

Saint-Denis Porte-Mortier, 1969.

BL 12 Amphibie, Berliet-built amphibious APC.

Tracteur sur Pneus, engine and driver in narrow front-hull, cargo box rear, 4 pneumatic tyred road wheels.

Engin Leger de Combat (ELC) (Even), 1962, small, low 7-ton vehicle, 5 bogie wheels, diagonally placed coil springs, 4 recoilless rifles on split turret.

ELC Canon de 90mm Even (Hotchkiss-Rive Light Fighting Unit), similar chassis, small oscillating (gimbal) T-profile turret w/90mm gun and Reibel mg, revolver-type loader, 17′ 5″ × 7′ × 6′.

ELC Canon Bitube de 30mm, same w/two 30mm and 2 mgs, 15′ 6″ × 7′ × 6′.

ELC avec Tourelle NA2, 1968, similar but 2 SS11 missiles on right and 1 on left or 2 SS11 on right and SS12 on left.

Alligator, US LVT4 w/40mm Bofors gun in turret.

M113 avec Tourelle AMX10P, US vehicle experimentally modified.

POST-WORLD WAR II MEDIUM VEHICLES

160

ARL44, 1946, Char basis, no hull gun, 90mm A/A (DCA) w/muzzle brake in large flat sided turret having large bustle, 34′ 6″ (overall) × 11′ 7″ × 10′ 6″.

Saute-Mines AMX de 1945, Char B1 w/articulated triple flanged mine rollers.

Sherman avec Tourelle AMX13, Fl 10 turret on US M4 tank.

Sherman/105, US M4A1 w/very long 105mm gun having muzzle brake but no bore evacuator.

Tracteur de la MDK2, unarmoured tractor, 5 road wheels, dozer blade front, fold-up trench digger rear.

Patton/105, US M47 tank w/105mm gun used on AMX30.

Char Moyen, 1949, Panther-type hull, large gimbal turret w/bustle, 90mm gun, 5 large bogies, final one trailing, may be AMX38.

AMX50 (Char Lourd M1949), same chassis arrangement as above, wider tracks, oscillating dome turret w/90mm, later 100mm gun, twin A/A mg on turret.

AMX50, smaller and low cast and welded hull, large cast gimbal turret w/bustle, 90mm, later 100mm gun, Panther-type overlapping wheel suspension.

AMX50, 1950, 120mm gun, flat sloping glacis, larger gimbal turret w/gimbal pivots visible, long bustle, cupola on left, 5 road, 5 support wheels, prototype.

AMX50, Surblindé, 120mm gun, overlapping bogies, faired bow, longer and wider, hull only completed but fitted w/lower mock-up turret, 34′ × 12′ 3″ × 11′ ½″.

161

AMX50 Surbaissé, 1950, large gimbal turret, 120mm gun using same ammunition as US M103 heavy gun tank, travel lock, wide tracks, overlapping bogies, 39′ × 11′ 2″ × 11′.

AMX50, 1950 model rebuilt w/lower hull, lower cupola, wedge glacis.

162

AMX50 sur Pneus, same vehicle w/5 large pneumatic tyred bogie wheels.

Automoteur de 120 de AMX50, 1950, Panther-type hull, 5 road, 5 support wheels, range-finder on roof, no turret, 120mm gun in front plate.

Char de Batignolles, predecessor of AMX30 w/6 road and 3 support wheels, no turret except for experimental superstructure.

Pepa, 1960, 120mm mortar SP.

AMX38, 1960, prototype only.

AMX30 (Char Moyen de Combat AMX30A), 1961, first prototype, cast hull and turret, sloping bustle, small cupola on right, range-finder, conical gun mantlet w/canvas weather cover, 105mm L/52, 5 slotted bogie wheel suspension, 4 return rollers, smooth glacis except driver opening on left, track-guards connected in front across bow, second prototype 1962 w/5 support rollers.

AMX30, 1963, 7 pre-production vehicles, pyramidal gun mantlet, metal weather cape replaced canvas cover, stowage rack around back of turret, square or round IR light, 20′ 8″ (31′ 2″) × 10′ 2″ × 7′ 5½″ (9′ 4″ overall).

AMX30, 1965, 2 pre-production vehicles w/thermal shield around gun, inspection doors right glacis, stowage rails around sides and rear of turret, connecting track-guard rail removed.

AMX30, 1966, same but new and higher commander's cupola, diesel engine, 20mm retro-fitted 1972, 21′ 7″ (31′ 2″) × 10′ 2″ × 9′ 5″.

AMX30 avec Roland, 1970, equipped w/Roland missile projector, 2 radar 2 tube projectors on flat-top hull.

AMX30 avec Pluton (Vehicle de Tir Pluton), equipped to project tactical nuclear Pershing-type weapon.

AMX30 avec Tourelle 5401A (AMX30 bitube de 30mm), twin 30mm Hispano-Suiza cannon and Doppler radar dish.

Char AMX30 Poseur de Pont, 1968, bridge-layer similar to that on AMX13 but larger.

Char de Depannage AMX30 (AMX30D), cupola on left, vehicle resembled German Leopard Bergepanzer.

AMX30/155, GCT M1971 (155/33 Mle F-3 AMX30), 155mm gun in large turret resembling that on Automoteur de AMX105B (GCT, Grande Cadence de Tir, high rate of fire), 34′ 1″ overall × 10′ 1″ × 9′ 8″.

AMX30/Lance-ACRA, 1972, 142mm weapon in squat cast turret w/large box mantlet.

AMX30–2, design study.

AMX30 AF, 1973, phased modification of existing vehicles, new fire control, stabilizer, laser RF and computer, coaxial mg replaced by 20mm gun separately controllable for A/A use.

AMX30S, Pays Chauds (hot countries), engine and transmission changes, sandshields, sold to Saudi Arabia.

AMX30, stripped-down commercial model, original type cupola w/mg, thermal sleeve on gun.

Rabtac, radar vehicle developed jointly by France and Germany.

GERMANY

Official Germany believed in 1914 that the war which had just started would be of short duration, and few new military devices were added to those already available. In 1915, instead of considering a vehicle as a means of breaking the deadlock of trench warfare, flame-throwers and poison gas were tried but without thorough exploitation. Major faith was placed in artillery and aircraft.

Already, however, pioneering suggestions had been made for armoured fighting vehicles. Günther Burstyn, an Austrian army officer, had shown a design for a small tracked vehicle to both the Austrian and German war offices before the war started. In March 1913 a German engineer from Riga had demonstrated to the German Commercial Testing Commission a model of a vehicle that lurched on pivoted legs. But the model was non-steerable and the commission asked him to produce a full-sized steerable machine. Eventually steering was achieved by putting the vehicle on giant ball bearings so that it moved as if on castors. This *Landpanzer-kreuzer* never went into production, however, despite the interest of the German crown prince, because by the time it had reached a feasible stage interest had turned to other designs.

Among these were a huge tricycle-like vehicle called the *Treff-As-Wagen*, a vehicle from the Orion company based on their agricultural tractor, and a *Marien Wagen* evolved by its designer Hugo Bremer from his 1915 cross-country lorry. Although neither was accepted as the basis for an armoured fighting vehicle that was worthy of full-scale production, the latter was used in half-track and fully-tracked variants as an un-armoured supply carrier.

These designs were the result of belated German recognition that tanks had a battle value–and even that recognition was not whole-hearted. As late as the beginning of 1918 Ludendorff was still unimpressed by tanks and was confident that his attacks would succeed without them. In the event they almost did.

When the British brought their new weapon onto the field in September 1916 the policy of the German High Command was to minimize its value. They did so with some justice, although this denigration might not have been shared by the front-line German troops who had to face it. Nevertheless the fact that tanks were committed to battle before they were available in numbers sufficient to make a decisive impact, and their subsequent misuse at Arras and Third Ypres, lent credence to the view (held not only on the German side of the hill) that the tank had an inherent defect as a weapon. Even the battle of Cambrai, which showed the irresistible power of tanks when they were used in sufficient numbers and on suitable ground, did not alter

this view because the failure that resulted from ineffective exploitation of the tanks' success was attributed to some innate fault in the weapon itself.

Behind the scenes, however, there were those in official Germany who took a different view. In October 1916 the German War Ministry convened a meeting of the A7V Committee (*Allgemeine Kriegsdepartment 7 Abteilung Verkehrswesen*) consisting of experts from the German automotive industry and members of the Commercial Testing Commission. From this committee came the A7V tank, the only German-built tank to see action in World War I. Its chief designer was Joseph Vollmer, whose first design of an armoured fighting track-layer was based on a Holt tractor brought to Germany from Austro-Hungary by Dr Leo Steiner.

It is somewhat staggering to realize that, compared to the 2,850 tanks that the British, for example, built in World War I, the Germans built only about twenty. Indeed only three of the eight companies which formed the total German tank strength were equipped with German tanks; the rest had captured British tanks re-armed with captured Russian guns. Apart from any antagonism to tanks as such, this minimal production output was the inevitable result of an over-worked economy that was turning out aircraft, submarines, ammunition, artillery and lorries all with a nominal top priority.

As well as their A7V tank, and the projected developments from it that were influenced in design by the captured British heavy tanks, the Germans also started work on a light tank programme which owed something to captured British Medium A Whippet tanks. The designer of the *Leichte Kampfwagen* (LKI, II and III), was Vollmer. His LKI was an adapted passenger car chassis (surplus, like so many in Germany, because of the fuel shortage) with an up-rated engine, a light armoured body and a small revolving turret, with track-frames and tracks.

Other tank projects begun were two for light tanks, one designed by Krupp, the other by Daimler; one for a heavy tank by *Oberschlesien Eisenwerk*; and one for a giant tank, the *K-Wagen*, partially designed by Vollmer and resembling a British heavy tank though weighing four times as much. Two of these were built but destroyed after the war under the terms of the Peace Treaty.

Hindenburg inspected the first A7V tanks and gave grudging consent to their use in action. His lack of confidence was not conducive to high morale, and when captured British tanks were also used the former policy of deriding them gave their German crews little reason for confidence. The original official anti-tank propaganda had its deleterious effects on tank production as well.

In the end the Germans recognized the true value of tanks–though recognition came too late for that war. Reporting on the Western Front situation at the end of September 1918 after the dominance of the battlefield by tanks had been indisputably proved at Soissons in July and at Amiens in August, Ludendorff, then Chief of the General Staff, wrote: 'Owing to the effects of the tanks our operations on the Western Front have now practically assumed the character of a game of chance. The General Staff can no longer work with definite factors'. Plans were made to build a thousand LKIIIs and two thousand heavy tanks. But not even the pilot model of the LKIII had been completed by the time of the armistice on 11 November 1918. Thus the last German tank built before construction officially began again with the *Panzer I* in 1933 was the LKII.

All German tanks were destroyed by Allied Disarmament Commission in the immediate post-war period and, under the terms of the Versailles Treaty, the Germans were denied the use of armour except for a few police cars. In addition, the General Staff was supposed to be abolished but in fact it continued to function secretly. As early as 1919 a special section in the General Staff was created to study armoured combat. Germany's weakness became her strength. The Allies were glutted with armour and could not afford to scrap it for newer designs, whereas the Germans had no tanks and could start from scratch. The Allies' 'Plan 1919' was studied, and the writings of Fuller, Liddell Hart, Martel and others were avidly analysed.

Both Germany and Russia were considered pariah nations after the war, and it was natural that collaboration should begin between them. Beginning in 1922, German and Russian technicians were exchanged, and from 1926 to 1932 Germans were stationed at the Russian tank centre at Kazan. To the amusement of the world, dummy tanks were used in manoeuvres, but the Germans were deadly serious, as the events of 1939 and 1940 were to show.

Vollmer had moved to Sweden after the war and supervised the completion of LK light tanks from parts shipped from Germany. Landsverk and Bofors in Sweden and Siderius in Holland were Krupp affiliates. Studies were exchanged between them. Vollmer then moved to Czechoslovakia.

Plans were drawn up for militarizing the German economy, and once again a short war was planned, this time with air and armour playing a large part.

Specifications were issued and Krupp, Rheinmetall-Borsig, Daimler-Benz, Henschel and MAN (*Maschinenfabrik Augsburg Nürnberg*) built tank prototypes. These were subjected to competitive tests, after which one of each type was selected for production. Ford and Opel did not receive armament work because of their American affiliation. Orders for

experimental tanks were secretly given as early as 1926, but actual quantity production did not begin until 1931.

By the time Hitler came to power, armoured formations were well on the way to reality, camouflaged as motor transport corps. A Russian purge broke up the previous technical exchange, but the Germans felt they had learnt all they needed to know.

Two officers were sent to the United States in 1933 to study mechanized tactics. Captain Adolph Von Schell returned in 1936 as colonel to spend a year in Detroit studying automotive production. Later, as General Von Schell, he developed an integrated system of spare parts simplification and standardization, production and stock control. Finally, he fell under Hitler's criticism and dropped from sight.

German rearmament began in earnest in 1933. In March 1935, Hitler publicly renounced without challenge the Treaty of Versailles. Six months later the first public showing of German armour took place. The following year four battalions of tanks were sent to Spain as part of the Condor Legion to participate in the Civil War. They used PzKpfwI light tanks as well as Russian T26 tanks captured from the government forces.

For purposes of secrecy the original German vehicles were given innocuous sounding names like agricultural tractor (*Landwirtschaftlicher Schlepper* contracted to LaS), heavy tractor, commander's vehicle (*Befehlswagen*) and similar titles. After this, experimental tanks were given a four digit number. The first digit or pair of digits indicated the weight class and the last two the vehicle number. A prefix VK (*Versuchs Konstruction*) showed that it was built for research purposes, and if there had been a multiple order the manufacturer's initials followed, e.g. DB for Daimler-Benz.

If standardized and accepted into service, the vehicle was given an SdKfz (*Sonderkraftfahrzeug*, special purpose vehicle) number as well as its class name followed by its type number, e.g. Panzerkampfwagen II usually abbreviated to PzKpfw or PzKw. Modifications were represented by the word *Ausfuehrung* (model, type) followed by a capital letter as A, B, C, etc. Thus PzKpfw IC was Model C of the first tank type.

Near the end of 1937 some of the Spanish Civil War lessons were embodied in new tank designs. In March 1939 the Germans over-ran Czechoslovakia and took over production of the Czech TNH tank which they renamed Panzer 38(t), the 't' being the first letter of the German word for Czechoslovakian. They also took over the LT35 tanks and renamed them Panzer 35(t).

The campaign in Poland in September 1939 gave the Germans additional experience which they made good use of in the invasion of the Low

Countries and France in May-June 1940. After that campaign they brought into service many captured French vehicles. They were deceived as to Russian trends but in the spring of 1941 had shown a Russian mission everything they had in the tank line. At Hitler's insistence nothing was concealed. Initially the Russian campaign went well but slowed down as the Germans over-extended themselves.

German production was fairly well centralized, but between 1939 and 1942 workers did not work overtime because it was still felt the war would be short. After the United States entered the war, the first real attempt at economic mobilization was made under the Todt Ministry. After Todt's death in an air accident, Albert Speer replaced him. In 1943 Speer's authority was increased, and by the fall of 1944 he was given power to forbid any design change that would interfere with production.

But Hitler, either through his personal representatives in the War Ministry or directly, made many engineering decisions, sometimes on obscure details. Almost any idea could be pushed forward with the proper political connections. Germany had four organizations collectively responsible for directing tank programmes. There was always opportunity for highly placed Nazis lacking engineering knowledge to interfere by throwing their weight around. And, in spite of totalitarian government, there was not always co-ordinated planning or decisiveness, and there was much extravagance in the number of vehicle types and in design complications. Very considerable use was also made of captured vehicles modified or intact. Relatively few Russian vehicles were used, principally because of lack of spare parts, but Russian cannon and ammunition were in full supply through capture. Such variety all led to difficulties of supply in the field.

Allied bombing caused some dislocation of production but from 1940 to mid-1944 German tank production increased ten times. Then it fell off but only partly due to Allied bombing. There were many other factors: the use of slave labour, oil shortages, transportation difficulties and extravagance in man-hours due to a lack of mass production knowledge and experience in the industries concerned.

Between 1939 and 1944, the Germans produced 23,487 tanks and 42,932 track-laying self-propelled guns. This was slightly less than the British tank production and just under one-quarter of the American, let alone Russian production, which was almost as large as the American. Against the Germans' 24,000 tanks, the British, Americans and Russians produced about 212,000 in World War II. All-out armour production in Germany started too late, as it had in World War I. Tactics, technique and training carried the load because German armour was always outnumbered by Allied armour. Tank training became so highly specialized that it never required more than four months once the war began.

After the trend of events in the war forced the Germans more and more on the defensive, design tended toward the assault gun and the tank destroyer instead of the tank. The armoured force wanted to continue 360 degree gun traverse while the other branches wanted limited traverse so that bigger guns could be mounted. Hitler favoured the latter which resulted in tanks being considered as artillery in the final phases of the war. It was true that more vehicles could be turned out for the same production effort, and more assault guns were turned out in the last three months of 1944 than in all of 1943.

Self-propelled guns during the war were first identified by the initials Sfl (*Selbstfahrlafette*, self-propelled carriage). Then gun calibre and type followed by tube length in calibres were added. These were accompanied by identification such as PAK (*Panzer Abwehr Kanone*, anti-tank cannon), Pz Jaeg (*Panzer Jaeger*, tank hunter), Stu K (*Sturm Kanone*, assault cannon), Stu H (*Sturm Haubitze*, assault howitzer) and Stu M (*Sturm Moerser*, assault mortar). Finally, popular names were applied such as *Hornisse* (Hornet), *Wespe* (Wasp), *Hummel* (Bumble-bee), *Brummbaer* (Grizzly Bear). Sometimes, for experimental vehicles, there were different names applied to the same vehicle produced by different manufacturers. An example is the *Grille* series produced by Krupp. The same series produced by Rheinmetall-Borsig was called *Skorpion*.

The original nationality of captured foreign vehicles taken into service was indicated by a small letter in parenthesis, which was the initial letter of the German word for the nationality concerned: for example, 'e' for English (*Englisch*), 'j' for Yugoslavian (*Jugoslawisch*) and 't' for Czechoslovakian (*Tschechisch*).

The war ended with development work being pushed forward on gas proofing, engine improvement and turbine applications, optical stabilization, rigid gun mounts, night vision equipment, A/A tanks and the design perfection of production vehicles, as well as on two super-heavy tanks, the Maus and the E100, the latter being part of an *Entwicklung* (Development) series ranging from tanks of 5 tons to the E100 (100 tons).

Just as occurred after World War I, Germany was denied the use of armour after World War II. But this time Germany was divided into East and West. When the Western Allies found that the Russians were rearming East Germany, they retaliated in kind. The Federal Republic of Germany received American equipment and later began producing armoured fighting vehicles it had developed itself.

Originally the French and Germans collaborated on the development of a new tank, but in the end they could not agree on details and each then went its own way, the Germans to produce the Leopard in 1965, the French to build the AMX30. To follow the Leopard the Germans entered into an agreement with the United States to develop a common tank known as U.S./F.R.G. MBT70. Joint work began in 1965, the tank to be available in 1970 or earlier. In the meantime the Germans continued to develop and build other armoured vehicles and exchanged vehicles for test with several NATO nations. By 1967 they were selling vehicles to smaller European nations and soon added Leopards to those vehicles they had to offer. In 1970 the joint MBT70 project was abandoned, the Germans concentrating on two advanced Leopard designs, the Americans experimenting with an 'austere' version of the MBT70 until even that was halted by Congress due to its high costs.

WORLD WAR I

Goebel Landpanzerkreuzer, 1915, long faceted hull eventually on large rolling spheres, not armed, if built would have been 118′ × 17′ × 17′, 550 tons with 4″ armour.

Flettner/BAMAG, 1915, large remote-controlled 'land torpedo', 4 large iron wheels connected on the inside by heavy drive chains which also acted as anti-bellying tracks, front wire-cutter also acted as self-contained flame-thrower, successfully demonstrated by inventor but rejected.

Treff-Aswagen, 1916, armoured tricycle w/11-foot main wheels and much smaller rear steering rollers, one 20mm gun forward, 1 mg each side for firing into trenches, 18 tons, 1 prototype built, name adopted to distinguish from agricultural tractor known as Treff-Bube.

163

Bremer Vierkettenfahrzeug (Bremer-Marienwagen Ueberpanzert), 1916, Bremer halftrack lorry modified to add 2 additional tracks, sheet metal box hull to simulate armour.

A7V (Allgemeines Kriegsdepartement Abteilung 7, Verkehrswesen), 1917, named for responsible department, prototype wooden working mock-up, anti-bellying rails fore and aft like

Renault FT tailpiece, centre cupola, unarmed.

A7V, 1918, partly faceted box hull w/rectangular centre cupola hinged front and back, hinged top hatches, 57mm gun forward, 6 Maxim mgs, 33 tons, 20 built, used in action, 24′ × 10′ × 11′ 2″.

A7V-1, same vehicle w/round cupola, not completed.

A7V Abaendert, A7V w/2 round vision cupolas and mg in semi-circular sponsons at rear corners.

A7V Projekt, basic vehicle w/larger hull and wide vertical sided oval cab, 7.7cm gun front, 2 × 20mm guns. 4 mg, not completed, 25′ 2½″ × 10′ × 12′ 11½″.

A7V Projekt, same chassis but smaller hull w/2 TUF (Tank und Flieger) and 2 Maxim mgs but 8 alternate mounts, box cupola, no tailpiece but wire-cutter in front, project only, 23′ 5″ × 11′ 11½″ × 10′ 10″.

A7V-U (Umlaufende Ketten, all-round tracks), 1918, resembled British heavy tanks but much larger sponsons set farther back, higher larger cab and spring suspension, 27′ 6″ × 15′ 5″ × 10′ 3½″.

A7V-U2, same w/somewhat smaller sponsons, no cab, 2 hull mgs, 1 Belgian 5.7cm gun and 1 mg each sponson, not completed.

A7V-U3, same as U2 but w/cab, 4 mgs in cab, 1 mg front, rear, each side and right sponson, Belgian 5.7cm gun in each sponson, project only.

Oberschlesien, 1918, 21 tons, 37mm in round turret, mg fore and aft in centre half-turrets, solid track frames, 2 built, 21′ × 11′ ½″ × 9′ 10″.

Fahrgestell A7V Mit Zwei 7.62cm Flak, experimental twin A/A guns on A7V Schlepper.

164

Orion Wagen, streamlined armour on tractor chassis, large track shoes, single steering wheel, unarmed, experimental.

K-Wagen, 1918, 165 tons, resembling British Mark VIII but much larger, broke into separate loads for railway travel, four 77mm and 7 mgs in massive sponsons, small round cupola centre front, hull sprung to rigid track frame roller, 2 600 HP engines, 2 built and broken up after war by Allied Disarmament Commission, 42′ 7″ × 20′ × 9′ 5″.

LKI, 1918, 2 prototypes built around lorry chassis called 'petrol gluttons', resembled British Medium A but higher and w/cylindrical turret w/mg, 16′ 8″ × 6′ 5″ × 8′ 9″.

LKII, 1918, 2 prototypes, similar but more streamlined, rear cab, 57mm in two-way rotor mantlet, 16′ 8½″ × 6′ 5″ × 8′ 3½″.

LKII Mit MG Drehturm, projected variation w/mg in cylindrical turret, parts sold to Sweden and assembled there after the war as Strv M21.

LKII Leichte Zugmaschine, projected fixed cab tractor.

LKII Kraftprotze, projected large cab ammunition carrier.

LKIII, reversed LKII w/engine rear and crew front, 57mm or TUF gun, not completed.

Krupp Leichter Panzerwagen, 1918, small mg carrier, rail and bogie suspension, cab front w/mg in bow, engine rear, 12′ 9½″ × 7′ 3½″ × 5′ 2″.

Daimler Sturmwagen, 1918, projected SP resembling German StuH of WWII.

Beute Panzerwagen St Chamond, captured French St Chamond fitted w/Sokol 57mm in place of 75mm, and German A/T rifles instead of mg, experimental.

Beute Panzerwagen Mark IV, 1918, captured British tanks w/Russian Sokol 57mm and Maxim mgs replacing original armament, used by Germans in action.

Beute Panzerwagen Mark A, 1918, captured British medium tanks which were modified in numbers for use by Germans.

Strassen Panzerwagen, 1920, improved A7V type box hull, w/mg in small cupola on Daimler half-track truck chassis.

POST WORLD WAR I VK (VERSUCHSKONSTRUKTION, RESEARCH MODEL VEHICLES) AND RELATED TYPES

VK31 (Le Traktor, Light Tractor, camouflaged title), 1928, sloping glacis, Swedish type turret w/37mm KwK26 L/45, 2 periscopes, enclosed track frames, 12 bogie wheels, 10 tons, 18′ 4″ × 7′ approx. × 8′ 6″.

VK301, small 2 man tank, project only, 11′ 8½″ × 6′ × 6′.

VK501, Buessing-NAG 2 man tank, project only, other manufacturers had similar projects.

VK601 (PzKpfwI n A, Panzerkampfwagen I neue Ausfuehrung, Tank I new model) (PzKpfwI Ausf C, Ausfeuhrung C, variation or model C), 1939, 8 tons, rectangular

superstructure, PzKpfwII type turret w/2cm EW141 gun and 1 mg, overlapping bogie wheel suspension, w/2 outer multi-spoked and 3 inner 6-spoked bogie wheels, 16′ 3″ × 6′ 3½″ × 6′ 7″.

VK901 (PzKpfwII n A) (PzSflIc, Armoured Self-Propelled Mount Ic) (2cm Pak38 auf PzKpfw Sd Fgst901 or 2cm Panzerabwehr Kanone auf PanzerKampfwagen Sonder Fahrgestell 901, 2cm anti-tank cannon on tank miscellaneous chassis 901), lighter version of VK1601 intended as a high speed 10-ton tank, overlapping suspension like VK1601 but narrower tracks, supplementary armour across front of rectangular superstructure and mantlet w/2 visors, stabilized gun, 1 vehicle experimentally w/4.7cm Pak(t), two later w/5cm Pak38 L/60.

VK903 (PzBeobWg, Panzer Beobachtungs Wagen, armoured observation vehicle), 1942, special turret w/rangefinder, wireless and BC scope for armoured division artillery, also reported to exist as PzSpWg (Panzer Spaeh Wagen, armoured reconnaissance vehicle) (PzKpfw fuer Gefechts Aufklaerung, tank for combat reconnaissance) (PzJaeg, Panzer Jaeger, tank hunter) (PzSfl 5cm, PzSfl fuer sIG33, Panzer Selbstfahrlafette fuer schweres Infanterie Geschuetz 33, armoured self-propelled mount for heavy infantry gun 33).

VK1201, details not available.

VK1202, details not available.

VK1301 (PzKpfwII nA) (Luchs or Lynx), 1942, prototype, almost identical in appearance to VK901 but all overlapping wheels were spoked, 15′ 2½″ × 8′ 1½″ × 7′ 3″.

VK1303 (PzKpfwII (2cm) Ausf L) (Luchs) (SdKfz123) (Sonderkraftfahrzeug 123, special purpose vehicle 123) (PzSpWgII (2cm KwK38)), improved production model, 4 man crew, front plate had 2 low narrow visors, rear of hull undercut, rotating turret, mg trigger on traverse hand wheel, overlapping disc type road wheels star spoked sprocket and idler, first 100 w/2cm gun, next 31 w/5cm. KwK L/20 later replaced w/2cm KwK39 L/60, 15′ 2½″ × 8′ 1½″ × 7′ 3″.

VK1601 (PzKpfwII nA verstaerkt, new construction strengthened), 1940, thick armour, 2 heavy front visors, 2cm gun, stabilized sight, wide tracks, overlapping road wheels, 2 outer wheels 6-spoked, round escape hatch left side of hull, round vision slit plate ahead of it, later converted to Bergepanzer II, 14′ 4″ × 8′ 8″ × 6′ 8½″.

VK1602 (le Leopard) (Gefechtsauf-

klaerer, Leopard) built of PzKpfwI, II and Lynx components, Lynx suspension, 5cm KwK39/1 L/60 in large open top slope sided turret w/large bustle.

165

VK1801 (PzKpfwIa nA verst.) (PzKpfwID) (PzKpfwIF), 1940, rebuilt PzKpfwIa, outgrowth of VK601, 20 tons, 2 mgs in turret, heavy curved mantlet, suspension as in VK1601, heavy visor on left only, wide tracks, round escape hatch on both sides, 14′ 4″ × 8′ 8″ × 6′ 8½″.

VK2001DB (ZW40) (Zugfuehrerwagen 40, unit commander vehicle 40, camouflage title), 1935, intended as replacement for ZW38 (PzKpfwIII Ausf B), first pilot w/3–4 speed transmission, second pilot fluid drive, 24 tons, 5 large road wheels w/4 holes each, 3 support rollers, torsion bar suspension, 3.7cm gun and 1 mg in squat turret w/round dome-lidded rear cupola, large sprocket and idler w/peripheral holes, Daimler-Benz built, 1 vehicle w/experimental diesel engine dropped when Russian campaign began, 16′ 10″ × 9′ 11″ × 7′ 10½″.

VK2001RhB (BW, Bataillonsfuehrerwagen, battalion commander vehicle, camouflage title), 1935, box hull, 5cm L/24 cannon, cylindrical turret open at rear, 19 tons, 8 road wheels on rail, second model w/8 road wheels in 4 pairs on arms, 3 support rollers.

VK2001K, 1935, forerunner of PzKpfwIV, originally overlapping road wheel suspension, later as in 1/BW, 3.7cm left and 2 mg right of mantlet, front plate straight across, project only, 17′ 1″ × 9′ 8″ × 8′ 2½″.

VK2002MAN, 1935, similar but square turret w/7.5cm L/60 gun, overlapping suspension, project only, 18′ 3½″ × 9′ 10″ × 8′ 10″.

VK2601 (m Leopard), medium Leopard w/7.5cm KwK41, 4 road wheels, skirts, miniature Panther hull, turrets built later were utilized on Puma 8 × 8 armoured cars.

VK3001H, 1941, Panther D prototype,, short 7.5cm cannon, overlapping road wheels, 3 support rollers, Henschel built.

PzSflV, 2 VK3001H later rebuilt as 12.8cm K40 L/61 SP in high faceted box hull w/rear overhang, rear idler moved back.

VK3001D, similar to Henschel but built by Daimler-Benz.

VK3001P (Porsche Typ 100) (Leopard) (SdFzI, Sonderfahrzeug I, special vehicle 1), two coupled engines, petrol-electric transmission, 21′ 8″ × 10′ 6″ × 9′ 11½″.

VK3002MAN, 1942, 38 tons, intended for 7.5cm KwK42 L/70, Panther D prototype, 19′ 8″ × 10′ 6″ × 5′ 9½″.

VK3002DB, overlapping leaf-spring suspension, no support rollers, diesel engine, 19′ 8″ (20′ 5½″) × 10′ 8″ × 8′ 10″.

VK3002RhB, 15cm sFH43 L/32.5, 22′ 10″ (overall) × 10′ 8½″ × 10′ 8″.

VK3601P, resembled VK4501P, project only, 19′ 10″ (22′ 8″) × 10′ 8″ × 8′ 7″.

VK3601H (PzKpfwVI), project w/Type 0725 gun, various types of motive power foreseen, turret never finished, design led to VK4501, 19′ 10″ (22′ 5½″) × 10′ 3½″ × 8′ 10½″.

VK4501H (PzKpfwVI H) (Tiger Ausf H2), forerunner of Tiger E to be made up of elements of VK3001 and 3601, 8.8cm KwK 36 L/56 or 7.5cm KwK 21 L/70, project only but Rheinmetall built 1 turret w/latter gun, 19′ 8″ (25′ 6″) × 10′ 3½″ × 9′ 4″.

▼ 166

VK4501P (Porsche Typ 101A) (SdFzII), Siemens Schuckert petrol-electric transmission, completed as Ferdinand SP (Tiger P, SdKfz184), 22′ (30′ 9″) × 10′ 3½″ × 9′ 2″.

VK4501P (Porsche Typ 102), Ferdinand suspension, hydraulic transmission, Tiger E turret and gun, 2 built.

VK4501P mit Rammhaube, Ramming head or sharp bow w/faceted carapace hull, 3 ordered converted by Hitler to demolish buildings in Stalingrad but not completed, 5 completed as Bergepanzer, 27′ 6½″ × 11′ 9½″ × 8′ 4½″.

VK4501P (Porsche Typ 103), same as Typ 102 w/radial cooling blower for transmission.

VK4502P (Porsche Typ 180) (SdFzIII), 1942, petrol-electric transmission, 6 road wheels, large squat turret well forward, 8.8cm KwK43 L/71 gun, Porsche models 180B and 180C w/Porsche-Deutz 16 cylinder diesel also reported, mock-up only but turret design was used for King Tiger.

VK4502P (Porsche Typ 181) (SdFzIII), same w/hydraulic transmission.

Porsche 205A (SdFzIV), details unknown but normal 2 track tank.

Porsche 205B, same w/1 wide track.

SdFzV, 3 versions: 18-ton tank, Fz2201SP and Typ 2115. reconnaissance vehicle.

SdFzVI, Porsche Typ 205 w/hydraulic transmission, Typ 255 w/mechanical transmission.

VK4503H, similar to Tiger E, mg left front plate, driver right, mock-up turret.

VK4504P, 8.8cm gun in rear mounted turret, project dropped because of great amount of copper required for petrol-electric transmission, 22′ w/o gun × 10′ 3½″ × 13′ 1½″.

VK6501 (PzKpfwVII) (SW), 1939, breakthrough-type tanks built by Henschel and Krupp, were to resemble PzKpfwIV but only mock-up turret made, small wheel overlapping suspension, 3 support rollers.

VK7001K (Loewe, lion) (Tiger Maus, tiger mouse), based on Tiger II, dome turret, engine front.

DWI, 1937, 35-ton Durchbruchwagen (breakthrough tank), short 7.5cm, later 10.5cm gun L/28, overlapping suspension, resembled PzKpfwIV.

DWII (PzKpfwVI verst), 1938, reworked DWI, short 7.5cm KwK gun, 2 mg.

▼ 167

le Sfl fuer TAK 3.7 (Tank Abwehr Kanone), 1927, small open semi-armoured agricultural tractor w/3.7cm gun dash-mounted w/faceted shield, first German SP adopted.

le Sfl fuer TAK 7.5cm, 1927, similar but larger Hanomag tractor, gun pedestal mounted w/shield.

RR160, Swedish Landsverk 30 wheel and track tank.

Geraet fuer le FH43 (Skoda), see Germany, Miscellaneous.

Geraet 040 and 041, see Germany, Miscellaneous.

Geraet 13 (PzGer13), see Germany, Miscellaneous.

Geraet 804, 807, 812, see PzKpfwIV.

Geraet 814, see PzKpfwIII.

Geraet 815, see PzKpfwIII.

Geraet 820, 821, 822, 823 and 824, see PzKpfwIV.

Geraet 873, see PzKpfwIV.

Geraet 5-1026 (le FH43 (Sf1) KpI) (Grille 10), Krupp Leopard project, see PzKpfwIV.

Geraet 5-1027 (le FH43 (Sfl) KpII), Luchs basis project, resembled Soviet T34, Krupp wooden mock-up only.

Geraet 5-1028 (le FH43 (Sfl) RhB) (Skorpion 10), Rheinmetall Borsig Leopard basis project.

Geraet 5-1211, see Panther.

Geraet 5-1212 (12.8cm K43) (Sfl) KpII (Grille 15), Leopard basis project, 22′ 10″ (33′ 6″) × 10′ 8″ × 10′ 8″.

Geraet 5-1213, 22′ 10″ (33′ 6″) × 10′ 8½″ × 10′ 8″.

Geraet 5-1528 (le FH43 (Sfl) RhB), Leopard chassis, wide sloping glacis, small AA/AT turret open in rear, mock-up only, also reported to be Krupp I Grille 15 on Panther chassis, see Panther.

Geraet 5-1529 (sFH43 (Sfl) KpII) (Grille 15), Leopard basis project, 21′ 2″ (23′ 5½″) × 10′ 8½″ × 11′ 8″.

Geraet 5-1530, see Panther.

Geraet 5-1702, see Tiger.

Geraet 5-2107, see Tiger.

Geraet 21-559, see PzKpfIV.

Geraet 21-561, see PzKpfwIV.

Grille 10, see Geraet 5-1026.

Grille 12/15, 15cm sFH43 or 12.8cm K43, wooden mock-up only, 22′ 10½″ × 10′ 8½″ × 11′ 8″.

Grille 15, see Geraet 5-1529.

Grille 17, see Tiger.

Skorpion 15, see Panther.

Grosstraktor I, heavy tractor I, 1927, World War I British heavy tank type track frames w/4 mud chutes, 2 screws for amphibious operation, long 7.5cm and 1 mg in forward turret, 1 mg in small rear deck turret, 1 vehicle had bow mg, Daimler-Benz vehicle designed by Dr Porsche, soft steel.

Grosstraktor II, 1929, made by Rheinmetall-Borsig, similar but 3 mud chutes, smaller rear turret, 7.5cm KwK L/20 in forward turret, bow mg.

Grosstraktor III, same made by Krupp.

NbFz (Neubaufahrzeug, new construction vehicle), 1933, large RhB main turret w/3.7cm above 10.5cm gun, nacelle-like mg mount on right of main turret, original 2 small auxiliary turrets, later changed, wireless antenna rails around turret, 2 built for propaganda purposes, mild steel plate, in 1942 name changed to PzKpfwVI and later called PzKpfwVI (Alter Art, old type) after PzKpfwVI designation was transferred to Tiger.

NbFz, 1935, similar Krupp main turret w/rear cupola, turret mounted on cylindrical super-structure, coaxial 7.5cm L/24 and 3.7cm gun w/parallel mg, small mg turrets right front and left rear, same suspension as VK2001RhB but 1 more roller, total 10, 4 support rollers w/mud chutes, 25 mm, mild steel plate, 3 built for bluff or propaganda purposes, in 1942 name changed to PzKpfwV and later called PzKpfwV (Alter Art, old type) after PzKpfwV designation was transferred to Panther, 21' 8" × 9' 6" × 9' 9½".

Wargel LW3, 1942, huge tricycle similar to WWI Treff-As, commercial prototypes only.

LW5-1, 1944, similar but reversed, intended as ARV for heavy tanks, prototype only.

PZKPFWI AND VARIATIONS

LKAI, 1933, 6 tons, forerunner of PzKpfwIa, sloping glacis, front plate straight across, driver on left, 2 mgs in turret, 4 large road wheels, 2 support rollers, trailing idler, no suspension beam, hooded side louvers, similar to SdKfz101, 11' 1" × 7' 8" × 6' 2".

LKAII, see PzKpfwII and variations.

LKBI (LaS-Krupp), rear of turret almost flush w/rear of super-structure, rear deck flat behind turret, then sloped down, side plates out to mudguards, muffler high on left rear and tilted slightly downward, front plate straight across except bevel on left corner, 2 mgs in turret, 4 road wheels, last 2 w/rail, trailing idler, 3 support rollers, Krupp diesel engine.

LKBII, similar but longer, no trailing idler, 5 road wheels, last 2 w/rail, 3 support rollers, rear deck sloped downward in double bevel, muffler on left rear and sloping slightly downward, Krupp diesel engine.

LKBIII, 3rd prototype of PzKpfwIa Landwirtschaftlicher Schlepper (LaS, agricultural tractor, camouflage title applied to all PzKpfw types), open chassis, 3 support rollers, used as personnel carrier.

SdKfz101 (IaLaS Krupp) (PzKpfwI (MG) Ausf A), similar to LKBI but rear of turret almost flush w/rear of superstructure, rear deck low, muffler on left rear mudguard, later 2 mgs, 13' 2½" × 6' 9" × 5' 7½".

SdKz101 (Ib LaS Maybach) (PzKpfwI (MG) Ausf B), similar to above but longer, no trailing idler but 5 road wheels and 4 support rollers, rear of turret ahead of rear step in superstructure, silencer on left rear mudguard, 1 experimentally w/diesel engine, 14' 6" × 6' 10" × 5' 7½".

SdKfz101 (PzKpfwI (MG) Ausf Tp) (IB LaS Maybach), adapted for tropical conditions by baffling exhaust upward and adding bellows-type air filter.

PzKpfwI Ausf C, see VK601.

SdKfz111 (PzKpfwI (A) Muni Schl, ammunition carrier) (Gep Muni Schl), turret removed and opening covered w/large hatch.

PzKpfwIA Fahrschulwanne, driving school chassis, turret removed or open chassis, originally w/hand rails around crew portion of hull, PzKpfwIb also so designated and used, 13' 2½" × 6' 9" × 4' 7".

PzKpfwIA Instandsetzungskraftwagen, repair vehicle, turret removed, PzKpfwIb also so designated and used.

PzKpfwIa (F), F/T installed by Afrika Korps to replace right hand mg.

Pi PzKwWgIa Pioneer armoured vehicle Ia, engineer vehicle, turret removed and box superstructure substituted, PzKpfwIb also so designated and used.

3.7cm Pak auf PzKpfwI, turret shield open at rear on PzKpfwI chassis, resembled 4.7cm Pak (t)Sfl.

4.7cm Pak (t) Sfl auf PzKpfwI Ausf B (PzJaegI fuer 4.7 Pak L/43 (t) or tank hunter I), pyramidal turret shield open at rear, a later shield not as deep and sloped back on top, gun also mounted on PzKpfwI Ausf Tp, 14' 6" × 6' 7" × 7' 4½".

4.7cm Pak (f) Sfl auf PzKpfwI Ausf B, same w/French 4.7cm A/T gun.

15cm sIG 33 auf PzKpfwI Ausf B or heavy infantry gun 33 (GWI fuer 15cm sIG 33, Geschuetz Wagen I, Gun Carriage I), infantry gun-howitzer on its complete field carriage mounted in box hull open at rear, 14' 6" × 8' 9½" × 11'.

Muni PzI, ammunition vehicle, front hull and turret removed, engine moved right front, 13' 2½" × 6' 9" × 4' 7".

PzKpfwIB Fe Lad Tr, Fern Ladungs Traeger, remote control carrier (Ladungsleger I), vehicle w/retractable arm holding 150 pound explosive charge, prototype only.

PzKpfwIc, one visor on left, vision cupola on turret, 2cm and mg, see VK1601.

PzKpfwId, see VK1801.

PzKpfwIf, see VK1801.

PzBefWgI, see Germany, Miscellaneous.

PZKPFWII AND VARIATIONS

LaS 100H (Landwirtschaftlicher Schlepper), 1934, open hull, cast rear idler, 6 small bogie wheels, leaf springs, 3 support rollers.

LaS 100MAN, resembled Carden-Loyd Mark VI but 6 small bogie wheels w/rail, became chassis for early PzKpfwII, 15′ 7″ × 7′ ½″ × 6′4½″.

LKAII(K), 1934 (LaS100K), chassis like LKAI but front of hull superstructure was recessed on right, larger turret w/2cm KwK 30 gun and 1 mg in wide mantlet, Zeiss tank periscope, Krupp and Henschel built, 14′ 8″ × 7′ × 6′ 2″.

LaS138H, prototype PzKpfwII Ausf D and E w/4 large bogie wheels, no support rollers.

SdKfz121 (PzKpfwII (2cm) Ausf al), 1935, Typ 1 LaS100, 6 small bogie wheels on rail, 3 support rollers, open idler, faceted turret, no reduction gear, driver cowl bevelled back on right, 15′ 7″ × 7′ × 6′ 6½″.

PzBefWgRhB, 1935 (Panzer Befehl Wagen, armoured command vehicle), 3.7cm and 2 mgs, 1 next to driver, turret like PzKpfwII.

▼ 172

SdKfz121 (PzKpfwII (2cm) Ausf a2) (1/LaS100), welded rear idler and change in engine compartment to improve cooling, 6 small bogie wheels on rail, 3 support rollers, faceted turret w/2cm KwK 30 gun and 1 mg coaxial, turret splash plate below gun across turret, 1 driver cowl and flap, bevelled on sides.

SdKfz121 (PzKpfwII (2cm) Ausf a3) (1b/LaS100), improved cooling and suspension.

SdKfz121 (PzKpfwII (2cm) Ausf b) (2/LaS100), 1937, final reduction gear added making bow square edged, new tracks, HP increased.

SdKfz121 (PzKpfwII (2cm) Ausf c) (3/LaS100), 1937, suspension changed to final type of 5 independently sprung bogies w/leaf springs, 4 return rollers, improved gears, last type w/front end rounded.

SdKfz121 (PzKpfwII (2cm) Ausf A) 4/LaS100), 1937, minor improvements, Zeiss tank periscope, first type w/square bow, 16′ × 7′ 7″ × 6′ 7½″.

SdKfz121 (PzKpfwII (2cm) Ausf B), 1940 (5/LaS100), squat vision cupola added, 16′ × 7′ 7″ × 6′ 9″.

SdKfz121 (PzKpfwII (2cm) Ausf C) (6/LaS100), additional armour on front of superstructure and mantlet, rounded bow, otherwise same as 3/LaS100, 15′ 9″ × 7′ 5½″ × 6′ 7½″.

SdKfz121 (PzKpfwII (2cm) Ausf D) (8/LaS138), 1938, 4 large bogie wheels, no support rollers, first use of torsion bars, front of hull vertical w/no corner bevels, epicyclic clutch and brake steering, cooling louvers in sides of engine compartment, 15′ 5½″ × 7′ 6½″ × 6′ 9″.

SdKfz121 (PzKpfwII (2cm) Ausf E) (8a/LaS138), similar w/minor improvements.

SdKfz121 (PzKpfwII (2cm) Ausf F) (7/LaS100), 1941, increased frontal armour, bow square, dummy visor right front, 5 small bogie wheels, 4 return rollers, bulging idler, additional vision slits, sometimes w/smoke grenade clusters rear of each mudguard, 16′ × 7′ 8″ × 6′ 9″.

SdKfz121 (PzKpfwII (2cm) Ausf G), 16′ × 7′ 8″ × 6′ 9″.

SdKfz121 (PzKpfwII (2cm) Ausf G1), thicker armour and wider driver's vision.

SdKfz121 (PzKpfwII (2cm) Ausf G3), thicker armour and wider driver's vision.

SdKfz121 (PzKpfwII (2cm) Ausf G4), thicker armour and wider driver's vision.

SdKfz121 (PzKpfwII (2cm) Ausf H), armour thickened, HP raised, prototype only.

SdKfz121 (PzKpfwII (2cm) Ausf J), 16′ × 7′ 8″ × 6′ 9″.

SdKfz121 (PzKpfwII (2cm) Ausf M), armour thickened, HP raised, prototype only.

SdKfz121 (PzKpfwII (2cm) Ausf A-F (Tp)), adapted for tropical conditions.

PzKpfwII Schwimmpanzer, 1940, each track was enclosed in a box fastened to sprockets and rollers, boxes of 3 compartments filled w/plastic tubes giving buoyancy and not rendered inoperative through enemy fire, power take off in front to shaft and screw at rear, intended for the invasion of Great Britain.

PzKpfwII (2cm) Ausf A-F Schwimmfaehig (amphibious) (FaGebr Sachsenberg Schwimmgeraet, Sachsenberg Brothers firm swimming device), screw propeller take off, cutout boat float added front and rear, resembled US flotation devices.

PiPzWgII, no details available.

Instandsetzungswagen II, repair vehicle, no details available.

Muni Panzer II, supply vehicle w/o turret, 15′ 9″ × 7′ 5½″ × 4′ 7½″.

PzKpfw Fahrschulwanne II, driver training chassis, turret removed, 15′ 9″ × 7′ 3½″ × 4′ 7″.

PzKpfwII Brueckenleger, bridgelayer (Brueckenleger I), short bridge carried on PzKpfwII Ausf a l, prototype only.

15cm sIG 33 auf Fgst PzKpfw II Sf, Fahrgestell, chassis of PzKpfwII (GWII fuer 15cm sIG 33) (Libelle, dragonfly), SP on open chassis, 3-sided shield forward, pilot model had semi-circular shield w/L/12 gun, 15′ 7″ × 7′ 4½″ × 5′ 3″.

15cm IG 33 auf Fgst PzKpfwII Verlaengert (lengthened), same as above w/1 bogie wheel per side added, front of hull higher than rear, armour more like pilot model.

SdKfz122 (PzKpfwII (Flamm) Ausf A-B) (8/LaS138), 1940, modified LaS138 chassis and hull, low turret w/1 mg34, F/T on each front mudguard, 15′ 7″ × 7′ 5″ × 6′ 9″.

PzBefWgII, command vehicle, prototype only, w/dummy armament.

PzKpfwII n A mit 4.7cm Pak(t)A5, project only.

SdKfz123 (PzSpWgII (2cm) Luchs) (PzKpfwII Ausf L), see VK1303.

Berge Pz Luchs, armoured recovery vehicle w/cantilever A frame, see VK1601.

SdKfz124 (le FH18/2 Sf Wespe, Wasp) (SflII) (le FH18/2 auf Fgst KpfwIISf) (GWII) (GWII fuer le FH18/2Sf), 1942 two similar types w/differing driver's cowls, gun cab rear w/downward sloping top edges, some guns w/armoured recoil cylinder, 3 return rollers, 15′ 9½″ × 7′ 6″ × 7′6½″.

Mun Sfl auf FgstPzKpfwII (Sf), similar but gun opening closed, carried 90 rounds as accompanying ammunition carrier for above.

5cm Pak 38 auf KpfwII (SdFgst901) (PzSflIc) (FgstPz901) (PzKpfwII fuer 5cm Pak 38), high front, swept back 3-sided hull curved downward in rear, gun w/muzzle brake, rebuilt VK901.

SdKfz131 (PzJaegII) (Marder II, marten II) (7.5cm Pak40/2 L/46 auf SflII Ausf A-C und F), sophisticated tank destroyer, V-front armour sloped upward and swept back amidship then recessed engine compartment, one vehicle experimentally w/one recoilless rifle, 15' 2" (20' 10½") × 7' 5½" × 7' 2½".

Minenraeumpanzer II (armoured mine exploder II) (Hammerschlag Geraet, hammerblow device), 1939, front mounted mine plough, project only.

SdKfz131 (Marder II Pak36(r)) (PzJaeg 7.62cm Pak36(r) auf FgstII Ausf A-C), resembled Marder II above but w/Russian gun and higher armour superstructure.

173

SdKfz132 (PzJaeg II Ausf D-E fuer 7.5cm Pak40/2), large bogies, bevelled-in hull w/gun in large shield, 15' 5½" (20' 10½") × 7' 6½" × 8' 6½".

SdKfz132 (PzSflII fuer 76.2mm le FK 296 (r) Ausf D-E), small swept back shield w/ or w/o muzzle brake on gun, 15' 2½" (18' 6½") × 7' 6½" × 8' 6½".

SdKfz132 (PzJaegII), muzzle brake, bevelled-in hull w/gun in large shield, large bogie wheels.

SdKfz135 (PzJaeg fuer 7.5cm Pak40/1 (Sf) Lorraine (f)) (PzJaeg Lr S fuer 7.5cm Pak40/1) (Marder I), French tractor chassis, box hull, double bevel open top, rear overhang, 17' × 6' 2" × 7'.

FgstII fuer 8.8cm Pak41, project only.

FgstII fuer 7.5cm KwK L/70, project only.

10.5cm le FH (Sf) Lorraine (f) (GW Lr S fuer FH18/3), similar to SdKfz135.

12.2cm FK (r) auf GW Lr S, Russian gun in streamlined turret on Lorraine tractor.

SdKfz135/1 (GWLrS fuer 15cm sFH 13/1), similar but w/trail spade.

sIG 33 auf Lr S (f), similar, 15' 7" 17' 7" w/spade (19' 5½" overall) × 6' 1" × 7' 2".

PzJaeg Lr S (f) fuer 4.7cm Pak181 (f) or 183 (f) 4.7cm Pak181 (f) auf PzJaegLrS (f), similar but smaller gun w/small shield, centre pedestal mounted.

Beob Pz Wg Lorraine, artillery observation vehicle on Lorraine chassis.

Mun Trsp Kw auf Lr S, ammunition carrier, 6 bogie pairs, 4 support rollers, open cargo body unmodified.

CZECH TNH LIGHT TANK VARIATIONS

PzKpfw38(t) 3.7cm (Cesko Moravska Kolben Danek Panzer) (38(t)) PzKpfwIII(t) Ausf A-F, G, H, M and S), see Czechoslovakia, 16' 1" × 6' 9" × 7' 9½".

PzKpfw38(t) Schulfahrwanne, turret-less, late in the war a wood-petrol device w/high vertical cylinder in rear was used at the factory for run-in tests to conserve petrol.

PzKpfw38(t) mit Turm PzKpfwIV, 7.5cm KwK L/48 in PzKpfwIV turret on 38(t) chassis, project only, 16' 1" (18' 3½") × 9' 1½" × 7' 1".

PzBefWg38(t) (PzBefWg LTH), several tank versions used as command tanks, one w/turret removed and low folding shield added to front and sides of hull superstructure.

SdKfzl38 (PzKpfw38(t) fuer 7.5cm Pak40/3) (PbJaeg38 Marder III) (Marder III) (Marder 38(t)) (7.5cm Pak40/3 auf Sfl38), small 3-sided shield, large mantlet, engine centre or rear, some w/louvers in centre sides, bow mg on models w/rear engines and front mounted main armament, final model w/gun in rear and cast driver's compartment cowl, 15' 3" (18' 11½") × 7' 3½" × 8' 1½".

SdKfzl38/1 (15cm sIG33 (Sf) auf 38(t)) (sIG33 (Sfl) auf PzKpfw38(t)) (15cm sIG33 auf GW38) (GW38 fuer sIG33), gun at front, 8-sided hull sloped to rear, variations existed, 15' 10½" × 7' 9" × 7' 10½".

MuniPz38 (Mun Fahrzeug auf Fgst PzKpfw38(t)), ammunition carrier, companion vehicle to SdKfzl38/1, driver relocated to right.

SdKfzl38/1 (15cm sIG33/1 (sf) auf 38(t)) (GW fuer sIG33/1), engine centre, 5-sided rear hull, variations existed, late models w/cast cowl as on SdKfzl38.

JagdPz38(t) (le StuG38(t)) (JagdPz38 fuer 7.5cm Pak39 L/48) (le PzJaeg38(t) fuer 7.5cm Pak39 L/48) (Hetzer, baiter), HP increased, suspension strengthened and tracks widened, low hull, gun in front glacis, partly skirted suspension, remote-controlled mg on top, originally narrow mantlet and 12 hole idler, improvements during production to cast mantlet, exhaust and suspension, idler w/6 holes but finally 4, 15' 7" (20' 5") × 8' 7" × 7' 1½".

PzJaeg38(t) fuer 7.5cm KwK42 L/70, similar, project only.

SdKfzl39 (PzJaeg38(t) fuer 7.62cm Pak36(r)) (PzSfl38 fuer 7.62cm Pak36(r)) (Marder III), gun

mounted in centre w/small shield, 15' 10" (19' 2") × 7' 8½" × 8' 2½".

SdKfz140 (Flak Pz38(t) 20cm, Flieger Abwehr Kanone Panzer, anti-aircraft armoured vehicle 38(t) (2cm) (Wirbelwind 38(t), whirlwind 38(t)) (2cm Flak 38 auf Pz38(t)), 2 types: gun rear in non-rotating diamond turret or in flat drop side turret, top sections of diamond turret were hinged to drop for fire at low elevations, 15' 1½" × 7' × 7' 4½".

FlammPz38, resembled Hetzer, flame-gun in large ball mount in front glacis.

SdKfzl40/1 (AufklPz38(t)) (Aufklaerungspanzer, reconnaisance tank) 38(t)), (PzAufKlWg638/11), intended as replacement for armoured car SdKfz222 and half-track SdKfz250/9, 38(t) w/2cm KwK 38 and mg in SdKfz222 turret on 38(t) chassis.

PzAufklWg638/12 (7.5cm K51), project.

PzAufklWg638/24 (2cm KwK38ZW), project.

PzAufklWg638/25 (12cm GrW42), project.

BergePz38 (BergePzWg638/16), Hetzer w/o gun and lower super-structure, equipped as tank recovery vehicle, 15' 7" × 7' 2" × 7' 1".

SchPzWg38(t), 1945, 2cm KwK38 in A/A type turret, 1 bogie added each side, intended as APC, wooden mock-up only.

FlakPzKugelblitz38 (KlKugelblitz (DB)38(d), ball lightning 38), FlakPzWg638/15 3cm MK103Zw), two 3cm MK103/38 and two 2cm Flak38 or MK151/20 in hemi-spherical turret, wooden mock-up only.

PzKpfw38(t) PAW(8cm) (Panzer Abwehr Werfer), A/T rocket, 1945, project to replace all tanks.

PzJaegWg638/10 7.5cm Pak 38 project only.

PzJaegWg639/9, project.

StuHaubWg638/13, 10.5cm Stu H42/3, project.

StuHaubWg638/14, 10.5cm Stu H42/2, project by Alkett.

GW638/17 fuer 8F43, project.

GW638/18 fuer 8F43/1, project.

GW638/19 fuer leFH18/40/4, project.

GW638/20 fuer sIG33/2, 6 bogie wheel chassis, project.

GW38 fuer sIG33/1 (Sf), project.

GW638/21 fuer le FH18/40/5, 6 bogie wheel chassis, project.

GW638/22 fuer 12.8cm K81/3 (Sf), project.

GW638/23 fuer sFH18/6, project.

GW638/26 fuer le FH18/40/5, 4 bogie wheel chassis, project.

GW638/27 sIG33/6, 4 bogie wheel chassis, project.

JagdPz38(d) (638/28), 10.5cm StuH42/2, project.

JagdPz38(d) (638/29) 7.5cm Pak 42/1 L/70, project.

GW638/30 fuer 12.8cm Pak80, project.

GW638/31 fuer s 10cm K18/1, project.

GW fuer 21cm GWSf2 (638/32).

GW38M fuer sIG33/2 (Sf), project.

Jagd Pz38(d) 8WK 40 H73, project by MAN.

PzJaeg38(d) Ausf W1806 und W1807, 1945, common chassis project, two types, diesel engine rear and engine beside driver, 7.5cm recoilless rifle first then 7.5cm Pak38/1 L/48 rigidly mounted, later 7.5cm KwK L/70, turretless chassis, 22′ 9″ × 9′ 2″ × 5′ 4″.

Krupp/Steyr Waffentraeger, 8.8cm Pak43/3 L/71, 4 large bogie wheels, bevelled turret, 38(d) chassis and RaupenSchlepper Ost components, 17′ 10″ (23′ 10″) × 8′ × 8′.

Rheinmetall/Borsig/Ardelt Waffentraeger, similar, 8.8cm Pjk43 (Panzer Jaeger Kanone) or KwK43 or 10.5cm le FH18/40 on 38(d) chassis, bevelled box hull.

PZKPFWIII AND VARIATIONS

ZW (Zugfuehrerwagen, platoon leader vehicle, camouflage title), prototypes built by MAN, Daimler-Benz, Rheinmetall and Krupp.

MKA, Krupp-built forerunner of PzKpfwIII, bevelled rear hull, flat-sided valance, driver's cowl set out, 3.7cm L/45 gun in divided type mantlet, Zeiss tank periscope, 6 simulated-spoked bogie wheels, 3 support rollers.

SdKfzl41 (VsKfz622) (PzKpfwIII Ausf A) (1/ZW, Zugfuehrerwagen,

platoon leader vehicle, camouflage title for all PzKpfwIII vehicles), 1936, similar to MKA but 5 large double bogie wheels, vertical coil springs, 2 support rollers, superstructure front vertical w/bow mg right, inner mantlet for 3.7cm KwK L/45, 2 mgs parallel in turret, cupola cover extending over sides of cupola, 8 hole sprocket, 15 tons, 17′ 9″ × 9′ 7″ × 8′ 6″.

SdKfzl41 (PzKpfwIII Ausf B) (2/ZW), 1937, 4 pairs small road wheels in 2 large horizontally placed leaf spring sets, 3 support rollers, 17′ 9″ × 9′ 7″ × 8′ 4″.

SdKfzl41 (PzKpfwIII Ausf C) (3a/ZW), 1937, 2-4-2 bogie wheel arrangement, 3 horizontally placed leaf springs, 3 support rollers, 17′ 9″ × 9′ 7″ × 8′ 4″.

Selbstfahrlafette IIIb (3a/ZW), Daimler-Benz prototype SP.

SdKfzl41 (PzKpfwIII Ausf D) (3b/ZW), 1938, all previous models redesignated Ausf D (3a/ZW), suspension similar to above Ausf C but front and rear leaf springs angled, 3 support rollers, smaller drive sprocket, increased armour, new cupola, 20 tons, (see also SdKfz266), 19′ 4″ × 9′ 4½″ × 8′ 9½″

SdKfzl41 (PzKpfwIII (3.7cm) Ausf E) (4/ZW), 1939, last model w/3.7cm gun, 2 mgs and inner mantlet, later changed to 5cm KwK L/42 and 1 mg in outlet mantlet as 4a/ZW, 6 bogie wheels, 3 evenly spaced support rollers, torsion bar suspension, 8 holed sprocket, 17′ 7½″ × 9′ 6½″ × 8′.

SdKfzl41 (PzKpfwIII (5cm) Aust F) (5/ZW), 8 holed sprockets, split driver's vision slot, stowage box rear of turret, outer mantlet for 5cm KwK L/42 and 1 mg, square bow mg mount, supplementary armour sometimes added, 17′ 7½″ × 9′ 6½″ × 8′.

SdKfzl41 (PzKpfwIII (5cm) Ausf G) (6/ZW), 5cm KwK L/42, new lower cupola, space between first and second support rollers increased, flat front plate, sometimes supplementary front armour w/bottom cut for new visor, single square bow mg mount, 8 hole sprocket, 8 hole idler, 17′ 7½″ × 9′ 6½″ × 8′.

PzKpfwIII (5cm) Ausf G (Tp), better cooling, air filters for tropical use, 18′ 1½″ × 9′ 8″ × 8′ 2½″.

SdKfzl41 (PzKpfwIII (5cm) Ausf H) (7/ZW), torsion bar strength increased, tracks widened, basic armour increased in front, spaced armour later added, new sprocket w/7 pie-shaped holes, spoked idler, new support roller spacing, new driver's visor.

SdKfzl41 mit 5cm Pak38, experimental.

SdKfzl41/1 (PzKpfwIII (5cm) Ausf J) (8/ZW), 1941, 5cm KwK L/42 gun, later L/60 and longer gun installed also in earlier model vehicles, basic armour increased, spaced front armour w/bottom cut for driver's visor, new ball mount for bow mg, side plates extended in front to form towing eyes, 17′ 9″ (18′ 3″) × 9′ 8″ × 8′ 2½″.

PzKpfwIII Ausf K (4c/ZW), hydraulic transmission.

SdKfzl41/1 (PzKpfwIII Ausf L (Tp)) (9/ZW), no peep slots on turret sides, 5cm KwK 39 L/60, 6 smoke dischargers, exhaust deflectors to reduce blast, supplementary spaced armour added to front of hull and turret, 17′ 9″ (18′ 3″) × 9′ 8″ × 8′ 2½″.

SdKfzl41/1 (PzKpfwIII Ausf M) (10/ZW), 5cm KwK 39 L/60, number of cannon rounds increased to 98 from 78 and mg rounds reduced to 2550 from 4650, some w/7.5cm KwK L/24 gun, better A/A gun and mount, some w/skirts (mit Schuerzen) for bazooka protection in 1943, some w/East tracks (Ostketten) which permitted attachment of grousers, smoke dischargers, water-proofed, high silencers introduced on late models, 17′ 11½″ (18′ 3″) × 9′ 8″ × 8′ 2½″.

SdKfzl41/2 (PzKpfwIII Ausf N) (11/ZW), main armament changed to 7.5cm KwK L/24, 17′ 9″ × 9′ 8″ × 8′ 2½″.

SdKfzl41/2 (PzKpfwIII Ausf O) (11/ZW), expedient vehicle w/7.5cm KwK L/24 to use up chassis.

SdKfzl41/3 (PzKpfwIII (Flamm)) (Flamm PzIII Ausf M), flame-gun in wide shield mantlet in turret, coaxial and bow mgs retained, 17′ 8½″ × 9′ 8″ × 8′ 2½″.

PzKpfwIII FAMO, 5cm KwK L/42, experimental overlapping 6 bogie wheel suspension, sometimes erroneously called PzKpfwIII/IV.

PzKpfwIII (Pak 7.62cm (r)), 1944, Russian modified w/Russian gun in modified turret, recaptured and used by the Germans.

149

▼ 176

PzKpfwIII, turret w/5cm KwK 39 L/60 on left side of mantlet, turret cupola on right, high silencers as in late Ausf M.

gpSfl fuer StuG 7.5cm Kan O-Serie (5/ZW), prototype SP.

SdKfzl42 (Gp Sfl fuer StuG 7.5cm KwK) (Gp Sfl fuer StuG 7.5cm Kanone, Ausf A) (StuGIII A fuer 7.5cm KwK L/24), PzKpfwIII Ausf E chassis modified to mount cannon on low hull, no mantlet, sight behind opening in upper front plate of superstructure, bullet deflector grooves on plates around it, spaced sloped armour on right along fighting compartment and on left in front of wireless box, louvers on left behind driver, 17' 8" × 9' 8" × 6' 5".

SdKfzl42 (GpSfl StuG 7.5cm Kanone Ausf B), higher HP, modified transmission, minor improvements to bullet deflectors, PzKpfwIII Ausf F chassis, 17' 7½" × 9' 7" × 6' 4½".

SdKfzl42 (Gp Sfl fuer StuG 7.5cm Kanone Ausf C), Stuk 37 L/24 gun, new sprocket and idler, otherwise similar to Model B.

SdKfzl42 Gp Sfl fuer StuG 7.5cm Kanone Ausf D, 1941, improved transmission, some w/Ostketten, sight projected above roof, upper front plates of fighting compartment changed.

SdKfzl42 (Gp Sfl fuer StuG 7.5cm Kanone Ausf E), spaced sloped armour along fighting compartment discontinued, wireless boxes on both sides, L/28 gun.

SdKfzl42 (7.5cm StuG 40 Ausf F), L/43 gun, reinforced armour, early model w/o, later w/muzzle brake, housing on roof top added to facilitate service of the long gun, later modified w/aprons and mg shield, some as command tanks w/wireless rail around rear deck, 17' 7½" (20' 8½") × 9' 8" × 7' ½".

SdKfzl42/1 (7.5cm StuG 40 Ausf G) (StuGIII 7.5cm StuK40 L/48), new gun, redesigned fighting compartment w/sloping sides, commander's cupola w/rotating periscope ring, additional armour in front, mg shield, smoke dischargers added, 17' 7½" (22' 2½") × 9' 7" × 7' ½".

SdKfzl42/1 Ausf G, 1944, sometimes incorrectly called Ausf H, cast 'saukopf' mantlet, cast left top plate w/bulge for protection of

commander's cupola (this also appeared on some of the previous Ausf G vehicles and some of these also were armoured w/the 7.5cm L/28 gun, some w/steel return rollers not rubber faced.

SdKfzl42/1 Ausf G, 1944-45, sometimes incorrectly called Ausf J, remote-controlled mg instead of mg w/hinged shield, smaller loader's hatch opening in 2 parts to the sides, travel lock for gun on upper glacis, single 'Nahverteidigungs-waffe' replaced previous smoke dischargers, steel return rollers w/o rubber facing, 17' 7½" (22' 2½") × 9' 7" × 7' ½".

SdKfzl42/2 (StuH42 L/28 (Sf)), 3 models, 1942 w/muzzle brake, fighting compartment as StuGIII Ausf F w/commander's cupola, 1943 w/muzzle brake, later w/o, fighting compartment as StuGIII Ausf G w/commander's cupola, 1944 w/o muzzle brake, cast top plate, remote-controlled mg, welded armour, w/ or w/o anti-bazooka plates, 20' 1½" × 9' 8" × 7' ½".

PzKpfwIII Tauchfaehig (submersible), turret sealed w/rubber 'bathing cap' having 22-foot hose connected to breather buoy which could be blasted away w/small explosive charge, submerge to 20', intended for the invasion of Great Britain and used in 1941 to cross the Bug River at the start of the Russian campaign.

MuniPzIII, ammunition carrier, StuGIII w/o gun, large rounded cast armour cover for gun port.

StuG40 als MuniPz, converted SP.

StuG40 mit Flammenwerfer, project only.

PzKpfwIII fuer 3.7cm Pak und RSF (Rueckstossfrei, recoilless) Waffen, 3.7cm gun and 2 recoilless rifles in large 3-sided shield, mock-up only.

▼ 177

Minenraeumpanzer III, mine resistant vehicle w/raised hull and spread suspension, 6 bogie wheels and rail, 3 support rollers, high track frame.

15cm sIG33 auf FgstPzIII (StuJG33) (sIG33B (Sfl)), much more armour added, high box hull, sloped sides, bow mg, 12 vehicles made but abandoned after adoption of SdKfzl66, 17' 8½" × 9' 6" × 7' 6½".

Instandsetzungs KwIII, repair and maintenance vehicle.

Berge PzIII Ausf E-N, no turret, wooden cargo box, usually w/Ostketten.

Schlepper III, armoured cargo carrier.

SdKfzl43 (PzBeobWgIII) (ArtPzBeogWg (PzIII)), artillery observation vehicle, mg only in turret with dummy cannon on extreme right of mantlet, chassis of all models used.

▼ 178

PzKpfwIII mit Waffe 0725 (Konischer Lauf, tapered bore) (PzKpfwIII Ausf L mit Turm PzKpfwIV), 7.5/5.5cm tapered bore gun w/muzzle brake, experimental.

Brueckenleger II, bridge carried on FgstPzIII, prototypes only.

GW634/6 le FH 18/40/6(Sf) (Geraet 814GW), project.

GW634/4 K8F 43/2(sf) (Geraet 815GW), project.

GW21cm GrW Sfl(634/3), project.

PiPzKWIII, turretless engineer vehicle, anti-bazooka skirts, racks on top for bridging material, etc.

PZKPFW IV AND VARIATIONS

▼ 179

BW (Bataillons Fuehrer Wagen), see VK2001 Rhb.

3.7cm Pak (Sfl) auf PzKpfwIV Fgst, prototype only.

Vs Kfz 622, Versuchskraft-fahrzeuge 622 (PzKpfwIV Ausf A) (1/BW), 1936, protruding driver's position w/round bow mg mount at right, also tried w/front plate straight across, 7.5cm KwK L/24 w/coaxial mg in turret, small inner mantlet, 2 hinged ports front of turret, single turret hatches, hinged side access doors in turret, drum-shaped cupola protruding through turret rear plate, single left of centre driver visor, 8 road wheels, 4 support rollers, 6 pie-shaped sprocket holes, pivoted wireless antenna on right, 19′ 5″ × 9′ 3½″ × 8′ 9½″.

SdKfzl61 (PzKpfwIV Ausf A-1) (1/BW), same but 2 hinged ports replacing hinged ports in front of turret and cupola w/slots instead of exposed periscopes.

SdKfzl61 (PzKpfwIV Ausf B) (2/BW), 1937, increased armour, 7.5cm KwK 37 L/24 gun, double driver's visor, hull flat across front, pistol port and peepslot instead of mg mount right front, cupola lower and no longer drum-shaped.

SdKfzl61 (PzKpfwIV Ausf C) (3/BW), 1938, wishbone wireless antenna deflector, turret armour increased, double driver's visor, hull flat across front, no bow mg, similar to Ausf B, internal mantlet, vision plugs in front turret plate, single turret door.

SdKfzl61 (PzKpfwIV Ausf D) (4/BW), driver's position again protruding, bow mg in square mount w/internal ball on right, L/24 gun, external gun mantlet, some later brought up to Ausf G standard.

SdKfzl61 mit 5cm KwK 39 L/60, one prototype only.

SdKfzl61 (PzKpfwIV Ausf E) (5/BW), 1939, single heavy driver visor, square bow mg mount w/internal ball, added armour front and sides of superstructure, no cupola bulge in turret rear plate, 23 tons, 7.5cm KwK L/24 gun, Afrika Korps modified 1 vehicle by placing a cylindrical section between turret and hull, this portion covered with heavy rags watersoaked to act as crude air-conditioner, 18′ 6″ × 9′ 5″ × 8′ 9″.

SdKfzl61 (PzKpfwIV Ausf F-1) (6/BW), 1941, heavier armour, wider tracks, turret prepared for 7.5cm L/43, double turret hatches, cupola moved forward, front ball mg mount, hull front straight across, idler made of tubing.

SdKfzl61 (PzKpfwIV Ausf F-2) (7/BW), 2 front turret ports removed, same chassis as Ausf F-1 but w/7.5cm KwK40 L/43, double turret doors, new dished sprocket, some later w/anti-bazooka plates, ball-shaped (single baffle) muzzle brake, some late vehicles may have had the double baffle muzzle brake as fitted on Ausf G, called Mark IV Special by the British, 17′ 9″ (21′ 9″) × 9′ 5½″ × 8′ 9½″.

SdKfzl61/1 (PzKpfwIV Ausf G) (8/BW), new double baffle muzzle brake, L/43 gun, system added for water interchange between vehicles

for winter starting, bow mg, main armament, all previous vehicles described later were changed to L/48 gun and additional armour as opportunity arose for modification, turret plugs reinstated, guard plate on top of turret bevel ventilator.

SdKfzl61/2 (PzKpfwIV Ausf H) (9/BW), basic frontal armour increased to 80mm, circular turret hatch instead of 2 part split, 7.5cm KwK40 L/48, some vehicles w/A/A mg, cast 6 spoke star sprocket, vision plugs on turret sides eliminated, 'aprons' around turret and hull sides introduced, front plate straight across, 19′ 4″ (24′ 2½″) × 10′ 9½″ × 8′ 8½″.

PzKpfwIV Ausf H (Thoma-Antrieb), 1944, with hydrostatic drive, sharply sloped-down engine compartment, small rear sprocket, front sprocket retained as idler.

SdKfzl61/2 (PzKpfwIV Ausf J) (10/BW), 7.5cm KwK40 L/48, fuel capacity increased, new transmission, simplified exhaust system, hand turret traverse to conserve petrol, new idler, anti-bazooka screen over tracks devised to reduce weight, w/Ostketten.

PzKpfwIV (Tp), several models w/improved air-filters and exhaust pipe baffles for use in North Africa.

PzKpfwIV mit Turm Panther, 7.5cm KwK42 L/70 in Panther turret on PzKpfwIV, mock-up only.

BergePzIV, crane and winch top of hull mounted above wireless operator position, no turret, rear deck built out, 19′ 4″ × 9′ 4″ × 8′.

MunPzIV Ausf F fuer Karlgeraet (PzKpfwIV Ausf F, Mun Tr fuer Karlgeraet), similar but rear deck boxed all around, ammunition vehicle for Geraet 040 (60cm Karlmoerser).

PzKpfwIV Tauchfaehig, submersible by same means as PzKpfwIII Tauchfaehig.

PzIV Brueckenleger (bridge-layer) (Brueckenleger III) (Sd Fz der PzPi, armoured engineer special vehicle), ramp bridge on turretless PzKpfwIV.

Inf Sturm-Steg, infantry assault ladder (Brueckenleger IVS), similar in appearance to bridge-layer, ladder extendable to 85′ in 5 collapsible segments.

PzBeobgWgIV, observation vehicle, resembled combat tank.

Mittlerer Waffentraeger (Waffentraeger 15cm sFH18 L/29.5) open PzKpfwIV chassis, also w/12.8cm K81(L/55), projects only.

180

Grille 10 (8.8cm Flak 41), also 10.5cm leFH43 or 10cm KwK, resembled Heuschrecke (grasshopper), PzKpfwIV chassis w/gun in circular mantlet in swept-back open box turret, 18′ 6″ (22′ 1″) × 9′ 6″ × 8′ 7″.

Geraet Nr 820 (StuGIV fuer 7.5cm StuK40 L/48), 1942, superstructure as StuGIII Ausf G, turretless vehicle, wedge-shaped recoil housing, separate driver's compartment w/top hatch, cast mantlet, 22′ × 9′ 8″ × 7′ 2½″.

181

Geraet Nr 822 (StuGIV 7.5cm StuK 40 L/48) (StuG (neu) L/70), with muzzle brake, same as above but no driver's visor, smaller hatch and periscopes on top of driver's compartment, sometimes w/remote-controlled mg on top.

Geraet Nr 823, 1943, same chassis but w/10.5cm H 42/2.

182

SdKfzl62 (JagdPzIV Ausf F 7.5cm Pak 39 L/48) (Guderian Ente, duck), squat, cast saukopf mantlet, no turret, first production w/rounded front corners on superstructure, 4 support rollers, skirted, originally w/muzzle brake, right and left hand mg ports on upper front plate closed by cone-shaped plugs when not in use, 1944 production front corners were square, command vehicles had 2 antennae, 22′ 5½″ × 10′ 5″ × 6′ 1″.

PzJaegIV 7.5cm StuK42 L/70 (VOMAG), 1944, first prototype, high superstructure w/vertical sides on unmodified PzKpfwIV Ausf H chassis, single silencer, ball mantlet, no muzzle brake, superstructure was wooden mock-up.

StuGIV (VOMAG), 2nd prototype, wedge bow in Ausf H.

PzJaeg 7.5cm StuK42 L/70, 1944, high superstructure, sloping sides, cast mantlet, second Vomag prototype, 18' 11½" (27' 6") × 9' 6" × 8' 9".

SdKfzl62/1 (JagdPzIV 7.5cm StuK42 (L/70)) (PzIV Lang) (PzIV/70) (Guderian Ente, duck), 1944, low superstructure, similar to SdKfzl62 but long gun w/o muzzle brake, eliminated cast triangular mantlet, nose heavy, frontal armour increased, left hand bow mg eliminated, 3 return rollers and first 2 bogie wheels steel tyred to take up excessive gun weight vertical exhaust, 27' 10" (overall) × 10' 5" × 6' 1".

Panzer IV Zwischenloesung, 1944, normal PzKpfwIV chassis w/modified PzIV/70 superstructure.

SdKfzl62, see Flak PzIb (Möbelwagen, moving van).

SdKfzl64 (8.8cm Pak 43/1 (L/71) auf Fgst PzKpfwIII/IV) (8.8cm Pz Jaeg (SF) IV L/71) (Nashorn, rhinoceros), 1942, gun rear, high sloping cab, open top, sloping glacis w/driver's cowl, some reported w/straight front plate, components from PzIII and IV, 23' 7" (27' 8") × 9' 4" × 9' 8½".

SdKfzl64 (8.8cm Pak 43/3 L/71 Pz Jaeg Hornisse, hornet), same as above, designation changed.

SdKfz165 (15cm sFH 18/1 (SF)) (Hummel, bumblebee) (15cm Pz Haub 18/1 auf Fgst KpfwIII/IV), 1943, prototype w/muzzle brake, later w/o, sloping glacis w/driver's cowl as in Nashorn, later front plate straight across w/2 vision ports, 19' 5" (23' 6") × 9' 9" × 9' 2½".

GWIII/IV (Mun) (Mun Traeg Hummel), similar w/o armament, companion ammunition carrier.

SdKfz165/1 (10.5cm le FH18/1 (Sf) L/28 auf GWIVb) (GWIVb fuer 10.5cm le FH18/1), shorter by 1 return roller each side, 18 tons, experimental, large sloping-back turret, semi-circular mantlet, artillery wheels carried on rear brackets at angle of 45 degrees, basic 9/BW chassis, 8 built and later converted to PzJaegIVb (E39), 19' 4½" × 9' 5" × 7' 4½".

PzJaegIVb (E39) fuer 7.5cm Pak39 L/48, 3 return rollers.

PzJaegIV fuer 8.8cm Pak L/71, 18' 9½" (24' 10") × 9' 8" × 8' 4½".

10.5cm K18 auf SflIVa, 1941, 2 built, resembled Hummel, faceted superstructure, separate box-like driver's and wireless operator's cowls, gun w/muzzle brake.

SturmPzIII/IV (Sf), StuG 7.5cm L/48 in turret, project only.

MuniPzIII Fahrzeug fuer StuPz III/IV (Sf), project only.

le PzH 18/40/2 auf FgstPz III/IV (Sf), project only.

MuniPz Fahrzeug fuer le PzH 18/40/2 III/IV, project only.

StuG 7.5cm L/70 auf FgstPz III/IV (Sf) (7.5cm StuG III/IV L/70), (le PzJaegIII/IV), project only.

10.5cm StuH auf FgstPzIII/IV (10.5cm Sturmhaubitze III/IV), project only.

▼ 183

Heuschrecke 105/8/1 GWIVb (GWIVb fuer 10.5cm le FH18/1) (Heuschrecke IVb), heavy mantlet w/crane for removing turret, crane stored on side track-guards, artillery field carriage wheels carried on rear brackets for attachment to turret for towing, 19' 4½" (21' 9½") × 9' 8" × 9' 4½".

Heuschrecke 15, 1942, low chassis w/built-in rear crane for removing turret and setting up weapon as field piece, project only.

▼ 184

SdKfz166 (StuPzIV fuer Stu Haub 43 L/14) (Brummbaer, grizzly bear), high front, sloped back, ball mantlet, first w/driver's visor, later w/o visor but periscopes, hatch layout on top plate improved, some w/Ostketten, later production w/skirts, cupola and ball mounted mg on left front plate, 19' × 9' 4½" × 8'.

▼ 185

PzKpfwIV fuer Zwei 7.5cm Rueckstossfreie Kanonen und 3cm MK, 3cm gun centre in open rear shield, recoilless rifle each side, 3 variations, intended as tank destroyer, mock-ups only.

FlakPzIV (Möbelwagen) (FlakPzIV (2cm Flakvierling) auf Fgst PzKpfwIV), 1943, drop sides.

FlakPzIV 3.7cm Flak43 (Möbelwagen), 1943, flat sides drop down to form platform, exposing gun w/3-sided shield.

FlakPzIV 2cm (FlakPzIV (2cm) mit PzFgstPzIV/3) (Wirbelwind, whirlwind), 1943, quadruple 2cm Flak in octagonal open top turret, 19' 5" × 9' 6" × 9' ½".

FlakPzIV (Ostwind, east wind) (Leichter Flakpanzer mit 3.7cm Flak43 auf PzKpfwIV Ausf J), 1944, 3.7cm gun in rotating diamond turret on PzKpfw Ausf J, 19' 6" × 9' 6" × 10' 2".

FlakPzIV MK103 Zwilling (dual) (Kugelblitz) (le FlakPzIV 3cm) (Vs Kfz604/4), dual 3cm MK103/38 in hemispherical turret.

FlakPzIV (OstwindII), 3.7cm Flakzwilling 44, project only.

FlakPzIV 3.7cm Flakzwilling 43, project only.

FlakPzIII/IV Kugelblitz, dome turret, project only.

Zerstoerer 45 (destroyer), 3cm Flakvierling 103/38, quadruple gun on PzKpfwIV chassis, project only.

PzKpfwIII/IV, prototype completed as a tank, PzKpfwII turret w/5cm L/42, components of both PzKpfwIII and IV, 6 bogie overlapping suspension (FAMO).

▼ 186

PzKpfwIV mit Waffe 0725, weapon moved slightly forward from location in experimental PzKpfwIII model w/same gun.

Lastentraeger 604/14 fuer 30.5cm Moerser (Geraet 565), project.

FlakPzWg 604/17 3.7cm Flak 43/1, project.

StuPzWg 604/16, sIG on PzKpfwIV w/special drive, project.

StuGIV fuer 7.5cm StuK40, project.

PzKpfwIV Ausf X, project.

StuG43 auf FgstPzIV 7.5cm L/70, Alkett project.

StuG43 auf FgstPzIV 10.5cm StuH42/2, Alkett project.

PzWg 604/9 (Alte Benennung PzWgIV Lang (A) 7.5cm Pak 43), project.

PzWg 604/10 (Geraet 21-559) (Alte Benennung PzWgIV Lang (V) 7.5cm Pak 43), diesel engine, project dropped, replaced by VsKfz 604/11.

PzWg 604/11, similar.

PzWg 604/15 (Geraet 561), details unknown.

GWIII/IV fuer le FH18/40/2 (Sf) (Geraet 804), project.

GWIII/IV fuer sFH18/1 (Sf) (Geraet 807), project.

GWIII/IV fuer sFH18/3 (Sf) (Geraet 812), project.

7.5cm L/48 PzJaegIII/IV auf FgstPzIV (Geraet 821), project.

Einheitsfahrzeug III/IV als PzKpfw (Geraet 824), Krupp Gruson, project.

PzKpfwIV fuer Raketenwerfer, small box cupola substituted for turret, 4 tube box projector rear mounted.

LePzJaegIII/IV, project only.

PANTHER CHASSIS AND VARIATIONS

SdKfz171 (PzKpfw Panther Ausf D) (PzKpfwV Ausf D2), 1942, sharply inclined glacis w/small flap opening on right for bow mg, driver's vision port on left of glacis, 80mm frontal armour, 7.5cm KwK42 L/70, originally w/ball-shaped muzzle brake, later double baffle muzzle brake, commander's cupola moved to right, eliminating bulge, later modified w/periscope ring, side plate extended down vertically in rear, exhaust pipes differed in the various Panther models, 22' 6½" (28' 4") × 10' 8½" (11' 3" w/skirts) × 9' 9".

SdKfz171 (PzKpfw Panther Ausf A) (PzKpfwV Ausf D1) (Panther Ausf E), 1943, ball mounted bow mg, early Pak75 L/70, ZF7 transmission, long sloping back track-guards, cupola bulge in turret side, 60mm front armour, otherwise similar to Ausf D, 22' 7" (28' 4") × 10' 8½" × 10' 2".

SdKfz171 (PzKpfw Panther Ausf G), thicker sloped side plates w/o vertical drop at rear, ball-mounted bow mg but no driver's vision port in glacis, later w/steel tyred bogie wheels, cooling improved, 22' 7" (28' 6") × 11' 3" × 9' 10".

PzKpfw Panther Ausf B, intended for Maybach-Olvar transmission but not built.

Panther II (PzKpfwV 7.5cm KwK44/1 L/100) (PzKpfw Panther Prototyp Ausf F), much thicker

armour, new ultra long gun, small turret w/saukopf mantlet, range-finder, gyrostabilizer, not completed.

PzKpfw Panther Ausf C, probably design study.

PzBeobWg Panther, two-way tapered dummy cannon in large mantlet, mg in ball mount right of gun, artillery observation vehicle converted from Ausf D, 22' 7" × 11' 3" × 9' 9".

Panther mit Nachtzielgeraet (night operating equipment), experimental IR device.

▼ 187

Panther H-1, Panther Ausf G w/clear glacis and Tiger B suspension.

SdKfz173s (8.8cm Pak 43/3 auf PzJaeg Panther (Jagdpanther V) (Jagdpanther fuer 8.8cm Pak43/3 L/71)), 1944, non-rotating superstructure, swept back hull, gun in glacis, cast mantlet, ball mount mg right of gun, variations in gun mount and top layout, 21' 10' (27' 10") × 10' 10" (11' 2" w/skirts) × 9' 4½".

SdKfz179 (Berge Pz Panther Ausf A) (Bergepanther), 1944, winch equipment in flat box top w/drop sides, large trail spade, see also VK3002MAN, 26' 9" (29' 1") × 10' 8½" (11' 2½") × 12' 1½".

Muni Pz Panther, similar but w/o winch and trail spade, converted from Ausf D.

Panzer Schlepper Panther, same but 1 less bogie, project only.

Panther fuer 8.8cm KwK43 L/71, project only.

Raumschaufel Pz Panther, Panther w/bulldozer, project only.

Minenraeumpanzer Panther, mine exploder vehicle, project only.

FlakPz fuer Schwere Flak (8.8cm Flak auf Sonderfahrgestell (prototyp)), only vehicle of Grille series to be completed, 8.8cm Pak41 w/small shield, box hull w/drop sides, first armed w/8.8cm Flak 18, 17' 7" (22' 11½") × 10' × 9' 2".

PzBefWg Panther, command vehicle, main armament retained, differing wireless sets.

Flak Pz Panther 8.8cm Flak41, gun in open top rotating turret, project only.

Flak Pz 'Coelian', Panther chassis w/3.7cm in Flakzw341 partly recessed rotating turret.

Gef Aufkl, Gefecht Aufklaerungs Fahrzeug Panther, combat reconnaissance vehicle, 5cm KwK39 L/60 in small turret, project later dropped.

Geraet 5–1211 (12.8cm K43 (Sfl) (Kpl) (Grille 15)), 1943, 12.8cm L/51 gun mounted at rear of Panther chassis, project only.

Geraet 5–1530 (sFH43 (Sfl) RhB) (Skorpion 15), 15cm FH L/32.5, 42 tons, large bevel-sided gun compartment mounted well back.

Panther Waffentraeger (weapon carrier), open bed hull, U-frame w/double A-frame in front box, 1 bogie wheel less, see Panther Schlepper Panzer.

PzJaeg Panther 12.8cm Pak80 L/55, hull built upon rear half of chassis, project only.

GW Panther fuer sFH18/4(Sf), project.

Panther mit HL230 bzw 254, MAN project.

Berge Panther Ausf F, project.

PzJaeg Mg605/4 8.8cm Pak 43/7 L/71, project.

PzMg605/5, project.

TIGER CHASSIS AND VARIATIONS

SdKfz181 (PzKpfw Tiger Ausf E) (Tiger I), 8.8cm KwK L/56, overlapping bogie wheels, originally concave and later flat studded, narrower tracks provided for rail transport, wide tracks for action, mg right glacis, turret had slight forward bevel, cupola later changed, 20' 8½" (28' 1½") × 12' 3" × 9' 4½".

SdKfz182 (PzKpfw Tiger II) (PzKpfw Tiger Ausf B), turret from VK4502(P), 8.8cm KwK L/71, first used w/mantlet and left side bulge for cupola, later w/saukopf and straight side plate w/cupola on top, steel tyred overlapping bogie wheels, narrow tracks for rail transport, 23' 9" (33' 8") × 12' 3½" × 10' 1½".

Tiger II fuer KwK L/68 (PzKpfw Tiger mit 10.5cm KwK L/68), larger gun, project only, 22' 3½" (35' 9") × 10' 1" × 10'.

SdKfz183 (PzBefWgIV) (PzBefWg Tiger), command tank.

SdKfz184s (Tiger P) (PzJaeg Tiger P) (PzJaeg Tiger (P) fuer 8.8cm Pak43/2 L/71) (Ferdinand), derived from VK4501, originally w/o bow mg but later added, later called Elefant, 22" 3½" (26' 8") × 11' 3" × 9' 10".

SdKfz185 (Berge Pz Tiger E), turret w/mantlet closed and crane

mounted on turret, 20′ 8″ × 11′ 7″ × 9′

188

Berge Pz Tiger (P) (Berge Pz Ferdinand), low flat pyramidal turret w/mg at rear, converted from VK4501(P).

Tiger H-2, mock-up, see VK4501H.

SdKfz186 (PzJaeg Tiger fuer 12.8cm Pak44 L/55) (Jagdtiger Ausf B), gun w/o muzzle brake mounted centre in sloping back box hull, overlapping bogies, 2 versions, the Henschel w/individual torsion bars as on Tiger II, the Porsche w/wider spaced bogie pairs, 25′ 7″ × 11′ 8½″ × 9′ 3½″.

SdKfz186s (PzJaeg Tiger fuer 12.8cm Pak80 L/55) (Jagdtiger), same as above w/different gun, some w/8.8cm Pak43/3, one experimentally w/modified engine compartment for 16 cylinder engine, 24′ 8″ (34′ 11½″) × 9′ 11″ × 9′ 8″.

Tiger fuer Moerser (R) (38cm RW61 auf StuM Tiger), 1944, sloped front plate mounting ex-naval anti-sub gun, later Tiger E suspension w/steel tyred bogie wheels, 20′ 8½″ × 12′ 3″ × 11′ 4″.

Tiger Jaeger 12.8cm L/66 (Jaegtiger fuer 12.8cm L/66), large turret set forward, gun tube retractable for travel, hull built up behind turret, project only, 21′ (37′ 3″) × 12′ × 9′ 4″.

189

10.5cm le FH43 L/68 Koenigstiger (Kingtiger), wide low glacis, flat-sided conical turret open in rear, mock-up only.

Geraet 5–1702 (17cm K43 (Sfl)) (Grille 17/21) (GWVI), Tiger basis project.

Geraet 5–2107 (21cm M18 (Sfl)) (Grille 17/21), Tiger basis project, identical chassis, swept back gun housing, huge sloped sides, mg in low glacis, not completed, 31′ 2″ (42′ 8″) × 10′ 4″ × 10′ 4″.

PzKpfw Tiger Ausf F, project only.

GW Tiger fuer 17cm K72 (Sf), project only.

GW Tiger fuer 21cm Mrs18/1 (Sf), project only on Elefant.

Stu Mrs Mg606/4, project.

GW fuer 30.5cm GrW Sfl (VsKfz606/9), project only.

24cm K4Sf, 1942, long 24cm gun mounted on a well frame suspended between 2 unarmoured Tiger E chassis, project only.

MISCELLANEOUS VEHICLES

SdKfz253 (le gp Beob Kw), 1936, hull similar to hull portion of halftrack, no turret, wireless rail antenna, 15′ 5″ × 6′ 5″ × 5′ 11″.

SdKfz254 (m gp Beob Kw auf RK7) (RR7), Saurer wheel-and-track command and reconnaissance vehicle w/bogie rail, see Austria.

RR7/1, similar, w/o bogie rail.

RR7/2, no details available.

RR8 (PzSpMg RK Ausf A), improved version w/rotating turret.

SdKfz265 (klPzBef Wg PzI, Klein Panzer Befehl Wagen, small armoured command vehicle), several varieties on SdKfz101 chassis as follows: 1k1A, 8-sided non-rotating turret offset to right on SdKfz101 Ausf A, no weapons, buggy-whip antenna on arm jutting out from right side rear of hull, double inverted-U antenna on right front mudguard; 2k1A, resembled British Carden-Loyd Mark VI carrier but larger, on SdKfz101 Ausf A chassis, rail wireless antenna; and 3k1B, on SdKfz101 Ausf B chassis, box hull, originally inside mantlet mg right front, and split hatch cover but no cupola, later w/flat-sided flare top cupola or flare bottom flat-sided cupola and ball mounting mg, wireless mast right rear of hull pivoted to raise from inside, some later w/auxiliary armour plates, 1 seen w/F/T in place of mg, rail wireless antenna, all about 14′ 6″ × 6′ 9″ × 6′ 5″.

190

SdKfz266 (PzBefWgIII Ausf D1) (3c/ZW) (Grossen PzBefWg, large armoured command vehicle), dummy gun.

Wireless differences were: SdKfz266, Fu2 and Fu6; SdKfz267, Fu5 and Fu8, this designation also applied

to Panther D, A, G, PzBef and Tiger PzBef Ausf E w/these wirelesses, and SdKfz268, Fu5 and Fu7, this designation also applied to Panther and Tiger command tanks as above.

191

SdKfz266, 267, 268 also included PzBefWgIII Ausf E (4a/ZW) formerly Ausf B, Ausf H (7a/ZW) and Ausf K (8a/ZW), some w/skirts and supplementary armour, dummy gun except on Ausf H which had 3.7cm KwK L/45, at least 1 vehicle in North Africa had large observation scope on right of mantlet, 18′ 1½″ × 9′ 8″ × 8′ 2½″.

SdKfz300 (B1 Spst) (Sprengstoff-traeger, explosives carrier), Borgward built, concrete box hull, 3 bogie wheels, also used as mine exploder pulling small serrated rollers, muffler left rear side, cable-controlled.

B2Spst, similar but w/4 spoked bogie wheels, 1 support roller, 3 tons, high hull, stubby glacis, higher HP, wireless-controlled.

B3Spst, similar to B2 but 5 spoked bogie wheels, charge carried on sloping glacis, steel hull, Borgward engine, 11′ 11½″ × 5′ 11″ × 3′ 10½″.

SdKfz301 B4a Spst (Grabenwolf), resembled B3, hull a little higher rear half, Zuendapp engine, steel hull, antenna behind driver, driver right, rubber pad track.

SdKfz301 (B4b Spst), similar, 11′ 11½″ × 5′ 11½″ × 4′ 6″.

SdKfz301 (B4c), wireless-controlled, small folding square turret for driver left centre, Borgward engine, 4 tons, turret slightly recessed, rear of hull overhung and undercut, 4 spoked bogie wheels, 13′ 5½″ × 6′ × 4′ 1″.

SdKfz301 (B4d), same but turret not recessed.

SdKfz301 (Borgward-Schlepper), 1942, ammunition carrier.

SdKfz302 (E Motor) (B1a), tiny .25 ton skeleton chassis explosive carrier, 4 disc bogie wheels, Type A w/flat top and 3 support rollers, Type B w/raised air scoop and 2 support rollers, 4′ 11″ × 2′ 9½″ × 1′ 10″.

SdKfz303 (V Motor) B1b (Funklen Pz, wireless controlled tank) (le Fe Lad Tr Goliath, light remote load carrier Goliath), three versions: B1, resembled tiny WWI British heavy tank, cable controlled; B2, same but wireless controlled; and B3, experimental, either type of control, 5′ 4″ × 3′ × 2′ ½″.

B4c Raketenwerfer (Kleinpanzer Wanze, small armoured bedbug), small rocket projector on B4c chassis, 13′ 5½″ × 6′ × 4′.

B4b Flak (Zerstoerer 45 destroyer, 3.7cm Flak43Zw, 3cm Flak MK103/38 or 2cm MKA/A guns mounted on B4b.

Ente (duck), amphibian remote-controlled explosives carrier, 4 disc type bogie wheels, rounded hull edges, 1 screw, 2 rudders, small round turret.

SdKfz304 (le Fe Lad Tr) (NSU Sprenger), more sophisticated explosives carrier, long sloping glacis, undercut rear, overlapping bogie wheels, 3 tons, 10′ 4″ × 4′ 8½″ × 4′ 9″.

SdKfz311 (le Fe Lad Tr) (Graeben-wolf), similar to SdKfz304 but skirted, folding 3-sided shield in rear for driver.

5cm Pak38 L/60 auf SdKfz301 (PzSfl 1a), gun w/large rear mounted faceted shield open top and rear, tubular trail spade, miniature SP.

10.5cm RSF auf Borgward (SdKfz301

fuer 10.5cm Rueckstossfreirohr, recoilless rifle), 2 mock-up types.

Pz Geraet 13, 1945, B4b w/thick armour, small PzKpfwII type turret w/small cannon, 3 smoke mortars on right of hull front super-structure, may possibly be the Lilliput panzer.

RSO (Raupen Schlepper Ost, Tracked Carrier East) Waffentraeger, 1942, original cargo type w/rounded bow and drop sides, no armour, portée for 10.5cm type 42 mountain howitzer w/o wheels.

RSO Waffentraeger V4, flat bow, carried wheeled Pak40.

RSO Waffentraeger, armoured cab, carried wheeled 15cm sIG33.

RSO Waffentraeger, armoured cab, carried wheeled 10.5cm type 42 mountain howitzer.

RSO (Raupen Schlepper Ost), standard Steyr supply tractor w/armoured cab having long glacis, /.01 suffix for petrol power, /.03 for diesel power, at least 1 experimental arrangement of a front cab and a wooden box connecting 2 units to an infantry carrier for 100 men.

Wf Schlepper Ost fuer 7.5cm Pak40 L/46, armoured bow, small gun shield, 14′ 6″ × 6′ 7″ × 6′ 2″.

Wirbelwind II (Steyr Fgst), 3.7cm Flak 44 on Ost chassis.

le FH43 L/30 (Sfl) Skoda (Geraet FH43 (Skoda)), 1943, Czech T25 chassis w/large bevel sided turret as AA/AT vehicle, project only, 19′ 9½″ (23′ 5″) × 9′ ½″ × 10′ 3″.

le Waffentraeger, 1944, 10.5cm le FH18/40 L/28 on low chassis, 4 large bogie wheels, 1 support roller, gun rear in swept-back rhomboidal rotating turret, gun demountable to wheels and trail, 21′ 1″ × 10′ 4½″ × 7′ 4½″.

M Waffentraeger, similar for 10.5cm le FH18/40, 20′ 2″ × 10′ 4½″ × 8′ 7″.

Einheitswaffentraeger (common chassis weapons carrier), 1944, similar but 6 large road wheels, 2 support rollers and spade, 10.5cm le FH18/40 L/28 or sFH18 L/29.5 or 8.8cm Pjk43 L/71, w/shield, project only, 22′ 2″ × 10′ 4½″ × 7′ 4½″.

Einheitswaffentraeger, similar for 12.8cm K81 L/55 or 15cm sFH18 L/29.5, 6 road wheels, 2 support rollers, project only, 28′ 5½″ (34′ 2½″) × 10′ 4½″ × 7′ 6½″.

WKH Geraet040 (Eva) (Karlgeraet), 1941, 54cm mortar on huge 11 bogie wheel 6 support roller chassis, transported on special railway carriage, 36′ 6″ × 10′ 4½″ × 15′ 8″.

WKH Geraet041 (Thorgeraet), same but 61cm mortar.

Karlgeraet II, 61cm mortar on modified chassis, suspension changed w/bogie crank arms on rail, 37′ 4″ × 10′ 4½″ × 15′ 8″.

24cm K 4 Sf, 1942, long 24cm gun on chassis like Geraet 040 but 1 less bogie wheel per side, project only by Rheinmetall-Borsig.

R1, 15cm coast defence gun on large tracked chassis, German Navy vehicle.

R2, 28cm coast defence gun on large tracked chassis, German Navy vehicle.

R3–R14, 15cm to 38cm guns on tracked chassis, German Navy vehicles.

E5, 1944, various uses intended, 6 tons, Belleville washer suspension, no evidence of completion.

E10, similar but 12 tons, various uses intended, no evidence of completion, suspension reportedly controllable.

E25 (Argus), 28 tons, various uses intended.

E25 (Porsche) (Porsche typ 245) (E2201) (le gp Mehrzweckfahrzeug, light armoured multiple use vehicle) (SdFzV), 5.5cm MK, 1 mg low in front, light reconnaissance or SP, project only, 16′ 1″ × 8′ 5″ × 5′ 8½″.

E25 (Alra), no details.

SdFzVI (Porsche Typ 250), hydraulic transmission project.

SdFzVI (Porsche Typ 255), mechanical transmission project.

E50, light tank to replace Panther, 55 tons, project.

E75, medium tank to replace Tiger, 80 tons, project.

E100, heavy tank, about 140 tons, appearance about like Tiger II, almost completed but turret not installed because it did not fit, 28′ 8″ (33′ 8″) × 14′ 8½″ × 10′ 10½″.

SdFzIV (Porsche Typ 205) (Maus I) (Mammut), 1943, huge skirted suspension vehicle w/dummy box turret, later w/conventional turret, 2 vehicles completed but blown up

to avoid capture in 1945, intended
for 12.8cm KwK82 L/55 and 7.5cm
KwK44 L/36.5 coaxial, later for
15cm KwK44 L/38 and 7.5cm
KwK44 L/36.5 coaxial, 206 tons,
33′ (41′ 6″) × 10′ 1″ × 11′ 11″.

Maus II, project only, 29′ 7″ (33′ 1″)
× 12′ ½″ × 12′.

*CAPTURED FOREIGN VEHICLES
AND VARIATIONS EXCEPT
LORRAINE TRACTOR AND
CZECH 38(t).*

19.4cm Kanone 485 (f), GPF,
standard French Schneider SP.

Infanterie Schlepper UE(f) fuer 28cm
Wurframmen UE(f) fuer RW,
French Chenilette w/dual 28cm
rocket projector mounted above
cargo body.

gp Muni Schl UE 630(f), French UE
Chenilette carrier used w/tracked
trailer (Anhaenger UE 840(f)).

Muni Schl UE (f), fuer RW,
Chenilette w/rocket projectors
mounted on sides.

Mg Tr UE 630(f), bevel-sided cab
open at rear added to UE.

Mg auf UE 630(f), several types as
follows: large curved shield and
mg at rear; mg in enclosed shield
on right side, now in Musée de
l'Armée in Brussels; mg in
pyramidal cab on right side and
pyramidal shield centre rear, now
in Austrian Army Museum, Vienna;
and mg in pyramidal cab on right
side but rear cab on high box, now
in Tøjusmuseet, Copenhagen.

3.7cm Pak auf UE (f), gun w/shield.

le Traktor 630(r) le Muni Schl (r)),
Komsolometz tractor.

le Traktor 630(r) fuer 3.7cm Pak,
gun w/shield, field modification.

PzSpWgVCL701(b), Belgian T15 light
tank.

PzSpWgVM701(f), AMR Renault
1933 Type VM.

PzSpWgZTI-702(f), AMR Renault
1935 Type ZT.

Moersertraeger AMR(f), faceted hull,
closed top, round cupola left front,
small square cab right rear, also in
open top open rear variety, 81mm
mortar.

PzSpWgZTII-703(f) (2.5cm), standard
French vehicle, gun mounted on
right of hull.

PzSpWgAMR(f) (2cm), similar but
German gun.

PzKpfw17R oder 18R-730(f), French
Renault FT M1917 or M1918, some
w/modified mg mount, and
w/MG34 replacing Hotchkiss mg,
some as modernised 1937.

PzKpfw17R-730(j), same captured
from Yugoslavia.

PzKpfw35R-731(f), commander's
cupola modified w/split hatch
covers.

PzKpfw35R(f) (mg), large low flat-
sided cupola w/mg replacing turret,
a field modification.

Muni Pz35R(f), conversion to supply
vehicle.

4.7cm Pak(f) auf 35R(f), French gun
in special turret w/bustle, turret
base higher in front so as not to
obstruct driver's vision.

4.7cm Pak(t) auf 35R(f), same
w/Czech gun.

Moersertraeger 35R(f), modified to
mortar carrier, turret removed.

Traktor 35R(f), turret removed and
opening covered w/split cover.

3.7cm Pak(t) auf 39R(f), special
faceted turret w/bustle and Czech
gun.

3.7cm Pak(f) auf 39R(f), similar
w/French gun.

PzKpfwFT731(h), Dutch Renault FT
w/MG34 replacing Hotchkiss mg.

gpMG Traeger Br732(e), British
carrier.

3.7cm Pak auf Fgst Bren (e), A/T
gun on British carrier.

gpMuni Schl Bren (e), British carrier
used for ammunition carrier.

Mun Schl fuer MG 08 (e), Maxim
mg pedestal mounted beside driver
on captured British carrier.

RSF Drilling auf Fgst Bren (e)
(Panzerjaeger Bren), triple recoilless rifle on Bren carrier.

leFe Lad Tr Bren (e), remote-
controlled explosives carrier made
from captured British carrier, also
used as remote-controlled supply
carrier.

Schneeschaufel auf Bren(e), 1
experimental model snow plough
on British carrier.

PzKwfwD-1 732(f), standard French
Char D1.

PzKpfw732(j), Yugoslav tank, Czech
SId.

PzKpfwD-2 733(f), standard French
Char D2.

PzKpfw35H-734(f), French 35H.

7.5cm Pak40 L/46 auf GW35H(f),
1942, similar to modified FCM but
on 35H chassis.

10.5cm le FH auf GW35H(f), similar.

PzKpfw39H 735(f), French 39H, some
w/tailpieces armoured over and
forming an extra fuel tank,
commander's cupola modified
w/split hatch covers.

10.5cm FH18 auf 39H(f), converted
to SP, 17′ 4″ × 6′ 1½″ × 6′ 10″.

7.5cm Pak40(f) auf GW39H)f),
French M1897 gun w/muzzle brake
on 39H, double bevel hull.

PzBefWg39H(f), converted to
command vehicle.

Muni Pz39H(f), converted to supply
vehicle.

Traktor 39H, similar.

PzKpfw39H mit turm SdKfz221,
German scout car turret substituted.

PzKpfw39H(f) mit 28cm Wurfrah-
men, 2 rocket projectors on each
side of hull.

PzKpfwZM736(f), captured French
40R light tank.

PzKpfwFCM737(f), French FCM
tank.

Moersertraeger 39H, 81mm mortar
carrier.

7.5cm Pak40 L/46 auf GW FCM(f), gun forward in bevel-sided faceted box on FCM chassis.

10.5cm le FH18 auf GW FCM(f), similar.

le PzKpfw737(r), Russian T26A light tank.

PzKpfwAMC738(f), French AMC35.

le PzKpfw738(r) Russian T26B light tank.

7.5cm Pak97/38(f) auf le PzKpfw738(r), French 75 on Russian T26 chassis.

PzKpfw35S 739(f), French Somua, turret modified w/split hatch covers.

FPzKjfw739(r), Russian OT26 flame-tank.

PzKpfwB1 bis 740(f), French Char B1 bis, some w/75mm gun in front plate removed and mg substituted, wireless mast moved forward, headroom increased above 75mm gun on all such captured tanks.

PzKpfwB1 bis Flamm (f), flame-gun substituted for bow-gun, vision visor added about F/T, F/T fuel tank added at rear.

10.5cm le FH auf Char B(f) (GW B2(f)), large front-mounted non-rotating turret and German howitzer substituted.

le PzKpfw740(r), Russian T26C light tank.

PzKpfw2C 741(f), French Char 2C.

le PzKpfw742(r), Russian Christie type BT7.

le PzKpfw Mark V(e) mit 10.5cm le FH16, British light tank w/German cannon replacing mgs.

Greuzer PzKpfwMKIV 744(e), British cruiser MKIV.

Kreuzer PzKpfwMKVI 746(e), British cruiser MKVI.

m PzKpfwM3 747(a), US M3 Medium.

m PzKpfw747(r), Russian T34, sometimes equipped w/PzKpfwIV cupola.

m PzKpfwM3A3(a), US M3A3 Medium.

m PzKpfwM4 748(a), US M4A1 Medium.

m PzKpfwM4A3 verst (a) US M4A3 Medium w/bow mg, and long supplementary glacis plate cover extending forward between horns.

200

Inf PzKpfwMKII 748(e) (SPzKpfw Matilda (e)), British Matilda.

4.7cm Pak181/183(f) auf SPzKpfw Matilda(e), flat chassis w/gun in centre, gun shield w/side wings, field modification.

Inf PzKpfwMGIII 749(e), British Valentines II and V.

SPzKpfw753(r), Russian KVI.

SPzKpfw754(r), Russian KVII w/15cm howitzer.

PzBefWg770(i), Italian L6/40 command tank w/o turret.

Sfl L6(i) (Semovente L6) (Semovente L40) (Semovente 47/32), see Italy.

mPzBefWg771(i), command tank w/o turret on Italian M13/40 and M14/41 chassis, 772(i) when on M42 chassis.

PzJaeg (Sfl) VA802(b), Belgian T14 SP.

RK PzKpfw KH70–945(tü), Czech KH50 type tank obtained from Turkey.

PzKpfw35(t) (LT35) (le PzKpfw Skoda Modell 35), Czech light tank.

PzSpWg 35(t), see Czechoslovakia.

201

Moerser Zugmittel 35(t) (Zug Kr Wg 35(t)) (Muni Pz 35(t)), Czech LT35 w/o turret, w/bows for tarpaulin cover, as mortar accompanying vehicle, 17′ 4½″ × 10′ 7″ × 4′ 11″.

le PzKpfwL6(i), standard Italian L6/40 light tank.

le PzKpfwL3/35(i), standard Italian tankette.

m PzKpfw 13/40(i), standard Italian Medium tank.

75/18 Sfl(i), standard Italian Semovente.

Sfl 122(r), Russian SU122.

12.8cm Pak auf SU152(r) German gun on Russian chassis.

SU85(r), Russian SP.

SU122(r), Russian SP, sometimes w/15cm sFH18 w/metal shield around recoil mechanism substituted for Russian gun.

SU152(r), Russian SP.

M PzKpfw Firefly(e), British Sherman w/17pdr.

202

Poche de la Rochelle, improvised SP on Schneider 19.4cm SP chassis, box hull bevelled inward, wide shield, 7.5cm Pak40.

POST WORLD WAR II VEHICLES

TT6–55, 1957, French APC w/4 disc road wheels, long glacis, small driver's cupola left front, small round turret behind it, prototype for SPz(Kurz), 13′ × 7′ 6″ × 6′ 1″.

SPz (Kurz) Transport (SPz Kurz 'Cargo') (Nachschub Pz CC–2) (SPz8), 1958, development of original French CC2–55 vehicle, 8 road wheels, long sloping glacis, 12′ 11½″ × 7′ 6½″ × 4′ 11″.

SPz (Kurz) Halbgruppe (Aufkl Pz) (SPz l), 1960, similar but 5 road wheels, 3 support rollers, spaced 2 and 1 from front, turret offset to left.

Kan Jaeg Pz mit 90mm Bord K (Kanonen Jagd Panzer), 2 built on SPzl chassis.

SPz (Kurz) Halbruppe/Funk (SPz1a) (SPz11–2), similar w/3 radios, 4′ 9½″ × 7′ 5½″ × 6′ 5½″.

SPz (Kutz) (SPz3), similar but turret offset to right, hull built up in rear, some w/recoilless rifle on top, horizontal louvers in sides near front, streamlined driver's cowl in glacis.

SPz3 Artillerie Beobachter (SPz 11-1 or SPz22–2), same chassis as above but closed top, 2 small cupolas w/mg on right cupola, no turret, 14′ 9½″ × 7′ 5½″ × 5′ 6″.

SPz (Kurz) Moerser (SPz1b) (SPz1b Panzermoerser 81mm) (SPz51–3), short APC as mortar carrier, 15′ 3½″ × 7′ 5½″ × 6′ ½″.

Spz Panzermoerser Leicht (SPz 52–3), 120mm mortar carrier.

Spaehpanzer mit 90mm Kanone (Spz1c), Spz Kurz chassis, 90mm cannon w/muzzle brake in low squat turret w/bustle, 15′ 3½″ × 7′ 5½″ × 6′ 9½″.

Spz4 KrKw (Krankenwagen, ambulance on HS30), 15′ 3½″ × 7′ 6″ × 6′.

AMX TT 12H, standard French APC but German welded turret on left w/20mm and 1mg, 15′ 10½″ × 8′ 1″ × 6′ 2″ (w/o turret).

SPW (Lang) (SPz 12–3) (SPz HS30) (Gruppe HS30), made in England by Leyland and in Germany by Hanomag and Henschel, 5 road wheels, 3 support rollers (2 front, 1 rear), bevelled hull sides, small conical turret on right w/20mm gun, later w/front bevel turret, some w/Wegman turret on left (similar but w/different mantlet), some w/single some w/double cluster smoke projectors in various positions on front glacis, some w/106mm recoilless rifles mounted at rear, 18′ 3″ (20′ 8″) × 8′ 4″ × 6′ 1″.

BeobPz HS30 (SPz Feuerleitpanzer 81–3), open top command vehicle, 3-sided shield in front, HS30 chassis.

SPz 21–3 Funkpanzer, similar as radio vehicle.

Sturmboote Traeger HS30, assault boat carrier, 2 versions.

RakWr HS30 (RJ Pz2) (SPz Rak Werf Mehrfach Leicht), 1960, 2 converted from SPz Transport, large box multiple rocket launcher on rotating mount at rear of hull, 20′ 7½″ × 9′ 9½″ × 6′ 3″.

HS30 Jagdpanzer Rakete (JPz 3–3 Mit Abschuss und Lenkeinrichtung 164 fuer Landrakete SS11, or mount and control for SS11 missile (Raketenjagdpanzer HS30), several variations, some w/wide bank of smoke projectors behind centre hull drop, 21′ 1½″ × 9′ 10″ × 8′ 6½″.

m Pz Moerser Tampella, 8cm mortar on HS30.

m Pz Moerser (SPz 51–3) (SPz Mrs Trg 81mm), 1960, long glacis, higher hull, one built.

Pz Moerser 120mm Leicht (Moerser-traeger 120mm) (SPz Mrs Trg 120mm) (SPz 52–3) (Panzermoerser 120mm auf HS30), similar.

HS30 mit 90mm Bord K (DEFA) (KJPz4–5), gun in large cast mantlet in nose, 20′ 5½″ (28′ 8½″) × 9′ 10″ × 6′ 10″.

HS30 mit AN/TPS33 Radar, surveillance and reconnaissance vehicle.

HS30 mit Turm A14, pot-belly hull, faceted turret w/HS 20mm cannon on either side of turret.

Rak Pz HS30 (HS30 mit Oerlikon Rak Wr Zw, dual rocket projector) (RJPz2), 1960, 20′ 7½″ × 9′ 9½″ × 6′ 3″.

HS30/HOT, casemate missile mount on HS30.

RJPzHS30, 1970, TOW (PARS 2) missile projector on cylindrical turret replacing RH turret on standard SPz12–3 prototype.

RJPzHS30, 1971, TOW missile projector pedestal mounted on standard SPz12–3 prototype.

HMK12 Pirat (HMK12–01SPW), 1960, Swiss Pirat manufactured in FRG by Henschel, 5 bogie wheels and 4 support rollers, L-shaped louver centre of side hull, commercial project.

HMK12–02SPW (Sanitaet), similar as ambulance.

HWK10, Raketenwerfer, rocket launcher.

HWK11 Mannschaft Transport-fahrzeug, resembling US M113 but w/bevelled sides.

▼ 203
HWK12 PzJaeg mit 90mm Rueck-stossanner Kanone (Wiesel), bevelled turret w/90mm recoilless rifle.

HWK13 Aufklaerungswagen mit 20mm MK, small conical turret w/20mm.

HWK14 Funkwagen, radio vehicle, also Befehls (command) and Art BeobWg (artillery reconnaissance vehicle), 16′ 7″ × 8′ 3½″ × 6′ 9″.

HWK16, Sanitaetswagen, ambulance.

HWK Mit Rak Werf Mehrfach Leicht, large box-type multiple rocket launcher rear mounted.

RU121 (RU12/1) (SPz neu Prototyp 1 Transport), short glacis, 4 built on same chassis as RU122.

RU122 (SPz neu Prototyp 1 Gruppe) (Schuetzenpanzer Gruppe), 1962, resembled HS30, turret right front, 5 road wheels, 4 or 5 support rollers,, 4 built.

HK131 (SPz neu Prototyp 1) (Jagd PzKan) (Kan Pz mit 90mm Bord Kan) (Kanonen Jagd Panzer), 90mm Rheinmetall gun in large

oval front mantlet, flat top, small cupola, 19′ 10″ (27′ 6″) × 9′ 10″ × 6′ 6½″.

Jagd Pz Kan (RU131 Prototyp 2), same w/rear of hull top cut down, smoke mortar cluster behind cut, rear and sloped back, 20′ 5½″ (28′ 8½″) × 9′ 10″ × 6′ 6½″.

HM Prototyp 1 (Mowag), APC, 2 built.

Jagd Pz Kan, 1 built on HM chassis.

3M1 (Mowag 211) (SPz neu Prototyp 2), 1966, APC resembling HS30, 6 road wheels, 3 evenly spaced support rollers, 7 built.

Jagd Pz Kan, 7 built on Mowag 211 chassis.

Pz Moerser, mortar vehicle on Mowag 211 chassis.

▼ 204
RU221SPz Flak Zw (Flak zw SPW), 1960, turret rear w/dual 30mm gun, 5 road wheels, 3 support rollers (2 rear close together), 4 built, production vehicles were to be on Leopard chassis, 19′ 8½″ × 9′ 8″ × 8′ 1½″.

RU234 Jagd Pz Rak, rear of hull top cut down, 21′ 1½″ × 9′ 10″ × 6′ 6″.

RU242 (SP neu Prototyp 2 Rak Werf) Oerlikon multiple rocket launcher, flat top, long glacis and suspension as on RU221.

▼ 205
RU251 Spaeh Pz, 1966, light recon-naissance tank, 20′ 4½″ × 9′ 9″ × 8′ 10″.

RU262 (SPz neu Prototyp 2) (SPz neu Gruppe), 1964, APC, flat top, long glacis, HS30 type turret right centre, large and small side access hatches, 5 road wheels, 3 support rollers (2 front close together), 20′ 3″ × 9′ 6″ × 7′ 7½″.

Jagd Pz Rak (Raketen jagdpanzer neu 342), 1 built on RU361, 18′ 6½″ (21′ 1″) × 9′ 9″ × 6′ 6″.

SPz Mrs Trg 81mm, mortar vehicle RU262 basis.

Pz Mrs 120mm, mortar vehicle RU262 basis.

SPz Rak Werf, SS10 rocket launcher vehicle, 2 built on RU262 chassis (probably RU342 series).

Mowag R312 (Prototyp 3), resembled HS30, 6 road wheels, 3 evenly spaced support rollers, turret front, 1 built.

RU361 Prototyp 3 (3RU6), resembled RU262 but 6 road wheels and 3 evenly spaced support rollers, turret centre, small dome cupola and remote-controlled mg rear top deck.

Jagd Pz Rak (Raketenjagdpanzer neu), 6 built on RU361.

Jagd Pz Kan (Jagd Kan 90), 6 built on RU361, large oval mantlet in nose, gun from US M47 tank, coaxial mg, called 'idiot proof'.

RU362 Prototyp 3, similar to RU361 but squat 2 man front turret w/remote-controlled 20mm gun, 6 road wheels, 3 evenly spaced support rollers, 10 built.

RU363 Prototyp 3, almost identical to RU361 but w/pedestals for SS10 rockets beside turret, high all around periscope in glacis for commander, 1 built.

Marder (O-Serie3002), pre-production same as RU362 but higher turret w/remote-controlled 20mm gun above it, rear deck remote-controlled mg, 22' 3½" × 10' 7" × 9' 8".

System Rapier auf Spz (neu), 1970, British missile projector on Marder.

HK222 (2HK2/2) Krankenwagen, ambulance, flat top, high hull.

HK231 (2HK3/1) (SPz neu Prototyp 2 Jagd Pz Kan), rear of hull top cut down, rear of hull slopes forward slightly.

Jagd Pz Kan Serie (widder), pre-production SP, 2 step cut in rear top of hull, 20' 5" (28' 9") × 9' 9" × 6' 10".

2HK3 Jagd Pz Kan, similar.

Roland (Fla Rak Wr SPz neu) (RU243) (PARS 3) (SPz neu mit Roland Waffensystem), radar-controlled rocket projector on SPz neu.

Marder II mit Roland II, large turret, missile tube each side of turret, radar dish.

SPz (neu) mit PzAbw System HOT, separate loading SS11 type rocket projector on each side of top hull, tubes tilt for reload.

K3E fuer RJPz 2A41, Marder w/right rear telescoping HOT projector.

1p SchPz 8.8cm gun in welded faceted turret, 7 road wheels, 6 support rollers, mock-up only.

NOTE: Even within a given series not all of the above SPz (neu) vehicles were identical. Some were designed with the engine and transmission at rear, some at front, some centre and some separated, depending on the intended use and partially for the purpose of giving optimum performance.

SPW(MTW) M113 mit HS828 (called Scheunen-Tor, barn door, due to its high silhouette), 2 cm gun in turret on American M113 APC.

MTWM113 Moerser Traeger, M113 rebuilt to carry 120mm mortar.

MTWM113 mit 6 Rüstsätzen Unterwasserfahren, carrier for 6 tank snorkel sections, 4 on top and 2 inside.

M113G1 KrKw Gep, ambulance.

M113G2 KrKw Gep, similar.

SPW(MTW) M113 mit MK Turm, flat AA cupola on US M113 APC, variations exist.

SPW(MTW) M113 mit Radar, 1964, US M113 w/counter-mortar radar.

MTWM113 (I), 1965, US M113 chassis w/new hull built commercially for Israel.

MTWM113 mit Marder Turm.

MTWM113 mit Rheinmetall T5-9 Turm, Rh202 20mm gun.

MTWM113 mit Rheinmetall T5-10 Turm, similar.

MTWM113 mit Rheinmetall Konische Turm, 1965, 20mm gun in conical turret.

MTWM113 mit Oerlikon GBD B20 KBH B25, 25mm gun in special turret.

Flakpanzer MTWM113, US M113 w/1, 2 or three 20mm guns.

MTWM113 mit Dornier Kiebitz Radar Geraet

Radargeraet Art Aufkl auf SF gep, US M113 w/British Green Archer radar.

MTWM113/Milan (PARS 1), missile vehicle.

MTWM113 C+R mit Reuckstossfrei 106, Lynx w/106mm recoilless rifle.

SPWM113/HOT (RJPz M113 mit PARS 3 HOT), US M113 w/twin missile projector.

PzMrs M113 (M113A1G PzM), 1970, US M113 remodelled for 120mm Finnish Tampella mortar.

Daimler-Benz Typ 714 (Tata/ Porsche/Daimler-Benz), 1955,

resembled Russian T54 but Belleville washer suspension springs, design project only for India, 20' 4" (33' 5½") × 10' 6" × 9' 2½".

Leopard AI (Porsche 723), 1961, streamlined design, diesel engine, single track guides, torsion bar suspension, 3 evenly spaced support rollers, 7 bogie wheels w/first 6 pivoted rearward, rear 2 pivoted forward, flat glacis, narrow horizontal engine louvers in hull sides, turret bulge for cupola on right, single piece loader's hatch, long RhB 105mm gun w/o muzzle brake, rangefinder, V mantlet, British 105mm gun w/rangefinder installed later, 22' 9" (29' 11") × 10' 4" × 7' 2½".

Leopard AII, no rangefinder but ranging mg, more streamlined turret, vertical hull louvers in sides, driver's hatch on right, all road wheels pivoted rearward, 26' 11½" (31' 2") × 10' 8" × 7' 3".

Leopard BI, (Rheinstal Hanomag T/1), 1961, flat glacis, same turret as AI, RhB 105mm gun w/rangefinder, no muzzle brake, driver left front, 6 bogie wheels, variable hydro-pneumatic suspension, 3 support rollers, double track guides, later w/British 105mm.

▼ 206

Leopard (O-Serie) (Standardpanzer) (Porsche 814), limited production, stabilized 105mm gun, rangefinder, turret w/rounded rear, multi-fuel engine in sharply raised hull, 2 engine louvers on left side, torsion bar suspension, 7 bogie wheels, 3 evenly spaced support rollers, 8 prism viewers (not a cupola) on right only, IR light centre front of turret, 23' (30' 4") × 10' 8" × 7' 2½".

Leopard 1 Los Nr 1-4, production, IR light moved to left of turret, loader's vision viewer added, 2 front support rollers close together and spaced from centre and rear rollers, engine compartment hull top smoothed out, forward left side engine louver shortened and w/hinged cover, later production w/armour skirts and thermal sleeve on gun tube, vehicles sold to other countries had mg variations, Dutch version engine louvers continuous instead of in 4 columns, 22' 11" (31' 4") × 10' 8" × 7' 9".

Panzerhaubitze, Leopard chassis w/large bevel sided turret and

120mm howitzer, mock-up only, similar mock-ups for 13.5cm SP and multiple rocket launcher.

Bergepanzer Standard (Porsche 807), 1964, pilot, lie-flat solid frame hydraulic crane on pivot base recessed right front of hull, no turret, 23' 6" × 10' 8" × 8' 10".

Bergepanzer Standard (O–Serie), production, raised turret-like superstructure, dozer blade, driver left, spare engine carried on rear deck, crane frame w/5 slots.

207

Pionierpanzer, 1968, similar but equipped w/wider larger dozer blade w/optional rake, hedgerow prongs, earth borer on rear deck in place of spare engine, 25' 11" × 10' 8" × 8' 10½".

StuG90, 90mm SP on Leopard chassis, similar to JgdPzKan.

208

Pz Flak Leopard (SPz Fla Zw) (Leopard Matador) (Panzerflak 1), 1968, prototype by Rheinstahl, modified turret, dual 35mm guns w/hemispherical firing radar between and search radar on top of radar bulge, has enemy-friend detection device, 23' 10" × 10' 6" × 9' 8".

Pz Flak Leopard Prototyp Oerlikon, conical turret w/35mm Oerlikon guns mounted right and left sides, otherwise similar to Rheinstahl model.

PfzB, same, production model, cylindrical turret.

Fla Pz Leopard mit 35mm Zwilling Oerlikon-Contraves (Gepard) guns in split turret, production model, 26' 10" × 10' 8" × 8' 10½".

Brueckenleger Panzer, hydraulic scissors bridge on lengthened HS30

chassis, 7 road wheels, 3 return rollers (1 front, 2 rear), front outrigger pedestals, mock-up only.

Leopard Brueckenleger Typ A and Typ B, former has folding bridge resting on a long girder frame, bridge slides into place, latter is scissors-type bridge resting on fore and aft platforms.

Biber (Brueckenpanzer), production Typ A, bridge-layer, 33' 6" (37' 5") × 10' 8" (13' 1½") × 8' 4½" (11' 6").

Pionier Schnellbruecken MAN, 1971, light skeleton bridge on Leopard chassis.

Kampfpanzer 70 (Keiler, wild boar), test rig w/o superstructure, elevatable suspension, 6 small road wheels on crank arms, 3 support rollers, 22' 11½" × 11'6" × 6' 6½" (8' 6").

209

Kampfpanzer 70, similar w/turret and bow vane added, armed w/Shillelagh, 17 prototypes built.

Leopard A1 LOS Nr 1–4 (Leopard 1A1), 1972, stabilizer, scalloped skirts, thermal jacket and bow vane, tracks w/replacement pads, deep wading kit, changes to be retrofitted to all Leopards, 22' 8" (31' 2½") × 11' 1" × 8' 7".

Leopard A2 LOS Nr 5 (Leopard 1A2), same w/cast turret, hull louvers w/o vertical bars, improved NBC protection, night vision equipment.

210

Leopard A3 LOS Nr 5 (Leopard 1A3), 1973, automatic loader added, welded spaced armour turret shaped like that on US M41.

Leopard A4 LOS Nr 6, same w/new fire control equipment and higher stabilized commander's sight, 22' 8" (31' 2½") × 11' 1" × 8' 7".

Leopard 2, development of KpfPz 70, 120mm automatic smoothbore cannon, spaced armour, laser rangefinder, stabilizer, MBT70

power train, retractable IR and white light device, 25' 4" (32') × 11' 7½" × 8' 2".

MBT 80 (Leopard 3) (KPz3), hull similar to but flat top and lower than Leopard, smoothbore 120mm gun, 7 road wheels, 3 support rollers, Anglo-German project, turretless, similar to Swedish Strv103.

SP70, joint Anglo-German project, British turret and 155mm howitzer on German Leopard 3 chassis, 7 road wheels, 3 support rollers.

Mz Schwimmfahrzeug, 1968, tracklayer w/side floats to be lowered for swimming or to form a bridge-pontoon, to carry cargo, etc.

211

Leopard mit Französisch 155 GCT Turm (155 GCT Leopard), 1973, experimental mounting of French GCT 155 turret and gun on Leopard chassis, 23' (34' 6") × 10' 8" × 10' 3".

GREAT BRITAIN

When Germany attacked Belgium and France in 1914, Captain (later Rear-Admiral) Murray Sueter, commander of the Royal Naval Air Service, was ordered to establish air bases at Calais and Dunkirk. He convinced Winston Churchill, then First Lord of the Admiralty, that armoured cars would be of help in defending airfields and rescuing pilots forced down in enemy-held territory. These cars were formed into squadrons which later saw service in other roles on many fronts in Russia, Africa and the Middle East.

After a few months the war on the Western Front stabilized to a continuous trench line without flanks and dominated by barbed wire and machine-guns. Both sides developed the same kind of tactics: large-scale infantry assaults preceded by artillery bombardment. The pattern was usually the same and even when salients were formed the attacker's own flanks became exposed to counter-attacks of the same kind. Except for local successes, such tactics failed. This was because the defenders went underground during the bombardment and came out later to stop the infantry assault with machine-gun and rifle-fire, while the artillery preparation frequently destroyed the attacker's ability to sustain his advance because his artillery could not be brought forward over the ground it had made impassable.

Colonel (later Major-General Sir) Ernest Swinton, Assistant Secretary of the Committee of Imperial Defence, had seen American Holt tractors towing guns for the Royal Artillery in France and suggested to the authorities that such a track-laying vehicle with armour might be an antidote to the machine-gun and would immediately open up the war. It has almost been forgotten that the first practical track-layer was the Roberts-Hornsby, patented in England under No. 16345 in 1904. It was mentioned to Roberts in 1907 (by Major Donohue) that the arming and armouring of such a vehicle would have a military use. But no development took place, the tractor was not adopted by the British Army, and the patents were sold to the Holt Company in the United States in 1911.

Swinton's suggestion was shelved. But Captain Sueter and others in the R.N.A.S. came to a similar conclusion about what an armed and armoured track-laying vehicle could achieve. Through the enthusiastic support of Churchill, a Landships Committee was formed on 20 February 1915 under (later Sir) Eustace Tennyson D'Eyncourt, a prominent naval designer.

After Swinton learnt of these activities he again contacted Sir John French, Commander of the British Expeditionary Force, and with the help of an interested staff officer, Major Glyn, was authorized to establish contact with the Landships Committee on the army's behalf.

It was under the aegis of the Landships Committee that the first experimental tanks were built, including Mother, which was first run on 3 December 1915 in Lincoln at the factory of William Foster and Co. where it was built and which gave an official demonstration in Hatfield Park on 26 January 1916. Mother was the first tank with the familiar rhomoidal shape that is perpetuated to this day in the arm badge of the Royal Tank Regiment.

The Landships Committee now became the Tank Supply Committee under the Ministry of Munitions. Its chairman was an R.N.A.S. Lieutenant, Albert Stern, who had been secretary of the Landships Committee. The new committee was given the responsibility for producing the new weapon in quantity. Swinton was assigned the task of organising training for its employment.

Swinton devised tactics and principles which were eminently workable and which had to be changed but little after active service experience. The project was highly secret and to assist in keeping it so, the hulls of the vehicles were originally described as water carriers. Some of the early vehicles had painted on them Russian characters which announced that they were destined for 'Petrograd With Care'. Workmen referred to them as 'those tank things'. Having

heard of this, Swinton adopted the word 'tank' in order to continue the secret in succinct fashion. Today it is a word used, with slight variations in spelling, in almost every army in the world.

The original force in March 1916 was called Tank Detachment; then successively during the year Armoured Car Section Motor Machine-Gun Service, Heavy Section Machine-Gun Corps, Heavy Branch Machine-Gun Corps, and finally, in the summer of 1917, the Tank Corps.

By then tanks were beginning to be produced in quantity. The pioneers who established the tank mechanically included W. E. (later Sir William) Tritton, Major W. G. Wilson–a brilliant automotive engineer–and H. (later Sir Harry) Ricardo. But most of the credit for organizing this early production must go to Stern, a banker in civil life who was now a Lieutenant-Colonel and who was, as were so many of the pioneers, in due course to be knighted. In the course of establishing tank production, first through the Tank Supply Committee, then the Tank Supply Department, and finally the Mechanical Warfare Supply Department of the Ministry of Munitions, Stern had upset a number of important people. Swinton, too, had become unpopular and had been shuffled off on a liaison mission to the United States. By this time Churchill had weathered his political eclipse after the Dardanelles controversy and had returned from the trenches to become Minister of Munitions. He bowed to pressure, and Stern was given the job of negotiating an inter-allied tank treaty, which he did successfully and which resulted in the Mark VIII.

Initially in their use of tanks British commanders ignored Swinton's ground rules for their employment, and the results were so disappointing as to bring into question the whole value of the weapon. By the end of 1917 they had learnt a little better how to use tanks, and in 1918 Colonel (later Major-General) J. F. C. Fuller devised a plan to be used should the war go on into 1919. It envisaged the deployment of tanks in mass as well as fast independent armoured forces supported by aircraft and supply tractors breaking through to strike at German rear areas and headquarters.

During World War I the British built about 3,027 tanks of thirteen different Marks and variants and had thousands more on order, plus 20,000 Newton tractors for supply of which about 200 were built. At its peak the Tank Corps had twenty-five battalions, including one equipped with armoured cars.

Lieutenant-Colonel Philip Johnson who, toward the end of the war had designed the Medium D tank which had a speed three times that of any earlier tank, headed an experimental establishment, the Tank Design Department, for several years until it was closed in 1923. The vehicles from

this department changed all over the world the nature of tank design and the approach to that design. The technical advances that Johnson initiated made practicable a great deal of the advanced tactical employment of tanks that was being evolved in the writings of those whose concept of the army's role was that it should aim at strategic paralysis of the opposing force rather than its physical destruction. The idea of swiftly moving forces striking at the key centres of the enemy, such as had been propounded in 'Plan 1919', could become a reality only if the tanks had the technical capacity to carry it out.

Such reality was far in the future, and when it did materialize it did so through the blitzkrieg. In the meantime the revulsion from war and the severe post-war reduction of the British Army threatened the very existence of the Tank Corps. Not only were most of its battalions disbanded in 1919 but the question arose as to whether to abolish the Tank Corps altogether or make it a part of the Royal Air Force–the logic of this latter suggestion being that the R.A.F. needed armoured cars for ground defence. But the Tank Corps survived (receiving the 'Royal' prefix in October 1923), although its strength was reduced to five battalions and eleven armoured car companies; and Colonel Johnson retired to civil life to found the Roadless Traction Company where he could continue his work.

The types and numbers of tanks produced in Britain in the years between World Wars I and II were determined by two factors: first, shortage of money for defence; second, the army's role. This role had four facets in the following order of priority: (1) policing the Empire, (2) minor expeditions and guerrilla warfare, (3) major expeditions and (4) a most unlikely eventuality it was felt, a major war. The resultant of these factors as far as tanks were concerned was an emphasis on vehicles that were small and as cheap as possible to produce. This in turn caused an erosion of interest until the design and supply of tanks faded to almost nothing. The only civilian firm that remained in the field was Vickers-Armstrongs Ltd., without whose 'solitary and pioneering efforts', as the official historian of British War Production in World War II has described them, 'the country would have possessed no facilities for the design and development of armoured vehicles'. After Johnson's Department was closed in 1923 only the Royal Ordnance Factory at Woolwich did any tank work in Britain apart from Vickers. Even in 1936 the British Army had only 375 tanks of which 209 were light and the remaining 166 medium. All but two of the mediums were obsolete as were 140 of the light tanks. Throughout the inter-war years, right up until 1938, the accent in Britain was on tank development, not tank production.

After 'Plan 1919' General Fuller continued to write on the subject of tank warfare and fostered a naval approach to it with light tanks as destroyers protecting the main battle fleet. The naval analogy found expression later on when the word 'cruiser' was applied to the type of tank designed for independent mobile operations. Captain (later Sir) Basil Liddell Hart in 1924 added the concepts of tank marines, self-propelled artillery, tactical air support, night operations and 'vertical envelopment' as he conceived paratroops to be. Their imaginative writing encouraged tank enthusiasts in Britain and elsewhere, especially in Germany, but it also engendered a a great deal of opposition.

Major (later Lieutenant-General Sir) Gifford Le Q. Martel devised a small one-man tank which he built in his garden from commercial components, and Captain (later Sir) John Valentine Carden and Captain Vivian G. Loyd, who had a London garage, also built a small tank or tankette as a cheap way of being able to produce swarms of small armoured vehicles. The Carden-Loyds went through a protracted evolutionary process and after the firm had been taken over by Vickers-Armstrongs the design led both to light tanks and the machine-gun carriers used by Britain and many other countries. The light tank series went from the Mark I of 1930 to the Mark VII and VIII of 1941, but the hey-day of its development was the Mark VI and its variants (the VIa, VIb and VIc) in the immediate pre-war years.

The medium tanks in service in the 1920s and 30s, the Marks I, Ia and II, were designed and built by Vickers. Altogether some 200 Mediums I and II were produced. Despite the concentration on the lighter type of tank, one heavy tank was ordered by the War Office at the end of 1922. By November 1926 it was ready for trials. It was called the Independent and although it turned out to be only a 'one-off' and never went into production its importance rests on the influence it had on tank design throughout the world, not only on the medium tanks built in Britain from 1926 to 1937 but also in Russia, Germany and France which took a close interest in the tank and all designed vehicles which showed the source of their inspiration. Indeed a famous spy trial in Britain (the 'officer in the Tower' case) concerned the Independent.

In 1926 it was decided to replace the Medium Mark II. Three A6 tanks were built by Vickers in 1927 and '28 and from these came the Medium Mark III. Because of the high cost of the Mark III, however, only three were built and attention turned to finding a cheaper replacement. This 'Woolworth medium tank' was designed by Sir John Carden, who was now with Vickers; it saw action in World War II as the A9, the first 'cruiser' tank. At the same time the A10 tank was built to the same specification but with heavier armour. Its intended role was to be an 'I' tank, operating in close support of infantry. In the event, the A10 was finally classified as Cruiser Mark II, while the first 'I' tank was the A11, lamentably under-gunned with only a machine-gun for armament.

The cruiser series was developed throughout World War II, progressing from the A9 and A10 to the Cruiser Mark III, the A13, which itself had three Marks, designated as Cruisers Marks III, IV and V, the latter being the first of the cruisers to be named. It was called Covenanter, which reputedly had more ways of destroying its crew than it had potentiality for destroying the enemy. Almost simultaneously with Covenanter (which never saw action) came Cruiser Mark VI, called Crusader. Both Covenanter and Crusader were produced in several Marks. All these cruisers after the A10 had Christie suspension.

Following Crusader came Cavalier, and then the Cruiser Mark VIII; with a Liberty engine it was called Centaur, with a Meteor engine it was called Cromwell. Both Centaur and Cromwell each had several Marks. Finally came Comet, the last of the cruiser line; for although Comet's successor, Centurion, was designed as a cruiser, by the time it went into production in 1945 the concept of two types of tank, cruiser and 'I' tank, had given way to the idea of a single multi-purpose 'capital' tank, later called a main battle tank.

The 'I' tank line which was started with A11 went on through the A12 Matilda, to the Infantry Tank Mark III Valentine and the 'I' Tank Mark IV Churchill. Matilda, Valentine and Churchill were all produced in several Marks and in considerable quantity. Output of A11s was 140, of A12 Matildas 2,987, of Valentines 8,275 (of which 1,420 were built in Canada) by far the greatest number produced of any British tank and of Churchills 5,640: a grand total of some 17,000 'I' tanks. Compared with this, output of cruiser tanks was a little over 9,000.

Before jumping to any conclusions in comparing the outputs of cruiser and 'I' tanks it must be borne in mind that from 1943 until the end of the war the most widely used tank in the British and Commonwealth armies was neither British built nor British designed. The tank which equipped the British, Canadian, New Zealand and South African armoured divisions in the latter years of the war was the American Sherman. In the 21st Army Group, in the North-west Europe campaign in 1944, there were thirty-two Sherman-equipped armoured regiments (American battalion size) compared with twelve Churchill and nine Cromwell units. And in Italy the proportion of Shermans was even higher. Nor were the Shermans the first American tanks to equip British units. Both American M3 Lights (known to the British as Stuarts or Honeys) and M3 Mediums (known as Grants or Lees) played a vital part in British armoured fighting before the Shermans arrived on the scene.

The British armoured divisions originated in the Experimental Mechanized Force of 1927, renamed in the following year as the Experimental Armoured Force–a change of title, wrote Liddell Hart, which 'expressed an aspiration rather than any change in reality'. Despite its inadequacies this was nevertheless the first armoured formation in the world. But it was not blessed by the War Office with permanence. Off and on for the next few years it appeared and disappeared, in one form or another. Then in 1934 four battalions of the Royal Tank Corps were permanently brigaded under Brigadier (later Major-General Sir) Percy Hobart. This was the foundation of the 1st Armoured Division which eventually emerged, after many vicissitudes, under that name in 1938. By that time, it is worth noticing, the Germans, who in 1934 had had only one tank battalion as against the British tank brigade, now had four panzer divisions. Meanwhile, the French had not decided that the tank was a supporting arm for infantry, the British were unable to decide whether the tank was a supporting or a primary arm and were consequently having a poor each way bet on 'I' tanks for support and cruisers for exploitation (with a side bet on light tanks because they were cheap); the Germans, under Hitler, had decided that the tank was the queen of the battlefield and that, as Guderian wrote, 'what was needed were armoured divisions which would include all the supporting arms needed to allow the tanks to fight with full effect'. The Germans were proved right.

Not only in Poland but in the campaign against Belgium and France the panzer divisions showed that the power of the tank was to cut its way through the opposition and that far from the tank supporting infantry it was the infantry that should support the tank. After Dunkirk the words 'panzer divisions', wrote the historian of the British 11th Armoured Division, 'assumed a near-mystical significance. We had to have armoured divisions'. At that time (June 1940) there were only two in existence: the 2nd in England and the 7th in Egypt. Both were under strength. The 1st Armoured Division was lying wrecked by the roadside in France. A daunting prospect–but the decision was taken to increase the number of armoured divisions to ten by September 1941. This was achieved although some were armoured divisions in name only, and were under-equipped and partially-trained. It was not until July 1942 that the first of the newly formed divisions went into action. By that time the organization of the division had been changed. One of the two armoured brigades was removed and replaced by an infantry brigade, while the division's artillery was increased. The day of unsupported armour–had it ever existed–was over.

As well as these new armoured divisions a number of tank brigades were formed whose task was the close support of infantry. At the maximum in 1942-43 there was a total of twenty-nine armoured and tank brigades in the British Army. In addition there were another twenty armoured and tank brigades in the armies of the Commonwealth countries.

Although the two tank roles of infantry support and independent operations became an outmoded philosophy before the end of World War II, there was still a kick left in the idea that the fully all-purpose tank was impossible. The outcome of this kick was the heavy gun Conqueror which, after a somewhat bizarre history of several intended roles, finally saw service for ten years until 1966 as a tank whose role was to destroy the enemy's heavy tanks at ranges which were beyond the capability of Centurion.

No doubt it was a reaction against the continual under-gunning of British tanks during the war–with the exception of the 17pdr Sherman Firefly–that gave rise to the Conqueror with its 120mm gun. And this reaction, if reaction it be, is continued in Britain's main battle tank of today, Chieftain, which mounts a 120mm gun as its main armament.

Over and above this it must also be mentioned that the 105mm gun mounted in Centurion is the British-built gun which has been adopted by West Germany for Leopard and by the United States for its main battle tanks. This is a far cry indeed from the machine-gun of the first 'I' tank in World War II and the terrible decimation that resulted from under-gunned British tanks throughout that war, let alone the abysmal misconceptions in the minds of some higher commanders as to how armour should be employed.

WORLD WAR I AND IMMEDIATE POST-WAR

Hetherington Big Wheel Machine, 1915, mock-up only, not completed.

Sueter Pedrail, 1915, 2 Pedrail machines articulated with centre turret, project only, 36′ × 12′ 6″ × 7′ 3″ (10′ 6″ overall).

Pedrail Machine, 1915, articulated chassis built, several hull forms projected, eventually completed for Trench Warfare Department with rigid chassis as flame-throwing vehicle, not used in service, 40′ × 13′ × 8′ 6″.

Killen-Strait Machine (Armoured), 1915, Delaunay-Belleville armoured car hull on 3 track American Strait's tractor chassis.

Greenhithe Machine (Hope Tractor) (Bullock Creeping Grip Machine), 1915, agricultural track-layer w/2 front steering wheels, not armoured.

▼ 212

Creeping Grip Tractor With Elephant Feet, 1915, 3 suspended log tamps on either side acting as pole vaults to overcome bellying, not armoured.

Tritton's Trench Crossing Machine, 1915, Foster steam tractor w/15′ girders to be paid down and picked up, not armoured.

Foster Trench Crossing Tractor, later design study, 60′ × 10′ × 15′.

MacFie Vehicle, model only but inventor claimed origin of track frame shape later adopted.

Nesfield Vehicle, model only, similar to MacFie vehicle.

Wheelock Armoured Tractor, American design study only, inventor claimed origin of track frame shape later adopted.

De Mole Vehicle, Australian, 1912 model resubmitted, appearance almost identical to later heavy tanks but no sponsons, approx. 37′ × 13′ × 9′.

Crompton Vehicle (ED1; Emplacement Destroyer), 1915, hull like French St Chamond tank on modified Pedrail Machine, 2 sets of Killen-Strait tracks in tandem, 4.5″ howitzer, model only, ED1a was to carry two 4.5″ howitzers, ED2 and ED3 were planned also but no details are available.

Bullock Track Machine, 1915, armoured box with small turret and dummy gun on track-laying chassis w/2 iron steering wheels in rear.

▼ 213

Little Willie, 1915, redesign of Bullock Track Machine but turret not completed, track frames like those on later Medium Mark A, approx. 15′ × 7′ × 10½″ w/turret.

Sims Land Torpedo, 1915, self-propelled track-laying land torpedo, project only.

Big Willie (Mother) (Wilson Machine) (HMLS Centipede), 1915, rhomboid shape, overhead tracks and outside sponsons w/long naval 6pdr, tail wheels for steering, boiler plate, short rivet pitch, rigid suspension continued in all subsequent wartime vehicles, 32′ 6″ × 13′ 9″ × 8′ ½″.

Mother with Daimler Transmission (Daimler Petrol-Electric Machine), 1916, original Mother with experimental transmission.

Mark I, 1916, production model of Mother, long rivet pitch, 6pdr L/40 gun and 4 Maxim or Lewis mg in male type, 6 mgs in female type, sponsons same size in both, some w/overhead bomb screens, some w/torpedo spar unditching gear, some w/unditching beams, tail wheels later removed from some, 28 tons, 26′ 5″ (32′ 6″ w/tail) × 14′ 4″ × 8′ ½″.

Mark I Supply, 1917, converted to cargo vehicles w/o sponsons.

Flying Elephant, 1916, 100-ton tank w/6pdr in nose and supplementary tracks between main tracks to prevent bellying, broken up for scrap after trial run, 26′ 9½″ (29′ 6½″) × 9′ 10″ × 10′.

Mark II, 1917, tail wheels eliminated, special grousers on every sixth track plate.

Mark III, 1917, same as Mark II but slightly thicker armour.

Mark IV, 1917, L/23 6pdr in male, Hotchkiss mgs replaced Lewis, female sponsons smaller than male, 26′ 5″ × 13′ 6″ (male) 10′ 6″ (female) × 8′ 1″.

Williams-Janney Hydraulic Machine (Mark IV modified), 1917, experimental transmission installed.

British Westinghouse Petrol-Electric Machine, 1917, Mark IV w/experimental stepless petrol-electric transmission.

Wilkins Clutch Gear System Machine, 1917, Mark IV w/experimental transmission.

Hele-Shaw Gear Machine, 1916, Mark IV w/experimental hydraulic transmission.

Wilson's Epicyclic Gear Machine, 1916, Mark IV w/Wilson planetary transmission, prototype of Mark V.

Mark IV with Special Unditching Gear, 1917, device to engage or disengage unditching beam w/o exposing crew.

Mark IV with St Chamond Petrol-Electric Transmission (St Chamond Petrol-Electric Machine), French transmission installed.

Mark IV Tadpole, 1918, Mark IV lengthened to increase trench-crossing ability, rear platform mounted 6″ trench mortar, both male and female, male 32′ 5″ × 13′ 6″ × 8′ 2″.

Mark IV Supply (Tank Tender), male sponsons rearmoured to create cargo space, several versions, engine horsepower increased.

Mark IV Wireless, weapons removed, wireless w/antenna added to create command vehicle.

Mark IV with Searchlight, 1917, early RE experiment for blinding enemy in night attack.

▼ 214

Mark IV with Mine Exploder, 1918, wood timber outriggers and heavy castor rollers suspended at ends.

▼ 215

Proposed Mark V, 1917, rear cab added and sponson gun mounts modified, wooden mock-up only.

Mark V, 1917, heavier armour, improved transmission, rear cab w/mg to fire to rear, male w/2 6pdrs and 4 mgs, female w/7 mgs, hermaphrodite w/male sponson on left, female sponson on right, 26′ 5″ × 13′ 6″ (male) 10′ 6″ (female) × 8′ 8″.

Mark V Lanchester Constant Mesh Gear Machine, 1918, experimental transmission.

Mark V Infantry Carrier, 1918, experimental vehicle w/sliding door replacing sponsons.

▼ 216

Mark V Experimental, 1918, spring and cable suspension w/laterally flexible narrow steel block tracks.

Mark V with Searchlight, 1922, continuation of experiment for blinding enemy in night attacks.

Mark V Tadpole, male Mark V lengthened for increased trench-crossing ability, prototype for Mark V*, 32′ 5″ × 13′ 6″ × 8′ 8″.

Mark V*, 1918, 6′ side panels inserted into Mark V to increase length, built as a troop carrier for 25 additional men, 2 cabs, unditching beam permanently installed, both male and female, 32′ 5″ × 13′ 6″ (10′ 6″ female) × 8′ 8½″.

Mark V* Workshop Vehicle, sliding doors in place of sponsons, built-up front cupola.

Mark V**, 1918, same length as Mark V* but built as lengthened vehicle instead of converted, both male and female, 38 tons, 1 larger cab forward, 1 fitted w/diesel engine in 1927, 39′ 1″ × 13′ 6″ (12′ 9″ female) × 8′ 7″.

Mark V**, Mine Sweeper (RE Tank), 1919, female w/heavy roller suspended in front of vehicle on jib to detonate land mines.

Mark V**, Bridging Tank (RE Tank), 1919, bridge laid by hydraulic jib, 2 slightly differing models.

Mark V**, Infantry Carrier, similar to Mark V Infantry Carrier.

Mark V*** (Mark X), designed but not built.

▼ 217

Mark VI, 1917, 6pdr in nose, small side mg sponsons, high suspension w/side mgs, wooden mock-up only.

▼ 218

Mark VII, 1917, two 6pdrs and 5 mgs, Williams-Janney hydraulic transmission, special cooling system, first vehicle w/electric starter, 3 built, 29′ 11″ × 12′ 9″ × 8′ 8″.

Mark VIII (Anglo-American Tank) (Liberty Tank) (International Tank), 1918, massive 45-ton vehicle resembling predecessors, one of soft plate w/Rolls Royce engine and 6 w/2 Ricardo engines and 1 V-type, differed from American-built Mark VIII which had Liberty engine, 34′ 2½″ × 12′ 5″ × 10′ 2½″.

Mark VIII*, designed but not built, was to have been 44′ long to cross 18′ trench.

▼ 219

Mark IX (The Pig), 1918, infantry carrier or supply vehicle, 2 large oval doors replacing sponsons, 31′ 11″ × 8′ 1″ × 8′ 5″.

Mark IX Modified, 1920, new box cab and long cylindrical floats added for amphibious experiments.

Medium Mark A Prototype (Tritton Chaser) (Tritton's No. 2 Light Machine), 1917, 2 engines in front, turret in rear from Austin armoured car, Little Willie-type track frames, 20′ × 8′ 4″ × 10′ 1″.

Medium Mark A, 1917, first production vehicles had rounded front air scoop, riveted plates at each bogie wheel, large mud chutes, high flat-sided rear cab, later production had only 6 round bogie plates and V-front air scoop, mgs only, 14 tons, 20′ × 8′ 7″ × 9′.

Medium Mark A with Tailpiece, 1917, experimental installation of French Renault FT tailpiece.

Medium Mark A with Tailwheels, 1917, experimental installation of Mark I heavy tank tailwheels.

Medium Mark A Modified (Medium A with Sprung Tracks), 1918, suspension changed to rollers and leaf springs, the hull later was raised considerably to change from 2 Tylor engines to 1 Rolls-Royce, maximum speed increased from 9 to 30mph.

Medium B, 1918, track frames compromised between heavy and Medium A types, box cab w/4mgs in front of vehicle, 1 mg sponson each side, engine rear, 22′ 9½″ × 9′ 3″ × 8′ 5″.

▼ 220

Medium C (Hornet), 1918, resembled Medium B but larger, 3 mgs in cab, cooling louver and other variations existed, 25′ 10″ × 8′ 10½″ × 9′ 7½″.

Gun Carrying Machine, 1916, open chassis w/low track frames, portée gun forward, box cab rear, tail wheels, prototype vehicle.

Gun Carrier Mark I, 1917, armour box hull w/driver and brakeman cabs over forward ends of track frames, portée gun, 29′ 9″ (w/tail) 42′ 10″ (w/gun) × 9′ 4″ × 11′.

Supply Tank (Gun Carrier Supply Tank), modified Gun Carrier Mark I, 30′ × 11′ × 9′ 4″.

Salvage Tank Mark I (Modified Gun Carrier Crane), 1917, cabs removed, jib crane installed.

Gun Carrier Mark II, 1917, resembled standard Mark V, field-gun carried on rear ramps, mock-up only.

Salvage Tank Mark II, converted Mark V w/jib crane.

▼ 221

Open-track Machine (Studebaker Tank) (Newton Tractor) (Buick Tank) (Ford Tank) (Overland Tank), 1919, small, low open top version resembling heavy tank to be used as a troop carrier under 'Plan 1919', made in England and USA to British order, only a few hundred of 22,000 completed, only the Studebaker had the lift-in armoured hull contemplated for all.

Medium D, 1919, resembled modern tanks, cylindrical bevel forward and sides, turret w/3 mgs, single cupola on turret, track frames higher in rear, spring and cable suspension, tracks like those on Mark V Experimental, also proposed 'male' version w/6pdr centrally in front and 2 mgs, only 4 pilots and a few production xehicles built, 30′ × 9′ 2″ × 9′ 11″.

D–2 (Medium D*), 1920, slightly larger and heavier version, track frames level, pressed steel tracks.

▼ 222

Medium D Modified (Medium D**), 1920, similar to Medium D but w/2 cupolas and minor changes asked for by Tank Corps.

Light D, 1920, not armoured, Overland touring car w/light track frames and long pitch tracks over pneumatic tyred wheels.

Light D*, 1920, 6 bogies and rubber track on Light D.

▼ 223

Light Infantry Tank (Johnson's Light Infantry Tank) (Hall-Scott Tank) (Tank 7–19–3), 1921, more sophisticated, smaller and lighter version of Medium D–2, 21′ long.

▼ 224

Tropical Infantry Tank, 1921, Medium D track frames w/louvered box cab forward, built for use in India.

▼ 225

Tropical Tank (Tank 8–20–10), 1921, similar but twin turrets like Austin armoured car.

Ammunition Carrier No. 1, closed top box hull w/spring and cable suspension, half metal tracks, amphibious.

Light Tropical Tank (Vickers Tank No. 1), 1921, Wolseley engine, later became FA Dragon Mark I.

Light Tropical Tank (Vickers Tank No. 2) (AT 2), 1922, open chassis, Armstrong-Siddeley engine, later became Dragon Mark II*.

Light Tropical Tank (Vickers Tank No. 3) (B6E2), 1921, completed as an 18pdr Gun Transporter.

▼ 226

Vickers Tank No. 1, 1921, chassis like Medium B but w/mg in dome

turret, skirted suspension, 18′ 4″ × 9′ × 8′ 9″.

Vickers Tank No. 2, 1923, similar but 3pdr gun in higher dome turret, exposed support rollers.

Armoured Amphibious 3pdr Gun (Hall-Scott), details unknown.

18pdr Transporter, Portée field piece on open chassis tractor, 5 bogie wheel pairs, 5 support rollers.

'A' VEHICLES

A1E1 (Independent), 1926, heavy tank, dome turret w/3pdr, Vickers mg in each of 4 small auxiliary turrets, modified 1928, 30′ 6″ × 10′ 6″ × 9′.

A2E1 (Light Tank Mark I) (Medium Mark I) (Vickers Medium Mark I), 1924, soft plate, cylindrical bevel-sided turret w/3pdr, Hotchkiss hull mgs, exposed bogie wheels, 17′ 6″ × 9′ 1½″ × 9′ 3″.

A2E2, 1924, Medium Mark I modified to 15pdr mortar and suspension as furnished later on Vickers Medium C as sold to Japan.

▼ 227

A3E1 (Light Dragon Machine-Gun Carrier) (3-Man Tank) (Carrier MG No. 1), 1925, 2-ended light tank built at Royal Ordnance Factory, 17′ 6″ × 9′ × 6′.

A4E1, 1929, squat vehicle w/mg in bevel-sided turret, 4 large bogie wheels on rail, 3 return rollers, leaf springs, 10′ 6″ × 6′ 2″ × 5′ 6″.

A4E2, variation of A4E1, see Light Tank Mark I A/A.

A4E3, variation of A4E1, cylindrical turret bevelled forward, 1 mg, 4 bogie wheels in half leaf spring pairs, 3 return rollers, box hull cut back in rear, 13′ 2″ × 6′ 1″ × 5′ 7″.

A4E4 (Carden-Loyd Mark VIII), variation of A4E1 w/suspension later changed to single horizontal coil springs and friction tape shock absorbers front and rear, raised box cowl, 11′ 11″ × 6′ 1″ × 5′ 6″.

A4E5, A4E4 w/higher cylindrical turret, controlled scissors suspension (interconnection added to bogies), shock absorbers eliminated.

A4E6 (Light Tank Mark Ia), similar to A4E1 except for turret, 4 bogie wheels in leaf spring pairs, 3 support rollers, later w/Horstmann suspension, 13′ ½″ × 6′ 1″ × 5′ 6″.

A4E7, A4E4 hull, high turret, large mantlet w/mg, leaf springs, 3 support rollers, later w/Horstmann suspension.

A4E8, variation of A4E6 w/hull bevelled-in, cowl raised, suspension changed to Horstmann type horizontal coil springs.

A4E9, variation of A4E7.

228

A4E10, 1930, A4E8 hull w/A4E3 suspension, prototype had dummy Besa in hull front, high turret w/1 mg above the other, new type suspension fitted 1932.

Vickers Carden-Loyd Light Amphibious Vehicle, 1930, prototype, 3⅓ tons, 2 double bogie wheels, leaf springs covered balsa rails cut square in front.

A4E11 (L1E1) (Vickers Carden-Loyd Light Amphibious Vehicle), 1932, covered balsa rails undercut and bevelled back, high driver's cowl w/bulge on top, engine louvers unprotected, leaf spring suspension, 13′ × 6′ 10″ × 6′.

A4E12 (L1E2), same w/low driver's cowl having swing-away cover w/flat top, box added over engine louvers.

A4E13 (Mark II Light Tank), 1930, bevel-sided rectangular turret and hull, suspension as A4E6 but horizontal coil springs later changed to diagonal, 3 return rollers, Wilson transmission.

A4E14, variation of A4E13, w/Armstrong-Siddeley transmission.

A4E15, A4E13 w/Rolls Royce engine and Wilson transmission.

A4E16 (Mark IIa Light Tank), 1933, turret flared at top w/either sliding or folding turret hatch, horizontal coil spring suspension, 2 return rollers, various tracks tested.

A4E17 (Mark IIb Light Tank), fuel tanks on sides only.

A4E18, A4E16 w/Rolls Royce engine built at Royal Ordnance Factory.

A4E19 (L2E1) (Vickers India Pattern No. 1 Light Tank) (Vickers Experimental 2-Man Tank) (Light Tank Mark IV) (Carden-Loyd Experimental), soft plate, octagonal turret, modified coil spring suspension, no return rollers, Meadows engine, 3½ tons.

229

A4E20 (Vickers India Pattern No. 2 Light Tank) (L2E2) (Light Tank Mark IV), resembled A4E19 but turret differed, thicker armour.

A5E1 (Vickers 3-Man Tank No. 2) (Carden-Loyd 3-Man Tank), 1930, hull like A4E6, low cylindrical turret w/.303 and .50 cal mg, 4.5 tons, half moon bogie connectors, 3 return rollers, w/novel suspension system.

A5E2-3-4, see Vickers Carden-Loyd Patrol Tanks Light Tanks.

A6E1 (erroneously called 16 Ton Tank), 1928, main turret w/3pdr and Vickers mg coaxial, 2 small auxiliary turrets w/conical tops and 2 mgs each, later 1 mg each, skirted suspension, Clark crash-type gearbox, 21′ 6″ × 8′ 9″ × 9′ 2″.

A6E2, 1930, slightly conical turret, single mg in each of 2 auxiliary turrets, SLM gearbox, Ricardo diesel engine later replaced by Armstrong-Siddeley engine.

230

A6E3, 1930, Armstrong-Siddeley V-8 engine, Wilson gearbox, Horstmann suspension substituted in 1937, new flat top auxiliary turrets, sometimes called 'The 16 Tonner'.

A7E1 (10 Ton Tank), 14 tons, cupola on turret, skirted suspension, 7 return rollers, leaf springs, AEC engine, mg in box beside driver.

A7E2, 1939, 4-sided sloping turret w/overhang, 11 bogie wheels w/volute springs, partly skirted, 7 return rollers, Armstrong-Siddeley V-8 engine.

A7E3, 1937, improved gun mantlet, 18.2 tons, wider tracks, 12 bogie wheels, helical springs, twin AEC diesel engine, forerunner of Matilda II, 22′ 6″ × 8′ 11½″ × 9′ 1″.

A8E1, 1937, similar to A7E3 but w/1 auxiliary turret, 2 Rolls Royce ZRR Phantom engines, 17.5 tons, Horstmann suspension, not completed.

A9E1 (Woolworth Tank) (Cruiser A9 Mark I), 1935, first tank w/Vickers-Gerlach tank periscope and power traverse, 14mm armour, 3pdr (later w/2pdr) and coaxial mg, cupola on main turret, 2 auxiliary conical top turrets w/single mg each, Vickers Horstmann (Valentine) suspension, engine changed from Rolls Royce to AEC diesel in 1936, 19′ 3″ × 8′ 4″ × 8′ 4″.

Cruiser A9 with Carpet-laying Device, 1939, experimental.

Cruiser A9 with Breathers, 1939, high air intake tubes mounted on right side w/parallel exhaust pipe leading from silencer.

A9E1CS Mark I, 3.7″ mortar main armament.

A10E1 (Cruiser A10 Mark I) (Cruiser Heavy Mark I) (Cruiser Mark II), 1938, no auxiliary turrets, 2pdr and mg in turret w/cupola, Bren gun left of driver added later, Valentine suspension, 30mm armour, intended as an infantry tank, 18′ 4″ × 8′ 4″ × 8′ ½″.

A10CS Mark I, same w/3.7″ mortar.

A10E2 (Cruiser A10 Mark Ia) (Cruiser Tank Mark IIa), 1938, main turret w/o cupola, coaxial Besa mg instead of Vickers, Besa beside driver, some vehicle variations in mantlet and bow mg, 18′ 1″ × 8′ 3½″ × 8′ 6″.

A10CS (Cruiser Mark IIa CS), same w/3.7″ mortar.

A10E3, 1940, 17 tons, forerunner of Valentine I.

231

A11E1 (Infantry Tank) ('I' Tank) (Matilda I), 1936, 60mm armour, first tank w/cast turret, mg main armament, 11 tons, 4 road wheel open suspension, splash rails on glacis removed in production and turret slightly more conical, 15′ 11″ × 7′ 6″ × 6′ 1½″.

A12E1, 1937, experimental 26.5-ton tank, 2pdr and Vickers mg in cast cylindrical turret, 70mm armour, concentric helical spring 11 road wheel skirted suspension, 6 mud chutes.

A12E2 (Mark II Infantry Tank) (Matilda), same but 5 mud chutes, 18′ 5″ × 8′ 6″ × 8′.

A13E1, 1938, first cruiser w/Christie suspension, dummy gun, 14mm armour, long pitch tracks, otherwise like A10E1, 18′ 1½″ × 7′ ½″ × 8′ 4″.

A13E2, many internal improvements, short pitch tracks, 19′ × 8′ × 8′ 3″.

A13E3, similar to A13E2 but thicker armour and turret bevelled at two horizontal angles, no cupola.

A13 Mark I (Cruiser Tank Mark III), production A13E3, bulged-out half cylindrical mantlet, coaxial mg in large cylindrical armour tube, some later reworked to A13 Mark II standards as Cruiser Tank Mark III*, and some of these had boxed-in mantlets, 19′ 9″ × 8′ 4″ × 8′ 6″.

A13 Mark II (Cruiser Tank Mark IV), thicker armour in front, mantlet same as Mark III or two-bevel plate over mantlet, cupola added, 19′ 9″ × 8′ 4″ × 8′ 6″.

232

A13 Mark IIa (Cruiser Tank Mark IVa), new flattened mantlet, Besa guns in conical armoured tube replaced Vickers mg, 19′ 9″ × 8′ 4″ × 8′ 6″.

A13 Mark IIa CS (Cruiser Tank Mark IVa CS), 3″ howitzer replaced 2pdr.

A13 Mark III (Cruiser Mark V) (Cruiser Mark Vc) (Covenanter), 1937, faceted undercut turret, small auxiliary turret w/Besa mg, 4 road wheel Christie suspension, 19′ 6″ × 8′ 7″ × 7′ 4″.

A13 Mark IIIa, weapon differences.

233

A14E1, 1938, similar to A16E1, soft plate, 29.3 tons, 8 small and 4 large road wheels, 4 boxed spring assemblies, 4 double return rollers, partial suspension skirting, 2pdr and coaxial Besa mg in turret, 1 Besa in each of 2 auxiliary turrets, Thornycroft V-12 engine.

A14E2, not completed.

A15E1, original design not completed, designation given to A16E1.

A16E1 (A15E1) (Cruiser Tank Mark VI) (Crusader Mark VI) (Crusader I), 1938, similar to A13 Mark III but 5 road wheels instead of 4, first cruiser w/Merritt-Brown transmission, 18 tons, prototype had A13 gun mantlet, 19′ 8″ × 8′ 8″ × 7′ 4″.

A16E2, Nuffield experimental heavy cruiser.

A17E1 (Tank Light Experimental Type PR) (PR51) (Tetrarch prototype), 1937, airborne, 7 tons, 15mm Besa mg, hydropneumatic suspension w/4 Christie-type road wheels.

A17E2 (Mark VII Light Tank) (Tetrarch) (PR) (Purdah), 1938, production model, 2pdr in turret, turret top sloped down in rear, 1 vehicle later fitted w/DD device, 13′ 6″ (14′ 1½″) × 7′ 7″ × 6′ 11½″.

A18E1, 1939, heavier version of A17E2, not completed.

A18E2, details unknown.

A19E1, 1939, cruiser w/auxiliary turrets on top of main turret, not completed.

A20E1, 1939, 25-ton infantry assault tank, chassis only completed, 14 road wheels, Matilda turret planned, 2pdr smoke mortar and mg in bow, mg in right and left sponsons.

A20E2, similar, 80mm armour, chassis only completed.

A20E3, A20E1 w/simulated box turret.

A21E1, projected development of A20 series, not built.

A22E1 (Infantry Tank Mark IV) (Churchill Mark I) (Churchill I), 1940, 2pdr and Besa in cast turret, 3″ howitzer in front plate, 11 road wheels, 38½ tons, 24′ 1½″ × 10′ 8″ × 8′ 2″.

A22F (Churchill VII), thicker armour, 75mm and Besa mg in cast and welded turret w/flared base, vision block cupola, redesigned welded hull, square side hatches replaced by round hatches, 25′ 2″ × 10′ 8″ × 8′ 2″.

A23E1, shorter and lighter A22, project only.

A24E1 (Cruiser Tank Mark VII) (Cavalier I), 1941, angular turret w/bolted-on applique armour, 26.4 tons, 6pdr and coaxial Besa, hull Besa, Liberty engine, Wilson gearbox, 5 road wheel Christie suspension, 20′ 10″ × 9′ 5½″ × 8′ 4″.

234

A25E1 (Light Tank Mark VII Revised) (Light Tank Carden-Loyd) (Light Tank Mark VIII) (Harry Hopkins I), 1941, faceted turret armour, cast 2pdr gun mantlet, 20mm armour, 14′ 3″ × 8′ 10½″ × 6′ 11″.

235

A25E2 (Harry Hopkins CS Mark I) (Alecto I), light SP converted from A25E1, 95mm howitzer, 14′ 3″ (18′ 1″) × 8′ 10″ × 4′ 2½″.

A26E1, lighter, faster version of A22, project only.

A27L (Cruiser Mark VIII L) (Cruiser Mark VIII) (Centaur I), 1941, similar to A24E1, 27.5 tons, 6pdr, Liberty engine, 21′ 10″ × 9′ 6″ × 7′ 9″

A27M (Cruiser Mark VIII M) (Cruiser Mark VIII) (Cromwell I), 1943, same but Rolls Royce Meteor engine, first tank so powered, 14″ tracks, rounded hood over bow gunner's periscope, commander's rotating hatch w/fore and aft periscope, early production in mild steel, 20′ 10″ × 10′ 1½″ × 8′ 2″.

A28E1, A27M w/suspension skirting, project only.

A29 (Clam), A27 chassis w/double tracks and 17pdr, 45 tons, project

A30 (originally called Centurion, later Challenger), A27M w/17pdr and Browning mg in larger turret, 15.5 tons, 1 road wheel added to Cromwell chassis, 32½ tons, Vickers built, no hull mg, 23′ 10″ (26′ 4″) × 9′ 6½″ × 10′ 10½″.

A30 (Avenger I), 17pdr SP, steamer turret roof, Leyland built, no hull mg, 24′ 3″ (28′ 7″) × 10′ × 8′ 3″.

A31, more heavily armoured infantry version of A27M, project only.

A32, heavier armour version of A27M, project only.

A33(1) (Assault Tank), Centaur-type chassis w/US T1 Heavy tank suspension, 45 tons, 22′ 8″ × 11′ 1½″ × 7′ 11″.

A33(2) (Assault Tank), same w/British suspension and skirting.

236

A33(3) (Assault Tank), US T14 built to British specifications, 75mm and coaxial mg, skirted suspension.

A34 (Comet Ia), 1944, 77mm coaxial Besa, hull Besa, strengthened Cromwell suspension and track w/o return rollers in pilot, 32.7 tons.

A35, Comet w/thicker armour and heavier suspension, project only.

A36, heavier version of A30 (Challenger) w/17pdr, project only.

A37, heavier version of A33 w/17pdr and 1 more bogie wheel, 52 tons, project only.

A38 (Valiant I), small assault tank, 6 small bogie wheels, 3 return rollers, 6pdr in massive cast turret, cast bow, 27 tons, GMC diesel engine, AEC gearbox, 17′ 7″ × 9′ 3″ × 7′.

A39 (Tortoise), 1944, 80-ton SP, 94mm 32pdr in massive cast turret, four 4 wheel bogies, each pair of wheels linked to a transverse torsion bar, 23′ 9″ (33′) × 12′ 10″ × 10′.

A40, thicker armour version of A30 (Challenger) w/17pdr, 35.5 tons, project only.

A41 (Centurion I), 1944, built at Royal Ordnance Factory, 5 w/17pdr, Polsten 20mm in left front turret blister, Besa mg in turret rear, skirted suspension, 24″ tracks, 5 w/rear escape door, 24′ 9½″ (32′ 3″) × 11′ 11½″ × 9′ 7″ w/o mg.

237

A41* (Centurion Mark I*), 70mm as in Comet, rear escape door, Besa mg in bow, 5 built.

A41 (SP IV), A41 hull w/32pdr in SP version.

A41a (Centurion II), 1946, shorter hull A41 w/cast turret and thicker frontal armour, vision cupola, hatch in rear of turret, stabilizer, Polsten gun eliminated, 17pdr, 5

built, later converted to Marks III and V, 24′ 6″ (29′) × 10′ 9″ × 9′ 3″.

A41T, see Centurion IV.

A42 (Churchill VIII), 39.5 tons, cast turret w/welded roof, protected turret race, 95mm howitzer.

A43 (Black Prince) (Super Churchill), wider hull and strengthened suspension to accommodate 17pdr, 28′ 11″ × 11′ 3½″ × 9′.

A44, A34 w/larger turret ring to accommodate 17pdr, project only.

A45 (Universal) (Capital) (FV201), 1946, heavier version of A41, steel rimmed resilient wheels, 8 road wheels, hull sides vertical, left front fender mg, Centurion turret w/17pdr, ball mounted mg left of driver, later w/20pdr in turret similar to A41, later hull used for FV214, chassis used for bulldozer.

FV202 AVRE (T), 6.5″ demolition gun in Centurion turret, cancelled.

FV203 AVRE (L), ARK type. cancelled.

FV204 Universal Flail, cancelled.

FV205 SP Medium Anti-tank, project only.

FV206 SP Medium Artillery, project only.

FV207 SP Heavy Artillery, cancelled.

FV208 Universal Bridge-layer, cancelled.

FV209 Universal ARV, cancelled.

FV210 Heavy Artillery Tractor, cancelled.

FV211 Medium Artillery Tractor, cancelled.

FV212 Assault Personnel Carrier, cancelled.

FV213 BARV, cancelled.

FV214, see Heavy Gun Tank Conqueror Mark I.

FV215a, heavy AVRE, w/mine-clearing roller, dozer and demolition gun, cancelled.

FV215b, heavy anti-tank SP, 180mm w/bore evacuator, massive turret w/exterior trunnions, Caernarvon chassis, mock-up only, cancelled.

FV216 Mini Flail, cancelled.

FV217 SP 120mm Medium A/T No. 1, project only.

FV219 ARV Mark I Caernarvon.

FV221 Medium Gun Tank Caernarvon, 1952, similar to FV201, Centurion III turret, skirted, w/road wheels visible.

FV222 ARV Mark II, driver in main crew compartment.

FV223 ARK, 75′ span, cancelled.

FV301 (A46), 1947, welded hull, Saladin turret, 75mm, project only for an airborne tank w/Christie suspension.

FV304, 25pdr in turret on FV301 light tank chassis, project only.

'C' VEHICLES

238

C1E1 (13pdr SP) (13pdr Transporter), open chassis vehicle.

'D' VEHICLES OF THE TRACK-LAYING VARIETY

D3E1 (Wheel-cum-Track Vehicle, Armoured Body), medium tank w/turret and cupola, sloping glacis, rear wheels concealed, 8 road wheels, 2 support rollers, later heavier suspension w/4 support rollers, 18′ × 8′ × 9′.

D3E2 (Vickers Wheel-cum-Track Car, Open Body), similar w/2 support rollers and later w/track frames strengthened and 4 support rollers, no turret.

D4E1 (Vickers Wolseley Armoured Car Tank) (Reconnaissance Car No. 1), armoured car chassis w/tracks between wheel pairs, 4 bogie pairs, 4 support rollers, dome turret.

D4E2 (Reconnaissance Car No. 2) same w/modifications.

D5E1 (Carden-Loyd Artillery Observation Car) (Artillery Observer Tractor), 4 bogie wheels, uncluttered glacis, high seats.

D6E1, Morris Martel 2-Man Tank, see Great Britain, Carriers.

'L' VEHICLES

L1E1 (Amphibian Light Tank No. 3), see A4E11.

L1E2, see A4E12.

239

L1E3, pilot amphibian vehicle, no screw, originally w/2 support

rollers, fluted sponsons, 14′ ×
7′ 7″ × 7′.

L1E3 No. 3 (Mark VIII Light
Amphibious Tank), 1941, 2 screws
in cowls, Besa mg.

L2E1, see A4E19.

L2E2, see A4E20.

L3E1 (Light Tank 3 Man) (Light
Tank Mark V Experimental)
(Three Man No. 1 Tank), experimental prototype of Mark V Light
Tank, bevel forward Mark VI Light
tank type turret w/2 mgs, return
roller on bogie, trailing idler, soft
plate, reverse steering.

▼ 240

L3E2 (Vickers 3-Man Tank No. 2)
(Light Tank Mark V), same
w/medium tank cupola added,
suspension later modified.

▼ 241

L4E1 (Experimental Light Tank DD
(M) 1411), built by Royal Ordnance
Factory, lighter and wider than
Mark VI Light Tank, wide hull,
cupola on turret, fully skirted.

CARRIERS

Martel One-Man Tank Pilot, 1925,
box hull w/sloping glacis, vertical
front radiator louvers, 2 trailing
steering wheels, 11′ 1″ × 4′ 6″
× 5′.

Morris Martel One-Man Tank, 1926,
improved production vehicle, wedge
shaped glacis w/top louvers, flat
cover over engine, tail wheels axled
to hull, 12′ 3″ × 3′ 9″ × 4′ 10″.

Morris Martel 2-Man Tank (D6E1),
1928, similar but wider crew
compartment, individual vehicle
differences, 9′ 10″ × 4′ 7″ ×
5′ 6″.

Morris Martel Single Wheel Steering,
2-man type modified to low axle
single rear steering wheel.

Crossley Martel, 1926, 1-Man
Tankette (Crossley Martel 1-Man

Semi-Track Tank), 1-man type
w/Citroën-Kégresse suspension,
several rubber track types tested,
12′ 3″ × 4′ 9″ × 5′ 4″.

Carrier MG No. 1, see A3E1.

Armstrong-Siddeley Armoured
Dragon (B1E1), 1924, open top
carrier 22′ long, no hull but front
engine covered, pivoting front
horns and laterally flexible track,
4 round holes in track frame and 1
oval hole in pivot section, silencer
over left track.

Armstrong-Siddeley Armoured
Dragon (B1E2), same w/low
armoured hull added.

Machine-Gun Carrier, 1924,
Armstrong-Siddeley Dragon B1E2
w/2 mgs on pedestal mounts.

Armoured Dragon B1E3, similar to
B1E2 but longer, hinge section w/2
round holes, 3 holes in balance of
track frame, silencer in rear.

Dragon PT (Protected Track) (B1E4)
(Woolwich Dragon), 2 front rollers,
2 grousered roller chain-driven rear
rollers, open top.

Carden-Loyd Tankette, 1925, pilot,
driver prone, unarmed, conveyor
chain tracks.

Carden-Loyd One Man, 1925, coffin
shaped hull, flat steel short pitch
stamped tracks, 14 double iron
rollers in track frame having no
springs.

Carden-Loyd Mark I, 1925, similar
but small turret shield w/auto rifle
added.

Carden-Loyd Mark I* (Carden-Loyd
One-Man Track and Wheel), 1925,
Mark I converted to tricycle wheel-
cum-track vehicle, small steering
wheel in rear.

Carden-Loyd Mark II (One-Man No.
2 Carrier), similar to Mark I but 4
soft rubber road wheels rail
mounted, no springs, 10′ 5″ ×
4′ 6″ × 4′ 10″.

Carden-Loyd Two-Man (Carden-Loyd
0.5 MGC) (Honeymoon Tank),
third model built, wider and lower
rebuilt version of One-Man model,
auto rifle later replaced by 50 cal
mg.

Carden-Lloyd Mark III, 1926, improved version of Two-Man model
but wheel-and-track type similar to
Mark I*, but larger rear steering
wheel, 9′ 11″ × 6′ 6″ × 3′ 4″.

Carden-Loyd Mark IV (Carden-Loyd
Two-Man No. 1 Track and Wheel),
improved version of Mark III, high
gun shield, no springs.

Carden-Loyd Mark V, 1928, similar to
Mark IV but low front armour and
uncovered wheel and track control
mechanism on front glacis, 9′ 11″
× 6′ 6″ × 3′ 4″.

Carden-Loyd Mark V* (Mark V
Modified), 1928, wheel-and-track
mechanism abandoned, first model
w/flat leaf spring connecting road
wheels, 1 vehicle tested w/upper
track rollers, 8′ 1″ × 5′ 7″ ×
3″ 4′.

Carden-Loyd Carrier (Smoke), 1928,
Mark V* w/o mg sponson, smoke
ejector tube extended rearward
from left rear corner.

Carden-Loyd Mark VI, 1928, similar
to MarkV*, rail for track return,
some w/stowage boxes over tracks,
differential covered, variously
armed, 8′ 1″ × 5′ 7″ × 3′ 4″.

Carden-Loyd Mark VI With 47mm
Infantry Gun, gun mounted in front
plate.

Carden-Loyd 60mm Mortar Carrier,
silencer right front, mortar in box
on glacis, front half of hull
covered, flat rear.

Carden-Loyd 3″ Mortar Carrier,
similar, mortar base mounted on
glacis.

Carden-Loyd Mark VI with Headcovers (Carden-Loyd Mark VI with
Armoured Tops), 1930, small
pyramidal headcovers hinged in
rear, some headcovers on peep-
slotted riser, some vehicles w/rail
wirecutters on either side of glacis
to hull top, 8′ 1″ × 5′ 7″ × 4′.

Carden-Loyd Mark IVa (AS Engine)
(B11E1), mild steel, 2 large return
rollers, Armstrong-Siddeley air-
cooled engine, sloped-up built up
armour, access door in glacis, mg
on right, 10′ 6½″ × 5′ 9″ × 5′ 6″.

B11E2, same but mg w/shield in
large built out sponson.

Carden-Loyd Mark VI* (Ford
Engine) (B11E3), same as B11E1
w/Ford Model A engine.

Carden-Loyd Carrier B11E4 and
B11E5, details unknown.

Carden-Loyd Experimental Mark VI
(B11E6), wider tracks, 2 return
rollers.

Carden-Loyd Mark VIa (Air-cooled)
(B11E7), 1929, Vickers air-cooled
engine, box hull sloped inward all
round, open top, 2 return rollers,
mg centre front.

Carden-Loyd Infighter (B11E8), 1930,
armour heightened in front, rebuilt
Mark V*, 10′ 6″ × 6′ 2″ × 5′ 6″.

Carden-Loyd Carrier B11E9, straight
sided box hull extending over
tracks, crew on raised seats, mg in
shield w/ball mount above level of
hull top, mg tripod carried on left
side, silencer left rear pointing
downward.

Carden-Loyd Three-Man Experimental Carrier (B11E10), similar
to Mark VI but Carden-Loyd

Patrol Tank hull, exhaust on left side over tracks, engine and differential offset to left, driver centre, mg on right, 1 man behind gunner, 1 return roller.

Carden-Loyd Mark VI (India Pattern) (B12E1 and B12E2), standard vehicles w/sunshade roofs, large engine fans and asbestos insulation.

Carden-Loyd Tractor, flat front plate, 1 large support roller, unarmed.

Carden-Loyd Mark VIb (Mark VI Improved Type), armour higher in front, armoured mg sponson, drop-down driver's door.

Carden-Loyd Mark VIb (Carden-Loyd Mark VI* Light Armoured Vehicle), original Mark VIb w/additional bevelled top w/hinged covers, access door in rear.

Carden-Loyd Light Tractor (One-Man Machine-Gun Carrier), 1934, tiny 2 road wheel one-man tractor, automatic rifle but not armoured, 6' 7" × 4' × 3' 11½".

Tractor Light GS Mark I, similar but sheet metal sides and Vickers mg right side.

Carden-Loyd Mark Ia Light GS Tractor, same w/heavier suspension and geared for higher speed.

Carden-Loyd Utility Tractor (Armoured), same but armoured and w/small square cupola, sold to Belgium, 7' 4" × 5' 4" × 5' 4".

Vickers-Armstrongs D50 Carrier, box hull, Vickers mg in right front plate, folding seats in rear, Horstmann 3 wheel suspension, 2 support rollers, 12' 1" × 6' 9" × 4' 5".

Light Dragon Mark III, unarmoured D50, horizontal fluting on droppable hull sides, headlights in boxes.

Tractor With 40mm Equipment, rebuilt D50, front suspension unit removed, 1 support roller, 40mm gun and trail above centre of vehicle.

Carrier, Machine-Gun, Experimental (Armoured), similar but Vickers mg on left could be raised or lowered, open top stowage boxes sloping outward each side of crew compartment, 12' 6" × 6' 6" × 5' 3".

GS Vehicle, same w/built out sponson w/Bren gun and rail on top left front and side, w/Boys gun on skate mount.

Carrier, Machine-Gun No. 1 Mark I, 1936, mild steel, right side of vehicle open for stowage, headlights in boxes, Vickers mg w/ or w/o shield on right, engine ventilators extended above hull, 11' 6" × 6' 9" × 4' 8".

Carrier, Armoured 2pdr, Carrier No. 1 Mark I, w/armour built up in rear and large shield w/2pdr and gunner in rear.

Carrier, Machine-Gun No. 2 Mark I, 1937, rebuilt No. 1 Mark I, headlight boxes removed, stowage box on left, open hull on right, Vickers mg in built-out sponson on left, both sides sloped downward to rear, front mudguards sloped forward, 1 support roller, later rebuilt to Bren Carrier No. 2 Mark I standard, 12' × 6' 9" × 4' 9".

Carrier, Cavalry Mark I, rebuilt No. 1, armoured only in front, carried 7 men, side seats w/wire mesh protection on prototype, fold-up hand rails, 1 support roller, sliding engine compartment doors in rear.

Carrier, Scout, Mark I, rebuilt No. 1 Mark I, carried wireless, engine ventilators in solid strip across top, battery box over rear axle, stowage box on left outside of sloping back hull side, Boys gun on left, 3" smoke mortar right side of hull, 12' × 6' 9" × 5' 2½".

Carrier, Scout, A/T, 1938, Scout Carrier w/Bren gun in sponson and Boys gun on pedestal mount on right.

Armoured OP No. 1 Mark I, Scout Carrier w/shutter in mg housing and wireless equipped.

Carrier, Bren, No. 2 Mark I, 1938, conversion of Carrier, Machine-Gun, No. 2 Mark I, hood over left mg sponson, Bren or Boys gun, rounded front fenders, right and left hull sides sloped down w/stowage box over tracks.

Carrier, Bren, No. 2 Mark II, same w/sloping rearward armour built out over left fender to form stowage box, 12' 2" × 7' 1" × 4' 8".

Carrier, Shuttered Projector, 1937, predecessor of CDL.

Carrier No. 1 Mark I Modified, 1937, 2 pdr and .50 cal mg fired to front through shield, gun w/travel lock.

Carrier No. 2 Mark I With Armoured Machine-Gun Sponson, similar to Scout Carrier but large armoured mg sponson.

LATER BRITISH CARRIERS

Carriers improperly called Bren Carriers are listed below. All had a steering wheel which functioned by warping track frames as well as by braking 1 track. The numbers under each Mark signify the following:

No. 1: 85HP British-produced Ford V8 engine, large lockers on right side;

No. 2: 85HP US-produced Ford V8 GAE engine, large locker at rear, standard Ford 1938–39 heavy duty type rear axle;

No. 2A: 85HP US-produced Ford V8 GAEA engine, large locker at rear, standard Ford 1940 heavy duty truck type rear axle;

No. 3: 85HP Canadian-produced Ford V8 engine;

Carrier, Machine-Gun, Mark I (Riveted), driver on right. No. 1, No. 2, No. 2A, No. 3, original type stowage, 3" mortar, mortar sometimes in left front seat. No. 1, tracked personnel carrier, Bendix brakes. No. 1, No. 2, No. 2A, No. 3, tracked starting and charging. No. 2, No. 2A, No. 3, tracked towing. No. 2, No. 2A, No.3 tracked personnel. No. 1, armoured O.P., no towing pintle, similar to Scout Carrier, cable drum in rear, adjustable shutter in place of mg.

Carrier, Machine-Gun, Mark II (Welded), foot step on side, spare wheel on glacis. No. 1, No. 2, No. 2A, No. 3, medium mg carrier, Vickers mg in sponson, another on pedestal over engine, one seen w/Vickers K guns in place of pedestal gun. No. 1, No. 2, No. 2A, No. 3, 3" mortar, new type stowage, no wheel on glacis. No. 1, tracked personnel, Girling brakes. No. 1, No. 1Z, No. 2, No. 2Z, tracked towing 6pdr or 4.2" mortar. No. 2, No. 2AZ, No. 3, No. 3AZ, tracked personnel. No. 1, armoured O.P., drums in rear.

Carrier, Mark III (Welded), No. 1, No. 2, No. 2A, No. 3, armoured O.P., sliding sponson aperture.

Universal Carrier, Mark I (Riveted), converted from Scout and Bren Carriers, flat top w/engine ventilator break upward, square rear, rear steps, 12' × 6' 9" × 5' 2½". No. 1, varied armament.

Universal Carrier, Mark I* (Riveted), No. 3, Canadian built, driver left, some vehicles w/sandshields, some w/3" mortar, 12' 6" × 6' 7" × 5' 2".

Universal Carrier, Mark II (Riveted), No. 1, No. 2, No. 2A, new type stowage, 4" or 2" smoke mortar left side of gunner or 2" mortar on engine cover, 2 foot steps each side, spare wheel on glacis.

Universal Carrier, Mark II* (Welded), No. 1, No. 2, No. 2A, modified air inlet and engine cover same as Mark II, Welsh Guard stowage, 12' 4" × 6' 11" × 5' 3". No. 1, No. 2, No. 2A, armoured

Z: US-produced axle;

* : symbol following Mark indicates Canadian produced vehicle.

O.P. similar to Mark II O.P., cable drum front and rear, mg sponson w/small door.

Universal Carrier Mark III*, No. 3, Canadian built OP equipped as British OP No. 1 Mark III.

Universal Carrier Mark I (Welded) (T16), US built, spoked bogie wheels, spare wheel right glacis, driver right, 12' 8½" × 6' 11" × 5' ¼".

Universal Carrier Mark I (T16E1), US built, flat glacis, no gun sponson, tarpaulin bows over cargo body.

Universal Carrier Mark II (Welded) (T16E2), solid bogies, reversed rear bogie.

Tugboat Carrier, rebuilt T16 hull width only to fenders, modified suspension, double track w/2 side bogie braces, 2 support rollers, low ground pressure for mine-field crossing.

▼ 242
Carrier, Universal (Overhead Cover), armoured roof.

Smith Gun, carrier w/high front armour sloping to the right, 3" smoothbore gun left front.

▼ 243
Smith Gun Modified, similar but gun centre, lower armour sloping to each side.

Carrier, 2pdr, Tank Attack, 1940, gun and shield centre mounted for all round fire, 13' 3" × 6' 7" × 6' 2".

Carrier, A/T, Boys gun sometimes replaced in the field w/US 50 cal Browning. German 20mm Solothurn, Italian 20mm Breda, etc.

Carrier, Universal, A/A, 4 Bren mgs on rotating mount in left centre, normal gun sponson plated over.

Carrier, Universal, A/A, all round traverse turret w/Vickers K guns over the gunner's seat.

Tapp Machine, 1939, 2 remote-controlled mgs on hydraulic scissors lift, 12' × 3' × 1' 7" to 9' 6".

Praying Mantis, 1943, outgrowth of Tapp Machine, increased track length, scissors raised 11½' and lowered to flat position, 2 types, 16' 4" × 6' 2" × 4' 5" to 12' 6".

Adey Martin Drain Pipe, flame-thrower on side of carrier, experimental.

Ronson Flame-thrower, large pipe over left front, 2 rear fuel tanks, feed pipe left side.

Wasp Mark I (F/T Transportable No. 2 Mark I), long flame-gun mounted left centre, 2 inside fuel tanks.

Wasp Mark I With DD Device (Dragonfly), same w/experimental flotation equipment.

Wasp Mark II (F/T Transportable No. 2 Mark II), F/T mounted in mg sponson, 2 outside fuel tanks.

Wasp Mark II (Canadian F/T Mark Ic), F/T mounted in mg sponson, 2 inside fuel tanks.

Wasp With MBSD, multi-barrelled smoke dischargers on sides and front to fire salvoes or single 8-barrelled smoke discharger.

Wasp Cree, experimental Canadian F/T.

Barracuda, 1944, Canadian F/T on right top using solid fuel.

Wasp Butterfly, Canadian experimental F/T.

Wasp Iroquois, Canadian experimental F/T.

Rattlesnake Mark II, Canadian experimental F/T similar to Wasp Mark IIc but F/T mounted on frame.

Carrier, Universal, with demolition device (Kid), explosive on flat frame raised when set on course after which driver jumped out.

Carrier, Towed, with Conger 2" Mark I line charge, engineless carrier w/5" rocket and box containing 330 yards of 2" hose fired into a mine-field and then pumped full of explosive and detonated.

Carrier, Universal, with Conger 1" device (Line Charge), Mark II Carrier used similarly but self-propelled.

Carrier, Towed, converted to trailer w/all equipment removed.

Carrier With Smoke Screening Apparatus, spray apparatus in rear stowage compartment of Wasp.

Carrier, Flotation Attachment Mark I With Assault Boats Mark I–II, 2 steel braces to which assault boats were attached on either side.

Carrier, Flotation Attachment Kapok Mark I, brackets to attach Kapok floats.

Carrier, Flotation Attachment Kapok Mark II, similar for 10 Kapok floats.

Carrier With Heightened Superstructure, various carriers w/panels added and vehicles water-proofed for Normandy Landing.

Carrier, Universal, with crossing device, skeleton overhead and front rails to store and lay wooden slats connected to two steel cables.

▼ 244
Carrier, Universal, with Carpet Device Mark I (Infantry), carpet on reel across front, carpet 11' 6" wide, 150' long.

Carrier, Universal, with Carpet Device Mark II (Infantry), carpet 11' wide for use from LCT.

Carrier, Universal, with Carpet Device Mark II (LCM), similar but 8' wide for use from LCM.

Carrier With Rocket Assisted Egress, 1945, twin 5" rockets on either side pointing toward rear at angle of 45 degrees to assist in egress from mud or muck.

Monitor, carrier w/high pressure water hose to dig out beach mines after WWII.

Carrier, Universal, experimental SP, dummy canvas turret w/recoilless rifle, sponson built out for commander on left, side steps near front, spare wheel on glacis.

Carrier, Universal With 106mm Recoilless Rifle, 1953, US 106mm pedestal-mounted at rear.

LOYD CARRIERS

G.S. Carrier, Loyd, 1939, Pilot unarmed vehicle, exposed differential and axle, short glacis, open top, 3 wheel Horstman suspension, Ford commercial parts, steering levers instead of steering wheel.

Mark I Tracked Carrier, Loyd (Loyd T21 Mark I) (35R Carrier), 4 bogie wheels, 2 support rollers, Bendix brakes, 13' 7" × 6' 9½" × 4' 8½".
No. 1, 2 pdr gun left front.
No. 1, 2 pdr gun w/shield centre front.
No. 1, No. 2, Tracked personnel.
No. 1, No. 2, No. 2A, No. 3,

Starting and charging, canopy top.
No. 1, No. 2, No. 2A, No. 3.
Tracked towing for 2 pdr AT gun.

Mark II Tracked Carrier, Loyd (Loyd T22) (35F Carrier), Girling brakes.
No. 1, No. 2, No. 2A, No. 3, Tracked personnel.
No. 1, No. 1Z, No. 2, No. 2Z, Tracked towing for 6 pdr or 4.2" mortar.
No. 2A, No. 2AZ, No. 3Z, Tracked towing for 6 pdr or 4.2" mortar.

No. 1, Stacey Lloyd (Armoured 2 pdr Mounting Mark I), engine moved forward, 2pdr w/3 sided shield rear mounted later modified to add suspension brace over final support roller.

Carrier, 6pdr T21 (Z) Mark II, Loyd, Gun mounted in front plate.

Carrier, 25pdr Gun/Howitzer Experimental, Loyd.

Carrier, Bridge SP Tracked, Loyd, 30' scissors bridge.

Carrier, Mobile Welding Plant, Loyd, welder across centre, canvas cab.

Carrier, Mortar T23 (Z) Mark II, Loyd.

Cable Layer, Loyd (Mechanized Cable Layer Mark I), 3 large wire drums on rear, cable payout in centre, crew, poles, etc., carried over tracks.

Carrier, Carpet-layer, Loyd, bobbin and wide carpet low down in front, improvised in Middle East.

Carrier, Quad Bren, AA, Loyd, armoured box and head cover for erect gunner and armoured box for seated driver.

OTHER CARRIERS

CT20 Carrier, Full Track Armoured (Oxford Carrier Mark I), skirted, upper support rollers concealed, resembled Universal Carrier, also mortar carrier and towing vehicle versions.

CT20 Carrier Modified, bevelled armour cupola added.

CT21 (35R), engine rear, 1 built.

CT22 (35F), engine front, 1 built.

CT23 Carrier (50cwt Carrier), similar to CT20 but 2 engines at rear.

CT24 Carrier, 2 models, 1 w/hull width only to fenders, 1 w/hull overhanging tracks, 4 bogie wheels, 1 support roller, flat leaf springs.

CT24 Carrier (CS Type), 1945, armed w/smoke mortar.

CT24 Mark VI A/A, triple mg mount.

CT25 Carrier, CT20 Carrier w/Rolls-Royce engine and Merritt-Brown transmission.

Red Achilles, CT25 Carrier w/F/T.

CT26 Carrier (VA Load Carrier), diesel engine based on A17 Light tank chassis, 15' 4" × 10' 5" ×6' 1".

Schofield Carrier (Griffiths Wheel and Track Tank), see New Zealand.

COMMERCIAL AND MISCELLANEOUS TRACK-LAYING TYPES

Vickers-Armstrongs Armoured Car Tank, 1928, 2 light types: 1 w/3pdr and 1 w/2 Vickers mgs, 8 road wheels, 2 support rollers, recessed rear wheels, exposed front wheels, 1 vehicle sold to Hungary w/o armament, 16' 8" × 7' 6" × 7' 8".

Vickers-Armstrongs 6 Ton Tank, pilot, 1929, sloping glacis, vertical front plate, sloping rear deck, cylindical twin mg turrets, 14' 11½" × 7' 6½" × 7' 2".

Vickers-Armstrongs 6 Ton Type A, 1930, twin turrets, sloping front plate right side only, flat rear deck, 4 return rollers, 8 bogie wheels in double pairs, 15' ½" × 7' 11½" × 6' 10".

Vickers-Armstrongs 6 Ton Tank with Straussler Trench Crossing Device, pole vault device fore and aft resembling similar device on 1911 Austrian Burstyn Motorgeschuetz.

Vickers-Armstrongs 6 Ton Tank Type B, single conical turret w/3pdr L/20 gun and coaxial mg, same hull as Type A, 15' ½" × 7' 11½" × 7' 3½".

Vickers-Armstrongs 6 Ton Tank Type C, similar but deeper hull and w/turret bustle, sold to China.

Vickers-Armstrongs 6 Ton Tank Type D, sloping front plate, long sloping rear deck, Type B turret w/flat cupola.

Vickers-Armstrongs 6 Ton Type E, sloping front plate right side only, larger 2-bevel driver's hatch, shorter sloping rear deck, w/improved deeper engine air louver, still deeper hull, 3pdr.

Vickers-Armstrongs 6 Ton Tank Type E (6 Ton Polish Model), twin turretted model w/mg ammunition boxes over turret bevels.

Vickers-Armstrongs 6 Ton Tank Type F (6 Ton Finnish Model), octagonal turret w/armament changes, extended mantlet, turret bustle, slightly deeper hull, shorter sloping rear deck w/engine ventilator cover.

Vickers-Armstrongs 6 Ton Close Support Vehicle, 1932, box hull on 6 Ton Tank chassis w/50 cal mg on pedestal mount.

Vickers-Armstrongs Personnel Carrier, 6 Ton Tank chassis w/high armoured front, low open top hull.

Vickers Three-Man Tank No. 1, 1932, resembled Mark V Light tank, high double bevelled cupola.

Vickers Carden-Loyd M1933, hull resembled Mark IV Light tank but long glacis, cylindrical bevel-forward turret, 2 bogie wheel pairs, leaf springs 2 return rollers, 1 mg, 11' 4" × 6' × 6' 5½".

Vickers Carden-Loyd M1934, similar but 6 sided conical turret, coil spring suspension, 2 return rollers, 1 mg, 11' 4" × 6' × 6' 4".

Vickers Carden-Loyd M1935, similar but higher turret w/rear edge on turret hatch, 1 mg.

Vickers Carden-Loyd With Self-Extricating Winch Device, pulleys and rollers on right glacis and fender, right sprocket w/extra hub.

Vickers Carden-Loyd M1935 (Swiss Type), similar but tool box built out on left side bevelled as armour, 11' 10½" × 6' 2½" × 6' 2".

Vickers Carden-Loyd M1935 (Argentine Type), same but high conical turret, and Colt mg.

Vickers Carden-Loyd M1937, similar to 1934 type but 2pdr w/muzzle brake or 20mm Oerlikon, sometimes identified as a tank destroyer.

Vickers Carden-Loyd (Belgian Type), see Belgian T15.

Vickers Carden-Loyd M1937 (Belgian Type Command Tank), conical turret w/dummy armament, suspension coil springs w/parallel shock absorbers, 4 bogie wheels, 2 support rollers, louvers on right glacis and right side, 13′ 8″ × 6′ 9″ × 6′ 7″.

Vickers Carden-Loyd M1938 (Dutchman), resembled 1934 type, 2 models: 1 w/1 mg, 1 w/2 mgs.

Vickers Carden-Loyd Patrol (A5E2–3), 1930, small mg turret on Carden-Loyd Mark VI Carrier chassis, leaf springs, differential cover on left, Danish model had a Madsen air-cooled mg w/o mantlet, 8′ 6″ × 5′ 9″ × 5′ 5″.

Vickers Carden-Loyd Patrol (A5E4), 1931, improved model w/coil springs.

Vickers Carden-Loyd Light Amphibious Vehicle, similar to A4E12 but swivelling-cowled screw, no rudders, sold to China.

Straussler 2 Ton, 1936, articulated suspension, Skoda-type turret.

Alvis Straussler, similar but larger than 2 Ton model, no turret ever fitted, 15′ 2″ × 8′ 3½″ × 6′ 9″.

▼ 248
Straussler 10 Ton, 1938, articulated suspension, wheel-or-track type, soft plate.

▼ 249
Vivian Loyd Two-Man Tank, 1940, long glacis, small 4-sided turret w/mg on right, 3 bogie wheels, exposed final drive.

Vivian Loyd Airborne Tank, 1941, similar.

▼ 250
English Workman, 1928, similar to

Vickers Mark IIa Medium, but less pronounced turret bevels, made for USSR.

▼ 251
Vickers Medium C, 1930, slope-sided cylindrical turret w/rear mg, mgs in side sponsons, outside fuel tanks, sold to Eire, 18′ 4″ × 8′ 4″ × 7′ 10″.

Vickers Medium D, same as sold to Japan.

Vickers 37 Ton (Vijayanta Mark I), 1961, based on Chieftain, built for India, 23′ 11″ (31′ 11″) × 10′ 5″ × 8′.

Vijayanta Mark II, resilient trunnions as on Centurion 8, mantlet like Centurion 10/2, 4 Swingfire missiles, 24′ 10″ (32′ 1″) × 10′ 5″ × 8′.

Vijayanta Mark III, front of turret ballistically improved, also front of hull.

Vickers 38 ton tank with Chieftain turret, experimental.

MARK NUMBERED LIGHT TANKS AND RELATED VEHICLES

Carden-Loyd Mark VII (A4E1), see A4E1.

Carden-Loyd Mark VIII (Light Tank Mark I), see A4E3, A4E4 and A4E5.

Light Tank Mark I AA (A4E2), twin 50 cal mg in open turret on Mark I Light tank chassis.

Light Aid ARV, Mark I Light tank w/turret removed and 2 large tool boxes on roof, improvised ARV.

Light Tank Mark Ia, see A4E6, A4E7, A4E8, A4E9 and A4E10.

Mark II, see A4E13, A4E14, A4E15, prototype called Light Tank Mark II (Close Rivets) and later fitted w/Rolls-Royce engine and Wilson gearbox, 11′ 8″ × 6′ 3½″ × 6′ 3″.

Mark IIa IP (India Pattern), rectangular bevelled cupola added, 11′ 9″ × 6′ 3½″ × 6′ 7½″.

Mark IIa (Wilson Steering), 1932, see A4E16 and A4E18.

252
▼
Mark IIb, see A4E17, those sent to India had small rectangular cupola w/drop sides, 1 w/experimental suspension, 11′ 9″ × 6′ 3½″ × 6′ 7½″.

Mark IIb (Lever Steering), 1932.

Mark III, based on Mark IIb, flat top turret in two planes, low front plate, 12′ × 6′ 1″ × 7′.

Mark IIIa, 1939, flat top turret in 1 plane, high front plate.

Mark IV, bevelled front plate, square turret w/flat top and high front plate, 4 bogie wheels, twin coil spring suspension, some vehicles w/o return rollers, 11′ 6″ × 6′ 10″ × 7′ 1″.

Mark IV Modified, 6-sided turret w/lower front protruding.

Browning A/A on Mark IV Light Tank, Quad Browning mgs in square drop-side cupola.

Bren A/A on Mark IV Light Tank, Quad Bren, otherwise same as above.

Mark V, prototype, 1933, originally w/o wireless box later w/added to rear of turret, some w/1 support roller between 2 bogie pairs, cupola removed, 12′ 10″ × 6′ 9″ × 7′ 3″.

Mark V, 1 support roller centred above first pair, 13′ × 6′ 10″ × 7′ 4″.

Mark V, Experimental, modified for extra bogie wheel and longer track as needed.

Mark V, with 10″ Continuous Rubber Track.

Light Tank Mark V, with twin Besa A/A, 12′ × 6′ 9″ × 7′ 3″.

Mark V, light tank with Boulton-Paul 4 Gun Aircraft turret.

Light Tank 2pdr, 1938, experimental A/T open-top turret on Mark V chassis.

Mark V, Light Tank with Perkins Diesel Engine.

Anti-Tank 2pdr on Mark V (Carrier Anti-Tank Gun Mark II Experimental), large sloping back turret.

Mark VI, light tank, front of turret modified, round cupola, wireless bustle, double radiator louver cover, 12′ 4½″ × 6′ 10″ × 7′ 3″.

Quad Browning on Mark VI, regular hull with large box top having drop sides.

▼ 253

Quad Besa on Mark VI (A/A Mark I) (Light Tank A/A Mark I) (Light Tank Mark VIa A/A I), Quad Besa .50 cal.

Roller Fascine (Special Trench Crossing Device), 1940, large double drum roller towed behind Mark VI as portable fascine.

Mark VIa, 1935, octagonal cupola.

Mark VIa*, flatsided turret w/2 forward bevels.

Mark VI a/L, 1936, Australian type.

Mark VIa, Modified, suspension w/shock absorbers parallel to coil springs, 2 support rollers, no cupola but 2 rounded split turret hatches.

Mark VIb, larger turret w/cylindrical cupola, single instead of double radiator louver cover.

Mark VIb, IP (India Pattern), no cupola but 2 rounded turret hatch covers, w/periscope.

Mark VIc, 1939, no cupola, 15mm Besa and 7.92mm Besa mg coaxial, 12' 11½" × 6' 9" × 7'.

Light Tank A/A Mark II (Light Tank IIIb AAII) Quad Bren, outside stowage on rear hull plate, modified sighting equipment.

Mark VII, see A17E2.

Tetrarch ICS, 3" Howitzer on Mark VII.

▼ 254

Tetrarch DD, first DD device.

Mark VIII, see A25E1.

Alecto I, see A25E2.

Alecto Recce (Alecto Mark II), 6pdr on Mark VIII chassis, several variations.

Alecto SP III, 25pdr.

Alecto SP IV, 95mm Howitzer.

Alecto Centipede, Alecto w/small yoke mounted anti-mine rollers.

Alecto Dozer, Alecto w/2-edged dozer.

Alecto APC, engine front, bevelled-box hull w/ports rear, hollow road wheels for amphibious capability.

Harry Hopkins II, improved Mark VIII.

Amphibious Tank Marks I*, I** and I***, 1942, details unknown.

MARK NUMBERED MEDIUM TANKS AND RELATED VEHICLES

Vickers Medium Mark I (Vickers Tank No. 2) (Light Tank Mark I), 1923, 3pdr in round turret having bevelled sides, Hotchkiss hull mgs, engine left front, exposed small bogies, Armstrong-Siddeley air-cooled engine, 1 later w/Ricardo diesel engine, various turret changes for A/A mg, wireless, cupola, tracks later improved, one w/Gutteridge vision device, 17' 6" × 9' 1½" × 9' 3".

13pdr on Experimental Mount (probably C1E1), gun front, caisson centre, radiators rear.

Mark I 18pdr SP (Mounting SP QF 18pdr Mark Ia 1936 Pattern), A/A gun w/recoil cylinder above gun tube on unskirted chassis resembling that of Mark I tank, 19' 4" × 8' × 8' 5".

Vickers Mark I CS, 15pdr mortar in place of 3pdr.

Medium Mark Ia, 1926, thicker armour, driver's cowl hinged upward in 1 piece instead of split and hinged to sides as in Mark I, later modifications in turrets and tracks changed identification to Mark Ia*, 17' 6" × 9' 1½" × 8' 10½" (later 9' 10½").

Medium Tank Mark Ia (Ricardo Engine), 1930, built-out bow w/protruding knob, protected engine radiator.

Medium Mark Ia Special (L) (Vickers Female Tank) (Vickers India Pattern), 1925, 4 Vickers mgs in turret only, also referred to as Indian Tanks Nos. 59 and 60.

Tank Medium Mark I with Wheel Equipment (Vickers Wheel-cum-Track Tank Mark I), 1926, small solid tyres hinged coil spring dollies with wheel pairs fore and aft between tracks, not D3E1 or D3E2, 21' × 9' × 9' 6" on wheels (8' 10" on tracks).

Vickers Dragon, Mark I tank chassis w/horizontal louvers in front.

Self-Propelled Bridge (Track) Dragon Mark IV, 1940, experimental Ark-type bridge.

Dragon Mark I 30 Foot Bridge Carrier, 1926, built-up hull supporting portable bridge girders.

255

Vickers Wheel-cum-Track Mark Ia, 1926, improved version w/larger rear wheels, not D3E1 or D3E2.

Vickers Mark Ia CS, 15pdr mortar in place of 3pdr.

Vickers Mark Ia Modified, ventilator stack on turret.

Mark II Medium, 1926, suspension skirts added, driver's cowl split and raised above hull roof level, Hotchkiss and Vickers mgs, 17' 6" × 9' 1½" × 8' 10".

Mark II (Wireless), command tank modifications.

Mark II 18pdr SP (Mounting SP QF 18pdr Mark Ia, Ib, Ic, Id, 1927 Pattern) (Birch Gun) (Close Support Tank), centre mounted A/A gun w/shield on chassis like that of Mark II, 12 tons, 4 vehicles made varied slightly.

▼ 256

18pdr Close Support Tank (Mounting SP QF 18pdr Mark Ie, 1929 Pattern), cylindrical gun housing w/high conical half shield appearing to be a turret, 13 tons, 19' × 7' 10" × 7' 6".

Mark II CS (Medium Mark II CS), 15pdr mortar in place of 3pdr.

Mark II Modified (Mark II* Command), enlarged stationary turret w/bustle, no turret bevels.

Mark II Medium Command Tank (Box Tank) (Brigade Command Tank), 1932, box hull on Mark II chassis.

Mark II Medium Tank 18 Foot Bridge Carrier, standard tank w/bridge girders fixed to hull and skirting on both sides.

Mark II Special (Wireless), may be one of the above command tanks or a separate vehicle.

Mark II* Medium, same modifications as Mark I* and Mark Ia*.

Mark II** (Mark II Special), special spaced asbestos sheeting for use in

Egypt, also had rear door blower.

Mark IIa, 1929, ventilation improved with box blower on left side forward hull, cupola added to turret, 17' 6" × 9' 1½" ×10' ½".

Mark IIa*, blower added on rear door, turret bustle and improved track, 17' 6" × 9' 1½" × 10'.

Mark IIa CS, 15pdr mortar replaced 3pdr gun, 17' 6" × 9' 1½" × 10'.

Mark IIa/L, Australian pattern, coaxial mg on left of 3pdr and ball mounted Vickers mg on right of 3pdr.

Mark III Medium (16 Ton Tank), designed out of experience with the A6 series, 3 built, large turret overhang, 21' 6" × 8' 10" × 9' 8".

Brigade Command Tank, modified Mark III Medium.

Mark I Cruiser, see A9E1.

Mark I CS (A9 CS Mark I), 3.7" L/15 mortar.

Mark II Cruiser, see A10E1.

Mark IIa Cruiser, see A10E2.

Mark IIa Cruiser CS (Cruiser A10 CS Mark Ia), 3.7" L/15 mortar.

Mark III Cruiser, see A13 Mark I, some later reworked to Mark IV standards, 1 w/20–30mm armour instead of 14mm, 19' 3" × 8' 4" × 8' 6".

Mark III* Cruiser, see A13 Mark I.

Mark IV Cruiser, see A13 Mark II.

Mark IV Cruiser CS, 3.7" L/15 mortar.

Mark IVa Cruiser, see A13 Mark IIa.

Mark IVa Cruiser CS, see A13 Mark IIa CS.

Mark V Cruiser (Covenanter I), see A13 Mark III.

Mark V* Cruiser (Covenanter II), cooling improvements applied to Covenanter I, driver had peep slot on left and right, 19' 6" × 8' 6½" × 7' 4".

Mark V** Cruiser (Covenanter III), air louvers changed in later production.

Martel Articulated Cruiser, 3 road wheel front section w/2 small mg turrets, 4 road wheel rear section w/Mark II Cruiser turret, project.

Covenanter IV, production version of Covenanter III, 19' 6" × 8' 6½" × 7' 4".

Covenanter I CS (Cruiser Mark V CS), 3" howitzer.

Covenanter II CS (Cruiser Mark V* CS).

Covenanter III CS (Cruiser Mark V** CS).

Covenanter IV CS.

Covenanter OP.

Covenanter Command.

Covenanter ARV, recovery vehicle.

Covenanter AMRA Mark Ic, mine exploder, 4 double ribbed rollers suspended from covered lattice frame.

Covenanter with Fowler Roller, similar but wider ribbed rollers.

Covenanter with Spigot Mortar, 1942, experimental mounting of 96mm petard howitzer.

Covenanter I, II, IV Bridge-layers, scissors-type hydraulically-controlled bridge.

Mark VI Cruiser, see A16E1.

Mark VIa Cruiser (Crusader II), heavier armour, 2pdr and mg coaxial, auxiliary turret and mg removed in later production and crew reduced to 4, 19' 8" × 9' 1" × 7' 4".

Crusader III, 6pdr, square recess in vertical turret face instead of bulging mantlet, some w/Vickers K A/A guns, 20' 7½" × 8' 8" × 7' 4".

Crusader I CS (Cruiser Mark VI CS), 3.7" mortar in place of 2pdr.

Crusader II CS (Cruiser Mark VIa CS), similar.

Crusader Bofors A/A, open chassis w/Bofors 40mm gun.

Crusader A/A I, Bofors in pyramidal turret, 19' 2" × 8' 9" × 9' 3½".

Crusader I A/A I, sloping front flat sided turret w/2 Polsten guns.

Crusader III A/A II, twin Oerlikon in A/A turret w/bolts on turret face.

Crusader III A/A III, similar.

Crusader with Triple Oerlikon, open chassis, partial shield.

257

Crusader with 5.5" Howitzer, open chassis.

Crusader III Tower (Gun Tractor Mark I), turretless vehicle as prime mover for 17pdr wheeled carriage w/ and w/o wading equipment, 20' 8" × 8' 10" × 7' 6" (w/raised canopy).

Crusader Gun Tractor Mark I w/5.5" SP Gun Mount, gun mount from post-war FV305.

Crusader OP, command vehicle, dummy 2pdr.

Crusader Command.

Crusader Rear Link, wireless vehicle.

Crusader ARV, turretless vehicle w/A-frame.

Crusader Mine Roller AMRA Mark Id, similar equipment to that on Covenanter AMRA Mark Ic.

Crusader Dozer, A-frame and centre rotating pyramidal winch.

Crusader Dozer with Special Grab, turretless dozer w/hydraulically-controlled bucket in front of dozer.

Crusader I with Flotation Equipment, outboard catamaran boats similar to Straussler.

Cruiser Mark VII (Cavalier I), see A24E1.

Cavalier I O.P, dummy 6pdr.

Cavalier ARV.

Cruiser Mark VIII (Centaur I), see A27L.

Centaur II, 6pdr, 21' 10" × 9' 6" × 7' 9".

Centaur III, 75mm gun and 2 Besas, 21' 10" × 9' 6" × 7' 9".

Centaur III, bulldozer, turretless.

Centaur IV, 95mm howitzer, 21' 10" × 9' 6" × 7' 9".

Centaur III A/A I, 2 Polsten guns.

Centaur III A/A II, similar.

Centaur A/A, experimental multiple Browning mgs.

Centaur IV A/A I, twin Polsten guns in Crusader A/A turret.

Centaur IV A/A II, turret modified for extra man.

Centaur A/A with Triple Polsten, mock-up only.

Centaur Cyclops, F/T in sawed-off 6pdr in turret.

Centaur Kangaroo, gutted tank as APC.

Centaur IVa OP, command vehicle.

Centaur Dozer, dozer w/small A-frame on turretless Centaur, w/ or w/o wading equipment, 2 staggered square cupolas.

Centaur Dozer (Hydraulic), high centre mounted rams controlling dozer.

Centaur Taurus, towing vehicle.

Taurus with 17pdr, gun forward, mock-up only.

Cromwell I, see A27M.

Cromwell II, 6pdr and 2 Besas, no hull mg.

Cromwell III, Centaur I w/Rolls-Royce engine and 14" tracks, originally Mark X, 21' 9" × 9' 6" × 7' 9".

Cromwell III D, same w/side opening bow gunner's hatch.

Cromwell IV, Centaur III w/75mm gun, Rolls-Royce engine and 14" tracks, 21' 4" × 10' × 8' 2".

Cromwell IV (FS), same, no hull mg.

Cromwell V, 75mm gun, 2 Besas, riveted hull, 14" tracks, differences in escape hatches.

Cromwell V (FS), same, no hull gun.

Cromwell Vw (Cromwell D), welded turret and hull, 14" tracks.

Cromwell VI, 95mm howitzer, 2 Besas, riveted hull, 14" tracks.

Cromwell VI (FS), same, no hull mg.

Cromwell VII, 75mm and 2 Besas, applique armour, riveted hull, 15½" tracks, first Cromwell w/all round vision cupola, 20' 10" × 9' 6½" × 8' 2".

Cromwell VIIw, welded hull, applique armour, 15½" tracks.

Cromwell VIII, 95mm howitzer, welded hull, applique armour, 15½" tracks, 20' 10" × 10' × 8' 2".

Cromwell IX, distinction unknown.

Cromwell X, Centaur refitted w/Rolls-Royce Meteor engine, see Cromwell III.

Cromwell Prong, Cromwell fitted w/Culin hedgerow device.

Cromwell Crocodile, F/T vehicle.

Cromwell Command (Cromwell AOP), wooden dummy gun, several wireless antennae.

Cromwell ARV.

Cromwell With Mercury Vapour Searchlight, experimental CDL in modified turret.

Cromwell With Two Mercury Vapour Searchlights, light in tube mounted low on each side of turret.

Cromwell CIRD, Canadian Indestructible Roller Device for A/M use.

Cromwell With Quadruple Mounting For Lilo Rockets, rockets mounted on right turret top.

Cromwell Dracula, details unknown, may be Crocodile F/T tank.

Cromwell Taby, details unknown.

Cromwell Vanguard, details unknown.

(Note that Cromwells were further

identified as C w/Valentine final drive, D w/assistant driver hatch, F w/driver hatch added, E w/lower final drive gear ratio.)

Challenger I, see A30.

SP 17pdr A30 Challenger I (SP II), 3 support rollers, steamer roof on turret (Venetian blind armour cupola).

Avenger (Medium A Tank), no support rollers, see A30.

Comet I, Comet Ia w/5 small bogie wheels and 4 support rollers, 18" track, early production w/o telephone box in rear, 21' 6" (25' 1½") × 10' 1½" × 8' 10".

Comet 1a, see A34.

Comet Ib, 2" longer than Comet Ia.

Comet Command.

Comet Bridge-layer, scissors type.

Commodore, 17pdr, 6 large bogie wheels, no support rollers.

Valiant I, see A38.

Valiant I, w/75mm gun.

Valiant II, 6pdr, engine changed to Rolls-Royce Meteorite w-Rolls-Royce transmission.

Charioteer VI (FV4101), Cromwell VII w/Carnaervon 17pdr turret, intended as tank destroyer, 200 converted, 21' 1" (29') × 10' × 8' 4".

Charioteer VII, 1955, Cromwell w/20pdr and bore evacuator.

Universal Tank, see A45.

Centurion 1, see A41, 17pdr w/o muzzle brake or bore evacuator.

Centurion 1*, see A41*.

Centurion 2, see A41a.

Centurion 3, 1948, 84mm 20pdr substituted for 17pdr, bore evacuator, 24' 9" × 11' 1" × 9' 7".

Centurion 3 Bridge-layer, 1957, similar to Churchill VII Bridge-layer, 45' 1" long × 14' 1" wide.

Centurion 3 Bridge-layer, Twaby Ark type, mock-up only.

Centurion 4, 1953, 95mm howitzer, project only.

Centurion 5 (FV4011), Mark III w/Browning instead of Besa mgs, later w/cupola mounted mg and 20pdr, bomb-thrower removed,

turret roof reshaped, rear escape hatch eliminated, 25' 9½" (32' 3") × 11' 1" × 9' 8" to top of cupola.

Centurion 5/1 (FV4011), Centurion 5 w/thicker armour, 105mm gun.

Centurion Flail (FV4001).

Dozer Tank (FV4019), FV4003 type dozer attached to any Mark.

Flame-thrower Centurion (FV4019), experimental conversion, w/accompanying fuel trailer.

Centurion 5/2, Centurion 5 up-gunned to Centurion 13 standard.

Centurion 5 ARV (AVRE Tank Centurion Mark 5) (FV4003), recovery vehicle w/boom and 1 A-frame or 2 A-frames and no boom, w/dozer and demolition gun, 28' 6" × 13' 4" × 9' 10½".

Centurion Bridge-layer Mark 5 (FV4002), 1961, hydraulically lifted 52' span similar to Churchill VII Bridge-layer, has rollers at end to ease lowering, prototype was on Mark VII, 53' 6" × 14' × 12' 9".

Centurion 5 Ark (Ark Tank Centurion Mark 5) (FV4016), 1963, Twaby Ark-type bridge-layer, front and rear extendable ramps, 34' × 12' 9" × 13'.

Centurion AOP, command version Mark 5 w/several radios.

Centurion 6, Centurion 5/1 w/105mm gun, thicker armour, longer hull for added fuel capacity.

Centurion 6/1, Centurion 6 w/IR.

Centurion 6/2, Coaxial ranging gun added.

Centurion DD (FV4008a), 2 types.

Centurion 7 (FV4007), new hull, thicker armour, Centurion 5 turret, 20pdr gun, increased fuel capacity, side loading ammunition hatch on left side, 24' 11" (32' 4") × 11' 1" × 9' 7½".

Centurion 7/1 (FV4012), thicker armour, first vehicle to have UNF standard machine screw threads.

Centurion 7/2 (FV4012), minor modifications, return to 105mm gun.

Centurion 25pdr (FV3802), gun rear mounted in cylindrical turret half covered by enclosed cab, 5 road wheels.

▼ 260

Centurion 5.5" howitzer (FV3805), 1959, similar.

Centurion Crocodile, F/T in glacis.

Centurion 8 (FV4012), Mark 7 w/20pdr gun in new resilient trunnion turret w/differing counter-rotating commander's cupola, split hatch covers on cupola.

Centurion 8/1 (FV4012), Mark 6 w/minor modifications including 20pdr gun and addition of IR.

Centurion 8/2 (FV4012), gun changed to 105mm w/bore evacuator.

Centurion 9 (FV4015), Mark 7 w/new 105mm gun and additional armour.

Centurion 9/1 (FV4015), Mark 9 w/IR.

Centurion 9/2, Mark 9 w/coaxial ranging gun.

Centurion 10 (FV4017), thicker armour as Mark 9, new 105mm gun on impact-resisting trunnions, 25' 8" (32' 2½") × 11' 1" × 9' 9".

Centurion 10/1, Mark 10 w/IR.

Centurion 10/2, Mark 10 w/coaxial ranging gun.

Centurion 11 (FV4015), Mark 6 w/IR equipment and coaxial ranging gun, skirts removed.

Centurion 12, Mark 9 w/IR and coaxial ranging gun and Browning between in Mark 5 mantlet.

Centurion 13, Mark 10 w/thermal wrap on gun, coaxial ranging gun instead of range-finder, IR equipped, Browning mg higher in mantlet than in Mark 12, 25' 8" (32' 4") × 11'1½" × 9' 9".

Centurion BARV (Centurion Beach Tank ARV) (FV4018), beach armoured recovery vehicle, Mark 3 basis, 26' 6" × 11' 9" × 11' 2".

Centurion ARV I (FV4006), Mark 2 basis.

Centurion ARV II (FV4006), raised superstructure, Mark 3 basis, 29' 5" × 11' 1½" × 9' 6".

Centurion ARV III (FV4013), Mark 7 basis.

Centurion CDL, high narrow CDL on left side of turret.

Centurion Viper, AVRE type w/dozer, no skirts, line charge as in Sherman Tapeworm.

Centurion with Rigid Panel Flotation Equipment (Amphibious Landing Kit) (FV4008b), DD type jettisonable through single blow-out pin located on top of turret, 29' 10" × 11' 9" × 12'.

▼ 261

Conway (FV4004) (Heavy Anti-Tank SP No. 1), 120mm gun in faceted slope sided turret on Mark III chassis, 24' 9" (35' 2") × 11' 1½" × 10' 6".

FV4005, 183mm gun w/automatic loader on open Centurion chassis.

Centurion with Swingfire, 2 Swingfire missiles on both sides at rear of turret.

Medium Gun Tank No. 1 (Carnaervon) (FV221), 1951, resembled Centurion, wide tracks, Centurion 3 turret and 120mm gun.

Medium Gun Tank No. 2 (FV4201), 1959, US 105mm gun in turret common w/US T95, design study w/several prototypes, originally w/small road wheels later enlarged and engine HP increased.

Trials Vehicle (40-Ton Centurion) (FV4202), 1956, components tester for Chieftain, 5 road wheels, 105mm gun, no mantlet, 25' 9" (35') × 11' 3" × 8' 4".

Constable, 1959, air-transportable SP, 105mm gun in Abbot turret.

Chieftain (FV4201), Mark 1 Chieftain), 1962, 120mm gun w/thermal jacket, domed cupola on domed turret w/split commander's cupola hatch, driver supine, 585HP engine, 6 bogie wheels, 4 support rollers, skirted, also fitted w/large barrel type snorkel, 25' 1" (34' 3") × 11' 6" × 9' 3".

Chieftain Mark 2 (FV4202), single door replaced split cupola hatch, wider angled smoke dischargers, w/or w/o aluminium dozer blade, production models w/semi-circular lip around driver's cowl, 650HP engine, coaxial mg between 120mm gun and 50 cal ranging gun, 24' 6" (35' 4") × 11' 6" × 8' 3".

Chieftain AVLB (FV4205), scissors-type bridge-layer, short bridge, demolition gun.

Chieftain AVLB, B/L w/boom launch.

Chieftain AVRE (FV4203).

Chieftain ARV (FV4204), dozer blade also acts as earth anchor, pilot R1 was design test, pilot R2 basically Chieftain 5.

Chieftain Mark 3, new cupola w/cupola mounted mg and non-reflecting periscopes, new air cleaner, IR headlight and turret mounted IR detector behind the headlight.

Chieftain 3/3, improved air-conditioning, laser sight.

Chieftain 4, design study only.

Chieftain 5, 750HP engine, will become Mark 8 w/new fire control.

Chieftain Mark 5P, as sold to Iran.

Chieftain Mark 6, Mark 2 brought up to Mark 5 standard, will become Mark 9 w/new fire control.

Chieftain Mark 7, Mark 3/3 brought up to Mark 5 standard, will become Mark 10 w/new fire control.

INFANTRY TANKS AND RELATED VEHICLES

Mark I, see A11E1, early cupola w/slit on one side, later low cupola w/o slit but both types seen on various Marks, 15' 11" × 7' 6" × 6' 1½".

Mark IM, same but soft steel pilot.

Mark I with Coulter Plough, elevatable twin finger-plough on girders for A/M use.

Mark II, 1937, see A12E2.

Mark IIM, same, mild steel training tank.

Mark IIa (Matilda II), Besa in place of Vickers mg.

Mark IIa/M, same, mild steel training tank.

Mark IIb/M, same, mild steel training tank.

Mark IIa* (Matilda III), same as Mark I but change in engines, 18' 5" × 8' 6" × 8' 3".

Mark IIa** (Matilda IV), Matilda III w/Clayton Dewendre air servo transmission.

Matilda V, Westinghouse air servo transmission.

Matilda with Cromwell Turret, experimental.

Matilda II CS, 3" howitzer in place of 2pdr.

Matilda III CS, similar.

Matilda IV CS, similar.

Matilda II CDL (Canal Defence Light), de Thoren flashing arc light to blind enemy.

Matilda V CDL.

Matilda Frog Mark I, F/T on Matilda IV and V developed exclusively in and for Australia, counterweight near muzzle.

Matilda Baron, turret removed, shaft driven rotor flail w/rhomboid-shaped flail-driving engines over rear of each track, small driver's cab.

Matilda Scorpion and Breach Marker, flail w/marker chute over rear of right track.

Matilda Murray, Cordite operated F/T.

Matilda with Tailpiece, 1940, 3 versions of tailpiece, raised suspension.

Matilda Scorpion Prototype, flail on lattice girder w/flail actuating engine on right side over tracks.

Matilda Scorpion I, flail operator in armoured box beside right track.

Matilda Scorpion II (♯1 Scorpion), similar to prototype but simplified lattice girder.

Matilda Lobster, crab rotor arms w/Baron rotor and flail.

Matilda Mine Roller (Matilda AMRA Ia), 4 ribbed rollers carried on front projecting girders w/deflecting shields for each roller.

Matilda with Carrot, similar but single deflector shield.

Matilda with Heavy Carrot, 600 pounds high explosive on a plain girder with double roller.

Matilda I with 2″ A/M Torpedo Mortar.

Matilda with Trench Crossing device, long lattice girders w/front end supported on modified Bren Carrier track frames, Middle East experiment.

Matilda with Inglis Bridge, long skeleton bridge pushed on orolo (track-laying bogie assemblies).

Matilda with Experimental Crane.

Matilda II TLC, see Churchill TLC Laying Device and Carpet.

Infantry Tank Mark III (Valentine I), 1940, based on A10E3, 2pdr and Besa, 17 tons, first British tank w/electric turret traverse and geared gun elevating mechanism, 2-man turret, narrow double pin tracks, AEC petrol engine, 17′ 9″ × 8′ 7½″ × 7′ 5½″.

Mark III* (Valentine II), diesel engine, 2-man turret, 17′ 9″ × 8′ 7½″ × 7′ 5½″.

Valentine III, 3-man turret, AEC diesel engine, 17′ 9″ × 8′ 7½″ × 7′ 5½″.

Valentine IV, 2-man turret, 2pdr and Besa, GMC diesel.

Valentine V, 3-man turret, similar to III but GMC diesel.

Valentine VI (Infantry Tank Mark III***), see Canada.

Valentine VII, see Canada.

Valentine VIIa, see Canada.

Valentine VIII, 6pdr in new 2-man turret, AEC diesel, welded bow, no coaxial mg, 19′ 4″ × 8′ 9½″ × 7′ 1½″.

Valentine IX, same as VIII but GMC diesel, 19′ 4″ × 8′ 9½″ × 7′ 1½″.

Valentine X, same as IV but 6pdr, 19′ 4″ × 8′ 9½″ × 7′ 1″.

Valentine XI, same as IX but 75mm gun, 19′ 4″ × 8′ 9½″ × 7′ 1″.

Valentine with Cast Hull, experimental.

Vanguard, improved Valentine, none produced but some features were incorporated into Archer.

Valentine 6pdr SP, gun w/curved shield mounted forward, box cab for crew.

Valentine 25pdr Gun Carrier Mark I (25pdr on Valentine) (Bishop I), 1942, high box turret open top and rear, partly bevelled turret front, 18′ 2″ × 8′ 7½″ × 9′ 1″.

Valentine 7.92″ Flame Mortar, large mortar on open chassis.

Valentine 17pdr SP, pilot, rear-mounted 17pdr firing front in faceted open top box.

Valentine 17pdr SP, production (SPI) (Archer I), larger open top turret sloping down in front and slightly more forward than on pilot, some later w/horizontal louvers in side of turret, 21′ 11″ × 9′ ½″ × 7′ 4½″.

Valentine Cordite I, II, IV (Valentine Flame-thrower Tank), Cordite operated F/T in small right front auxiliary turret.

Valentine Pressure Type II (Valentine Flame-thrower Tank), Nitrogen operated F/T.

Valentine CDL, pilot CDL vehicle in WWII.

Valentine Scorpion III, rotor flail suspended from lattice frames, faceted welded turret replaced regular turret and housed 2 rotor driving engines, 27′ × 11′ 10″ × 7′ 5½″.

Valentine with Spiked Rollers, 2 rollers leading tracks, 1 roller centre rear.

Valentine AMRA Mark 1B, 4 ribbed rollers carried on girders, no deflecting shields.

Valentine with Fowler Roller, similar but wider ribbed rollers.

Valentine-Straussler Anti-Mine Vehicle, 2 long double half-leaf spring frames each w/4 electric solenoid controlled grub hooks.

Valentine Snake, extensible tube exploder for mines.

Valentine IV with W2/700 Jet Engine, 1946, centre mounted in front as mine exploder.

Burmark, Valentine chassis w/double Twaby bridge.

Valentine OP, dummy gun.

Valentine Bridge-layer, scissors type.

Valentine Margic Carpet, carpet bobbin low in front, vehicle controlled by tank commander.

Valentine III DD, also Valentine V, IX and XI.

Jumping Tank, 1946, Valentine w/hinged hydraulic jacks fore and aft.

Rota Tank, Valentine w/free rotor for air-dropping, project cancelled.

Infantry Tank Mark IV (Churchill I), see A22E1, 2pdr gun and Besa mg.

Churchill ICS, 3″ howitzer in both turret and bow.

Infantry Tank Mark IVa (Churchill II Pilot).

Churchill II, 2pdr and Besa in turret, Besa in front plate, those used at

Dieppe had Ronson F/T in place of hull Besa, 24′ 5″ × 10′ 8″ × 8′ 2″.

Churchill II CS, 3″ howitzer in turret, 2pdr in front plate.

Churchill III, welded turret w/6pdr, one experimentally w/Sherman 75mm gun, some converted to Mark VII status, first production vehicles had early air intakes and uncovered tracks, later longer 6pdr w/counter-weight, 25′ 2″ × 10′ 8″ × 8′ 2½″.

Churchill IV, cast turret w/6pdr, some converted to Mark VII basis, 25′ 2″ × 10′ 8″ × 8′ 4½″.

Churchill IVa, cast turret w/Sherman 75mm gun and Browning mg.

Churchill IVb (Churchill IV/75) (NA75), Sherman 75mm gun, no hull mg.

Churchill V, cast turret, Mark IV w/95mm howitzer, 2 Besas, some converted to Mark VII status, 25′ 2″ × 10′ 8″ × 9′ 2″.

Churchill VI, cast turret, Mark IV w/75mm, 2 Besas, some converted to Mark VII status, 25′ 2″ × 10′ 8″ × 8′ 2½″.

Churchill VII, see A22F and A42.

Churchill VII with All Round Cupola, commander's cupola w/replaceable periscopes, 25′ 2″ × 10′ 8″ × 9′

Churchill VIII, welded hull, cast turret, w/flared base, Mark VII w/95mm howitzer, 2 Besas, 24′ 2″ × 10′ 10″ × 8′ 11″.

Churchill IX (FV3903), Churchill III –IV w/applique armour on turret and hull, 6pdr gun.

Churchill IX LT, same as IX but original turret retained.

Churchill X, Churchill III, IV, VI w/75mm gun and Besa in heavy welded turret, applique armour, new visor and glacis, heavy suspension, new transmission.

Churchill X LT, VI w/applique armour but original turret.

Churchill XI, Churchill V–VI w/applique armour and 95mm howitzer.

Churchill XI LT, same w/original turret.

AVRE Churchill IV (Armoured Vehicle Royal Engineers), 96mm petard howitzer, several variations.

AVRE Derrick Generator, front mounted crane.

AVRE Churchill VII (FV3903), 6½″ petard howitzer.

AVRE 75mm QF (AVREII), 75mm gun AVRE.

Ardeer Aggie (Ardeer Projector), 1943, experimental AVRE, 6½″ petard howitzer in new turret on Churchill III, 1 built.

Woodpecker, AVRE w/4 rocket propelled petards on either side of vehicle.

Churchill Adder, periscope type F/T on rear deck.

Churchill VII Crocodile, F/T in left front plate replacing Besa, trailer for fuel.

Churchill Cobra (Mamba), same w/F/T hooded, some fitted w/Culin device.

Churchill Oke, original F/T.

Churchill Salamander No. 1, F/T below 75mm gun.

Churchill I 3″ Gun Carrier Mark I, box hull gun in hull mount in left front plate, 25′ 2″ (26′ 1″) × 10′ 8″ × 9′ 1″.

Churchill Atherton Jack, jib crane mounted on turret.

Churchill Prong, Churchill fitted w/Culin type hedgerow cutters.

Churchill ARV, turretless prototype recovery vehicle.

Churchill II ARV Mark I, similar, cranes carried on sides and mounted for use.

Churchill II ARV Mark II, 1944, twin small cylindrical turrets, A-frame at rear, some w/6-sided cupola.

Churchill IV ARV I, fixed turret w/dummy 6pdr gun.

Churchill VI ARV.

Churchill BARV, beach armoured recovery vehicle, Churchill XI w/turret replaced by large cylinder.

Churchill I CDL, experimental.

Churchill Kangaroo (FV3904), 1947, gutted Churchill VII as APC, open top hull, small superstructure forward.

Churchill Minefield Marking Flag Discharger (Whyman Mine Marker), flags carried in box dispenser over right track frame to outline cleared minefield.

Churchill Marking Light Discharger, similar w/lights on rods.

Churchill Interim Flail, 1956, turretless, large hydraulic rams low at rear of track frames, flail folded over rear deck when not in use, covered flail chain drive.

Churchill Toad (FV3902), Churchill IV w/flail supported by wheels carried on semi-circular rocker arms which could be folded over rear deck when travelling, equipped w/Whyman Line Markers to outline cleared areas.

Remote-Controlled Churchill Flail, gutted Churchill w/flail, radio controlled, experimental.

Churchill AMRA Mark IIe, 4 flanged rollers on reinforced girder frame followed by 2 heavy rollers to cover gaps between pairs.

Churchill AMCR No. 1 Mark I, A/M
reconnaissance caster roller, 2 roller
pairs on swivels.

Churchill with 16″ CIRD and 18″
CIRD, Canadian Indestructible
Roller Device Mine Exploder, also
experimentally w/15.5″ and 21″
CIRD.

Churchill Farmer Track, 2 very large
rollers behind a harrow on a frame.

Churchill Farmer Front, large twin
rollers behind multi-fingered wide
mine plough, also w/large disc
wheels in place of rollers.

Churchill II with Farmer Deck
Plough, double plough carried on
high lattice frame.

Farmer Deck IIIa, similar plus rollers.

Churchill IV with Plough A
(Churchill OAC Plough A) (OAC
Mark I) double plough preceded
by double rollers mounted on
counter-weighted latticed girders.

Churchill with Bullshorn Plough B
(Bullshorn Mark II), 2 heavy
ploughs w/curved centre deflector
on small hinged frame.

Churchill Plough C (OAC Mark II),
similar to OAC Plough A but 1
barrel-like roller in front of each
plough.

Churchill IV with Plough D (Atherton
Equipment), similar but w/o rollers,
plough controlled by small rear
deck mounted Atherton jib crane.

Churchill IV with Bullshorn Plough
Mark IIIc, 4-fingered ploughs with
deflectors on crossed I-beam framework, variations existed.

Churchill IV with Jeffries Plough,
similar to Bullshorn Plough IIIc
but w/V-shaped-fingered ploughs.

Churchill with Senior Equitine
Cultivator, wheeled farm cultivator
pulled behind Churchill.

Churchill Harrow, wheeled farm
harrow pulled behind Churchill.

Churchill Light Carrot, light steel
extension outrigger on vehicle bow
holding explosive charge to be
dropped.

Churchill with Bangalore Torpedo,
long iron pipes containing explosives
carried on framework over both
tracks, fitted together and pushed
into minefield.

Jet Mine Clearing Device, frame w/3,
6 or 12 five-inch rockets mounted
on Churchill bow at 60 degree angle
to the direction of travel, also
w/rockets in armoured box.

Churchill IV 3″ Snake, short snake
sections carried over tracks, no
main armament.

Churchill Gun Carrier Snake, similar
but much longer snake.

Churchill AVRE Conger, 2″ Mark I
line charge device similar to
Sherman Tapeworm.

Churchill Goat, at least 12 different
types existed, including Elevatable
Goat, Goats Mark I–III, Single
Onion, Jones Onion, AVRE Goat,
Quinson Device, Porton Apron, all
of them devices for suspending
explosive charges from a front
frame for placing on near, far or
both sides of walls, Carrots and
Onions were dropped, Quinsons
were hung, Goats slid their charges
into place, one Onion carried two
parallel snake pipes vertically as a
Bangalore torpedo device.

Churchill Great Eastern Ramp, 1945,
60′ span rocket-projected sliding
section bridging ramp, pilot
Churchill I basis, production
Churchill IV w/Churchill VII
suspension.

Churchill Girder Bridge-layer (SBG
Bridge) (Jumbo), 34′ bridge
supported in front from A–frame.

AVRE with Folding SBG Assault
Bridge, similar but bridge hinged in
centre.

Churchill III and IV Bridge-layer
(30-foot Tank Bridge No. 2), span
on pivot arm carried on top of tank
until lifted forward on pivot arm,
37′ 6″ × 10′ 6½″ × 11′ 1″.

Churchill VII Bridge-layer (30-foot
Tank Bridge No. 3) (Towed
Standard Box Girder Bridge), 1948,
SBG type w/bridge cable supported
over a kingpin to a rear deck
mounted winch, bridge normally
carried on 2-wheel trailer.

Churchill Ark I (Armoured Ramp
Carrier I), bridgeway mounted on
top of turretless chassis with hinged
bridgeway front and rear, entire
vehicle being used as a bridge of
type known as Twaby Ark,
Churchill II and IV basis.

Churchill III–IV Ark II Italian
Pattern (Churchill Twaby Ark)
(Octopus), 53½′ span, interchangeable M1 (Long) and M2 (Short)
front and rear spans supported by
kingposts front and rear.

Churchill Ark II UK Pattern, 47½′
span, front ramp only supported by
kingpost, rear span later added,
Churchill III and IV basis.

Foldups, resembled Ark II, US
treadway bridge launched by rocket,
experimental.

Lakeman Ark, Churchill Gun Carrier
w/ark whose centre portion could
be raised hydraulically to permit
using vehicle to surmount a high
far wall.

Churchill Skid Bailey, Bailey Bridge
pushed into place.

Churchill Prototype Bailey, Bailey
Bridge supported on 2 turretless
Churchill chassis.

Churchill Mobile Bailey (BMB), 90′
span hinged at tracked support
bogie assembly (orolo), pushed by
Churchill.

Churchill Brown (Mobile Brown), 1
Churchill w/turret, 1 w/o supporting Bailey Bridge, disengaged by
small explosive charge.

Churchill Dalton, improvement on
Brown, Churchill Ark in front,
Churchill AVRE rear, bridge dis-
engaged by firing cartridge within
AVRE.

Churchill VII Bridge-layer (30-Foot
Bridge Tank No. 3), 1956, improved
version of Churchill III–IV Bridge-
layer for heavier post-war vehicles.

Hudnott Ark, flexible treadway rolling
over large side plate guides, one
track each way, rocket actuated,
experimental.

Linked Ark Folding Assault Bridge
(Churchill Twin Ark) (FV3901)
(Linked Dog), paired Churchill
Twaby Ark, on Churchill IV, could
be used singly or coupled.

Churchill Ark Churchill II, trackway
on top of Churchill slid open like
extension ladder by winch-
controlled cables.

Woodlark, double Twaby type but
centre span considerably higher.

Churchill Chespale Fascine, brush
fascine carried at bow of AVRE
and released by cable, several
versions including Dumbbell
Fascine.

Churchill Moyens Fascine Launcher, 1948, 4-segment steel frame fascine mounted in cradle on turret.

Churchill TLC Laying Device and Carpet (Type A Mark I), 1939, originally intended for cruisers and infantry tanks and experimentally on a Matilda, weighted carpet dropped which was pulled from roller by tracks.

Churchill TLC Laying Device and Carpet (Fascine Type), small bobbin carried like fascine on bow.

Churchill Carpet-Layer (Bobbin) (Medium Bobbin), originally an experiment for Dieppe landing.

AVRE with Type B Twin Bobbins, 2 bobbins, giving choice of surface material.

Churchill Bobbin Type C Mark II, single bent side arms supporting bobbin.

Churchill Bobbin Type D, large drum, fixed side arms.

Churchill with Log Carpet-Layer, logs fastened to cables as carpeting.

Churchill Pussyfoot, rubber-tyred road wheels and modified engine and transmission.

Black Prince, see A43.

Black Prince Ark, bridging tank, project only.

Black Prince Bridging Tank, hydraulic bridge-layer, project only.

Black Prince Flame-thrower Tank, project only.

Conqueror I (FV214) (Heavy Gun Tank Mark I), 1953, 65 tons, US 120mm 60pdr gun w/coaxial mg, prominent glacis weld, massive cast turret high in rear, cupola w/cross-cupola range-finder, 8 road wheels, 4 support rollers, outgrowth of Universal Tank, see A45, 25′ 4″ (38′) × 12′ 11″ × 11′ 10″.

Conqueror II (SP Heavy Anti-Tank Mounting) (Heavy Gun Tank Mark II) (FV215a), smooth glacis weld, single driver periscope, skirted, 180mm 2pdr gun, 2-piece turret hatch, 25′ 4″ (38′) × 13′ × 10′ 6½″.

Conqueror Heavy AVRE (FV215b).

Conqueror ARV (FV209), turretless, prototype only.

Conqueror ARV Mark I (FV219), prototype.

Conqueror ARV Mark II (FV222), no turret, prototype.

Conqueror Flail (FV204), details not available.

Conqueror Ark (FV223), bridging tank.

Conqueror Viper (Giant Viper) (Baby Viper), explosive line charges of 2

sizes projected by rocket, name dependent on length and width of path cleared.

US TANK DESIGNATIONS AND US TANK MODIFICATIONS

Scott, US M8 Howitzer Motor Carriage.

Stuart I, Light Tank M3 w/Continental engine.

Stuart II, same w/Guiberson engine.

Stuart Hybrid II, later model M3 w/Guiberson engine.

Stuart III, Light Tank M3A1 w/Continental engine.

Stuart Hybrid IV Light Tank M3A1 w/Guiberson engine.

Stuart V, Light Tank M3A3.

Stuart VI, Light Tanks M5 and M5A1.

Stuart Kangaroo, gutted Stuart VI used as APC.

Stuart Tower, gutted Stuart VI used to tow A/T gun, similar to Kangaroo.

Stuart Recce, turret removed, several versions, some w/grenade netting.

Stuart II and VI Command, turret removed, several versions.

18pdr on Stuart, Middle East improvisation, square shield, gun fired forward.

Chaffee I, Light Tank M24.

Locust I, Light Tank M22.

274

▼

Locust with Littlejohn Conversion, conical bore gun device applied to standard M6 37mm gun.

Lee I, Medium Tank M3, additional stowage boxes usually and suspension mud rails sometimes added, cupola usually removed and mg ring mount sometimes substituted.

Lee II, Medium Tank M3A1.

Lee III, Medium Tank M3A2.

Lee IV, Medium Tank M3A3, Continental engine.

Lee V, same w/diesel engine.

Lee VI, Medium Tank M3A4.

Grant I (ELH) ('Egypt's Last Hope'), Medium M3 w/British turret, no cupola.

Grant II, Medium M3A5, with cupola.

Grant CDL, new flare top turret w/dummy gun and flashing arc light.

Grant ARV, recovery vehicle w/dummy turret.

Grant ARV I, turret removed, twin AA mg.

Grant ARV I, US T2 Recovery Vehicle w/added bracing legs in rear and mortar mounted on front glacis.

Grant Scorpion III, lattice frame and flail rotor on Grant I, engine for flail over right rear track.

Grant Scorpion IV, same but rotor engine over both tracks.

Grant Command, no hull gun, 75mm dummy gun in turret.

Priest I (M7 Howitzer Motor Carriage), some w/armoured jacket over recoil mechanism.

Priest Kangaroo, gutted M7 as APC.

Priest Modified, 254mm mortar replacing 105mm howitzer.

Sherman I, US M4 Medium w/75mm gun.

Sherman Hybrid I, US M4 Medium w/cast glacis and 75mm gun.

Sherman Ib, US M4 Medium w/105mm howitzer.

Sherman Ib*, US M4E8 w/suspension skirts and horizontal volute spring suspension.

Sherman IbY, US M4 w/105mm howitzer and 23″ track.

Sherman Ic, US M4 w/17pdr.

Sherman II, US M4A1 Medium w/75mm gun.

Sherman IIa, same w/75mm gun and wet ammunition stowage.

Sherman IIb, same w/105mm howitzer.

Sherman IIc, US M4A1 w/17pdr.

Sherman III, US M4A2 Medium w/75mm gun.

Sherman IIIaY, same w/23″ track and 76mm gun.

Sherman IV, US Medium M4A3 w/75mm gun.

Sherman IVa, same w/76mm gun.

Sherman IIIaYE876, US Medium M4A3E8 w/23″ track.

Sherman IVb, US M4A3 w/105mm howitzer.

Sherman IVc, same w/17pdr.

Sherman V, US M4A4 Medium w/75mm gun.

Sherman V (Guards) (Sherman Tulip), same w/Typhoon rocket projectors on turret.

Sherman Vc (Firefly), with 17pdr, bow mg eliminated, 20′ 2″ (23′ 8″) × 8′ 7″ × 9′ 4″.

Sherman VI, US M4A6.

Sherman VII, US M4A6 w/75mm gun.

Sherman VIIc, same w/17pdr.

Sherman Prong, same as US hedge-row removal prongs, MKI on Sherman and M10, MKIII on Cromwell.

Sherman Porcupine, 2 spiked rollers on harness attached to high cross bar 8′ in front of tank.

Sherman Minefield Marking Lights, 1943, experimental, small chute over left rear idler containing 12 spiked box canes containing battery operated lights visible to the rear, released by cable to spiked drum ratchet over right rear idler.

Sherman with Whyman Mechanical Lane Marker, 1944, 2 banks of 12 firing tubes on each side at rear containing 7′ long flagged pickets fired by cartridges for marking cleared minefield lanes.

Sherman with Lane Marking Hopper, drum at rear to release powdered chalk at intervals to mark mine swept lane boundaries.

Sherman du Toit Sweeper, forerunner of flails, 2 simple I-beams supporting geared 6″ flail rotor w/chains.

Sherman Scorpion IV, same assembly as Grant Scorpion II.

Sherman Crab I Pilot, similar but large rotor.

Sherman V Crab I, more advanced version on heavier girders, driven by engine over rear of right track, hydraulic ram on each side controlled rotor height, each end of rotor had wire-cutting knives, periscope had dust protection cowls, mantlet and turret were sealed.

Sherman V Crab II, hydraulic ram on left side replaced by counter-weight, rotor engine moved forward, with minefield edge marker chutes.

Sherman Marquis, originally Sherman Octopus, similar to Crab II but large welded flat sided turret containing hydraulic rams and rotor engine.

Sherman Lobster, crab rotor arms w/Baron rotor and flail.

Sherman Pram, partly covered chain drive in roller supported outriggers.

Sherman Pram Scorpion, combination low wide flail and 4 ribbed rollers.

Sherman BARV Flail, Beach Armoured Recovery Vehicle w/flail.

Sherman Centipede, 24 small rollers on 2/axled yoke dragged behind flail equipped Sherman.

Sherman with 15½″ CIRD, 2/heavy rollers in front of each track mounted on heavy 2/way spring loaded frames extending forward of rollers.

Sherman with 18″ CIRD, similar but larger rollers.

Sherman CIRD (Rigid Stirrup), 1946, similar but heavier springless frame.

Sherman CIRD with tapeworm.

Sherman V AMRCR No. 1a Mark I, A/M reconnaissance caster roller, 4 rollers, 1 pair ahead of the other on swivels suspended from heavy frames.

Sherman Lulu (originally Zulu), heavily-ribbed wooden barrel rollers suspended from retractable arms in front of each track and 1 pivoted centre rear, entire assembly folded up behind turret for travel, rollers could detonate A/P mines but not A/T mines, each also was a mine detector, producing both an audible

signal and a light indicating which roller was over a mine.

Sherman Porpoise, waterproof towed sledge, not a tank.

Sherman with Bullshorn III Plough, similar to Churchill Plough B.

Sherman with Bullshorn IVc Plough, similar.

Sherman with Jeffries Plough, similar to Churchill Jeffries.

Sherman with MD1 Plough, similar to Jeffries but simplified frame.

Sherman 3″ Snake, ratchet actuated snake, 20′ lengths of 3″ water pipe pulled or pushed into minefield to clear a 21′ lane.

Sherman Tapeworm, snake in a trailer, pulled out by the tank after trailer is unhooked and then detonated, 500 yards of 2¼″ hose, the 50′ of hose nearest the tank was filled w/sand rather than explosive, usually used with CIRD equipped tank.

Sherman Petard (Sherman AVRE), Sherman fitted w/96mm petard howitzer in turret.

Sherman Woodpecker, 1944, Sherman fitted w/four 96mm petard howitzers per side fired singly or in ripple.

Sherman with 2″ Conger Mark I, 1944, towed engineless Bren carrier with rocket and projector, 300 yards of 2″ woven hose fired, then pumped full of explosive by compressed air and detonated.

Sherman CIRD with Flying Bangalore Torpedo, 1943, for wire clearance, Bangalore projectors on side arms of mine roller assembly, each holding 2 Bangalore torpedoes with small grapnels.

Sherman V Adder (Sherman Cobra), 1944, periscope type on rear deck, fuel tanks rear, also seen mounted in wireless mast base, 22′ 2″ × 8′ 7″ × 9′ 9″.

Sherman Crocodile, periscope type F/T w/trailer for fuel.

Sherman Scorpion, 1945, 4 small F/T to fire in all directions on standard Sherman, capable of separate or salvo fire, intended to prevent laying of satchel charges.

Sherman Salamander No. I, Wasp Mark IIA F/T in armoured tube below dummy 75, on M4A3 and M4A4.

Sherman Salamander No. II, on M4, dummy 75 with Wasp F/T with extended barrel and F/T in gun loader's periscope opening.

Sherman Salamander No. III, on M4, F/T in dummy 75.

Sherman Salamander No. III*, alternate A or B in dummy 75.

Sherman Salamander No. IV, on M4, Wasp IIa F/T in mantlet below dummy 75.

Sherman Salamander No. V, on M4, F/T below and coaxial with main armament.

Sherman Salamander No. VI, F/T in blister on left side of turret.

Sherman Salamander No. VII, F/T in wireless antenna base on right side.

Sherman Salamander No. VIII, similar to No. VI.

Sherman Ramp, details not available.

Sherman Bridge-layer, long double bridge girder hinged to front and supported from heavy A-frame.

Sherman Bridge-layer, short double bridge girder supported fore and aft from centre Kingpole, turretless Twaby Ark type.

Sherman Twaby Ark, short folding girders fore and aft w/centre runway, entire assembly acting as a bridge.

Sherman Ark, similar to Twaby Ark but longer lattice type girders.

Sherman Octopus, Ark type, hinged lattice girders.

Sherman Plymouth Bridge-layer, huge Bailey Bridge carried on Sherman.

Sherman Dachshund, similar to Plymouth.

Sherman Fascine, brush fascine carried on rail framework on turretless Sherman.

Sherman Wooden Crib Carrier, wooden cradle w/wooden crib fascine.

Sherman with Assault Boat Mounting, assault boat carried on support rack on combat tank.

Sherman III DD (M4A2), original DD, DD collapsible canvas screen as flotation device w/twin screw power take-off.

Sherman III DD Mark I (M4A2), strengthened top rail and 8 self-locking struts fitted.

Sherman III DD Mark II, modified Mark I.

Sherman III DD Mark III, US built on M4A2, both original and HVSS types.

Sherman III DD with Rocket Egress, five 5″ ATOG rockets on either side to assist in climbing slippery banks.

Sherman III aY DD III.

Sherman V DD (M4A2), original DD on Sherman.

Sherman V DD Mark I, same as Sherman III DD I.

Sherman DD II Ginandit, sections of matting released by mechanical device under hull used with DD vehicles to gain initial footing on loose soil.

Sherman DD with Belch, 1944, motor driven pump drawing sea water and sprayed through jets to extinguished a fire in case a flame barrage was met during a landing operation.

Sherman V DD APC, turret replaced by mushroom shaped cover, used as APC.

Sherman with Grapnel, rocket projector on rear of turret to fire a grapnel and line for use against barbed or accordion wire or for cliff assaults.

Sherman Topee, armoured hinged side section boat built around tank.

Sherman BARV, flare to box-like superstructure beach armoured recovery vehicle, several versions.

Sherman BARV Crab, same fitted w/A/M flail.

Sherman II ARV III, US M32 Tank Recovery Vehicle.

Sherman III ARV I, British conversion to tank recovery vehicle.

Sherman V ARV I, similar, 20′ × 8′ 7″ × 6′ 10″.

Sherman V ARV II, British conversion w/dummy gun and turret.

Sherman Rear Link, multiple wireless and telephone equipped tank.

Priest OP, US M7 SP converted to OP vehicle.

Priest Kangaroo, US M7 w/howitzer removed and embrasure plated over, used as an APC.

Sherman CDL, bolted-on oval mg mount in new turret w/CDL unit.

Sherman Kangaroo, several Marks of Shermans gutted for APC use.

Sherman Special Suspension, experimental installation of Horstmann scissors-type suspension.

SP 3″ M10 (Wolverine), US 3″ Gun Motor Carriage M10.

SP 17pdr M10 (Achilles), British modified US M10 w/ and w/o muzzle brake.

Tower M10, turretless M10 used as a prime mover.

M10 with Experimental Mine Plough, turretless M10 w/US-type concave-V snow plough.

Sherman Tropicalized, various modifications for use in the South Pacific including suspension skirts.

FV100, 300 & 400 SERIES VEHICLES

FV 15,000, 1964, test rig prototype of Scorpion, hydraulic suspension, aluminium tracks.

FV101 (Alvis Light Tank) (Scorpion), 1968, Jaguar engine ,high HP/wt ratio, 76mm gun as on Saladin A/C w/coaxial mg, FV433 (Abbot) flotation screen, low diamond-shaped rear mounted turret, torsion bar suspension, 14′ 5″ (w/gun) × 7′ 2″ × 6′ 10½″.

FV102 (CVR (T) GW) (Striker), same chassis, Swingfire A/T missile, turret similar to Ferret Scout Car Mark 5, 14′ 1½″ × 7′ 2″ × 7′ 3″.

FV103 (CVR (T)) (Spartan), same chassis, small cupola, APC, 16′ × 7′ 3″ × 7′ 4″.

Spartan with ZB 298 Radar Surveillance, target acquisition radar.

FV104 (CVR (T) ARM AMB) (Samaritan), ambulance vehicle, no turret, 15′ 6″ × 7′ × 7′ 2″.

FV105 (CVR (T) CMD) (Sultan), similar to Spartan, command vehicle, 16′ × 7′ × 7′ 2″.

FV106 (CVR (T) REC) (Samson), ARV on basic vehicle, rear trail spade, internal winches, 15′ 6″ long, 7′ wide.

FV107 (CVR (T) ANTI) (Scimitar), basic vehicle w/Fox A/C 30mm gun turret, idler higher than drive sprocket, 14′ 4″ × 7′ 2″ × 6′ 11″.

FV301, 1945, Light tank w/77mm gun, chassis only complete, see also A46.

FV302 (GPO/CP Vehicle), project only.

FV303 (20pdr SP A/T Gun), project only.

FV304 (25pdr SP Gun), project only.

FV305 (5.5″ SP Gun), project only.

FV306 (Light ARV), project only.

FV307 (Radar Vehicle), also envisaged as a radio vehicle, project only.

FV308 (Field Artillery Tractor), project only.

FV309 (Royal Artillery Section Vehicle), project only.

FV310 (Light APC), project only.

FV311 (Armoured Load Carrier), project only.

FV401 (Cambridge Carrier) (Universal Carrier Tracked No. 4), 1950, 4 road wheels, torsion bar suspension, prototype for FV402.

FV402 (AOP Team Carrier) (OP No. 4), command vehicle w/armoured cupola roof, based on FV401.

Cambridge Carrier DD, carrier w/flotation device.

FV403, A/T artillery tractor.

FV404 Starting and Charging Vehicle.

FV405 Light General Purpose Carrier.

FV406 Command Carrier.

FV407 (Tentacle) (Air Co-operation Signals Vehicle).

FV408 Armoured Ambulance, 2′ longer than FV401 to accommodate stretchers.

FV409 GPO/CP (Command Post Vehicle).

FV420 (Malkara Mounting), basic FV432 chassis w/A/T missile mount, experimental.

FV421 Load Carrier, predecessor of FV432, high hull w/horizontal fluted drop side doors.

FV422 Armoured Personnel Carrier.

FV423 Command Post Vehicle.

FV424 Royal Engineers Section Vehicle.

FV425 REME Section Vehicle.

FV426 (Orange William), A/T missile vehicle.

FV431 Load Carrier, 1958, armoured cab, removable body w/hinged-up sides, FV432 components.

FV432 Prototypes, 6 w/Rolls Royce B81 engine, 6 w/Rolls Royce K60 multi-fuel engine, 2 headlamps, flotation screen sloped downward rear to front.

FV432 Mark 1/1 (Trojan), production, resembled US M113, 4 headlamps, smoke mortars left and right front, flotation screen followed hull side outlines, protruding air intake filters right side, silencer box protruding left side near bow and exhaust pipe along left side, 16′ 9″ × 9′ 9″ × 6′ 2″ (7′ 6″ overall).

FV432 Mark 1/2.

FV432 Mark 2, exhaust over left top.

FV432 Mark 2/1, right side air intake flush w/hull, w/the following variations (1973): cargo; ambulance for 4 stretchers; FACE (Field Artillery Computer Equipment), on Mark 2/1 basis, wire rack over hatch, vertical exhaust pipe extension; command vehicle with penthouse (tent extension), extension mast sections in rack on left side; with Sperry vehicle navigator, outrigger device on glacis; sonic detection equipment, 1971, rear superstructure and two erectable telescopic masts; with ZB298 ground surveillance radar; Cymbeline, a lighter radar than FV436 Green Archer; with Rarden turret, Rarden 30mm, 17′ 3″ × 9′ 3″ × 8′ 10″; with Ferret turret; with Vixen turret, 16′ 9″ × 9′ 9″ × 8′ 4″; SCAT, duel mg on commander's cupola, later w/small rear turret having 1 mg and two 3 barrelled smoke dischargers; rocket assist, 3 booster rockets each side to assist in extricating vehicle from mud, etc.; AVR (Armoured Vehicle, Reconnaissance), 1960, 75 or 105mm gun and Swingfire missile in squat front mounted turret of limited traverse, hull built up behind turret, project only; Blue Water Missile, project only; Carl Gustav, Swedish 85mm A/T rocket device; Wombat, 120mm A/T recoilless rifle on top of hull, gun originally carried inside and lowered on ramps for firing on ground; mortar 81mm, mounted on Mark 1/1, this version had a large round split top hatch instead of the normal square split hatch; with mine-layer, a tractor for mine storage to feed 2 wheel Bar Mine-layer trailer; Ranger A/P Mine-layer, mounted box resembling missile projector and comprising a laying rig, a fire control unit and a package of 72 disposable magazines each containing 20 minelets ejected up to 100 metres at a controlled rate; Rapier, front-mounted high turret w/2 missile projectors on each side; 5-Ton A/T Vehicle, 1964, Wombat or 75mm gun in rear mounted turret, project only; and 105mm Portée Vehicle, 1964, similar, gun could be fired from vehicle or dismounted to fire, hinged for armour, resembled French Hotchkiss airborne carrier, project only.

FV433 105mm Field Artillery Self-propelled (Abbot), 1958, FV432 basis, rear mounted howitzer, cylindrical cupola, 16′ 8″ (19′ 2″) × 8′ 8″ × 8′ 2″.

Value Engineered FV433, no flotation screen, no rubber track pads, split hatch cover, minor internal simplification, 17′ 6″ (18′ 9″) × 8′ 8″ × 8′ 2″.

Falcon, Abbot basis, 2 turrets w/30mm Hispano Suiza guns for A/A use, 17′ 6½″ × 8′ 6½″ × 8′ 3″.

FV434 Armoured Recovery Vehicle, collapsible crane right rear, winch and earth anchor, 18′ 9½″ × 9′ 4″ × 9′ 3½″.

FV435, details unknown.

FV436 SP Mortar Locating Radar (Green Archer), cut down rear hull, rear mounted radar.

FV437 Pathfinder, internal capstan w/hawse hole in bow, rocket projected earth anchor, hydrojet water propulsion, no flotation screen.

FV438 Swingfire, twin wire-guided missile projector, 16′ 9″ × 9′ 9″ × 8′ 10½″.

FV439 Royal Signals Vehicle, box superstructure in rear, power actuated masts.

MISCELLANEOUS VEHICLES

TOG I, 1940, WWI-type hull w/Matilda turret and rigid suspension designed by 'The Old Gang', WWI tracks, electric transmission, French 75mm gun from Char B in nose.

TOG Ia, rebuilt TOG I, over-hanging hull w/lower track frames, massive 6-sided turret w/slight bevel forward, skeleton tracks, 31′ × 9′ ½″ × 10′ 3″.

TOG II, massive 5-sided turret w/slight bevel forward, 6pdr, WWI tracks.

TOG II* (2R) (TOG II with Stothert and Pitt Turret), 17pdr in Centaur turret, electric drive, skeleton tracks, 80 tons, 31′ (33′ 3″) × 9′ 9″ × 10′.

Armoured Bulldozer D7, similar to US Armoured Cabs but square and faceted armour.

Armoured Bulldozer with SBG Bridge, bridge supported in front by A-frame.

Armoured Holt Tractor, rear cab w/2 machine-rifles and trench mortar.

D8 Tractor (Amphibious) flared box hull similar to but smaller than BARV.

Experimental Mine Plough on D8 Tractor, first British experiment w/V-shaped fingered mine plough.

90-Ton Tank, 1940, mock-up only.

Turtle Mark I SP resembling A39 but welded instead of cast armour, project only.

Agag, small light vehicle for crossing minefields, 2 triangular bogie wheel frames, rear bogie included 1 support roller.

Beetle I, small British equivalent of German Goliath, rail outside suspension, electric vehicle cable-controlled, also called MLM (Mobile Land Mine).

Beetle II, similar, suspension rail eliminated.

Amphibious Beetle, Beetle II w/floats added, 2 screws.

Ruston-Bucyrus NLE I (Naval Landing Equipment) (White Rabbit No. 6) (Cultivator No. 6), infantry and officer type, huge track-layer resembling Churchill, intended for digging 5′ trench w/3′ parapet, carried marines to occupy trench as it was completed, infantry type 77′ 6″ × 6′ 6″ × 8′, officer type 77′ × 7′ 6″ × 8′.

FV201 (Red Cyclops), no details available.

Neptune Prototype, British-designed amphibious vehicle similar to US LVT4, rear ramp.

Neptune AF1 (Amphibian Tracked 4-Ton GS) (FV501), improved version, 30′ 2½″ × 11′ 8″ × 10′ 6½″.

Sea Lion (Amphibian Tracked 4-Ton Recovery) (FV503), ARV on Neptune.

Turtle (Amphibian Tracked Workshop Vehicle), similar.

Argosy Prototype, APC type, 6 small road wheels, 3 support rollers, boat-like hull.

Argosy (Argosy Freighter Ferry), production models, more boat-like in appearance.

LVT(F) (Sea Serpent) (FV502), US LVT w/2 horizontal pyramidal F/T turrets and 1 cylindrical rear mg turret.

LVT(R), US LVT(A)4 w/turret removed and rocket projectors added.

LVT Carpet-Layer, US LVT w/double carpet-layer device.

Rodent, US M29 Weasel w/light 4-axle ribbed roller frame for A/M use.

Weasel with Light Mine-clearing Plough, no details available.

CV3/35, 1942, captured Italian tankette w/Lewis gun replacing

original armament, 2 converted at Asmara, Eritrea for local defence.

11/39 with Ark, captured Italian medium tank fitted w/Twaby Ark bridging device.

CET, 1972, amphibious air transportable combat engineer tractor, water jets, 4 road wheels plus trailing idler, rocket-powered earth anchor and obstacle clearing device, resembled US CET.

APC70, 1970, GKN Sankey commercial APC w/Rarden turret and hull firing ports.

APC70, 1973, Anglo-Dutch APC project.

SP70, British 155mm howitzer on German KPz70 chassis, a joint project.

FMBT (Future Main Battle Tank) (MBT80), Anglo-German project on same chassis.

M113 with One-Man Turret, US APC w/Peak Engineering/Rarden gun and coaxial Besa turret, a small cast turret fitted on either cargo hatch or commander's hatch by means of clamps.

M113 with No. 16 Lightweight AFV Cupola, 1972, MEL Equipment Company commercial offering, high cylindrical vision cupola w/remote-controlled mg and spotlight.

M113 with Rarden gun in Fox turret mounted rear of centre.

M113 with Green Archer, radar vehicle.

M113 with Rapier, US M113 w/Rapier 4 missile turret rear mounted, 20mm remote-controlled gun top right front.

Wheelbarrow (Remote Handling Equipment) (Tracked EOD, explosive ordnance disposal) (Rollerskate), 1973, tiny Carden-Loyd type remote-controlled TV inspection vehicle used in Ulster, also involves use of another similar vehicle equipped w/remote-controlled shotgun for detonating bomb devices, 48″ × 27″ × 30″.

Wheelbarrow Mark 1, same w/Tiller steering through lanyards.

Wheelbarrow Mark 2, same w/power steering.

Wheelbarrow Mark 3, same w/4-wheel skid steering.

Wheelbarrow Mark 4, same as Mark 3 w/tracks.

Wheelbarrow Mark 5, same w/24-volt electrical system.

Wheelbarrow Mark 6, same w/minor improvements.

Rapier on M578, 1974, 4-missile Rapier projector on US M578 chassis.

HUNGARY

The first tanks in Hungary were Italian L3/35s obtained from Italy. These were locally modified to add a cupola. Nicholas Straussler, before he emigrated to Britain, designed and built some interesting light tanks having novel suspension systems and one wheel-and-track tank. However, these were not adopted. The Hungarian Army purchased tanks from Czechoslovakian manufacturers, and Manfred Weiss and Csepel Steel Works of Budapest built a number of tanks and self-propelled guns under licence from Landsverk AB in Sweden.

Since World War II Russian armour has been in use.

(CV3/35), Italian tankettes modified in Hungary by the addition of a small square commander's cupola.

Toldi I, Swedish L60 (3rd Series), design built under licence in Hungary, half-cylinder ventilator in front glacis later removed and armoured over, rail wireless antenna on front glacis, 15' × 6' 6½" × 6' 4".

Nimrod, Swedish Landsverk 'Anti' built under licence in Hungary, Toldi chassis, 40mm Bofors in large open-top, moulded and swept-back turret, 18' 8½" × 5' 11" × 9' 2½".

Turan I (HK40M), Skoda type T22, 2 double bogie pairs, 1 single lead bogie wheel, 5 support rollers, large riveted turret w/40mm gun and 2 mg, mg left hull front, square turret cupola, built by Weiss and Csepel Steel Works, 18' ½" × 8' × 7' 6½".

Turan II, turret modified with long bevel on cupola and gun changed to short 7.5cm.

Turan III (T75), same as Turan II but long 7.5cm w/muzzle brake.

Zrinyi, SP on Turan chassis, 10.5cm L/20 howitzer in hull resembling Italian SPs, also reported w/German Pak40, 17' 10" × 9' 6" × 6' 3".

Straussler Light Tank, 1938, amphibious wheel-and-track type, laterally-hinged leading sprocket and trailing idler, 2 laterally-hinged bogie wheels on heavy girder, 2 support rollers, 8-sided turret w/37mm gun.

INDIA

India was armed with a mixture of American and British armour after becoming an independent nation in 1947 and still uses some of it. Negotiations with several nations to build tanks in India culminated with the decision to produce the Vijayanta (Freedom) tank, as the Vickers 37-ton Main Battle Tank is known in India. This tank was produced in the Madras tank arsenal as well as in England. India also has Russian PT76 tanks.

Martel Four Track Tank, 1929, developed to test use of commercial parts, smoothness of 4 separate tracks and André silent block rubber jointed tracks, forward half of the articulated vehicle resembled Loyd Carrier but had 2 bogie wheel scissors suspension, rear half was open chassis for engine, 11' 6" long.

Tata/Porsche/Daimler-Benz, 1955, see Germany, Daimler-Benz Typ 714.

Sherman, US M4A4 w/high velocity Canadian 76mm gun substituted for 75mm gun.

Vijayanta, see Great Britain, commercial, 23' 11" × 10' 4½" × 8'.

PT76, see Soviet Union.

IRAN

The Iranians have long been interested in armoured vehicles, having purchased foreign-made tanks from the United States, Sweden and Czechoslovakia as early as 1931. After World War II other vehicles came from Britain and the United States. Today the Iranian Army has three armoured divisions equipped with American M24, M47 and M60A1 tanks, American M107 SPs, M113s with and without TOW missiles, and Russian ZSU57-2, ZSU23-4, BTR50P, BTR60PB and BM21 Katyushas. Deliveries of British Chieftain Mark 5P tanks, ARVs and AVLBs began in 1973.

ISRAEL

Israel became a nation in 1947 and almost immediately faced war with her Arab neighbours. A great deal of armour was purchased from European scrap dealers and from British and French sources. Some of this equipment was modified and up-gunned and used in the second and third Arab-Israeli Wars. In 1965 and 1966, American armour was purchased. Some use also was made of modern Russian vehicles captured from the Arabs.

(39H Modified), former French light tank modified by substituting a British 6pdr w/muzzle brake.

Shermak, 1950, Sherman w/75mm Krupp M1911 field gun.

Sherman Modified, 1951, Sherman w/76mm gun from US M10.

Sherman M50, 1956, US M4A1 w/French 75mm gun.

MK.51, US M4A3E8 w/US 76mm gun.

Sherman MK51, w/AMX13, 75mm gun, turret bustle added for balance.

(Sherman Modified), swept-back, open-top turret undercut in rear, French 75mm Mle 1897 gun w/muzzle brake.

Isherman (M51HV) (Super Sherman), 1962, several Sherman models w/French 105mm, L/51 gun in T23 type turret, new 460HP Cummins diesel engine, HVSS suspension, 23″ tracks, weight increased to 39 tons.

(Sherman Modified), US M4A1E8 w/French F1 10 turret from AMX13.

(Sherman Modified), Sherman w/US T23-type turret and British 20pdr.

293

▼ M50 (Sherman Modified), gutted Sherman w/French 155/23mm mounted in rear of hull, armour sides later heightened, Cummins diesel engine.

(Priest Modified), US M7 w/new French 105mm howitzer.

M48A2, US Medium Tank rearmed w/British 105mm, new diesel engine.

M113, US APC modified to add light mortar behind cupola and mg pedestals on either side at rear.

TI 67, Russian T54 w/new Continental diesel engine and power train requiring larger engine compartment, new electrical system, air conditioning, laser range-finder, British 105mm.

Tsaber, 1970, reported to be locally built tank.

L33, 1973, French 155mm howitzer in high box hull on Super Sherman chassis, 28′ × 10′ 11″ × 11′ 4″.

Mortar Tank, same hull and chassis w/Finnish 120mm Tamgella mortar.

Ambutank, 1969, M50 modified w/wider hull, engine moved to right front, removable 4 stretcher cell in rear, mg in cupola, 20′ 4″ × 10′ 11″ × 9′ 4½″.

Supply Tank, similar to ambutank.

Ben Gurion, British Centurion Mark 5 w/105mm and Centurion 3, up-gunned to Mark 5 status w/longer-barrelled British 105mm gun, GE hydraulic transmission and air-cooled Continental V12 diesel engine.

E48, US M48A3, unmodified.

E3 Patton (M48A3), US medium tank rearmed w/British 105mm gun, new diesel engine, original cupola eliminated in favour of German-type periscope cupola.

M113J (Zeida), US APC modified to add light mortar behind cupola, mg pedestals on each side towards rear, bow vane removed, exhaust pipe points downward.

K107, US M107.

K109, US 109.

K110, US M110 SP.

Alpha, US M548 carrier.

(- - - - -), W. German-built APC hull on US M113 running gear components.

Tsaber, 1970, reported to be locally-built tank

(- - - - -) Sherman chassis w/cherry-picker (extendable platform for artillery observation) comprising rear-hinged telescoping ladder w/heavy bow-mounted travel lock.

ITALY

Italy, like many other countries, improvised armoured cars before World War I. During that war, Lancia armoured cars based on a touring car chassis were used, mainly at Gorizia, Caporetto, second Piave, and in the Vittorio Veneto offensive. In Italy, too, the tank idea took shape as it did in Britain and France, and again the first steps were taken without consultation with Allies. Actually, the first Italian tank certainly antedated the first French tank and probably just antedated the first British tank by a small margin of months.

This first Italian tank was a large, twin-turreted cleated wheel vehicle designed by Captain Luigi Cassali and built on the Pavesi principle of an articulated chassis to follow ground conformations. Armament was heavy, and the vehicle was fitted in front with wire-cutters. But after being built at the Pavesi factory it was found to be impractical and was dropped.

As soon as British tanks appeared in action, the Italian high command became interested. After learning that the French also had tanks, the Italians ordered 1,500 from Schneider, but the French government politely

suggested that the Italians build their own. However, the French did furnish Italy with one Schneider and one Renault. The Italian Army Commissary asked that 1,500 be made in Italy, but for various reasons that was not considered practical.

The Fiat Company began working on a locally-designed heavy tank, the Fiat 2000, and later on a smaller, redesigned lower and lighter version of the Renault FT, the Fiat 3000. Because Fiat had no previous experience with track-layers delays were inevitable, and the few vehicles made were not completed until 1919.

Only a company-sized tank organization existed from 1919 until 1927, at which time an independent five battalion regiment was formed. Although several experimental vehicles like the wheeled Pavesi and Ansaldo tanks were built during the 1920s and early 1930s, none was adopted. Instead, in 1931, British Carden-Loyd Mark VI carriers were built under licence. These were followed by an Italian version, the L3/33 and the later improved L3/35.

In 1936 and 1937, five *Reggimento Fanteria Carrista* were equipped and made part of the infantry, following the limited combat experience of the campaigns in Italian East Africa and Ethiopia. Italian troops including armour were sent to Spain and participated in the Civil War. There, the two Italian battalions equipped with the light L3/35s were unable to cope with the heavier Russian vehicles used on the government side. The Press exaggerations of the Italian defeat at Guadalajara almost sounded the death knell of armoured forces all over the world.

In Italy there resulted some large light tanks as well as the medium M11/39, but in the Albanian campaign in 1939 only the L3/35 vehicles were used. At home during this period an independent *Divisione Corrazzata* (armoured division) was formed and used in manoeuvres and two more were planned. There was also a *Divisione Celere* but it was partly mechanized and partly horsed. In spite of the existence of these units, in the French campaign and in Libya in 1940 and 1941, tanks were used in small units attached to infantry. But in 1941 three armoured divisions sailed to North Africa and became part of the German *Afrika Korps*.

Italian tank design was little influenced by the Germans. In 1942 a group of Italian officers was sent to Germany to study the Panther tank and its production with a view to building Panthers in Italy also, but the Italian General Staff decided instead to continue with the Italian designed P40 and P43 tanks.

The Italians were handicapped by shortages in raw materials and by limited steel production. Italian steel production was one-fourth that of Britain and one-eighth that of Germany. Nevertheless, 1,222 medium tanks were made in 1941, which compared favourably with other production for that year and was about one-third of German production.

After World War II, the Italian forces were equipped with a variety of British and American armour, and when the previous armoured divisions were reconstituted to form a part of NATO forces, re-equipping with newer American vehicles began. The U.S. M113 A.P.C. was produced in Italy but a plan for producing U.S. M60 tanks was rejected by the Italian government in 1966. Some American tanks were re-armed and re-engined and commercially offered for sale.

WORLD WAR I VEHICLES AND DERIVATIVES THEREOF

Pavesi (Pavesi-Tolatti) (Pavesi-Cassali), 1915, two turrets, double wire-cutters in front, probably preceded both original British and French tanks.

Fiat 200 Prototipo, 1918, slope-sided box hull w/4 rectangular openings near top edge, small cylindrical turret, 8 paired bogie wheels, skirted, unarmed.

Fiat 2000, 1918, similar but 6 mg in cylindrical mantlets at hull corners and side centres, jutting out rounded driver's cowl, driven by periscope vision, 65mm gun in hemispherical turret, 44 tons, 24' 4" × 10' 2" × 12' 5½".

Renault, Renault FT w/Italian mg.

Fiat 3000A Prototipo, 1918, smaller version of Renault FT M1917 w/low centre of gravity for mountain use, engine mounted laterally, 1 Fiat 14/35 mg mounted high in high turret, 5 tons, 14' 1" × 5' 6" × 7' 2¼".

Ansaldo-Renault, 1918, stripped-down Renault FT w/105mm howitzer and shield arranged to fire to rear.

Carro Armato M21, production version of Fiat 3000A w/dual air-cooled mgs, mounted low in turret, also seen w/1 Lewis gun.

Carro Comando M21, dummy cannon, loop antenna on top of turret.

Carro Armato M25, same w/strengthened track frames.

Carro Armato M28 (Carro d'Assalto Leggero 3000B), 6¼ tons, improved version, double jacks built into tailpieces, watertight hull, w/37/40mm gun.

Fiat 4000, chassis of Carro Armato M28 as artillery tractor, armour over engine only.

Fiat 4100, similar but smaller.

L5/30, same w/dual Fiat 29 mg mounted low, Fiat 14/35 mg mounted high or dual SIA mg mounted low.

Carro Armato M30 (M30C) same w/strengthened track frame of 4 vertical braces having 3 holes each.

Carro Armato M30/r, 37mm version w/wireless and inverted-U wireless antenna on turret.

Carro Armato M36 (L5/21), same as M30 but w/dual 37mm guns.

POST WORLD WAR I TANKETTES

Carro Veloce 29 (CV29), original name for British Carden-Loyd Mark VI with headcovers.

Carro Armato 29, 14 mode in Italy w/Italian Fiat aircooled aircraft mg.

CV29, same but 14 made in Italy w/Fiat air-cooled aircraft mg.

Carro Veloce CV3 Prototipo, 1933, small Carden-Loyd type vehicle, long sloping glacis,' 2 double and 1 single bogie wheel on rail, tool-box behind sprocket served as upper track support, open-top hull, no turret, rear hull side louvers, unarmed, 10' 2½" × 4' 7" × 3' 3".

CV3, partly welded hull, 2 small square hullside peepholes, water-cooled mg in large sponson, side louvered engine compartment, 6 bogie wheels.

CV3 CA29, similar but side louvered hull, top louvered engine compartment.

CV29 Studio di Trattore Cingolato, CV29 w/high sloping side and rear armour, intended as either an artillery tractor or a light tank w/rotating turret but the latter was not completed.

Carro Veloce 33 (L3), similar, 2 water-cooled mgs in left front sponson, riveted hull, high engine compartment sides, rectangular door on louvered part of upper rear hull bevel, sold to China.

L3 Variante, welded hull, 1 mg, 3 double bogie wheels, rubber torsion suspension, 2 support rollers.

Carro Veloce 33 Speziale, armed w/37mm gun, project only.

Carro Armato Veloce 33 (CV33) (L3/33), 2 slope glacis, welded hull, 1 mg in 2-way mount on left, small peep slot low in centre of top hull bevel, no tool-box but 2 forward skids, flat track adjustment bracket.

L3/33, riveted hull, 4 bogie wheels, rubber torsion suspension, no support rollers, 20mm gun, sold to Brazil.

Carro Veloce 35 (L3/35) (Scatola di Sardine, sardine tin) (Cassa de morto, coffin), 1935, improved model, dual air-cooled mgs, top bevel peep slots moved forward, later outside lipped peep slots, gun mount later streamlined and gun barrels partly armoured, some w/pillar antenna, tropical model w/added louvers rear of crew compartment, fluted track adjustment bracket, 10' 4" × 4' 7" × 4' 2½".

L3/35 Recupero, small A-frame rear mounted to serve as ARV.

47/32 da L3/35 (Semovente L3 da 47/32), 47mm gun w/shield mounted left front, forward hull cut down, 12' 7" overall × 6' × 5'.

L3/33 (LF) (Lancia Flamme, flamethrower), long barrel hooded F/T replaced one or both mgs, hood sometimes removed, F/T fuel carried in armoured box over engine, later in wheeled trailer.

L3/35 (LF) (CA3/35LF), self-contained flame-thrower, fuel box above engine compartment.

L3/35 (P) (L35/p) (Carro Veloce Passarella, bridging), 1930, long double path girder bridge supported on H-frame w/winch for launching.

Carro Radio (Carro Armato Comando), loop wireless antenna, peep holes replacing mg mount.

Cingoletta Bren, British carrier w/Italian mg.

Cingoletta Fiat 2800, direct copy of British Universal Carrier w/side step in centre, Breda mg.

Bren Carrier met 37mm Kanon, Universal Carrier w/US 37mm gun.

Cingoletta Fiat 2800, resembled US T16 Universal Carrier, mg in LF sponson, 13' 10½" × 3' 11" × 4' 5".

WHEELED TANKS POST WORLD WAR I

Pavesi P4 Prototipo, 1924, articulated Renault FT-type hull and mg turret on 4 large spoked and cleated tractor wheels.

Pavesi P4, improved w/larger hull and turret, wheels w/grousers, 2 tons.

Pavesi Anticarro (anti-tank), similar but smaller, no turret, small cupola, 57mm gun mounted low in front plate.

Pavesi Mezzocarro, very large articulated hull w/mg in front, moulded turret w/mg front and rear, front of hull rounded w/horizontal louvers, 6 tons.

Ansaldo, more sophisticated version, round concentric engine ventilator in front, large cylindrical turret w/bustle and mg in rear, 47mm gun, 4 large simulated-spoke disc wheels w/cleats.

Ansaldo Carro di Fanteria, similar but 6 wheels closely coupled, articulated, cylindrical hull, T-shaped turret w/47mm gun and small mg turret each side of main turret each w/thimble-shaped stroboscope cupola, project only.

POST WORLD WAR I MEDIUM TANKS

Carro de Rottura 8T (breakthrough tank 8T) (Carro Ansaldo I), semi-rigid suspension, covered track frames w/mud chute rear two-thirds, box cab in front w/47mm gun in large ball mount on right, mg centre, driver left, engine compartment sloped downwards towards rear, 12' 10" × 6' × 6' 3".

Carro de Rottura 10T (Carro Ansaldo II) (CA 12T Mod 32), 1932, hull overhung left track, square door w/ball-mounted mg on left side, vertical louvers in engine section of hull, 6 bogie wheels, 2 visible support rollers, otherwise similar to 8-ton model, 16' 4" × 6' × 6' 5".

300

Carro de Rottura (M11 Prototipo) (CA12T Mod 37/26), 1936, prototype of Carro M11/39, 2 double and single bogie wheel sets, 3 support rollers, sloping glacis, 37mm in outset cylinder-like mount on right front, centre of hull hung over tracks, small wedge-shaped 8-sided turret w/mg, later w/opened-up suspension skirt, 15' 6" × 7' 2" × 6' 5".

M11 Secondo Prototipo, hull and suspension modified, 8 bogie wheels.

Carro Armato M11/39, improved leaf spring suspension, 10-sided turret, later conical turret w/dual mg, 37mm gun in right front sponson, 15' 11" × 7' 2" × 7' 4½".

GL4, 1939, 75mm gun and 4 mgs, 38.5 tons, existence not verified.

WORLD WAR II LIGHT TANKS AND VARIATIONS

CL5/21 (Carro Leggero 5/21, Light tank 5/21), 1940, massive Vickers Carden-Loyd 6-ton tank type suspension, 2 support rollers, low glacis, square box hull, driver right, large faceted turret w/37mm gun overhung hull front, RH mg in turret, built-in step in centre of mudguards, 5.5 tons, 11' 6" × 5' 7" × 6' 6".

CL5/30, same w/dual Fiat 29 mg in turret.

CL Sperimentale 5T, CL6/40 suspension but 2 support rollers, 37mm gun left front plate, 2 mg in turret, 11' 5" × 5' 6⅓" × 6' 6".

L6 Carro Cannone, faceted turret w/37mm left, mg right, 2 support rollers.

CL6/40, 1940, similar but larger, 7.25 tons, bevelled glacis, 1 mg in bevelled, slope-sided turret, front corners of hull bevelled, large strap step at centre of mudguard, torsion bar suspension but similar in appearance, 3 support rollers, reverse gun locations in sloping rounded turret, 12' 4" × 6' 5" × 7' 3".

L6 Carro Cannone, sloping rounded turret, torsion bar suspension, 3 support rollers, 37mm gun right, mg left.

CL6/40 Modificare, glacis bevel similar to US M5 Light tank, hull bevelled inward on sides from turret forward.

L6, production model w/13.2mm gun.

Semovente L6/41, L6/40 chassis, open-top hull, 20mm A/T gun in nose.

Semovente 47/32 (Semovente L40 da 47/32), resembled British Bren Carrier but larger, 47mm gun left front, some w/mg and shield added on right top, 12' 6½" × 6' 1" × 5' 2½".

L6/40 (LF) (L40LF), F/T mounted in turret of L6/40 in place of 20mm gun, torsion bar suspension.

L6/40 (R) (L40 Centro Radio), standard vehicle w/2 wirelesses, dummy cannon.

L6/40 Semovente Comando, command tank, high hull, no turret, mg or 20mm gun left front, several variations, 12' 6½" × 6' 1" × 6' 2½".

L6/40 Trasporte-Munizione (Cingoletta L6/40), turret and hull top removed, used as a carrier, mg on pedestal mount, 12' 6½" × 5' 11" × 5' 1½".

Cingoletta L40, turret removed, mg left sponson, used as a carrier, 12' 9½" × 6' 3½" × 4' 9".

Cingoletta L40 Modificare, 13.2mm gun in place of mg.

WORLD WAR II MEDIUM TANKS AND VARIATIONS

Carro Armato 13/40 (CA13/40) (M13/40), similar to M11/39 but w/larger partly-faceted turret, 47/32 gun w/heavier mantlet in turret, full mudguards later partial, originally 1 mg in ball mount and later 2 mg jut forward in right sponson, 105HP engine, 16' 2" × 7' 4½" × 7' 5½".

Semovente Comando M40, command tank on M13/40 chassis, 1 mg later 13.2mm gun right of nose, no turret or top armour.

M13(S) (Carro Recupero, recovery vehicle), turret replaced by low slope-sided superstructure.

Semovente 75/18 (L40 da 75/18), 75mm howitzer w/sieve-type muzzle brake in ball mount in centre of front plate, resembled German assault guns, M13/40 chassis.

Semovente 75/27, Carro Comando w/75/27 cannon.

Carro Centro Radio, command tank, wireless antenna on right side of turret.

Carro Medo Veloce, M13/40 chassis w/mock-up flat front plate, bevelled hull, low turret.

Carro Comando, 75/18 Semovente w/mg only.

Carro Comando, same w/13.2mm gun.

Semovente 75/34, same w/75/34 cannon.

CA14/41 (M14), CA13/40 w/125HP engine, full mudguards, other minor changes, 16' 1½" × 7' 5½" × 7' 9".

M14 Sperimentale, slope-sided round turret w/cupola and range-finder ears.

Semovente 75/18 (L41 da 75/18), same as 75/18 on 13/40 but on 14/41 chassis.

Semovente Comando M41, command tank on M14/41 chassis, turret removed, 1 mg in right front sponson, 16' 1½" × 7' 5½" × 5' 11½".

Semovente 90/53, long 90mm gun w/5-sided open rear shield on modified 14/41 chassis.

CA15/42 (M15), thicker armour, access hatch moved to right side, rear of hull vertical instead of angled to accommodate new 192HP engine, 47/40 gun, 16' 7½" × 7' 9½" × 7' 10".

M15 Modificare, rear of crew compartment built up.

CA Ante Aereo, turret removed from 15/42 and quad Isotta-Fraschini 20mm A/A gun mounted.

Semovente Comando M42, turret removed from CA15/42, 13.2mm right front sponson.

Semovente Comando M42 per Aero Cooperazione, turretless special air liaison vehicle on M40, M41 or M42 chassis, mg in M41, 20mm gun in others.

Semovente 75/18 (Semovente L42 da 75/18), same as 75/18 on M13/40 but on 15/42 chassis.

Semovente 75/34 (M42M da 75/34), similar but longer gun, 16' 7½" × 7' 2½" × 6' 1" w/o gun.

Semovente 75/46 (M42T da 75/46), long gun on lengthened 15/42 chassis, 17' 1" × 8' 2½" × 5' 9".

Semovente 90/53, long gun on M41 chassis partial shield on prototype, 3-sided shield on production, 16' 8" × 7' 5½" × 7' 1½" w/o gun.

Semovente 105/25 similar to 75/18 but bigger gun, partly skirted, also on M42 chassis, 16' 7½" × 8' × 5' 9" w/o gun.

Semovente 149/12, project only.

Semovente 149/13, project only.

Semovente 149/35, 149mm gun on open 13/40 chassis, partly skirted, 21' 9" × 9' 10" × 5' 6".

Semovente 155, similar to 149/35.

Semovente 155 (M43), similar to 105/25.

P75, Medium tank w/2 supplementary turrets, later designated P40 w/cupola on main turret and small turrets eliminated, mock-up only, 24' 6" (overall) × 9' × 11' 4".

▼ 301

P40 Primo Prototipo, Medium tank w/suspension similar to CA13/40 but 4 support rollers, faceted hull w/turret-like 13/40 but larger mantlet, 75/18 howitzer, mg in right front sponson, 2-bevel glacis, driver left, buggywhip antenna left rear, 18' 8½" × 9' ½" × 8' 2½".

P40 Secondo Prototipo, 75/32 cannon substituted.

P40 Terzo Prototipo, hull enlarged, turret bustle added, sponson mg eliminated.

P40 Quarto Prototipo, same w/75/34 cannon.

P40 da 105/23 (P40 Variante Finale), top of hull notched for greater tube diameter at maximum depression, wireless antenna left front, smooth mantlet.

▼ 302

Crociero 43 (P431) (Carro Celere Sahariano), closely resembled British Crusader but w/M11/39 turret, 4 large road wheels, 2 large support rollers between front and rear bogie pairs, partly skirted, forward half of hull faceted.

P43, final version of P/40 w/German Panther turret, mock-up only, 20' 1" (overall) × 10' × 7' 4".

MR35, captured French Char 35R.

POST WORLD WAR II

▼ 303

OTO–Fiat M47R (M47), US M47 w/M60 diesel engine and British 105mm gun, offered commercially.

M47 Pasarella Astra, aluminium scissors-type bridging tank.

Carro Ante Aero, US M2A4 light tank w/o turret and w/modified hull, .50 cal Browning mg w/shield.

VTC M113, US APC produced in Italy, some equipped w/mortar locating radar.

PI M113 A1, (Tipo 676) US vehicle produced in Italy, smaller trim vane, hull to be common with 4×4 APC 35mm remote controlled Oerlikon gun.

M113A1, US vehicle produced in Italy, some experimentally fitted w/Swiss Oerlikon KBA 25mm cannon mounted above GBD–B–22 squat vision cupola.

AMX13 VTT, French APC used in Italy, variously armed w/Browning MG 42/49 or FAL BM–59 mg, 106 recoilless rifle and 81 or 120mm mortar.

Semovento M10, US M10 w/shortened 3" gun, tube sleeve added for weight compensation.

Semovento M109, US armed w/either a 105/14 pack howitzer or an Italian 155mm L/25 gun.

Leopard, German tank manufactured in Italy.

OTO–Melara M109, 1972, US M109 w/Italian FH70 155mm type howitzer w/bore evacuator in middle of tube, 20′ ½″ (23′ 2″) × 12′ 1″ × 12′ 1½″.

OTO–Melara SP70, 1972, Anglo-German vehicle w/Italian FH70 155mm howitzer w/bore evacuator toward rear of tube.

(- - - - -), 1973, 100mm assault gun resembling Jagdkanone, small left front cupola w/mg, 21′ 8″ (22′ 4″) × 11′ 2″ × 5′ 7″.

JAPAN

In 1919 Japan obtained a few World War I tanks from Britain and France for use as reference equipment. The tanks were Medium Mark A Whippets, one Mark IV, and some Renault FT tanks; but studies based on them failed at first to arouse any interest. The appearance of the British Vickers Medium in 1923 changed this negative attitude, and the new enthusiasm for tanks in Japan was reflected in a programme to modernise the equipment of the Imperial Japanese Army. Unable to purchase tanks abroad—except for Renault FTs which they did not want—the Japanese started their own limited tank-building operation in 1925.

The discussion about a mechanized force in Britain added to Japanese interest in tanks and their employment. Some Carden-Loyd tankettes and a Vickers Model D tank (which had been developed for the British Army but not adopted) were bought. These too served for study and formed the basis of several light, medium and heavy experimental designs. The prototype of the first tank, a heavy was completed in February 1927, twenty months after design work was started. In due course the various experiments crystallised into a series of light and medium vehicles which, with the addition of some Renault NC bought from France, saw action in China and Manchuria. Because of petrol shortage and in order to reduce fire hazard (which was dramatically illustrated when the Vickers D caught fire on test) the Japanese developed diesel engines for their tanks.

Although Japan eventually had three armoured divisions, several independent armoured regiments, and an armoured battalion with most infantry divisions in World War II, Japanese armour was usually frittered away in small packets by commanders who ignored the official doctrine to employ them in mass.

Japanese marines were also equipped with armour. Some vehicles were the same as those used by the army, but after the army ceased to develop amphibious vehicles the navy took over. Some of the vehicles they developed were capable of being carried on the decks of submarines.

Japanese vehicles had a high degree of parts interchangeability, but suffered from lightness—although heavier tanks with more powerful armament were developed later in the Greater East Asia War (World War II) they were not produced in sufficient quantity to have any significant effect. Japanese industrial capacity was limited and whereas the United States was building tanks by the tens of thousands, the Japanese counted their production in hundreds, reaching a total of only 3,600 tanks and 900 self-propelled guns and other armoured vehicles. The fuel shortage was acute, to the extent that a small steam engine was in the process of development for tank use. Substitute fuels were also being developed from fish oil, soyabeans and alcohol.

Some explanation is necessary of the way in which the Japanese designated their tanks. The basis is the year of the Emperor's reign in which the equipment was adopted. The reign began in the year 2586 (Western year 1926). Up to Western year 1940 the last two digits only were used. Thus the Type 89 Medium tank was standardized in the year 2589 (Western year 1929). The petrol engine version was Type 89A, the diesel engine version was Type 89B. These A and B designations were also supplied to prime movers and cargo trucks, the exception to the rule being the Renault tanks purchased from France: the Renault FT was known as the Renault A and the Renault NC as the Renault B.

From the year 2600 (Western year 1940) designations were simplified. Equipment adopted that year was called Type 100, followed by Type 1 for the year 2601, Type 2 for year 2602, etc. Prototype equipment was re-designated when it was adopted for production: thus Prototype 91 Heavy Tank became known as Type 95 Heavy tank on standardisation. Japanese tanks were also referred to by names: thus, in the case of Medium tanks, Chi–I, Chi–Ro (the Type 89), Chi–Ha (the Type 97), Chi–Ni, Chi–He, Chi–Nu, Chi–To and Chi–Ri. Light tanks also had names, e.g. Ha–Go (Type 95), Ke–Ni (Type 98), as had command tanks (Shi–Ki) and engineering tanks (Ri–Ki), while self-propelled guns were called Ho–Ni, Ho–ro, Ho–tu, etc.

After 1945 the Japanese were not permitted to have armed forces by the terms of their postwar constitu-tion. The Korean War changed this, and a small defence force was authorised. In 1954 work was begun on the development of a new Japanese main battle tank, and the first two prototype vehicles were completed in March 1957. From them came the Type 61 MBT. Some interesting self-propelled guns and armoured personnel carriers have also been developed.

LIGHT TANKS AND VARIATONS

Ot–su A, 1923 (Type Koh), Renault FT, both 37mm and mg types.

Ot–su B, 1927, Renault NC1 modified in 1929, 6 cylinder Mitsubishi 75HP diesel replaced 4 cylinder Renault 60HP engine, some w/tailpieces, some w/o, 57mm gun or 1 mg, 9 tons.

I–go (No. 1 Light Tank) (Prototype No. 1 Infantry), 1929, resembled Type 2589 Medium and forerunner of that tank, vertical bow w/mg on right, faceted sponsons w/fuel tank caps, conical turret w/1 mg and no cupola, 9 bogie wheels, 4 support rollers, 10 tons. 14′ 1½″ × 7′ 1½″ × 7′ 2½″.

Type 2589, 1929, (Prototype No. 2 Infantry), almost identical but 57mm gun in turret and mg offset at rear of turret, no cupola, designed as a tropical tank for invasion of the Philippines, mg on right of flat hull front, driver left w/leg room built out, rectangular entry door below bow mg.

Combat Car Type 2592 Prototype, very similar to Kei–sen–sha but 2 bogie wheel pairs, 3 support rollers, leaf springs, and flat top 20mm gun sponson, 14′ 7″ × 5′ 11″ × 6′.

Type 92 Heavy Combat Car, first production, similar to prototype but 3 two-wheel disc road wheel pairs w/4 bolt heads each visible, 3 support rollers.

Kei–sen–sha (Light Tank M2592), second production, mg in bevel-front conical turret, 20mm gun in ball mount in curved top sponson jutting out on right hull front, driver recessed on left, sloping glacis, welded armour, 2 square access hatches, bevelled engine compartment, horizontal louvers, 4 spoked road wheels, leaf springs, 2 support rollers, one front one centre, 4 tons, 14' 8½" × 5' 11" × 6'.

Ho–go, (Issikawajima M2594) (Cho–Kei) (Cho–Kei Sen–sha) 3-ton tankette, 2 bogie wheel pairs, 2 support rollers, horizontal coil springs between support rollers, small conical turret w/1 mg partly blocked by raised crew cowl, sloping glacis w/raised hatch frame and cover for maintenance, hinged box louver left side of hull w/exhaust pipe looped over it, later w/flat hinged door w/exhaust pipe below, finally return to box louvers, later production hatch cover had rounded raised section and small round inspection plate left centre of differential armour cover, 10' 1½" × 5' 4" × 5' 4".

Type 2594, similar but somewhat longer because of trailing idler, an accident on the first trial run killed the driver-designer and the project was abandoned.

So–koh–sha, 1934, similar to Ho-go but w/trailing idler and long sloping glacis, round inspection plate in centre of differential armour cover, experimentally w/7mm gun, 3.2 tons, 11' 2" × 5' 4" × 5' 4".

(- - - - - -), an APC derived from So–Koh–sha, also used as cargo carrier, observation vehicle, wire carrier, and balloon control, experimentally as 37 or 47mm SP A/T, 2 bogie wheel pairs, 2 support rollers, small driver cupola and cowl jutted out, open top rear w/tarpaulin bows.

Ha–go, 1934, first prototype of Ke–go, 2 bogie wheel pairs w/bogie support pivot above bogie axle line, short horizontal spring, 1 support roller, toothed idler, later plain, mg in ball mount on left front plate which was straight across, conical bevel-front turret w/37mm gun, rounded edge, split-turret hatch, no cupola, engine compartment sloped downward to rear, flat-sided crew compartment bulge w/pistol port left side, engine silencer left side, no louvers.

So–to, first Ha–go chassis lengthened, 37mm gun in place of front mg, low superstructure in place of turret on left side w/flat hatch in

front and square dome hinged cap in rear, open rear w/folding ramps to load A/T field piece.

▼ 307

Ke–go, same as Ha–go second proto-type but bogie support pivots below axle line, also supported additional small road wheels, long suspension spring, rounded conical crew compartment bulge, louvered, cupola, rear mg, special model for Manchuria, 14' 1" × 6' 9½" × 7' 5½".

Kyu–go, engine silencer right side, mg left front of hull first omitted then later added, front plate recessed for driver on right, 37mm L/37 gun, mg offset at turret rear, flat edge split cupola hatch, engine compartment louvers, 2 support rollers.

Kyu–go, final production, same except bogie support pivots again above bogie axle line, split rolled edge cupola covers, modifications included some vehicle w/hull built out on left side for auxiliary fuel tank, instead of mg, some w/47mm howitzer in larger 'Type 90' turret, some had Kapok floats in iron frames and 2 outboard engines for river crossings, experimentally in 1944 hooked to Ku7 Maeda glider but project abandoned, 14' 1½" × 6' 9½" × 7' 3".

Ke–ri (Light Tank Type 3), Kyu–go w/Chi–ha turret, 7.4 tons, 57mm gun and coaxial mg, 1 rear mg, 1 mg front of hull, 14' 1½" × 6' 9½" × 7' 5½".

Ji–ho, gun carrier or SP, modified Kyu–go w/type 35 120mm gun and shield, 4 bogie wheels.

Ho–to, miniature Ho–ni, 120mm howitzer front mounted on Kyu–go chassis.

▼ 308

So–Ki, dual 20mm A/A guns w/shield on built-up hull on lengthened Kyu–go chassis, 3 bogie

wheel pairs, 3 support rollers, gun crew seats rear top of hull.

(- - - - - -), So–ki w/top hull build-up removed, large open turret w/bustle and one 20mm A/A gun.

(- - - - - -), 47mm gun on Kyu–go miniature tank destroyer resembling German StuK.

▼ 309

Chi–ni–sha (trial light tank), 1936, 11 tons, 4 bogie wheel pairs, 3 support rollers, partial potbelly hull open at bottom and baffled for ventilation, long glacis, horizontal engine compartment louvers, 57mm gun on left side of turret, driver slightly outset, mg right front, small tailpiece, silencer on right side, intended as the standard light tank and so approved but the Japanese-Chinese War began the next day so it was cancelled w/decision made to continue w/the Chi–ha medium tank because it was already in production.

Ji–ro, 100mm gun in rounded rear cab mount on chassis of Chi–ni–sha.

Ke–Ke(Te–ke), small 4½ ton tank, bevelled hull, angled tool-box over left mudguard, driver left, driver's cowl slightly forward and raised, 37mm gun in cylindrical turret w/rounded bulging turret cover, 2 bogie wheel pairs, 2 support rollers, engine right, horizontal coil spring suspension, silencer centre right side, one tank experimentally hooked to Ku6 Maede glider in 1944 but project abandoned, 13' 1½" × 6' 6½" × 6' 3".

Type 98, Te–ke w/bogie wheel supports inside of bogie wheels, 3 support rollers.

Light Tractor Type 3, based on Ke–ke chassis.

Te–re (Type 100 Observation Vehicle), Te–ke chassis, silencer exhaust to front. small fixed box cupola, open rear hull w/canvas covers.

So–ha, Te–ke used as control vehicle for miniature radio-controlled demolition vehicles, 12' 2" × 6' 3" × 5' 1½".

Ke–ni (Type 2598 Light), 1938, 8 tons,, 3 bogie wheel pairs, 3 support rollers, potbelly hull, driver set out slightly, long 37mm gun w/coaxial mg in conical turret having round hatch cover lifting

forward, 13′ 5½″ × 6′ 11½″ ×
5′ 11½″.

Ke-ni (Light Tank Type 2) (Modified
Type 98), 1941, same w/cylindrical
turret and still higher velocity
37mm gun.

Ke-to (Keni-B), 1944, Ke-ni w/4
large bogie wheels in Christie-type
suspension, 'Type 100' turret w/mg
in rear, 7.2 tons, 13′ 5½″ × 6′ 11½″
× 5′ 11½″.

Ku-se, 1944, SP based on Ke-to,
Type 99 75mm gun w/shield,
intended as a tank destroyer,
16′ 8½″ × 7′ 7½″ × 6′ 2″.

Ke-nu (Light Tank Type 4), Ke-ni
w/Chi-ha turret, 14′ 1″ × 6′ 9½″
× 7′ 5½″.

Ke-Ho (Light Tank Type 5),
experimental, similar to Ke-ni but
Chi-ha turret, 3 bogie wheel pairs,
horizontal coil spring suspension,
3 support rollers, mg front of hull,
10 tons, 15′ 4½″ × 7′ 2½″ × 6′ 6½″.

LIGHT AND MEDIUM
AMPHIBIOUS VEHICLES

Trial Type 1 Amphibious Armoured
Car, 1928, wheel-and-track
convertible, designed to study
amphibious possibilities, ran
forward or backward on either
wheels or tracks, submarine-type
hull, turret w/stroboscope in
centre of hull, 1 mg, based on
study of Citroën-Kégresse car
purchased in France.

Trial Type 2 Amphibious Armoured
Car, rebuilt No. 1 w/larger conical
turret, no stroboscope.

(------), 1930, experimental
amphibian, pointed bow, pointed
stern, boat hull, small 3 road wheel
and trailing idler suspension under
fore part of hull, long rear
overhang, small superstructure
w/Ho-go turret, 13′ 1½″ × 5′ 3″
× 6′ 3″.

A-I-go, amphibious light tank,
chassis similar to Kei-sen-sha but
leaf springs reversed, hull over
tracks built up for buoyancy,
rotary jet pumps in tubes provided
propulsion in water, 14′ 8″ ×
5′ 11″ × 6′.

Type 2592A, similar but no bow mg,
single screw, large ventilator cover
left top of engine compartment,
14′ 9½″ × 6′ 2″ × 6′ 10½″.

B-ro-go, 1933, 2 variations similar
to above but 1 support roller, turret
had very decided front bevel
w/ball-mounted mg in bevel,
16′ 9″ × 6′ 2½″ × 6′ 10½″.

SR-I, very similar to A-I-go but
w/higher driver's cowl.

SR-II, 1937, rectangular box
buoyancy chambers over tracks,

8-sided conical turret w/8-sided
rounded top cupola, mg in square
mount on left front, 25mm gun in
turret, retractable bow surfboard
operated by rack and pinion,
2 screws in tubes w/rudder behind
each, 3 bogie wheel and trailing
idler suspension, 1 support roller,
16′ 5″ × 5′ 8½″ × 6′ 2½″.

▼ 310

SR-III, similar but rounder edges of
buoyancy chambers, final Japanese
Army amphibious design, 13′ 9½″
× 6′ 2″ × 7′ 10″.

Ka-mi-sha, 1941, Japanese Navy
design, 4.3 tons w/o detachable
boat-shaped floats fitted fore and
aft, 4 bogie wheels, 2 support
rollers, large low turret w/37mm
gun and 1 mg on left front of
faceted hull, could be transported
on deck of a submarine to depth of
300′.

Ka-mi-sha Type 2, 1942, 10 tons
w/o floats, light tank 2595 basis,
'Type 100' turret w/37mm gun and
mg front of hull, 4 bogie wheels, 2
support rollers, 2 screws, rear
conning tower, 15′ 8″ (24′ 7″
w/floats) × 9′ 2″ × 7′ 6½″.

▼ 311

Ka-chi-sha Type 3, similar but
8 bogie wheels, 4 support rollers,
added cupola on turret, 47mm gun
and mg coaxial, 1 mg front of hull,
25 tons, 33′ 8½″ × 9′ 9½″ ×
12′ 6½″.

Ka-chi-sha Modified, same general
conformation but w/Chi-he turret,
37mm gun front of hull, rear
conning tower, 23′ 4″ (35′ 5″) ×
9′ 10″ × 12′ 6″.

Ka-tsu-sha Type 4, 18 tons, 4 bogie
wheel pairs, 4 support rollers, could
carry 40 marines, sheet-metal boxes
over tracks filled w/buoyancy
material, twin screws, oval-dome
ventilator top of flat top hull, small
square turret at bow, 36′ 3″ ×
10′ 11″ × 11′ 3½″.

▼ 312

Ka-tsu-sha II, Type 4, similar but
smaller, 14 tons, could carry naval
torpedo on either side of hull, boat
shaped bow.

To-ku-sha Type 5, similar to
Ka-chi-sha Modified but 31 tons,
47mm gun and mg in Chi-ha turret,
25mm gun front of hull, not
completed, 35′ 5″ × 9′ 10″ ×
11′ 1″.

MEDIUM TANKS AND
VARIATIONS

Experimental Tank No. 1 (18-Ton
Tank), 1927, first Japanese tank,
bore general resemblance to Type
89 Medium, 70mm gun in large
turret w/stroboscope cupola w/dome
cover, small bevel-sided mg turret
left front and centre rear, 4 bogie
wheel pairs on vertical concentric
coil springs, 4 support rollers, on
rail, partly skirted, 25 tons.

Experimental Tank No. 1 Modified,
1930, track frames strengthened,
5 support rollers.

Type 40, Vickers Medium D Tank
purchased in Great Britain.

▼ 313

Koh (Type 89) (2589 Medium),
forerunner of Type 91 Heavy
Tank, based on Vickers Medium
D, second Japanese tank, original
weight 9.5 tons, after modification
12 tons, suspension similar to
Experimental Tank No. 1
Modified, stroboscope later
remover and replaced by hatch
cover, 57mm gun and mg, 1 bow
mg, 20′ 5″ × 8′ ½″ × 7′ 2½″.

Light Tank 89 Modified, 1929, pilot
of Type 89 Medium, No. 1 Light
Tank w/front of hull now sloped,
armour thickened, mg on right
front, hinged cap cupola.

Japan

314

Medium 89A (Chi-i-A), 1929, faceted hull fuel tanks over tracks, petrol engine, 9 bogie wheels, 5 support rollers w/girder, 57mm gun, 1 mg rear of turret, small hinged cap cupola, mg right front, some later w/modified heavier mantlet, 17' 6" × 8' 4" × 8' 6½".

Medium 89B (Chi-i-B), larger cupola w/split cover, towing pintles, 18' 8½"(20' 10½") × 7' 2" × 8' 4½".

Medium 92, Medium 2589 w/larger hinged cap cupola, towing pintles and other modifications.

Chi-ri (Medium 94), similar to 89B but w/tailpiece from Ot-su B, 4 support rollers, split hatch cover cupola, mg left front of hull, internal mantlet for 57mm gun, girder under support rollers removed, diesel engine.

(Gas and Smoke Tank), Type 2594 Medium converted to gas and smoke projector.

Chi-ha, prototype medium tank, 6 large-spoked double wheels in 3 bogies, exposed horizontal suspension springs, 3 large support rollers.

Chi-ha (M2597), 1937, 6 road wheels w/first and last independently sprung, covered horizontal coil spring suspension, 3 support rollers (centre one smaller), low sloping glacis, 57mm gun in low turret w/wireless rail antenna, low cupola, split hatch cover, mg left front, mg rear of turret, front plate originally straight across but later protruding, rounded driver's cowl, some used as command tanks w/o 57mm gun but not to be confused w/Shi-ki, 18' 2" × 7' 7½" × 7' 3½".

Chi-ha, modified, 5 road wheels plus 3 additional overlap road wheels, 4 support rollers, lowered coil springs.

Shin-ho-to Chi-ha (new turret Chi-ha), larger Chi-he type 1 turret w/bustle and long 47mm gun, turret used because demand for Chi-he tanks could not be met, 1 vehicle seen w/dome cupola and A/A gun on right, 1 w/hydraulic steering, Chi-ha modified on Saipan by eliminating cupola and space between turret bustle and hull.

Type 98 (Chi-ho), lower 97 type w/long 47mm gun, mg blister left turret front, 2 support rollers, tailpiece.

Ho-ro, Chi-ha chassis as SP, Type 38 150mm howitzer in square box shield at front of vehicle, 18' 1" × 7' 7½" × 7' 8".

Ho-i (Gun Tank Type 2), Type 97 w/short 75mm howitzer in large turret, later w/longer 77mm howitzer, 18' 9½" × 7' 7½" × 8' 5½".

315

Ho-ni I (Gun Tank Type 1), similar to Ho-ro but w/long Type 90 75mm gun, 19' 4" × 7' 7½" × 7' 10".

Ho-ni II, same w/105mm howitzer.

Ho-ni III (Type 3 Gun Tank), same as Ho-ni but w/armour added at top and rear of shield.

Type 5 Self-Propelled Howitzer, 20cm gun on Chi-ha built by Japanese Navy.

Type 5 Self-Propelled Gun, 120mm L/45 naval A/A gun on open chassis Chi-ha, built by Japanese Navy.

Ho-K, 1938, ramming tank, Chi-ha w/o turret, long sharp steel prow designed for use in forests of Manchuria and Siberia against USSR, 24' 8" × '9 6" × 5' 11".

Ho-tu, 2cm L/45 naval gun SP on Chi-ha chassis.

Shi-ki, Chi-ha command tank, wireless rail around turret but no turret gun, 57mm gun mounted in bow in place of mg, 18' 1" × 7' 7½" × 7' 4".

(- - - - - -), Chi-ha command tank, turret had peep slots beside mantlet and large top-hinged hatches on either side of turret, no cannon.

Chi-ho (Type 2598), experimental medium tank.

Ka-se, modified Shi-ki w/'Type 1' turret having range-finder ears.

Chi-nu (Type 3 Experimental), 1944, Chi-ha chassis w/massive welded turret and hull, turret w/bustle, square turret doors side and rear, Model 1930 French Schneider 75FG gun w/muzzle brake, cupola w/split hatch covers, 18' 8" × 7' 7½" × 7' 8".

Shin-ho-to Chi-nu, same w/new turret.

Ho-ri I (Type 2 Experimental) (Gun Tank Type 2), 1944, Chi-nu w/75mm howitzer, mg left front, 21' 4" × 11' 8" × 10' 9".

Ho-ri II, experimental, resembled German Hummel, long 100mm gun, 47 tons, project only.

Sa-to, 1938, Type 98 20mm A/A gun on open Chi-ha chassis, wheels for field gun carriage carried on rear hubs.

316

Ho-ki, components from Chi-ha used to create an APC, 4 bogie wheels, 2 support rollers, open top box hull, driver left, engine forward right, louvers in hull in front of engine, tarpaulin bows, 15' 8" × 7' 2" × 8' 2½".

Se-ri, engineering vehicle on Chi-ha chassis, low conical turret, A-frame and jib crane at rear, 18' 5½" × 6' 6½" × 7' 5½".

(Engineer Vehicle), Se-ri w/large girder crane mounted on turret.

Ri-ki (Engineer Tank), Chi-ha chassis w/jib crane at rear.

(Engineer Vehicle and Prime Mover), Chi-ha chassis w/2 huge front-mounted cranes and removable boom in rear, equipped w/winches, driver front between crane bases, 17' (20' 8") × 7' 5½" × 7' 11".

(Engineer Vehicle), Chi-ha chassis, enclosed hull, centre front pivoted crane, large rear porcupine bracing sprocket w/hydraulic jack.

K, Chi-ha w/bulldozer but w/o turret.

TG-Ki, 1943, Chi-ha w/o turret, small cupola, rocket-assist bridge launcher and girder bridge.

G-Ki, double flail on standard Chi-ha.

Chi-he (Type 1), 1942, tank similar to Shin-ho-to Chi-ha but front of hull straight across, heavier armour, and welded instead of riveted.

Ta-ha, Chi-he w/new open top turret w/two 37mm A/A guns and 2 mgs, not completed, 19' 8" × 7' 7½" × 6' 6½".

194

Chi–ne, similar to Type 89 Medium but lower, 8-sided turret w/o cupola, had tailpiece, 2 bogie wheel pairs, 3 support rollers, project only.

Type 2 Experimental, welded, rounded bow, rounded hull front, slightly conical turret w/rolled top edge, round hatch cover, torsion bar suspension, 6 bogie wheels, 3 support rollers, not armed when found by US troops in Japan.

Chi–to, prototype w/57mm gun.

Chi–to (Type 4 Experimental), 1943, welded hull, front of hull straight across, mg left front 3 piece cast turret w/bustle, Type 4 long 75mm gun, hydraulic steering, 7 bogie wheels, 3 support rollers, 2 part horizontal suspension, 21′ 8″ × 9′ 4½″ × 9′ 4½″.

Chi–ri (Type 5 Experimental), 8.8cm gun in massive welded turret having turret basket, large flat-sided bustle, small cupola, straight-sided hull, short almost flat glacis, A/A mg mount top right side of turret, 57mm bow gun, 2 silencers across rear of hull, 8 bogie wheels, 3 support rollers, 2 section horizontal coil springs, 23′ 11″ × 10′ 1½″ × 10′ 1½″.

Chi–ri II Type 5, details not known.

HEAVY TANKS

▼ 317

Chi–i–sha, 1927 (Heavy Tank T95), 21′ 2½″ × 8′ 10½″ × 9′ 6″, first heavy tank, details of original unknown but it was modified and underwent the following name changes: Chi–ro–sha, 1930; Chi–ha–sha, 1932; Chi–ni–sha, 1934; this last had a 70mm howitzer in a bevel-forward turret, mg left rear, 37mm gun in small turret left front and centre rear, 1 leading bogie wheel and 4 bogie wheel pairs on 2 rocker arms, 4 support rollers, hull resembled Medium 89.

Heavy Tank 2591, resembled above but had 16 bogie wheels and 1 leading bogie wheel, cupola resembled but was not a stroboscope, mg turret left front and centre rear, main turret bevelled forward w/offset mg left rear, 57mm gun main armament, 31 tons, almost vertical bow, minor modifications later made.

Heavy Tank 2595, Type 2591 Heavy Tank basis, 10cm gun w/shield front mounted.

A–i–chi 2596, 75mm and 35mm in turret, 2 bow mgs, resembled Russian T32, existence not verified, 31′ × 10′ 8″ × 9′ 2″.

Heavy Tank 2597, two 37mm guns in turret, 2 mg in bow, resembled Russian T28, 24′ 5″ × 9′ 10″ × 9′ 6″.

O, 1940, 110-ton tank reported built and then scrapped.

O–i, 1944, 130-ton tank, Mitsubishi official history in 1957 reported 1 vehicle completed, 105mm gun in main turret, 47mm and 1 mg left front, mg rear of turret, 2 engines, 2 double bogie wheel pairs each on crank arms sprung from 1 coil spring, 32′ 9″ × 13′ 9″ × 13′ 1½″.

MISCELLANEOUS CHASSIS VEHICLES

(- - - - - -), British Carrier captured at Singapore w/hull covered and small conical turret w/mg added.

▼ 318

Ha–to, 1943, engine front, armoured crew cab centre, 300mm trench mortar mounted on open rear, 1 mg, 7 bogie wheels, 19′ 7″ × 7′ 10½″ × 8′ 11½′.

Na–to I, 1945, 75mm Type 4 A/A gun mounted at rear on Ha–to chassis, engine front, riveted hull, 16½ tons, 19′ 6½″ × 7′ 10½″ × 9′.

Na–to II, details unknown.

Ka–to, 1944, high velocity 100mm gun, 40-ton vehicle, design study only.

Ho–to, details unknown.

Ho–gi, 1937, track and rail vehicle, two 4 bogie wheel sets, leaf springs, 4 support rollers, streamlined hull and turret, auxiliary railway wheels between tracks front and rear operated by hydraulic jacks, w/railway couplers, 14′ 10½″ × 8′ 2½″ ×8′ ½″.

So–da, armoured transport vehicle based on Ho–gi.

(Engineering Vehicle A1), large rear mounted crane, 1 mg left front, 8 disc type bogies w/simulated spokes rail mounted, 2 support rollers.

(Engineering Vehicle A2), same chassis, streamlined welded armour hull, single crane centre forward.

(Engineering Vehicle A3) ARV on Ho–gi chassis.

(Engineering Vehicle A4) (Engineer Vehicle Type E), chassis similar to M2594 Medium tank but two 4 bogie wheel sets, 3 support rollers, curved crane centre mounted, bridge girders on pivoted forks carried over tracks, 1 flame-thrower, 1 mg, several versions existed, 20′ 2½″ × 8′ 2″ × 9′ 10″.

(Swamp Crossing Vehicle) (SAB), unarmoured track-layer with track pads inflated by air-compressor.

REMOTE-CONTROLLED VEHICLES

Nagayama, 1929, Fordson tractor w/torpedo shaped hull and stationary turret of sheet metal, radio-controlled demonstration vehicle.

K–Ni–go, K–2, 1934, M2589 Medium w/hydraulic and later electrical controls, remote-controlled by radio, 18′ 10½″ × 7′ 2″ × 8′ 4½″.

A, Ya–go, 1935, cable-controlled demolition vehicle, resembled German skeleton type Goliath, 56″ × 25″ × 18″.

B, 1935, similar radio-controlled, 78″ × 46″ × 22″.

Tei-kei, 1936, M2594 tankette w/electrical controls, remote-controlled by radio.

K–san–go, K–3, 1939, specially built experimental radio-controlled vehicle, 3 bogie wheel pairs, 2 bump bogie wheels, 2 mg, 21′ 9½″ × 7′ 11″ × 7′ 9½″.

K–yon–go, 1945, Miniature vehicle, 6 bogie wheels, 5 radio frequencies for remote-control, television control was under experiment, 16′ 10½″ × 7′ 6½″ × 5′.

K–2, very small demolition vehicle, resembled Ka–tsu–sha Type 4.

POST WORLD WAR II LIGHT TANKS AND RELATED VEHICLES

Ko–ma–tsu SS Mark I, 1955, two 105mm recoilless rifles in squat right side hydraulic lift turret, driver in set-out rounded cowl on left ,4 bogie wheels, 3 support rollers, rubber torsilastic suspension, improved in 1957 w/square driver's cowl, 13′ 5½″ × 7′ 2½″ × 4′ 4½″ (6′ w/guns raised).

Mitsubishi SS Mark II, 1955, similar, 4 bogie wheels, 3 evenly spaced support rollers, square driver's cowl, guns on right more to rear, 13' 2" × 7' 2½" × 4' 8½" (guns in low position).

SS Mark IV Type 60, 1959, production type, rounded driver's cowl, two 106mm recoilless rifles w/travel locks, 3 support rollers w/2 forward rollers near one another, 14' 1" × 9' 4" × 4' 6" (6' guns raised).

319

Experimental Type 60, same but w/two 105mm recoilless rifles on each side.

Type 56, APC, 5 bogie wheels, 3 support rollers, hull like SU–I, 15' 11" × 7' 10½" × 5' 7".

SU–I, APC, chassis similar to Type 60, 6 bogie wheels, 3 support rollers, low rear hull, 2 large rear doors, 50 cal mg w/shield on top, mg in front plate, 6 cylinder Boxer type diesel engine front mounted, 15' 10½" × 7' 10½" × 5' 7".

SU–II, similar, manufactured by a different firm, 8 cylinder V-type diesel right centre mounted, other modifications.

SV, became Type 60, 81mm mortar and rear ramp, SU–II chassis, 15' 11" × 7' 11" × 5' 7" to top of hull.

SX, Type 56, rear of hull slopes downward, 4.2" mortar, 50 cal mg w/shield mounted forward, 15' 10½" × 7' 10½" × 5' 7".

320

SY, Type 56 chassis w/higher box hull and 105mm howitzer in front plate, 15' 11" × 7' 8" × 9' 4".

(– – – – –),1960, 10-ton light tank w/76mm gun, not verified.

SUB–1, 1970, experimental APC resembling US M113, hinged suspension skirts, 5 large bulging disc road wheels, twin centre cupolas, 20mm gun in right, bow mg.

SUB–2, 1970, similar but overhanging rim, hollow bogie wheels, hinged fluted skirts, RH centre turret w/several weapons, driver in centre front cupola.

SUB–2 Production, no skirts, higher hull.

POST WORLD WAR II MEDIUM TANKS

SB, Bridge-layer tank Type 67, prototype on US M4A3E8 chassis, production on ST (Type 61) tank chassis.

SG, US M4A3E8 chassis and hull w/folding bridge-launcher.

SD, US M32A1B3 tank recovery vehicle as armoured engineering vehicle w/bulldozer.

SK, tank recovery vehicle based on ST (Type 61) tank chassis.

GK, mine destroyer vehicle, no details available.

STA–1, 1956, resembled 1965 German Leopard, 90mm gun w/muzzle brake and coaxial mg, heavy A/A mg, cast turret w/cupola bulge and bustle, 7 bogie wheels, 4 support rollers, 21' 8" (28' 2") × 9' 8" × 7' 4".

STA–2, similar but 6 bogie wheels, 3 support rollers, turret resembled US M47 medium w/mg cupola like US tanks, higher than STA–1, 19' 8" (26' 8") × 9' 8" × 8' 2".

STA–3, similar, gun had blast deflector, single stowage rails around turret, 19' 8" (26' 4")× 7' 8" × 9' 4".

321

STA–4 (Type 61), similar to STA–3 but double stowage rails around turret, range-finder at base of cupola, 20' 8" (28' 1") × 9' 8" × 8' 1½".

STB–1, similar but w/hydraulic controllable suspension, 21' 8" (29' 7") × 10' 6" × 7' 4" to 8' 10".

Type 67 Bridge-layer, Type 61 tank basis, resembled US M60 AVLB, 23' 10" × 11' 3" × 11' 3".

Type 67, Armoured Engineering Vehicle, Type 61 tank chassis, 27' 7" × 9' 8" × 10' 2".

Type 70, Armoured Recovery Vehicle, Type 61 tank chassis, telescoping A-frame base-mounted front of turret, boxed winch rear deck, dozer blade, mortar on front glacis, 50 cal mg top of turret, 24' 6" × 10' 6" × 10' 2'.

JORDAN

Jordan's armoured force is equipped with American and British tanks, American M113s, British armoured cars, and some self-propelled guns. One interesting local vehicle was an American Sherman with a French 105mm firing to the rear.

(– – – – –), US M113 w/Commando armoured car turret substituted for commander's cupola.

(– – – – –), 1948, French Lorraine tractor modified locally to rear mount US 4.7" A/A gun M1920 w/shield, resembled German SdKfz135.

(– – – – –), French 105mm gun w/shield facing rear on turretless US Medium M4A4, small strip protecting turret race below shield.

KOREA (Republic of)

M47VTR, M47 tank basis w/tubular A-frame hinged to bow to form makeshift ARV, modified turret w/inside winch, supplementary front bracing legs.

NETHERLANDS

Pantrado, 2 automobile wheel and idler Trado units connected back to back by ball-bearing race, used w/ or w/o auxiliary tracks, conical top turret w/mg on each unit, not completed, name derived from Pan (first syllable of the Dutch word for armoured vehicle) and Trado (Captains van der Trappen and Van Doren).

Jaguar, Lynx, Poeme and Panter, 1935, British Carden-Loyd Mark VI with headcovers, added mg shield.

Centurion Bruglegger, US scissors mounted on British Centurion chassis, 36' 8" × 13' 2½" × 13' 1½".

Leopard/Contraves, German medium A/A vehicle w/Dutch radar equipment, called Pfz–C.

M113 C + R met Oerlikon 25mm, US vehicle w/Oerlikon 25mm gun mounted above clam shell-like GBD–B20 vision cupola, 15′ 1″ × 7′ 11″ × 6′ 7″.

APC70 , 1973, Anglo-Dutch APC project.

VTT met TOW, 1973, French APC w/US TOW missile projector pedestal mounted left front.

LVT4 met Veldgeschut, 1944, US Amtrac w/field howitzer on its carriage, mounted behind cab for normal and high angle fire.

LVT4 met Vlammwerfer, 1944, self-contained F/T unit w/shield mounted behind wedge-shaped armour.

NEW ZEALAND

▼ 322

Bob Semple Tank, 1940, modified US Disston design inspired by photo in US magazine, fluted armour (simulated), 2 mgs in hull, 1 mg in turret, built on commercial tractor, 14′ × 8′ 3″ × 11′.

▼ 323

Griffiths Wheel and Tank Track (Schofield Carrier), 1940, box hull, large open top turret w/2pdr and Besa mg, 2 bogie wheel pairs and support units, front wheels between horns, rear wheels on sides, wheels connected to sprockets and idlers when in use, carried on brackets when on tracks, 13′ 2½″ × 8′ 5″ × 6′ 7½″ on tracks; 14′ 1″ × 8′ 5″ × 6′ 10½″ on wheels.

Carrier, LP No. 1 (LP–local pattern), identical to Australian No. 1, 1939, mild steel training version for manufacturing experience.

Carrier, LP No. 2 and 2A, identical to Australian No. 2 and 2A.

Carrier, ambulance, lengthened hull w/canvas top, for carrying stretchers.

Valentine SP, 1944, Valentine tank w/Matilda IV 3″ howitzer installed, continued in use until 1955.

Sherman Fascine Carrier, 1945, gutted US M4A1 Medium w/skeleton braced steel frame for fascine, field modification.

Grant ARV, US Medium w/M3 75mm gun in sponson, 37mm gun removed from turret and crane fastened to turret base and supported by rear mounted A–frame.

M113, US M113 w/Commando twin mg A/C turret, similar to Australian modifications.

NORTH VIETNAM

▼ 324

(-----), Soviet T34 w/turret removed and well plated over, new turret resembling German WWII Wirbelwind mounting Chinese-type 63 dual 37mm A/A gun, turret travel lock in rear, 19′ 11″ × 9′ 8″ × 13′.

BTR50PK, 1972, Soviet vehicle w/twin ZPU–2 A/A guns in a rear-mounted tub.

NORWAY

M24, US Light tank modernized in 1973 w/French GIAT 90mm gun, Detroit diesel engine and new suspension and tracks, bow mg opening plated over, offered commercially and marketed by France.

Weasel, US M29 Cargo Carrier mounting 106mm recoilless rifle.

M109G, US M109 SP.

PAKISTAN

Pakistan has not developed its own armour but is equipped with

American and Chinese tanks—M47 (OTO Melara) and M48A2 American Medium tanks, M24 and M41 American Light tanks, T59 Chinese Medium tank, T60 and T61 Chinese versions of the Russian PT76, and the ubiquitous American M113.

PERU

Tanque M37/38, Czech LTP.

POLAND

The Poles received their first armour in the form of Renault tanks from France during the Polish war with Russia in 1920. A few years later, one of these was modified into a smoke projector, and another was fitted with tracks made up of steel cables held together by cross-pieces.

In the early 1930s a Carden-Loyd Mark VI and some Vickers-Armstrongs 6-ton tanks were obtained in England. The series of Polish TK tankettes evolved from the former while the 7TP tanks evolved from the latter. Arrangements were made to buy two Christie tanks in the United States, but the vehicles were not accepted by Poland and were taken over by the United States Army. However, very similar wheel-and-track vehicles, the 10TP and later the 14TP were built in Poland, but only experimental models existed.

The Polish army continued to be armed with modernized World War I Renaults, newer French R35 tanks, TK tankettes, Vickers 6-ton tanks, and 7TP tanks. In total there were forty-eight companies equipped with 830 tanks. The older vehicles were committed to combat while the newer ones were held in reserve when the Germans attacked. The 35R battalion took no part in the fighting and crossed the Romanian border when the outcome was no longer in doubt.

The Free Polish forces were equipped with British, Canadian, French and American armour. After World War II, Poland was equipped with Russian armour.

PRE-WORLD WAR II TANKETTES

Lekki Czotg Szybkobiezny wz 30 (high speed light tank model 30) (TeK 1001) (TK–1) (TK wz 30), Polish built Carden-Loyd Mark VI type w/mg in semi-circular shield mount jutting out from right front, Ford engine, 2 leaf spring road wheel pairs on rail w/large leaf spring, 4 support rollers on rail.

TK–2 (TK wz 30), higher hull, shorter glacis, cut-out for mg, louvers below mg, built out on right front, new heavier suspension, engine and transmission, trailing idler, 7' 9" × 5' 9½" × 3' 5½".

Czotg Rozpoznawczy TK–3 (reconnaissance tank TK–3) (TK wz 31), 1930, similar but top of hull covered and bevelled-in all round, cylindrical mg mantlet, stronger suspension, 8' 5½" × 5' 10" × 4' 4".

TKS, ball-mounted mg, driver recessed on left, stepped glacis, Gundlach periscope, 1 mg fixed parallel to hull axis for use by driver, added hinged armour cowl for driver on some vehicles, new engine, A/A mg on fork on right rear of hull, wider tracks, 8' 4½" × 5' 9½" × 4' 4½".

TK/TKS zKM kal 20 PK, 1939, some TK and TKS vehicles modified w/large bulbous mantlet for 20mm gun.

Czotg TK–D (TKS–D), 47mm Bofors w/shield mounted in front, later 37mm Bofors A/T, high vertical sided hull.

TKF, 1934, TKS w/Fiat engine, 2 mg, 1 w/A/A capability, no outside mg fork, prototype only, 8' 5½" × 5' 10" × 4' 4".

TK zwieza (turreted TK) (TKW), 1933, TK–2 w/right hand turret having bulging mg mantlet, 2 turret versions, 6 vehicles built, resembled British Carden-Loyd patrol tank, 8' 4½" × 5' 9½" × 5' 3".

Autotransport Dragoweyo, experimental wheel-and-track vehicle comprising unarmoured 4-wheel chassis towed behind tankette, tankette driven onto trailer when vehicle was to be moved on wheels, tracks then removed and chain drive to wheels fitted.

C2P (CTK) Ciagnek 2P (tractor 2P), experimental 4-ton tractor on TKS chassis.

LIGHT AND MEDIUM TANKS

Renault Kardaszewics, 1923, French FT17 w/tracks made of 8 cables w/cross-pieces, 16' 2½" × 5' 9" × 7' 2½".

Renault Fumatory, 1923, turret removed from French FT17, large chemical tank over each track w/centre blower for chemically created smoke.

Renault FT17 Modernzacji, 1932, modernized French FT17, 37mm gun and 2 mgs, frontal armour increased.

WB 10, 1926, Medium tank project, details unknown.

Czotg Bojowy w31 (battle tank 1931) VAU 33 (Vickers-Armstrongs Ursus 33), 1933, British Vickers 6-ton tanks built in Poland from

imported parts but w/Saurer diesel engine, 16' × 7' 11" × 6' 10".

VAU 33 dw, original twin-turreted Vickers 6-ton tanks retrofitted w/Saurer engine, necessitating raised engine compartment, louvers over tracks.

VAU 33 jed, same but original single turret models.

7TP dw (two turret), 1934, Polish-built Vickers 6-ton tank variation, twin turrets w/bevelled mg ammunition box built on top front of each turret, variously armed w/Browning cal .30, Maxim 08, Hotchkiss 7.9mm or 13.2mm mg, later w/2 Browning water-cooled mgs in armoured jackets, same vehicles later rebuilt to 7TP jed standard, 15' 11" × 7' 11" × 7' 2".

7TP jed (one turret) (7TP jw wczezniejszy, original turret), 1936, same but single Swedish type turret, 37mm Bofors, 1 mg in armour jacket, 2 road wheel pairs, 4 support rollers, silencer mounted low in rear and louvered rear doors, 16' × 7' 11½" × 7' 6½".

7TP jw pozniejszy, same w/turret bustle and turret pistol parts, new engine, rear louvers eliminated, silencer mounted high in rear.

7TP jw wzmociony, new lighter diesel engine w/no hull change, prototype only.

C7P (Originally C6P), artillery tractor on 7TP chassis.

4TP (Pz Inz 140), 1938, reconnaissance tank resembling British Mark I Light tank, 20mm gun in 7TP turret, faceted bow, almost vertical stern, 4 road wheels, 2 support rollers, prototype only, 12' 7" × 6' 10" × 6' 1".

Pz Inz 141, Pz Inz 140 w/flamethrower, project only.

Pz Inz 342 (C4P), 1938, artillery tractor on 4TP chassis, prototype only.

(- - - - -), bridging tank on C7P chassis.

(- - - - -), armoured recovery vehicle on C7P chassis.

9TP, 1939, similar to 4TP, new lighter diesel engine in smaller engine compartment w/horizontal side louvers, thicker armour, streamlined driver's position, prototype only.

325

10TP, 1936, Christie-type wheel-and-track tank resembling US T3 Medium, 7TP turret, mg in right centre front ball mount, 4 road wheels, prototype only, 17' 8½" × 8' 4½" × 7' 2½".

14TP, 10TP built as an assault tank w/thicker armour, 37mm gun, 1 mg, prototype only.

20/25 TP (BBT), 1939, 25-ton tank, large bevel-front cast turret, armament not determined, 47mm, 60mm, 75mm and Bofors 40mm considered, 1 mg coaxial, 2 mgs in small right front auxiliary turret, 7 road wheels on heavy track frame, project not completed, based on a Special Committee (KSUS) project of 1934.

Pz Inz 152, details unknown.

Pz Inz 160–161, 1937, tank destroyer resembling Carden-Loyd Mark VI but larger, Bofors 37mm low in bow, 1 A/A mg, 4 road wheels, 2 support rollers, 4TP chassis, project only, 13' 1½" (15' 9") × 6' 10½" × 5' 3".

Pz Inz 425, details unknown.

T54, Soviet T54 Medium tanks built under licence.

T55, Soviet T55 Medium tanks built under licence.

Waczkiewicz, 1970, tiny slope-sided 5 road wheel utility tractor.

(- - - - -), modified Soviet SU85 as ARV, mg in front plate, driver left, hydraulic spade rear.

(- - - - -), modified Soviet SU100 as ARV w/conical mg cupola right front.

(- - - - -), modified Soviet SU100 as dozer w/hydraulic control cylinders on sloping glacis.

Mazur D–350, tractor resembling Soviet AT–5, 5 road wheels, 4 support rollers, engine behind cab, unarmoured.

TOPAS–2AP, Czech OT62 w/turret from Czech Skot 2AP.

FREE POLISH FORCES (WORLD WAR II)

Kaczka, 1944, gutted US M3 and M5 Light tanks used as Kangaroos.

ROMANIA

R–1, see Czechoslovakia.

326

R–2, Czech LT35.

R–3, Czech MUV6.

(- - - - -), rebuilt R–2 as assault gun
using captured Soviet 76.2mm gun.

(- - - - -) (Storm Gun), rebuilt Soviet
T60 mounting Soviet 76.2mm gun
w/3-sided shield immediately behind
driver, resembled Japanese Ho-ni I.

SOUTH AFRICA

Command Tank, US M3A3 Light
Tank, turret removed, mg mounted
on pedestal forward.

SOUTH VIETNAM

M24, US light tank w/mg and shield
mounted on turret top.

M113, US APC modified in at least
the following forms: .50 cal mg on
top w/3-sided shield; cupola on
riser on left side w/parallel mgs
and screen protected searchlight;
small turret on right w/57mm
recoilless rifle; 30 foot aluminium
treadway bridge-launcher, H-frame
towing eyes, and dome cupola
centre front behind hatches and
106mm recoilless rifle right rear.

SOVIET UNION

The Russian automobile corps was
formed late in 1914 with armoured
cars purchased in Britain and many
armoured in Russia. A great deal of
use was made of them. After the
French Schneider tank was used in
combat in France, the Russians tried
to order 200 but were refused. They
later tried to order an equal number
of St Chamond tanks and finally of
Mark VIII tanks. Upon on being
turned down for these last they asked
for blueprints in order to build them
in Russia. However, the Russian
break-up appeared so imminent that
this too was refused for fear the
prints would fall into German hands.

In recent years, the Russians have
claimed that Mendelyeef invented the
tank in 1911. They also claim that
in 1915 there was built a Lebedienko
armoured tricycle and a Porochow
tank, as well as the Wesdechod

tankette in 1919.

After World War I the British and
French sent troops with tanks to
assist the White Russians and when
they were withdrawn the armour was
abandoned and fell into the hands of
the Bolsheviks. Some of the French
Renaults were rebuilt by the Kharkov
Locomotive Works by substituting
Fiat engines and adding a machine-
gun to the right side of the turret.

Upon the death of Lenin, Frunze
became *de facto* chief of the Red
Army. He introduced many reforms
including standardization of equipment. After his death in 1927 his
work was carried on by Klim
Voroshilov.

Some experimental vehicles were
built. But the Russian lack of
engineering and industrial capacity
obliged them to buy foreign tanks,
whose design characteristics they then
copied.

In 1928 the first five-year plan was
started to strengthen the national
economy. Albert Kahn, the famous
American factory architect, was
invited to visit Russia. He was
encouraged by Henry Ford to accept.
Kahn built 521 strongly reinforced
plants of various kinds from Yukhutsk
to Kiev and trained 4,000 technicians.
(Kahn later built the tank arsenal at
Warren, Michigan, as well as the
Willow Run Bomber Plant.) Henry
Ford also offered and sent engineers
to Russia at his own expense and
trained Russian engineers in Detroit.
Other industrialists followed suit.

The Russo-German Kazan arrangements were of more benefit to the
Russians because they led to the
purchase of a German aircraft engine
which the Russians needed badly for
study and which became the basis
for the engine used for tanks and
aircraft.

From the early 1930s the Politburo
regarded very seriously the possibility
of war and began gearing the nation's
industrial fabric to military production. The first two five-year plans
contemplated setting up a base capable of adding new industries. This
was built around the great iron and
coal deposits in the Urals. Nizhni
Novgorod, Chelyabinsk, Stalingrad
(as it was later called) and Kharkov
began producing materièl between
1931 and 1933. A complete optical
plant was bought from Zeiss in
Germany and moved to Russia.

The United States recognized Russia
in 1933 in order to counter a Japanese
attack on Manchuria. From then on
the Soviet Union purchased many
machine tools in the United States
and also purchased the Christie tank
which was the American T3 Medium
tank. The Kazan agreement with
Germany was broken off in 1932.
Stalin ordered the Commissariat of
Defence to stop copying foreign
designs and to develop purely Russian
designs that would be superior to all
others. Torsion bar suspension, the
diesel engine, and wide tracks for use
in snow became their outstanding
features. In this development, combat

experience in Manchuria against the
Japanese was of more value than
Russian combat experience in Spain
during the Civil War.

A non-aggression pact with Hitler
was signed in order to buy time. The
Finnish War in 1939 showed some
serious deficiencies in tank design.
Changes were made immediately, but
they took some time to get into production. Germany attacked Russia in
June 1941. Initially Russian armour
was dispersed and was handled badly.
Existing tank plants were in danger
of being overrun unless moved. In
August 1941, the tank and tank component plants at Kharkov, Mariupol,
Kirov, Stalingrad, Voroshilovgrad,
Kiev, Donbas, Krivoi Rog, Dniepro-
petrovsk and Zaporazhe were moved
by rail to the Urals and installed
there. Later the Leningrad plant was
moved. Within a few months production was resumed in the Urals,
Central Asia and Siberia. The tank
plant at Saratov north of Stalingrad
and at Gorki east of Moscow were
not moved until late in the war.

In spite of the tremendous problems
of moving the tank industry, the
Russians claimed that T34 tank production man-hours were cut between
1941 and 1943 from 8,000 per tank to
3,700 and on the KV from 14,600 to
7,200. (By contrast, the American
M46 tank of the immediate post-war
period required 75,000 man-hours per
tank.)

The Russians were handicapped by
having to transport tanks by rail from
the Urals to the fronts, but they
simplified handling by completely
equipping the tanks so that receiving
troops could pick them up at the
railhead and take them into action
immediately, if necessary.

Both men and women worked in
war plants. Three-quarters of the
non-slave labourers were women. Late
in the war the slave rate was very
high. In addition to Soviet production
of 95,099 tanks and SPs between July
1941 and June 1945, the United States
gave Russia 13,303 combat vehicles
and 15,340 self-propelled guns, and
other equipment including a complete
rubber factory. The Russians received
preferential treatment under the
American Lend-Lease pro-
gramme and no questions were raised regardless of their demands. The British
also gave Russia 4,260 tanks and
Canada gave 1,220 tanks while both
contributed huge numbers of Universal Carriers. The Russian official
history credits America and Britain
with giving her a total of 11,567 tanks
and self-propelled guns.

The Russians were critical of both
British and American armoured
vehicles. Russian tanks were built to
do a job. They were simple, lacked
crew comfort but were effective.
Russian tank casualties were never
released but were believe to have
exceeded 100,000.

After the war, Swiss sources
claimed that the area in the Urals
was developed even more with
machine tools taken as reparations

from Germany. They also stated that at least eighteen plants were engaged in tank production at a time when the West had ceased production entirely.

During World War II there were 520 Soviet divisions which incorporated a tank regiment, plus other divisions without tanks. There were also twenty-five armoured and thirteen mechanized divisions in six armoured armies in addition to 400 smaller autonomous armoured units.

Many Russian vehicles were named, many others were numbered, some were both named and numbered. For a time it appeared that light tank two-digit numbers ended in zero while medium tank numbers ended in four and heavy tanks were numbered 100 and above. But this system, if it ever existed, is no longer used. Vehicles which form the basic chassis and are used for other purposes receive an extra letter, such as O for flame-thrower, M or S for bridging and T for ARV. Thus, OT34 would be the T34 tank equipped as a flame-thrower tank and ST34 would be the T34 chassis as a bridge-layer. Self-propelled guns have the initials SU followed by the calibre of the weapon mounted. When the Stalin chassis was used for an SP, the initials were JSU. Captured German chassis had an additional 1 added, as SU761. American tanks with petrol engines carried their American designations but when fitted with a diesel engine, the designation was followed by an M. Russian tank design since World War II has been imaginative and progressive, and the Soviet Union exports a considerable amount of armour.

LYAWCHKIS TANKOV, LIGHT TANKS AND VARIATIONS

Poroshovstshikov Vesdyekhod (Advance Rover), 1915, 4 tons, moulded hull built around wide track.

Stetanoska (Maximov), 1919, 1 man prone, shaped armour, bow mounted gun, small forward cupola, 10 road wheels, skirted, design study only.

Sormovsky (KS) (Tankov Tip M), 1920, copy of Renault FT, later modified for Maxim mg w/limiting chute as on Austin armoured car.

Reno Russkij, 1920, Renault FT tanks captured from the Wrangel 327

army, modified to substitute Fiat truck engine and to add Hotchkiss mg in ball mount on right side of turret, mg had to be removed to fire 37mm gun.

Teplokhod, 1920, 3-man amphibious tank, 76.2mm gun in turret, design study only.

Izhozavod, amphibious tank design based on above, partially completed.

(Gun Carrier), 1922, open tractor, driver on projecting front seat, front ramps for portéed 45mm wheeled carriage, gun crew seated in rear.

T16, 1927, Renault type, 5.5 tons, small road wheels, short hull, prototype for MSI.

T17 (Lilliput), 1938, engine front, driver left, mg or 37mm gun right in box cab surmounted in rear by smaller box cupola, mg in right sponson, tailpiece, 3 bogie pairs on vertical coil springs, 3 support rollers, Kégresse half metal tracks, 4 tons.

MSI (Maly Suprovizdyiniya I, little supreme Soviet I) (Maly Sovietski, little Soviet), Renault type w/tailpiece, faceted riveted hull, 6-sided turret, 37mm gun and mg on adjoining turret faces, cupola w/dome cover, 3 bogie pairs on 3 vertical springs plus 1 lead bogie wheel, 3 support rollers.

MSII (T18), 1928, similar but 3 support rollers w/leaf spring grouped at front for track tension, one rear support roller, 14′ 4½″ × 5′ 9″ × 6′ 11½″.

MSIII (T19), 1931, heavier version, 4 support rollers, rear of hull level, turret side plates form bustle.

T20, similar to T19, 3 four bogie wheel suspension units like French NC1, no tailpiece, rear of hull sloped downward, prototype only.

T23, 1931, suspension similar to T20 but 4 bogie wheel pairs, 2 support rollers, open top box hull resembling British Carden-Loyd Mark VI, 4 tons, 1 made.

T26A1, 1931, British Vickers-Armstrongs 6-Ton Tank built under licence, Vickers mgs in twin turrets higher than original and cut away in front forming rear cupola, 15′ 9″ × 7′ 10″ × 6′ 9″.

T26A2, same but air-cooled mgs in platter mounts in each turret, low rear deck.

T26A3, same but heavy mg in right turret, light mg in left.

T26A4, same but 27mm gun in right turret, light mg in left.

T26A5 (T26 Tu), same but short 37mm gun right turret, light mg in left turret, some w/long 45mm gun

instead of 37mm, w/ and w/o wireless rail.

T26V, T26A4 or A5 w/wireless rail antenna around hull.

T26VI, same as T26V but 20mm gun in right turret and no left turret.

T26B1, 1933, Vickers-Armstrongs 6-Ton Tank built under licence, BT5 cylindrical turret w/bustle, rounded mantlet w/long 37mm gun, later 45mm and mg, Zeiss tank periscope sight, some w/rear turret mg, 16′ 3″ × 8′ × 8′.

T26B1–V, same w/wireless rail around turret.

T26Pkh, 1943, same fitted w/snorkel.

Su5–1 (Samachodnaya Ustanovka 5–1, self-propelled 5–1), T26 chassis, rear cab open top, short 76.2mm gun firing to rear, high side shields protruding above cab top.

SU5–2, similar w/122mm howitzer on T26 chassis.

OT130 (OT26B1), flame-thrower converted from SU5–2.

SU5–3, similar but 152mm howitzer.

OT133, flame-thrower converted from T26, box-like mantlet.

T26S (T26C), new slope sided turret w/bustle, large rounded mantlet, welded hull, hinged dome ventilator in left front glacis, some w/double searchlights mounted on 45mm gun, buggy whip wireless antenna, 15′ 2″ × 8′ × 7′ 7½″.

OT26A (Ogon Tankov 26, flame tank 26) (DT26), T26A w/twin turrets, smoke emitter on left rear mudguard, flame-gun in right turret, left turret later removed.

OT26B, T26B w/long flame gun and coaxial mg.

328

OT26C (OT26S), T26S w/ special large wedge-shaped mantlet, F/T on left side and sighting opening right side, later w/supplementary armour plates on hull front and turret sides w/added curved plate over mantlet.

AT26, T26 w/76.2mm gun and mg in turret.

AT26B2, welded hull and turret.

AT26B2–V, same as command tank.

ST26, 1932, double track girder bridge carried on T26 w/fixed turret.

T26K, T26 artillery tractor w/modified hull and no turret.

T27 (MT27, Malyenki Tankov 27), Carden-Loyd Mark VI with head-covers built under licence, 2 bogie pairs, 8' 8" × 5' 4" × 4' 5".

T27A, headcovers joined, ball mounted mg in front plate, 3 bogie pairs.

329

T27B, same but mg mounted in jutting-out sponson.

(- - - - -), T27 w/37mm gun intended as an A/T weapon.

Morskoij 33, Vickers Carden-Loyd Light Amphibious Tank.

T33, very smilar but scissors suspension, 2 bogie wheel pairs, 2 support rollers, flat deck, driver right, square faced left side turret w/mg, high rounded edge turret hatch.

SU45, 45mm gun w/shield on T33 chassis.

T37, 1932, similar to T33 but buoyancy floats over tracks, turret right side, dome cupola, 2 bladed screw w/rudder behind, 12' 6" × 6' 8" × 6' 1".

T37A, same but welded turret centre front.

T37–3–2T, same as T37 but turret was one of the auxiliary mg turrets from T28 heavy tank.

T37–V, T37 w/wireless rail antenna on supports over tracks as command tank.

T38, 1936, larger, 4 tons, turret again on left side, driver's head in raised box on right, rear deck louvers w/raised sides, 12' 4" × 7' 8" × 5' 4".

T38–M2, 1938, same w/20mm cannon in turret on right side and probably engine change.

T40, 1940, 5.4 tons, designed to make maximum use of automobile components, faceted hull, rear sloped downward, flat glacis,

driver centre, small turret set back on left side, 12.7mm mg and 1 mg in rectangular mantlet w/rounded top and bottom edges, torsion bar suspension, 4 disc bogie wheels, 3 support rollers. dual lifting eyes on nose plate, 13' 6" × 7' 8" × 6' 4½".

T40A, same but single lifting eye, faired glacis, trim vane.

BM8–24, 28 tube rocket projector on T40 chassis.

T41, 1932, high hull, right hand turret w/mg in mount permitting high angle fire, modified Horstmann suspension, 4 bogie wheels w/trailing idler, 2 support rollers.

T50 (Maly Klim, little Klim), 10 tons, almost a miniature of the T34 but 6 small bogie wheels, 3 support rollers, 45mm gun and 1 mg in cast turret, w/small cupola having replaceable prisms, 17' 1" × 8' 1" × 7' 1'.

T60 Prototype, similar to T40 but glacis sloped upwards, flat-sided bustled turret w/rectangular mantlet and rectangulatr armoured box mount for Solothurn 20mm gun, large louver left side of glacis, 13' 6" × 7' 8½" × 5' 9".

T60, 1940, not amphibious, long sloping glacis w/driver cowl centre top, left hand turret w/flat sloping sides, 20mm gun in rectangular armoured box at mantlet, 4 spoked bogie wheels, 3 support rollers, torsion bar suspension, 13' 8" × 7' 10" × 5' 10".

T60A, same w/disc road wheels and truncated conical turret.

KT (Kry'yataya Tanka winged tank), 1942, Antonov biplane and twin tail assembly glider w/quick release by tank driver who acted as glider pilot, glider failed to take off, project abandoned.

SU45, 45mm gun w/shield on T60 chassis.

T70, 1942, resembled T60 but larger, engine front, 45mm gun and 1 mg in rounded mantlet in large sloping sided turret w/rounded rear, driver hatch w/periscope left side of glacis, hatch on lower right glacis, torsion bar suspension, 5 bogie wheels, 2 or 3 support rollers, amphibious, 14' 1" × 7' 4" × 6' 8½".

T70A, same, flat turret rear.

SU37, 37mm L/63 gun w/flash hider rear mounted in open top V-front cab on lengthened T70 chassis, 6 bogie wheels, 3 support rollers, 17' 2½" × 9' × 6' 10½".

SU37, T70 chassis, 37mm L/39 gun (excluding muzzle brake) rear mounted, 3-sided cab w/handrails, 12 tons.

SU76, similar w/76.2mm gun,

1 added bogie wheel, originally w/rear fold-up doors.

SU76, later w/conventional hinged doors and bigger engine, 11' 8" × 9' × 7' 2".

T34, (?), airborne tank, 1948, miniature tank, 3 small bogie wheels, 2 support rollers, hull sloped in all around, slope-sided turret w/large mantlet, 45mm gun, 3 tons, utilized components from T70, SU76 and T34, 12' 3" × 7' 6" × 6' 6".

BM8–24, T70 chassis w/rocket-projector.

T80, T70 w/heavier mantlet, round cupola and applique armour on turret sides, 14' 6" × 8' 2½" × 7' 2".

PT76 (Plojushchtij Tankov, amphibious tank 76), 15.5 tons, 6 medium-sized bogie wheels, no support rollers, low bevelled glacis, driver centre, squat conical turret w/76mm gun and bore evacuator at the muzzle, double turret hatch w/double bulges for greater head-room, IR equipped, hydrojet propulsion in water from ports in hull, steered w/deflector plates, 22' 8" (25') × 10' 4" × 7' 5".

PT76 (PT76 Model 2), 1962, similar but 76mm gun w/bore evacuator in the middle of gun tube and w/muzzle brake.

(Armoured Reconnaissance Patrol Vehicle), PT76 w/various radiation meters and w/large bulbous cupola on top of main turret giving audio and visual warning of the presence of chemical agents, also has mechanical device to set out markers to outline zones of contamination exceeding five roentgens per hour.

PT76 Model 3, overhung rear hull, ventilator stack on rear deck, shorter gun w/muzzle brake.

ASU57 (Aviadezantnaya Samochodnaya Ustanovka) (L/73), airborne 57mm assault gun, 4 large bogie wheels, 3 × 2 support rollers, w/and w/o muzzle brake and bore evacuator, 12' 3" (19') × 6' 9" × 5' 3".

330

ASU85, PT76 chassis airborne SP, 85mm L/53 w/bore evacuator and muzzle brake in centre front glacis ball mount, potbelly hull front, driver right, 20' (28') × 9' 2" × 6' 11".

BTR(50)P, 1952, amphibious APC on PT76 chassis, open top front hull higher than rear portion, 2-bevel glacis, driver centre, cupola left front, 1 heavy mg right front, later models w/closed top w/2 rectangular doors and cupola on left, then 2 oval doors, this last type then was built up w/cupola moved to right side, finally another cupola was added on the left, some w/IR equipment, 22′ 8″ × 10′ 4″ × 6′ 1″.

BTR60 (PB), similar, small revolving turret w/14.5mm mg on right w/recoilless rifle, 22′ 9″ × 9′ 3″ × 7′ 6″.

BTR50(PU), 57mm M1942 A/T gun w/shield on BTR50(P).

ZSU23–4 (Shilka), 1965, PT76 chassis, large square turret w/quad 23mm guns and radar dish, driver left, latest model w/vertical air scoops replacing previous louvers and slots, 19′ 9″ × 9′ 3″ × 8′ w/o radar.

Luna 1 (BB–1) (SSM Type 1) (Frog 1 and 2, NATO title), PT76 chassis w/bulb nosed missile resembling US Honest John missile, mounted in 5 segment skeleton cradle ramp hydraulically elevated for firing on rear turntable pivot, 31′ 6″ × 10′ 1″ × 10′ 1′.

▼ 331

Luna 2 (BB–1) (T5C) (Frog 3), similar but missile head larger w/o bulbous nose.

Luna 3 (Frog 4), same but missile same diameter throughout length.

Frog 5, same but shorter missile, 2 upper rollers added.

BMD, 1967, low profile modified, BTR50P type w/5 road wheels and 2 support rollers, low barge-like hull, low turret w/57mm gun and coaxial missile similar to French SS11, carries 8 men plus crew, 21′ 4″ × 9′ 10″ × 6′ 1″.

▼ 332

Ganef (SA4), 1964, PT76 basis, 7 bogie wheels, 4 support rollers (2 in centre), 2 Frog 4 missiles.

(- - - - -), 1971, mine-layer on Ganef chassis.

▼ 333

Gainful (NATO title) (SA–6), redesigned Frog 1–2 chassis w/3 Frog 4 missiles facing rear.

SREDNY TANKOV OR MEDIUM TANKS EXCLUSIVE OF CHRISTIE TYPES

Anglieski Padokhij (English Workman), Vickers tank purchased from Britain, see Great Britain.

T12 (T1–12), 1928, prototype of T24, 20 tons, first tank w/45 mm gun in fixed box turret having side mg and large cupola w/mg, 5 bogie wheel pairs, 2 upper rollers, tailpiece, 111 built.

T24, 1932, armour faired away to either side of sponson for mg on left front glacis, 45mm gun in cylindrical turret w/mg cupola, 4 bogie wheel pairs, each pair on vertical coil spring assembly w/4 support rollers, 21 tons, 25 produced, suspension also used on Komintern tractor, 21′ 4″ × 9′ 10″ × 9′ 2½″.

T26, (?) 1932, 5 bogie wheel pairs plus leading and trailing rollers, 4 upper rollers, covered suspension, large forward bevel main turret w/45mm gun, mg in ball mount to right, 2 small forward mg turrets.

T28, Model 1933, 1933, 31 tons, 76mm L/16.5 gun in cylindrical turret w/wireless rail antenna, mg in ball mount in right turret front, small

auxiliary mg turrent w/45mm gun right front, 45mm in left rear auxiliary turret, 2 small dome ventilators in glacis, 4 bogie wheel pairs, skirted, 6 support rollers, 24′ 5″ × 9′ 2½″ × 9′ 2½″.

T28A, 1933, similar, top edge of turret rounded, lighter.

T28 Model·1938, (T28B), similar but mg in right front auxiliary turret, no rear auxiliary turret, short 76.2mm gun in main turret, 6 bogie wheel pairs, 4 support rollers.

T28 Model 1939 (T28C) (TG2/T22) (T28M), 5 piece cast turret, main gun lengthened to L/30, mg in hooded ball mount on right turret front, driver cowl raised, dome vent left glacis, armour later thickened.

T28 Model 1940 (T28D), similar, 1 piece cast turret, cast frame mantlet, auxiliary turrets w/welded applique armour circles w/narrow slits, some vehicles w/armoured recoil mechanism for main armament.

T28F (T28M?).

JT28, 1939, T28 tank chassis w/only 2 front auxiliary turrets retained, used as carrier for large girder bridge.

Direnkova, 1930, not verified or identified.

T46, 1935, T26 type hull and turret, 4 large road wheels, 2 support rollers, 45mm gun.

T46-5 (T–IV) (T–11), 1937, 31 tons, flat top hull, T26S type turret w/slope back bustle w/ball mounted mg, 45mm gun and 1 mg coaxial, 2 searchlights on gun, 6 small bogie wheels, 3 support rollers.

CHRISTIE-TYPE VEHICLES

▼ 334

BT1 (Bystrij Tankov, fast tank) (Betka, beetle) (Tri Tankista, three tanker), 1931, US T3 Medium Convertible wheel-and-track tank built in Russia w/o royalty to J. W. Christie, leading disc bogie wheels w/peripheral holes, others 5 spoked, V-shaped glacis, double skin hull, cylindrical forward bevel turret w/1 or 2 mgs in mantlet, 1 mg in right turret front, 10½ tons, 18′ 1″ × 7′ 4″ × 7′ 3″.

BT2, 1931, same as BT1 but w/37mm gun, 1 mg in ball mount to right of main armament, perforated bogie wheels, 18′ 11″ × 7′ ½″ × 7′ 4½″.

BT3, same as BT2 but disc wheels and 45mm gun.

BT4, twin turrets as in T26A, experimental.

BT–DT (Dmovaya Tankov, smoke tank).

BT3–IT, crude bridging tank.

BT3–PT (Podiemniya Tankov, crane tank), crude ARV.

BT/MU, simple short 2 track bridge hinged at the bow of BT, bridge normally carried resting on mudguards, connected by chain to log which, when run over by tracks, pulled bridge down, after which tank could back, leaving bridge to slide off by friction and gravity.

BT5 (R34), 1932, bevelled hull sides, projecting driver's cowl, turret w/large mantlet and bustle, 18′ 11″ × 7′ ½″ × 7′ 4½″.

BT5V, same w/wireless rail antenna around turret.

BT5/OT, 1934, disc bogie wheels, cylindrical turret w/eccentric bustle and box mantlet from OT133, flame-thrower and mg coaxial.

BT5A, (Artilleriyskich Tankov), 76.2mm L/16.5 gm and mg.

BT5 PKh, same as BT5 but fitted w/snorkel device for fording.

BT5–IT, bridging tank.

BT6, pneumatic tyred bogie wheels, 2 small pneumatic tyred wheels on axle at wider bow, mg ball mount right hull front, 45mm gun and mg coaxial in turret, mg in large bulging ball mount right and left sides of turret, sometimes confused w/BT7M and BT8.

BT7–1, original BT7 w/BT5 cylinder type turret, short pitch tracks.

BT7 (BT–M/C) (R37), 1936, slope-sided turret w/bustle, smaller rounded mantlet, shorter glacis w/driver's cowl extending across hull, 18′ 7″ × 7′ 6″ × 7′ 11½″.

BT7–V, same w/BT5 turret and wireless rail.

BT7A, BT5 w/short 76.2mm gun front and ball mounted mg rear plate of large turret, trailing idler.

BT7M, BT7 w/76.2 mm L/16.5 gun and one of the first tanks to be fitted w/diesel engine, conical turret w/2 periscope heads.

BT8 (BT–M/D) (T29–5), 1934, 26 tons, BT7M chassis w/hull from T28, 2 forward auxiliary mg

turrets, short 76.2mm gun in main turret, 4 bogie wheels per side, all driven.

T46, 1937, BT5 turret having wireless rail antenna but mg right front, suspension comprising 4 large bogie wheels and 2 support rollers, driver set out on left front, BT7 turret later substituted.

BT/JS (BT/IS) (Ispitatelniy, investigator), 1937, long sloped glacis, wide bevel all round hull, T26S turret w/searchlights, 4 large bogie wheels partly skirted, may have been amphibious, 18′ 11½″ × 7′ 6″ × 7′ 6″.

A20 (T29–5), 1937, T34 predecessor, 45mm gun, otherwise very similar to final T34, 4 large bogie wheels, three rear axles driven, 1 built, 17′ 10″ × 8′ 9″ × 7′ 9″.

T29, Christie-type wheel-and-track version of T28, 4 large double rubber tyred road wheels, double rubber tyred front idlers w/idler axle across bow, 23′ 1½″ × 9′ 6″ × 8′ 8″.

T29–5, improved version, smaller road wheels and 3 support rollers, front axle eliminated.

T32, predecessor of T34 but higher hull, convertible feature eliminated, slope-sided hull, short 57mm gun in ball mount.

A30, identical to A20 but 76.2mm L/11 howitzer in ball mantlet, may also be T32.

T34, prototype, similar w/57mm gun.

▼   335

T34/76A (T34A), 1939, slope-sided plate turret w/bustle, 76.2mm L/30.5 gun w/bulb mantlet above gun, mg in turret rear, riveted nose plate, 115 made, a few early production w/BT7 petrol engines, later w/diesel, gap between second and third bogie wheels, 19′ 9″ (21′ 7″) × 10′ × 8′ 2″.

T34/76B (T34B), partly-welded turret w/1 hatch, steel rimmed bogie wheels w/peripheral holes for heat dissipation, riveted nose-plate, L/41.5 gun, new angular bolted recoil cylinder cover below gun, some w/smoke candle discharger in box on left rear fender.

T34/76C (T34C), bogie wheels steel rimmed or mixed, new welded and cast turret w/bulging mantlet, grab irons and 2 turret hatches, welded nose plate, 19′ 11″ × 9′ 8″ × 8′ 8½″.

T34/76D, KV turret and 76.2mm gun, later w/2 periscopes.

T34/76E, model D w/cupola on left top of turret, commander's tank.

▼   336

T34/76F, L/34.7 gun in all cast turret, 4 speed transmission replaced by 5 speed.

SU85, 1943, turretless T34, large eyeball mantlet right front w/85mm L/49 gun, driver left, small cupola right top, 30 tons, 19′ 5″ (26′ 8″) × 9′ 10″ × 7′ ½″.

85T (SU85T), SU85 w/armament removed, gun mount closed over, used as ARV.

SU100, 1944, very similar to SU85 but 100mm L/53 gun almost centre front, 19′ 5″ (32′ 8″) × 9′ 10″ × 7′ ½″.

SU100T, SU100 w/armament removed and front plate covered over, used as ARV.

SAU122, 1942, very similar to SU100 but 122mm howitzer in massive mantlet protecting recoil mechanism, 30 tons, later w/eye-ball mantlet.

(- - - - -), tank dozer on T34.

(- - - - -), V-type snow plough on T34.

MDK–2M (GB409 original German designation), unarmoured and reversed T34 w/cab and fold-up trench digging device.

T34/85–I, 1944, T34 chassis, KV85 cast turret w/bustle, 85mm L/39 gun, 1 man added to crew, single dome ventilator on turret top, 20′ (26′ 9″) × 9′ 10″ × 8′ 11″.

T34/85–II, improved vision and fire control, double turret ventilator, cupola added, 20′ (26′ 9″) × 9′ 1″ × 9′ 1″.

T34/85 Fascine Carrier, double fascine on centre axle apparently carried on rear deck and dropped by backing into opening.

ST34, 1942, simple bridging device on T34, operated as described under BT/MU.

MTU (MT34) (Mostovoy Tankov, bridge tank), bridge carried on rollers on hull of turretless T34.

MTU34, scissors-type folding bridge, hydraulic erection and laying device on turretless T34, 32′ 10″ × 10′ 6″ × 12′ 2″.

OT34 (T34/76B ATO41), regular T34 w/KV turret but F/T substituted for front glacis mg, fuel container rear of hull.

T34/PT3, mine roller, common axle carrying 2 sets of thick serrated edge discs on double I-beam whiffletree mount yoked to tank bow.

TT34 (T34T) (JT34), turretless T34 used as ARV, some w/double boom pivoted above driver w/double pillar travel locks for boom bases.

TT34 (T34T) (SKP–5), built-up rear hull, turretless, rear mounted winch, some w/demountable crane pivoted amidships, 26′ 3″ × 9′ 10′ × 8′ 6″.

T34STU, T34 w/dozer blade.

T34, 1944, propaganda tank w/armoured loudspeaker w/frontal louvers on each side of hull, used to tempt Germans to defect.

PT8, T34 chassis w/1 added road wheel, unarmoured personnel carrier.

T43, T34/76C w/thicker armour, not adopted because gun calibre no longer considered adequate.

T44, lower and longer than T34, wider tracks, driver's hatch left side of glacis, bow mg muzzle flush w/glacis hole, splash rail across centre of glacis, 85mm gun w/o muzzle brake, conical sleeve at mantlet, later 100mm gun w/o sleeve, oval turret, 2 large flat cupolas on turret, long turret bustle, vertical hull sides, first spoked and perforated road wheel spaced from others, 20′ 3″ (25′ 2½″) × 10′ 4″ × 7′ 11″.

T54 Pilot, 1947, similar but short pitch track, turret like T44 but faired at rear bottom, loader's hatch raised.

▼ 337

T54 (T54A), 5 large bogie wheels, front 1 separated from rear 4, squat bulbous cast turret w/base under-cut to turret ring, ventilator right centre, commander's hatch left, external mantlet, 100mm L/56 gun w/vertical stabilization, AA mg on right turret hatch added later, no bore evacuator originally, but

later at muzzle end, 21′ 2″ (29′ 7″) × 16′ 9″ × 7′ 10″.

T54 (T54B), second model, bore evacuator at end of tube, hemi-spherical turret w/base overlapping hull sides, raised cupola on loader's hatch, internal mantlet, driver has fixed mg in front plate, computer, IR devices.

T54 (T54C), same equipped w/snorkel devices, narrow trim vane on glacis.

T54 (T54D) (T55), 1961, flush internal mantlet, some w/fasteners for mine rollers, some w/snorkel periscope, also w/high snorkel tower for commander, new cupola for commander, no commander's mg, gunner's cupola almost flush, stowage boxes, number and shape of rear deck engine louvers, jettison fuel tanks and stowage of snorkels at rear, and IR devices, 43 rounds instead of 34, bore evacuator at end of gun tube, horizontal turret grab irons.

T54E, see T55.

SU–ZAM–57–2 (ZSU57–2), 1957, modified and shortened T54 chassis, 4 bogie wheels, 2 support rollers, large square open top turret w/twin 57mm A/A guns, 18′ 4″ (28′) × 10′ 9″ × 9′ 10″.

▼ 338

MST54 (MT54), 1959, 2 lengths: 40′ and 65′, skeleton girder bridge on turretless T54, hydraulic control for laying by means of extensible U-arm, 12.7mm mg in cupola.

T54/PT3, same type of mine-roller as on T34/PT3.

T54–T, tank chassis used as ARV, trail spade and snorkel tower added, later w/extensible boom hinged at base of special rotating turret, resembles German Leopard ARV.

OT54 (PT54), mine-roller similar but w/o common axle, each roller set suspended from curved beam and held in line by chain attached to hull, variations existed.

PT54 Mine-Roller, two 5-roller units w/spikes mounted on a common frame.

PT54, 2 serrated 3-roller caster units chain supported and chain anchored suspended from goose neck supports, sometimes w/centre leading roller.

PT54, 2 serrated 6-roller units on similar goose necks (centre

counter-weighted), sometimes also w/ploughs.

PT54, 2 serated 3-roller caster units centre supported.

PT54, 2 five-spoked rollers on hinged cradle on separate yokes, chain anchored.

ORT54, trench digger on T54 chassis.

ORT54, trench digger on T54 chassis.

▼ 339

T55 (T54E), same as T54 but w/IR equipment having several variations, turret basket, turret hatch low in first model, w/high rim in second model, new commander hatch, no A/A mg, bore evacuator just ahead of centre of tube upper front turret ventilator dome eliminated, 20′ 4″ (29′ 7″) × 10′ 9″ × 7′ 9″.

(-----), 1968, T55 w/armour covered hydraulic package on bow to control toothed and bladed mine plough in front of each track.

T55T, 1973, ARV, small commander's turret right front, crane along left top.

BAT/M, combination recovery crane and bulldozer on T54 chassis.

▼ 340

T62, 1963, similar to T54 but gap between third and fourth and between fourth and fifth road wheels, larger turret placed further back, 115mm gun w/bore evacuator in middle of tube, cupola further back than loader's hatch, 22′ 4″ (31′ 2″) × 10′ 10″ × 7′ 7″.

T70 (T64), 1971, similar but six smaller road wheels, 3 support rollers, long glacis on larger hull, 120mm gun, turret near centre of hull, launcher 45 tons, also referred to as T64.

TYAZHELYI, HEAVY TANK TYPES

Tyjawlij Tankov Mendelyeef, 1898, purported to resemble German WWI A7V.

Bronivikh Lebedienko, 1915 giant tricycle w/two 30' diameter wheels, T-shaped hull, small rear steering roller, dome turret in centre of frame, stated as not completed, photo appeared in Pravda in 1968.

T32 (M–11), 1930–31, inspired by British Independent tank and developed from TG series, five turrets, main one centrally placed w/76.2mm gun, two diagonally right front and left rear each w/a 37mm gun, all three w/a co-axial mg, two each w/7.62mm mg next to the 37mm turrets, skirted suspension, driver left front, 45 tons, 30' 6" × 10' 6" × 10'.

T35, replacement to above similar but w/many detailed improvements, two 45mm guns instead of 37mm guns, more powerful petrol engine (500 hp instead of 345 hp), 31' 6" × 10' 6" × 11' 3".

T35 Model 33V, same w/wireless antenna rail round central turret.

T35–1 (T32A), similar but no rear turrets.

T35A (TG–3/T–40), 1933, similar to T32 but sloping hull and dome turret, 4 road wheel pairs, skirted suspension.

T35B, same but flat sided turret w/bustle.

T35C (T35 Model 1935), same but slope-sided turrets.

SU7, SU14 and SU141, T35 chassis w/203mm howitzer.

SU14–BR–1, 1935, long heavy 152mm gun centre mounted on open T35 chassis, rear ammunition loading crane.

SU–BU–10, 152mm howitzer SP on T35 chassis.

SU14 BR2, similar, 152 howitzer resembled German Ferdinand SP, auxiliary skirts for front one-third of suspension, T35 basis.

SMK (Sergei Mironovich Kirov), 1937, cylindrical superstructure mounting large cylindrical turret

and 76.2mm gun, smaller auxiliary turret w/45mm gun in front of main turret, 31' 6" × 10' 6" × 10' 6".

TG (Tank Grotte), 5 large road wheels, partly skirted, 4 upper rollers, long flat glacis, driver left, centre mounted slope sided turret w/dome cupola, 76.2mm gun w/muzzle brake.

TG1/T22, variation, details unknown.

TG3/T29, variation.

TG5/T42, variation.

T100 (Sotka) (Sotyna ?) (100), 1937, SMK w/105mm gun in main turret, 8 bogie wheels, 4 support rollers and wider tracks.

SU100Y (Igrek), same chassis w/130mm gun in large mantlet in centre of hull, 8 road wheels, 4 support rollers.

KV (Klim Voroshilov), prototype 1939, almost identical to SMK but smaller, driver centre, large cast turret w/76.2mm gun, mg in rear of bustle, smaller auxiliary cast turret w/45mm gun in front of main turret, skirted, 4 bogie wheel pairs, originally spring suspension but later torsion bar, crew 5, 4 support rollers, used in Finnish War in 1939, 22' 6" × 11' × 9'.

KV76 (KV1 Model 1940), KV chassis w/welded flat-sided square bustle turret w/square rear door, no rear mg, L/30.5 76.2mm gun in early T34 type mantlet, no auxiliary turret, some w/mg left of driver, 40 tons, 22' 2" × 10' 8" × 10' 8".

KV1 Model 1941 (KVIA), 76.2mm L/41.5 gun in large mantlet w/cast outer mantlet mg left of driver, cast slope-sided turret w/bevelled bustle, 6 road wheels, 3 support rollers, some w/auxiliary front plate, later, 21' 10½" (22' 4") × 11' × 10' 8".

KV1 Model 1942 (KV1B) (Ekranami), same as KV1 Model 1941 but heavily rounded mantlet and appliqué armour on hull and turret.

KV1 Model 1942 (KV1C), cast turret, thicker hull armour, spoked road wheels.

KV122, 1940, short 122mm howitzer in high massive turret, 3 mgs.

SU122, hull like JSU122 howitzer but long gun, 19' 5½" (22' 9½") × 9' 10" × 7' ½".

SU152, 1943, 152mm howitzer in chassis similar to SU122, 22' 5½ (29' 2½") × 10' 8" × 8' ½".

KV1C, cast turret faired in front, wider tracks, thicker armour.

KV1s (Skorotsnoy, fast), 1942, lighter and faster version, sloping rear deck, cupola on turret, bustle mg offset to left, weight reduced 5 tons w/thinner armour and smaller hull, new transmission, 76.2mm gun and 3 mgs.

KV85, KV1C w/85mm L/49 gun, thicker armour, turret faired in front, cupola, crew 4, 46 tons, no bow mg, turret later applied to T34, 22' 4" (28' 3") × 10' 8" × 9' 2½".

SU122, hull like JSU 122 howitzer but long gun, 19' 5½" (22' 9½") × 9' 10" × 7' ½".

KVIIA (KV2 Model 1940) (SU152) (Zveroboy, conquering beast), 152mm L/20 gun-howitzer w/blast deflector in huge bulging mantlet, 50 tons, 21' 10½" (22' 4") × 11' × 10' 8".

SU203, no details available.

KVII–1, KVII w/85mm gun.

KVII–2, KVIS, w/122mm A/A gun.

KVIIB, new turret, wider tracks, asymmetric mantlet some W/F/T.

KV7, 1941, turretless KVI chassis w/one 76.2mm and two 45mm guns, prototype only.

KV8, flame-thrower on KVIC chassis 45mm gun and F/T in cannon tube.

KV9, 1941, KV w/dual 76.2mm guns.

KVT, turretless KV as ARV or prime mover.

JSI (JSIA) (JSIB) (JS85) (Josef Stalin), 1944, KV85 w/lowered suspension, 22′ 2″ (28′) × 10′ 2″ × 8′ 11½″.

JS100, same w/100mm gun.

JS122, JSI w/122mm L/43 gun w/muzzle brake in new larger cast turret w/left rear mg, single faired front hull casting, driver centre, rear of hull sloped as on T34, 22′ 2½″ (28′ 2½″) × 10′ 1″ × 8′ 11½″.

JSII (JS122), flat sloped front plate, 122mm gun w/muzzle brake, cast and welded hull, front plate faired, driver bulge instead of visor, two stage planetary steering added, 22′ 2½″ (34″ 3′) × 10′ 2″ × 8′ 11½″.

JSIII (Shuka, pike), 1945, squat cast overhanging dome turret w/small cupola, 122mm L/45 gun w/stabilizer, V-glacis, sloping hull sides, 6 bogie wheels, 3 support rollers, 21′ 10½″ (32′ 9″) × 10′ 6″ × 8′.

JSU122 (D258), 1944, 122mm field howitzer L/45 w/blast deflector in huge rectangular cast mantlet, box-like front, low rear deck, 6 bogie wheels, 3 support rollers, 50 tons, 22′ 4″ (32′ 4″) × 10′ 1″ × 8′ 11½″ to top of hull.

345

JSU122 (A19), 1944, 122mm field howitzer, no muzzle brake, 22′ 4″ (32′) × 10′ 1″ × 8′ 11½″.

JSU249 (JSU 122 D258), 1955, JSU122 chassis w/122mm L/43 gun less muzzle brake, same gun as on Stalin tank.

JSU152, 1944, 152mm L/28 gun w/o blast deflector, 22′ 4″ (29′ 3″) × 9′ 10″ × 8′ 2½″.

JSU-T, JSU152 w/armament removed, designated by NATO as Model A ARV.

JSU-T Model B (JSU-TE), storage bin and small folding crane added.

JSU-T Model C, trail spade added.

JSU-2T (Model D), similar but large squat dome replaced regular Stalin turret, snorkel tower added.

JSU-T Model E, large slotted fold-back A-frame hinged on glacis of Model D.

(JSU Command), same appearance as Model E, but w/o storage bin or trail spade.

JS4 (K-1), 1948, 122mm gun w/bore evacuator, bogie spacing same as T62 of 1965, w/bigger engine.

OVM (Viacheslav Molotov), 1948, existence not verified.

T10 (Lenin), 1957, Stalin III chassis with 7 bogie wheels, 3 support rollers, 122mm gun w/bore evacuator and 2/baffle muzzle brake, V-glacis, wide tracks, 25′ 2″ (32′ 4″) × 11′ 7″ × 10′ 10″.

T10M, 1967, improved, longer gun, muzzle brake w/5 baffles, IR equipped, improved fire control equipment, turret bustle, 23′ 11″ × 11′ 8″ × 7′ 11″.

T14, project only.

(- - - - -), 1957, 8 bogie wheels, 4 support rollers, 310mm gun may be ram jet but more likely light beam controlled missile projector, gun tube extends beyond vehicle for most of its length, 33′ 2″ × 11′ 8″ × 10′ 10″.

(- - - - -), 1958, similar but 420mm 3 stage rocket light-beam controlled missile projector, suspension strengthened in 1961.

(- - - - -), 1965, appeared to be an even longer 420mm tube w/additional springing on 4 front bogie wheels (rear bogie wheels when firing).

BB-2 (T7A) (Scud A, NATO title), 1957, Stalin-type chassis w/side forward cabs, large missile in ladder-like cage, 36′ 1″ × 10′ × 10′ 10″.

BB-3 (T5B) (Scud B), missile carried in warming jacket, had bulbous nose w/long snout, heavier chassis, 41′ × 10′ × 10′ 10″.

Shaddock (NATO title), same, 6 bogie wheels, 3 support rollers, larger missile in jacket like Scud A, new tail base.

Easter Egg (Iron Maiden) (Scamp SS14, NATO title), 1965, lengthened T10 heavy tank chassis, 8 bogie wheels, 5 support rollers, large box hull w/⅓ of huge blunt-nosed missile overhanging the bow.

Scrooge (NATO title), another even larger missile overhanging the bow even more, 8 bogie wheels, 5 support rollers.

MISCELLANEOUS VEHICLES

Komsolometz (STZ), 1939, artillery tractor, slope sided, armoured bow, ball mounted mg in large oval mount right front, open rear w/seats for 3 men each side w/bows for tarpaulin cover, 2 leaf spring bogie wheel pairs, 2 support rollers, 4½ tons.

SU45, 45mm gun in auxiliary turret from T28 heavy tank on Komsolometz tractor.

SU57, 57mm gun w/shield on open chassis Komsolometz.

SU76M, 76.2mm A/T gun w/shield rear-mounted on open chassis Komsolometz.

SU14, lengthened Komsolometz chassis, 3 bogie wheel pairs, 2 support rollers, low faceted hull like German Scout Car SdKfz221, 76.2mm gun w/muzzle brake in nose, 2 low cylindrical cupolas.

GAZ47 (AT-L), 1956, automobile-type artillery tractor, semi-armoured 1 mg in sponson right front glacis, 4 disc type bogie wheels and trailing idler, 2 support rollers.

ASU57, 1956, modified GAZ47 chassis w/one less bogie wheel, 2 support rollers, open top box hull, 57mm L/73 gun w/muzzle brake mounted left front, airborne SP.

(- - - - -), 1962, similar to US Ontos on GAZ47 basis chassis.

ASU76 (ASU57), same chassis as ASU57, but very long 45mm gun w/multi-baffle (muzzle brake and bore evacuator), airborne SP.

346

T8 (BM14) (STZ-5), ATS M1950 automobile-type artillery tractor larger than ATP, 4 bogie wheel pairs, 4 support rollers, 2 banks of six 140mm rockets each on rear mounted pedestal.

ATP, similar to GAZ47 but 5 disc-type road wheels, 3 support rollers, front armoured cab w/heavy mg in heavy mantlet right front, some later w/rotating commander cupola, cargo body, 13′ 4″ × 7′ 8″ × 5′ 7″.

AT-S, 1950, unarmoured tractor, 6 spoked road wheels, 3 support rollers, engine front, 9 tons.

AT-S (M54), cargo tractor, also used to carry medium artillery or BM24 rocket projector, bonnet protrudes in front, 8 small road wheels, 4 support wheels.

AT-S59, T54 tank basis, hauls A/A missile on wheeled trailer attached by king-pin, engine forward.

AT–T (M50) (K–10), T54 tank basis tractor for heavy artillery, also used for trench digger or Lorain type crane, engine front, 28 tons.

AT–L–M, unarmoured tractor for heavy wheeled mortar, engine front, cargo box rear, 6 spoked road wheels, 3 support rollers (later eliminated), 9.1 tons.

GT–S, squat unarmoured AT–P used as personnel carrier, engine front, ASU57 components, 4 road wheels, trailing idler, 5 tons.

GT–SM, similar, 5 road wheels and trailing idler, canvas top, arctic personnel carrier, unarmoured.

GT–T, partial armour, engine front tractor intended for arctic use, PT76 components, 6 road wheels, armoured cab, 11 tons.

GSP (PT8), long unarmoured personnel carrier, amphibious, fluted sides, also used to carry inverted bridging pontoon w/hydraulic release device.

MODIFIED FOREIGN VEHICLES

M3C, US M3 Light Tank.

M4M, US M4A2 Medium Tank w/Russian 76.2mm gun.

SU60, 3 bogie wheel and trailing idler Belgian Carden-Loyd chassis captured from the Germans, w/60mm A/T gun and rounded open rear shield.

SU762, PzKpfwIII chassis, bevelled in turret w/bustle, round cupola, 76.2mm gun in bulging mantlet, 17′ 7½″ (20′ 8″) × 9′ 6½″ × 7′ 9½″.

SU76I, PzKpfwIII chassis, slope-sided square superstructure mounting Soviet 76.2mm gun.

SU761, German sIG33 150mm gun on KV hull w/o turret.

SU Valentin, 85mm gun on turretless Canadian Valentine chassis.

AMX–51, Russian name for French AMX13.

AMX–63, Russian name for French AMX30.

SPAIN

The Trubia and Verdeja Light tanks built from 1926 to 1932 were very interesting vehicles but did not re-place the French-built vehicles in use in the army. The Trubia had roller tracks. The Verdeja had a cannon which could fire at either ground or aerial targets.

During the Civil War the rebels were equipped with German and Italian armour and the government with Russian armour. For a time the Spanish Army retained a mixture of such armour, but in recent years it has been completely rearmed with American equipment.

Carro de combate Trubia, 1925, 10-ton Renault FT type but covered track frames w/horizontal mudguards, high bow, no bow gun, small front roller for obstacle crossing, tailpiece, conical turret w/2 mgs and several ball mounts, domed stroboscope, no bogies, roller tracks w/sprung track frames, 17′ 8″ × 6′ 11″ × 7′10″.

▼ 347
Carro de Combate Trubia (Ligero Tipo A–4, light tank type A–4), 1933, improved model w/added mg centre right in glacis, 17′ ½″ × 5′ 11″ × 7′ 10½″.

Rudimentado Tanque Blindado Aznalcollar, 1936, improved, hull similar to French Schneider CA.

Landesa, 1934, experimental armoured hull on commercial agricultural tractor, small peaked cupola, 1 mg in rear cab, resembled US Disston tank.

Tanque Libertad (Tanque de Juguete, toy tank), 1936, similar but quite small, ventilator louvers completely around top portion of engine compartment w/additional louvers below in rear only, round turret w/several mg mounts, rounded glacis flush w/mud-guards, partially concealed suspension, several built, 13′ × 6′ × 6′ 6″ (approx.).

▼ 348
(- - - - -), makeshift improvised armoured hull on agricultural tractor during Civil War, large rear box cab, large box over engine w/armour overhanging forward part of track frames, 1 mg.

(- - - - -), 1936, improvised hull on agricultural tractor, resembled US Disston but faceted armour, mg right and left bow, ventilator shutters both sides of wedge-shaped bow, mg in low flat cupola.

Carro de Combate Ligero Verdeja, 1938, prototype, engine front,

PzKpfwI turret w/2 mgs modified to permit installation of Russian 45mm gun in centre of mantlet, long sloping glacis, 4 bogie wheel pairs on leaf springs, 4 support rollers.

▼ 349
Carro de Combate Ligero Verdeja No. 1, 1938, same but w/cylindrical turret w/large rounded mantlet elevatable to angle of 75°, 2 mgs, crew 3, 14′ 9″ × 6′ 7″ × 5′ 2″.

Carro de Combate Ligero Verdeja No. 2, 1940, similar to No. 1 but shorter glacis, larger engine, 3 mgs, crew 4, 16′ 9½″ × 6′ 11½″ × 5′ 8½″.

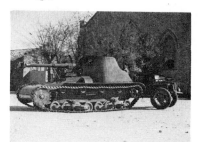

▼ 350
Pieza Autopropulsada Verdeja, 1940, rebuilt No. 1 vehicle as SP w/Russian 75mm gun in 3-sided turret, vehicle resembled British Archer.

(- - - - -), Civil War Light tank resembling Czech SId but front plate rounded off at top and rear of hull rounded downward, 4 road wheels on leaf spring bogies, suspension skirts, ball mounted mg right front.

MODIFIED FOREIGN VEHICLES

L3/33, Italian tankette w/lowered hull, strengthened suspension, modified bow mg mount, small turret w/cupola and 20mm gun.

Krupp, PKpfwI w/high welded turret having flared base, 20mm gun in mantlet permitting elevation to angle of 85 degrees.

Krupp Negrillo, PzKpfwI, so called because of slate grey colour.

(Leopard), Leopard mounting Belgian gun in place of the British 105mm.

(AMX30), 1972, French tank built in Spain under licence.

SWEDEN

After World War I parts for ten LK Light tanks were obtained from Germany. With them came Joseph Vollmer who had been the leading tank designer in Germany. He supervised the construction of the tanks, thus keeping Germany in touch with tank development despite the prohibition of the Versailles Treaty. When the tanks were ready they were allocated to an experimental unit of the Svea Life Guard. In 1921 the Gota Life Guard took over. By 1930 the original ten had been re-modelled and a few foreign tanks were added.

The Swedish tank industry began in 1930 with the creation of A.B. Landsverk, an affiliate of Krupp. They built and sold in and outside Sweden a variety of Light tanks and other armoured vehicles. By 1939 two mixed infantry and tank regiments had been formed in the Swedish Army. The war in Europe showed the need for change and in 1942 an armoured force of four armoured regiments was created. Both Landsverk and Scania-Vabis were producing tanks in this period. After World War II the last stages of the use of armour in Europe were studied, and there was a question as to whether armour had any future. Finally, it was decided that it did have one and in 1953, eighty Centurion Mark 3 tanks were purchased from Britain.

A.B. Bofors, in collaboration with the Swedish Army, began a study of tank design in 1958. In 1963 a revolutionary new tank was announced. It had no revolving turret, and the gun was fixed. All aiming was done by the aiming of the entire vehicle through an ingenious arrangement controlling both steering and suspension. This Strv 103, or S-Tank, and other vehicles were offered commercially by Swedegroup, made up of Saab Aviation, electronics manufacturers, and the National Defence Industries–somewhat as the organisation is in France.

An interesting feature of manufacture in Sweden is that much of the country's industry has moved underground into atomic bomb-proof plants. Construction costs were found to be 20 per cent higher than for ground level plants, but maintenance costs are apparently virtually non-existent. Swedish workers apparently like these plants where both lighting and temperature are better than on the surface, and possibly for this reason there is much less absenteeism.

POST WORLD WAR I TANKS AND RELATED VEHICLES

Strv M21 (Stridsvagn, tank), 1921, WWI German LKIII light tanks assembled in Sweden, engine front, rear cab w/round turret having round cupola, 37mm gun, 1 mg

w/several mounts, 16' 8" × 6' 5" × 7' 6½".

Strv M21/29, same rebuilt, new Scania-Vabis 60HP engine in place of Daimler 55HP.

L5 (Landsverk 5), name of manufacturer, 6-ton wheel-and-track tank, 16' 8" × 6' 5" × 7'6½".

351

Carden-Loyd Mark VI, British carrier modified for 1-man operation, higher hull, mg pedestal mounted on centre glacis instead of side.

L10, 1931, 37mm or 47mm gun w/armoured coaxial mg in rectangular mantlet in conical turret w/large access doors on either side, 2 Zeiss tank periscopes, gun sight on turret top, 2 large bogie wheel pairs on leaf springs, no support rollers, rear of hull sloped down, armoured mg right front, rear drive, 17' ½" × 7' ½" × 7' 2½".

L10 (M31), 1933, second series (Strv M31), suspension bogie pairs connected and supplemented by centre coil spring, 2 support rollers, rear of hull undercut, wireless rail antenna around hull front, 12 tons, could be fitted w/catamaran floats having outboard motors, only Swedish tank w/geared steering, 17' ½" × 7' ½" × 7' 2½".

L30 (FM31), 1931, wheel-and-track tank, 2 bogie wheel pairs each leaf sprung, similar to L10 Second Series, 2 support rollers, skirted to protect pneumatic tyred wheels on leaf springs and crank arms to lower for road operation by 2 shafts from centre gear, 47mm gun, 2 mgs, 17' ½" × 7' 10½" on solid tyres, 8' ½" on balloon tyres × 8' 1½" on wheels (7' 3½" on tracks).

L30, 1933, second series, skirting removed, shaft centre gearing supported on heavy bracket, 12½ tons, 17' ½" × 8' ½" × 7' 4½" on tracks (8' 2" on wheels).

L60, 1934, similar to L10 but 7½ tons, 4 bogie wheels, 2 support rollers, rear of hull slightly undercut, no hull mg, 20mm Madsen gun and 1 mg in turret w/Zeiss periscope, driver left, 13' 7½" × 6' 4" × 5' 11½".

L60 A(M33), 1934, second series, trailing idler, otherwise as above, 15' 1" × 6' 6½" × 6' 1".

L60, B(M38), 1935, third series, 20mm gun and 1 mg, rectangular mantlet in larger turret slightly undercut in rear, buggy whip wireless antenna rear top of turret, spoked bogie wheels, trailing idler, front sprocket, hull partial potbelly w/louvers side centre, half cylinder ventilator centre of glacis, 15' ½" × 6' 8½" × 6' 4½".

352

(L60 Fourth series), same w/37mm gun and 1 mg in turret having large low cupola, protected peep slots and bustle, 8 tons, in 1943 armament changed to 37mm gun on left, 2 air-cooled parallel mgs right, 15' ½" × 6' 8½" × 6' 4½".

Strv33 (Strv M40/L), 1941, M/38 w/front glacis ventilator removed, door in centre of glacis, large bulging inspection plate low right.

Strv M40/K, improved Strv 33, no door in glacis but small dome ventilator right front, 16' 3½" × 6' 10" × 7'.

L61 (Strv M/37) (AH IV SV), Czech designed, Swedish built, 6 tons, sloping glacis, square box hull w/bevelled front corners, sloping back engine compartment, 4 large bogie wheels, 1 centre support roller, 2 Madsen mgs in left side of mantlet, driver right, raised dome cupola on left turret top.

L80, 1933, 7½ tons, miniature L30, 4 bogie wheels w/skirts, 20mm gun and 1 mg, bulging turret hatch, 13' 1½" × 7' 4½" × 7' 2½" on tracks, 8' 2½" on wheels.

L80, 1935, second series, skirts removed, 15' ½" × 7' 8½" × 6' 4½" on tracks, 7' 6½" on wheels.

L100, 1933, 4 tons, hull and turret lines continuously pyramidal, driver left, 2 bogie pairs, leaf springs, no support rollers, 1 mg, 11' 3" × 5' 6½" × 5' 5".

L100, 1934, second series, rear of hull w/overhang, trailing idler, 2 support rollers, 13' 5½" × 6' 3" × 5' 11".

L100, 1935, third series, rear of hull w/large overhang, louvers in centre hull sides, sold to Norway, 13' 5½" × 5' 7" × 5' 5".

L101, 1931, chassis similar to 1933 L100, intended as a tank destroyer, 20mm gun in larger turret, 11' 9½" × 5' 7" × 5' 7".

353

Landsverk 'Anti' (LVKV40), chassis similar to L60 third series but 5 bogie wheels and 3 support rollers, sloped out hull, large open-top turret w/Bofors 74mm AT/AA gun, 17' 1" × 7' 9½" × 9' 10".

Strv38, imported Czech TNH, mg in ball mount left front, driver right, large turret w/37mm gun and ball mounted mg, bustle and octagonal cupola, 4 large bogie wheels, 2 support rollers.

Strv40, same w/first tank installation of a torque converter.

Strv41 SI, same w/Scania-Vabis 145HP engine.

Strv41 SII, same w/Scania-Vabis 160HP engine.

354

SAV101, Stormartillerivapen 101 (SAV M/43), converted from Strv M38, resembled German Hetzer but 105mm L/9 howitzer in ball mount, rectangular cupola left front, 13.3 tons, 15' 1" × 6' 2½" × 7' 6½".

SAV M/44, 1957, same w/cupola removed and howitzer drawn back so that only 12" of recoil cylinder remained visible, 15' 1" × 7' × 7' 7".

PBV301, Pansarbandvagn 301, prototype APC converted from Strv38, mg ring right top of box hull, open louvers left hull front, later w/dome-shaped mg cupola and cover over louvers left hull front.

PBV301, slope-sided hull w/cupola right front, 20mm remote-controlled gun, flat glacis w/slight bulge on right for driver's vision, wider tracks than original.

Strv39, 37mm gun and 2 mgs, not identified.

Strv M/42 (Strv 71) (Lago) (IVK73), 1943, resembled M/38 but 75mm gun w/2 mgs on right of rounded mantlet, spare bogie wheels carried rear of turret sides, cupola set back, rounded cast bow, 6 bogie wheels, 3 support rollers, 24 tons, 16' 1" (20' 5") × 7' 2½" × 5' 3".

355

Strv74 (L71), 1958, Strv M/42 fitted w/new streamlined cast turret w/cupola and bustle, long 75mm gun w/bore evacuator in cone-like cast mantlet, 3 wirelesses, wide tracks, Strv 74H carried 45 rounds, Strv 74V carried 40 rounds, 19' 11½" (24' 7") × 7' 11½" × 9' 10".

LVKV M/70, Luftvaernskanonvagn M/70, A/A cannon vehicle, Strv M/42 chassis, square slope sided open top turret, 40mm L/70 Bofors A/A gun.

IVK73, InfanterivagnKanon 73, 1958, Strv M/42 (Strv71) w/75mm howitzer in larger turret as SP.

(------, M/42), ARV w/crane on turret top, chassis of Strv M/42.

PVKV71, PansarvaernsKanon 71, A/T cannon 71 (PVKV M/43), resembled German assault guns, 6 heavy rimmed bogie wheels, 3 support rollers, handrail top of hull, 75mm L/54 gun w/sieve muzzle brake in ball mount, some w/cupola and closed top, in 1957 new gun w/bore evacuator installed, 20' 5" (24' 7") × 7' 9" × 8' 5".

IVK72, 1953, infantry version of above, shorter gun, part of recoil mechanism visible, 9 tons, 16' 1" (18' 10") × 7' 4" × 5' 3".

LVKV41 (LVKV FM/43), 5 bogie wheels, 2 support rollers, faceted hull, high cylindrical turret, open top, twin Bofors 40mm L/60 guns, bustle w/brackets on either side for spare bogie wheels, 19' ½" (19' 5½") × 7' 10" × 7' 10½".

LVKV42, 1954, similar but w/1 Bofors gun, adjustable suspension, experimental, 19' × 7' 10" × 7' 10½".

IKV102, 6 bogie wheels, 2 support rollers, altered IVK72, 105mm L/20 gun w/blast deflector, no recoil cylinder visible, 10 tons, 15' 9½" (19' 8") × 7' 4" × 6' 2½".

IVK103, 1956, similar but more powerful engine, L/22 gun w/blast deflector, recoil cylinder above gun tube, cupola added 1957, 1 w/experimental rig extending around front of tracks for testing feasibility of 'crowbar steering' for minute changes in traverse for accurate gun laying at a halt, 16' 4" (18' 5½") × 7' 9" × 6'.

IKV120, 1957, 155mm automatic gun, 5 bogies, no support rollers, 20' 8" (25' 11") × 9' 8" × 6' 9".

155SA, 1960, 155mm gun in rear cab, flat front deck 14 round semi-automatic loader, 6 bogie wheels, trailing idler, 3 support rollers, prototype.

Bofors SAV (155mm Bandkanonen 1A), 155mm L/50 gun, sloping glacis, improved version w/loading mechanism and hopper, 21' 6" (36' 1") × 10' 10" × 11' 6".

Bofors VK155, similar but lower turret, driver and assistant driver cabs built up, shorter glacis, 21' 6" (36') × 11' 1½" × 10' 8".

Bofors VK, similar, w/Strv 103 suspension, driver position built up only on right.

356

Bofors 120mm SP, 1948, assault gun w/5 large road wheels, resembled Soviet SU122.

Strv 81, British Centurion w/105mm L/51 gun.

Strv 102, British Centurion III w/105mm L/62 gun.

Strv Panther, gift from Germany during WWII.

Strv Firefly, captured British tank, gift from Germany.

Strv Firefly Modified, experimental rig w/internal 'crowbar steering' and experimental stationary turret w/fixed mount 150mm gun.

Strv KRV, 1957, experimental 45-ton vehicles, 2 built, resembled French AMX50, smoothbore automatic loading 150mm gun but turret never completed, 6 large road wheels, no support rollers, suspension later changed to 4 smaller road wheels and 3 support rollers, 1 chassis suspension modified to become adjustable, other chassis became test rig for hull-mounted unarmoured British 105mm L/51 gun.

Strv 'S', prototype turretless tank w/fixed 105mm L/62 gun and controllable suspension, duel mg boxes over each mudguard resembled German assault guns, 4 large road wheels, no support rollers, steel tracks, 38 tons, conventional engine and gas turbine used separately or in combination, small cupola right top, 2 made.

Strv 103 (Strv M/64), pre-production model of 'S' tank, gun w/bore evacuator and tie-down bracket, more powerful gas turbine, dozer blade, new optics, some w/2 mgs left front mudguard, 1 ranging mg right front mudguard, 10 made, some w/2 return rollers added, some w/3.

Strv 103, production model Type A w/o flotation screen like Straussler screen on British FV432, Type B w/flotation screen, new cupola and sight stabilization, armour covers for periscopes, rubber pads for tracks, larger engine, ribbed armour, 22' 8" (28' 10") × 10' 10" × 6' 2½".

VEAK40, Strv 103 chassis basis, twin Bofors A/A guns in bevel-front square turret w/fold-down radar antenna, 20' 10" × 10' ½" × 10' 4"

MLC941 (MLC50) (Brobv941), armoured bridge-layer, 49' bridge on Pbv302 chassis, 21' 11½" (45' 3") × 10' 8" × 10' 7½".

Pbv302, APC resembling US M113 but rounded edges, small conical turret on left w/20mm gun, partly skirted, 15 tons, 5 large road wheels, small dome vision cupola right top, driver vision dome centre front, amphibious, later turret rear raised, hull smoothed out and left front ventilator moved to left, 17' 10½" × 9' 4½" × 7' 2½".

GPbv, 1972, tracked artillery control vehicle on Pbv302 chassis.

PbvM113, US M113 w/Haegglunds 20mm gun turret.

IKv91, light tank resembling Soviet PT76, 90mm gun w/bore evacuator, amphibious, 21' (28' 8") × 9' 10" × 7' 11".

Type 82 Bgbv82, armoured recovery vehicle on Pbv302 chassis, 22' 2" × 10' 6" × 8' ½".

SWITZERLAND

Before World War II the Swiss Army was equipped with Vickers-Armstrongs Light tanks and later with Czech Kolben-Danek Light tanks. The latter were assembled in Switzerland from imported parts but were equipped with Swiss engines. Immediately after the war, some G13 self-propelled guns –actually the German Hetzer on the PzKpfw38(t) chassis–were purchased in Czechoslovakia where the chassis had originated.

In the 1940s several experimental self-propelled guns were modified and four new self-propelled guns with squat cast hulls were built but not adopted for service. Additional tanks were obtained in France, Britain and the Republic of South Africa. Failing to find any foreign country interested

in building tanks to Swiss specifications, the Swiss themselves built several pilots of the Pz58 tank and later, after modifications, this vehicle, re-named the Pz61, was put into production and is standard equipment–though now being replaced by the advanced Pz68.

Mowag, Saurer, and Hispano-Suiza have built armoured vehicles commercially, but none have been adopted for the Swiss Army. Some of these were armoured personnel carriers but the American M113 was adopted instead of either Swiss or French designs.

IMPORTED TANKS AND VARIATIONS

Praga Panzer (Pz39) (KW Danek) (LTL–H), 1939, Czech Light tank w/24mm gun and 2 mgs, assembled in Switzerland from imported parts but w/Swiss Saurer diesel engine.

G–13, 1946, Czech SP same as German WWII Hetzer, 75mm L/48 gun, w/diesel engine called G–13(D), 15' 11" (20' 6") × 8' 8" × 7' 2".

NKI Ausf I (NAKA I) (Nahkampf Kanone I, Infighter Cannon), 1943, lengthened LTL–H chassis w/5 bogie wheels, 4 support rollers, 75mm gun in centre w/3-sided shield having sides higher in rear, resembled Japanese Ho-ni I.

NKI Ausf 2, 1943, similar but w/105mm L/22 howitzer, lower side shield w/sides sloping down in rear, 18' long.

LePz51, 1953, French AMX13.

Pirat Probepanzer (experimental tank),1957, AMX13 chassis w/large multi-sided welded turret w/multi-sided cupola, 90mm Mecar gun.

Flabpanzer (Flakabwehrpanzer), 1960, open AMX13 chassis w/twin Oerlikon 30mm A/A guns.

Flabpanzer, 1960, open AMX13 chassis w/4 HS 20mm A/A guns.

Flabpanzer, 1960, Open AMX13 chassis w/40mm Bofors gun.

mPzWg55, 1955, British Centurion 3, recoil buffer specially modified at Swiss request to reduce recoil travel, later upgunned to 105mm, other Centurions were mPz56 or Centurion 5 and mPz57 or Centurion 7.

Entpannungspanzer mit Krahn (repair tank with crane) (Entpannungs-panzer 56), 1960, Centurion ARV.

SPz63, 1963, US M113 APC w/slight modifications.

PzH66 (M109–U), US M109 modified to speed up loading device.

MwPz64, 1963, US M106A1 originally w/81mm mortar, changed in 1971 to 120mm mortar.

SPz63, US M113A1.

KdoSPz63, same w/additional wire-lesses as command vehicle.

Feuerleit Pz63, M113 w/2 accessory boxes on top as artillery fire control vehicle for M109–U.

SPz63/73, M113 w/Swedish Haegg-lunds 20mm gun turret.

SPz63 Mowag, US M113 w/centre mounted Mowag turret w/20mm gun.

Genie Pz63, M113 w/dozer blade, 19' 4" × 8' 10" × 9' 2".

M113/KBA–B 25mm, M113 w/special turret and 25mm gun.

M113 C+R/Oerlikon, Oerlikon GBD 25mm gun turret resembling German Marder turret, 15' 1" × 8' 10" × 8' 4".

Pz80, US/German MBT70 tested in 1973.

DOMESTIC TRACK-LAYERS

357

▼ NKII (Gustav), 1944, torsion bar suspension, 6 small bogie wheels, 3 support rollers, 75mm gun in cast turtle-back hull, small cupola, 4 built, 17' 2½" (19' 10") × 8' 5½" × 7' ½".

KW 30–I, 1956, prototype of Pz58, perforated road wheels, 83.4mm gun.

KW 30–II, 1956, same but dished road wheels.

Pz58, 1959, prototype, cast hull, cast turret w/small cupola on right side top, 90mm L/60 gun in cast cone mantlet, 20mm L/100 gun coaxial on left, A/A mg, 6 road wheels, 3 support rollers, steel tracks, 21' 6" (31') × 9' 10" × 8' 8".

Pz61, 1961, improved turret w/cupola on left side, British 105mm gun w/bore evacuator substituted, Belleville washer suspension, 42 tons, second prototype, mg in place of 20mm gun, port in left side of turret, rubber padded tracks, 21' 11" (30' 6") × 10' × 8' 11".

Pz61 Ausf 2, 1967, cupola again on right, new type of rubber-lined track.

Pz68, new rubber block tracks, increased HP, stabilizer, improved fire control, British 105mm gun, mg replaced 20mm.

Pz68 Modified, 1972, experimental version w/variable suspension.

Entpannungspanzer 65, prototype ARV, Pz61 chassis, low cargo-type hull, dozer blade, front A-frame, production on Pz68 chassis, 24' 10" × 10' 4" × 10' ½".

Brueckenpanzer 68s, similar vehicle but bridge-layer, open girders originally, later solid steel and finally solid aluminium.

PzKan68, 155mm gun on Pz61 chassis, resembles French Automoteur 105 but larger, 21' 6" (30' 11") × 9' 10½" × 8' 7½".

Chenilette VP90, almost identical to French Fouga but made by Rexim-Geneve, tiny amphibious 2-ton vehicle w/nose-mounted US 75mm recoilless rifle or 20mm cannon, crew prone.

Chenilette VP90A, similar but top-mounted long-barrelled rocket projector.

Pirat I, 1956, Mowag-built APC, low bow, higher passenger compartment in rear, 5 bogie wheels, 2 support rollers located centre and rear, 16' 7" × 7' 10½" × 5' 11".

Pirat II, 1958, level glacis, small dome cupola, 5 bogie wheels, 4 support rollers, also used as Krankenwagon or ambulance w/4 stretchers, 18' 4" × 7' 10" × 6' 8".

Pirat III (Pirat 14), 1960, similar but 5 bogie wheels having 8 peripheral holes, 4 support rollers, 2 bevel glacis, small conical bevel-front turret on right w/20mm Oerlikon gun, 18' 4½" × 8' 2½" × 7' 4½".

Pirat IV, no details available.

Pirat V, 1962, similar to III but engine behind turret instead of beside turret, turret centre, 1 bevel glacis, 6 bogie wheels, 4 support rollers.

Pirat 18, 1965, same w/higher, faceted open top hull, dual 20mm Oerlikon guns, 20' × 9' 6" × 6' 8½".

Jagdpanzer Pirat, 1959, Pirat II w/90mm Mecar gun.

Tornado, 1970, improved Pirat w/remote control 20mm gun on cupola, 2 rear remote control mgs later experimentally fitted w/HS30 turret, 19' 6" × 9' 10" × 6' 7" w/rise, 7' 4" w/HS30 type turret.

Tartaruga, 1960, Swiss Saurer version of Austrian Saurer APC and all purpose vehicle, similar to Pirat but sloped-in hull w/louvers near front, centre mounted conical bevel-front turret w/20mm gun, 2 large flat ventilator covers on rear deck, rear of hull undercut w/2 large exit doors, 18' ½" × 8' 2½" × 5' 9½".

Gepard, 1973, 90mm gun on Tornado, resembling German JagdKanone.

HS30 TTL, 1959, similar to Pirat, slope-sided box hull, twin mg on ring mount, large circular ventilator plate right, 2 rectangular ventilator plates left rear deck, 5 bogie wheels, 3 irregularly spaced support rollers.

F1A PzA14-HS30 (CC30), 1955, HS30 w/faceted hull, large centre mounted faceted welded turret w/multi-sided cupola, twin 20mm HS831 L/78 guns, 15' 11" × 8' 2½" × 7' 4".

F1a PzA14 D-HS30 (Oerlikon-Contraves), same chassis, four 20mm A/A guns in large box turret w/rear mounted radar dish.

Mowag mit Turm 20DLA, 1960, similar to Tartaruga w/turret like German HS30, rear of hull vertical 20mm Oerlikon 204 GK gun, 5 bogie wheels, 4 support rollers.

Skorpion, 1957, 11 tons, 5 six spoked bogie wheels, 3 support rollers, large conical open top turret w/90mm Mecar gun w/muzzle brake and shield projecting above top turret edge, pillar type travel lock.

SYRIA

(- - - - -) T34/85 w/turret removed and Russian 100mm A/T gun mounted at right front.

UNITED STATES OF AMERICA

Interest in track-laying combat vehicles existed in the United States even before the American entry into World War I in April 1917. Most of this interest was civilian in origin. It mainly resulted from British war orders as well as from news stories after tanks first began to be used in combat in September 1916, although some of the activity predated that.

Cleve Shaffer of San Francisco conceived the idea of armouring and arming the little Fageol orchard tractor as a one-man combat vehicle. He offered the idea to the local German consul who promptly rejected it. E. M. Wheelock of Winona, Minnesota, was the designer of the Pioneer Tractor which was manufactured there. In early 1915 a salesman, Francis S. Lowe, went to England to sell tractors. He carried with him blueprints for a 30-ton armoured tractor designed by Wheelock. Lowe gave the plans to Lieutenant (later Major) W. G. Wilson of the Admiralty Landships Committee but later could not get satisfactory replies

regarding them. Although Lowe and Wheelock claimed that the British heavy tanks used in World War I basically were of the same design and shape as those specified in these plans, no credence was given to their claims by the War Claims Commission who stated that prize money for war inventions was available only to British inventors.

An application for a patent for a turreted 'amphibious vessel' that bore a crude resemblance to the modern LVT(H) 6 was filed by W. T. Taylor on 15 March 1915 and patent No. 1,161,267 was granted on 23 November 1915, but there is no evidence that such a vehicle was built. Still, it is interesting that all three of these proposals antedated the public appearance of the first French and British tanks.

The Alligator Tractor, manufactured by Automatic Machine Company in Connecticut, formed the basis for two successive designs proposed in 1915 by Norman Needs as the Automatic Land Cruisers I and II. In appearance they were somewhat like the German A7V built two years later.

The C. L. Best Tractor Company in San Leandro, California, built a CLB75, a simulated tank, early in 1917. The Holt Manufacturing Company built one called Special 18 (Scat the Kaiser) which closely resembled the commercial Disston Tank of the 1930s. Another Holt design was the tiny one-man motorcycle-engine-powered vehicle resembling the British heavy tanks, which led to the Wickersham robot tracked torpedo. The Holt Company also built armour around a standard Holt Tractor, calling it the G9. It was tested by the Ordnance Department. In conjunction with General Electric, Holt also built the Holt Gas-Electric Tank and participated in the design of self-propelled artillery and the huge tricycle Steam Wheel Tank. The Endicott Shoe Company built a steam tank resembling British heavy tanks. J. Walter Christie proposed several self-propelled guns.

The American Military Mission in Paris had reported unfavourably on tanks about the time the United States entered the war in 1917, but after General John J. Pershing arrived in France special committees were set up to study possible American use of tanks. They decided that French and British tanks should be used, although the British required that American units equipped with British tanks should serve with British formations. However, interest lagged until the Battle of Cambrai on 20 November 1917, and the signing of the Anglo-American Tank Treaty on 19 January 1918, under which the new Tank Mark VIII—the International or Liberty Tank—was to be built jointly in large numbers.

There was almost complete industrial confusion in the United States; nevertheless Pershing's headquarters were constantly given firm production dates for the copies of the Renault FT tanks which were to be built in the United States for the American Light tank battalions, although at the time the blueprints had not even been converted from the French metric system. It was not until J. L. Harwords was appointed in August 1918 to run the tank programme that order began to emerge from chaos.

Several plants began building the 6-ton tank copied from the Renault. Ford began producing the little Ford two-man tank utilizing commercial Model T components. Buick, Overland and Studebaker produced versions of the British Newton Tractor and a Victoria or Hamilton Tank resembling today's armoured personnel carriers resulted from Buick's experience. Production of the British Mark VIII was started at the Locomobile plant but was completed at Rock Island Arsenal in 1920 from the parts made for 100 vehicles. The ambitious Mark VIII programme failed partly because of the failure of the American aviation programme since the same Liberty engine was to be used for aircraft.

In December 1917, Colonel (later Brigadier General) S. D. Rockenbach was appointed Chief of the Tank Corps in France and placed on Pershing's staff. The War Department in February 1918 authorized a Tank Service National Army under the Chief of Engineers with the 65th Engineers forming the cadre. Colonel Ira C. Welborn was the first Director of the Tank Service which the following month became the Tank Corps. Lieutenant-Colonel (later General) Dwight D. Eisenhower commanded the Tank Training Centre. Five brigades each of one heavy and two light battalions, one repair and salvage company, and brigade headquarters, were formed. At the end of the war, 23,405 tanks were on order. None reached combat; ten got to France and only a few hundred more had been completed.

The Westervelt or Caliber Board set up in 1918 to formulate post-war equipment policy decided that light and medium tanks and self-propelled guns should be developed. In 1920 the Tank Corps was abolished, and under the National Defense Act of that year, as a result of a political deal between Congress and the army, tanks were assigned to the infantry. The War Department built its first medium tank in 1921; this was redesigned the following year, by which time a 15-ton limit had been imposed on medium tanks by the General Staff. Both prototypes exceeded the limit and were held in abeyance. In the meantime J. Walter Christie had produced the first of a series of tanks, all tested by the army.

Economy measures after World War I limited expenditures for tanks. The concept of their use was merely as infantry accompaniment ('to facilitate the uninterrupted advance of the rifleman in the attack' said a General Staff directive in 1922) and

for some time existing supplies were sufficient to develop that concept. Policies also fluctuated. In 1922 the War Department decided to utilize, when they could be produced, only truck-transportable Light tanks of five tons and a medium tank of fifteen tons due to the limitations imposed by railroad flat cars and highway bridges, and, principally, the weight limit of existing engineer pontoon bridges. In 1924 the infantry decided that they wanted only medium tanks, but two years later, when a 22-ton Medium T1 had been built, changed their minds in favour of light tanks only. Design studies in collaboration with the Society of Automotive Engineers led to the Light Tank T1 series, one of which was standardized prematurely as the M1. The Light Tank T1 series began with the engine in front, which was standard automobile practice but was not too suitable for a tank.

This method of designation had been adopted in 1925. Until 1920, model years had been used to designate a given piece of ordnance. There was also some use made of the naval term 'Mark'. In 1922 M stood for model year (thus, M1922), and an additional M followed by a Roman numeral represented a succeeding modification. The 1925 system established T for experimental and E for alteration of an experimental nature. M thereafter stood for standardized model and A for a standardized modification. Each was followed by a sequential Arabic numeral. Every type of ordnance was so numbered, so that there was, for example, an M3 Light Tank, an M3 Medium Tank, an M3 rifle, and an M3 75mm gun, and so on.

The influence of the British Experimental Mechanized Force caused breakthrough and exploitation missions to be assigned to the cavalry. In 1928 a Mechanized Force was established. Since, by law, tanks belonged to the infantry, the cavalry used the words 'Combat Car' for the same vehicle as a means of circumventing the law. Cannons were eliminated by the infantry in favour of .50 cal machine-guns and a barbette hull was preferred to the rotating turret. Later a change in Chief of Infantry caused the barbette type of hull to be dropped.

The Christie designs, although poorly built, began to attract attention. A few Christie tanks were purchased as medium tanks for the infantry and as combat cars for the cavalry. However, Christie was an inventor rather than an engineer. He attempted to make use of political pressure and his designs required a great deal of re-engineering. Because appropriations were limited during the depression years and the army resented the political pressures, it was decided that such funds as were available might better be used to obtain more vehicles of tested Ordnance design so that troops could receive more adequate training.

The infantry tried to gain control of the Mechanized Force but Colonel (later General) Chaffee convinced the Chief of Cavalry and General Douglas MacArthur, then Chief of Staff, that it should be retained in the cavalry although the bulk of the cavalrymen generally were incensed, seeing tanks as a rival to horses. The two branches bickered over appropriations, meagre at best.

The War Department raised the light tank weight limit to 7.5 tons because that was the load limit of the divisional engineer bridge, a fact angrily referred to by the Chief of Cavalry, who complained that the only divisional engineer bridge in existence was the one 'designated in General Grant's directive for his advance on Richmond in 1864-5'. The bickering continued and during the depression years Congress had to step in and specifically earmark funds for aircraft and armour to keep the army from diverting funds to personnel and pay.

All through the 1920s and 1930s there were two other schools of thought, one firmly believing in tanks and the other placing its faith in artillery. These and the insistence on economy were not conducive to the development of outstanding vehicles. Only thirty-four tanks were built from the end of World War I to about 1936, and some of these were rebuilds of one another. A few 6-ton light tanks of World War I had been modified with Franklin air-cooled engines about 1928. However, mechanical performance and reliability were achieved. In addition, standard components were developed and the experimentation with commercial engines likely to be available in a future emergency proved later to have been invaluable. Industry was not greatly interested during this period because of the anti-war movement which pinned the 'merchant of death' label on any manufacturer who engaged in any form of war material production.

The Spanish Civil War which broke out in 1936 was at first thought to discredit armour, and in 1938 the budget appropriation was cut except for a few so-called medium tanks, in reality only enlarged light tanks. In the 1939 manoeuvres, tanks were used piecemeal until the last day when the mechanized cavalry broke out en masse and had a field-day. That and the German invasion of Poland awakened the War Department. Redesign of the M2 Medium was undertaken, with the M3 being standardized before it was built. The contract was given to industry. The light tank was also redesigned and contracts were let. And for the first time development of a heavy tank, the T1, quickly took place, a tank that proved to be far ahead of its time and was developed into the M6 Heavy Tank.

The result of the nomenclature system in use was that there was an M3 Scout Car, M3 Personnel Carrier,

M3 Light Tank and M3 Medium Tank. By 1942 all subsequent combat vehicles were to continue receiving T numbers as before, but M numbers were assigned so as to eliminate duplication. By 1944 confusion was less, but to eliminate it finally, T numbers were assigned so that they could be directly converted to M numbers.

The navy system of numbering amphibious vehicles for the Marine Corps was to assign L.V.T. (Landing Vehicle, Tracked) sequence numbers, as LVT1, LVT2, etc. Later, when such vehicles were armoured, they were numbered LVT(A)1, etc.

Infantry-cavalry differences were buried in the creation of the Armored Force on 10 July 1940, and formation of armoured divisions and separate GHQ tank battalions began. Strong factions attempted to break up the armoured divisions in favour of all separate battalions to be assigned as needed to each infantry division. A strong artillery faction continued to fight for artillery. One highly placed artillery man advanced the proposition that 'all we'll need to win this war is the old horse-drawn French 75—provided we can get enough of them'. (That officer was later placed in charge of evaluating self-propelled artillery.) To neutralize the infantry-cavalry problem, an artillery officer was placed in command of the Armored Force, just as had been done when the first British armoured division was formed in 1937.

President Franklin D. Roosevelt set up production goals of 45,000 tanks for 1942 and 75,000 for 1943, which included anticipated Lend Lease needs. In March 1942, the army was reorganized into Army Air Forces, Army Ground Forces and Army Service Forces. After this the Armored Force became the Armored Command and could no longer go directly to the War Department but only through A.G.F. By the end of 1942 there were sixteen armoured divisions, all eventually used in Europe. There were also sixty-five separate GHQ battalions as compared with the fifty-four battalions in the armoured divisions. In the Tank Destroyer Command there were 106 tank destroyer battalions, later reduced to sixty-eight. In addition, most cavalry regiments were mechanized. The GHQ battalions eventually were made interchangeable with the armoured division battalions, an indication that the infantry finally had succeeded in gaining control over armour policy.

A.G.F. constantly changed design and quantity requirements, and British and Russian demands under Lend Lease also shifted constantly. A.S.F. set up a system of requirements versus stocks which was revised monthly and attempted to control production as if it were a tap. No room was left for judgement, foresight or skills. There was no latitude for error or the inevitable padding of

requirements for which the military are notorious. A.S.F. and the General Staff never seemed to understand the implications of 'lead time', despite production expert William Knudsen's early explanation that 'it still takes nine months to make a baby'.

Tools and spare parts requirements also complicated the issues, as did the needs of civilian production which A.S.F. wanted to shut off completely. Conflicts between A.S.F. and the Civilian War Production Board were fanned into flames over matters such as these. Even when it was obvious that the war was almost over, A.S.F. resisted reconversion. In spite of all the controversy. 28,919 Light tanks, 57,027 Medium tanks and 2,300 heavy tanks were completed. In total, 318,768 combat vehicles were produced plus 18,620 LVTs together with enough spare parts to have produced half as many more again. In all this there was much waste and much wasted effort. Among the waste was that put into the Tank Destroyer Command. Vacillation and hesitation marked their demands until the vehicles the Command finally were willing to accept were tanks to all intents and purposes.

Early in the war tank projects were often dropped because they violated regulation AR850–15, which specified that tanks could not exceed thirty tons or 103 inches in width. In 1942 the heavy tank project was cancelled because a heavy tank was not wanted by the Armored Command. But in 1944 the M4 Medium tank was criticized as being unable to combat the German Panther or Tiger. General Eisenhower sent his Armor Officer to the United States to expedite the development of a heavy tank; ironically this officer had to reopen a project he himself had been instrumental in cancelling. Other improved medium tanks had been rejected in the same way. One, the Pershing, was continued in the face of opposition. In early 1945 two later heavy tanks were released for production by General Staff directive in spite of the lack of interest on the part of the A.G.F., but after V–E Day the order was cut to a few test models only.

A Light Tank T7 series had been designed to incorporate ease of maintenance, cast armour and the British 6pdr gun. It became so weighted by demands from the Armored Command that it became the M7 Medium Tank with a 75mm gun which was ordered into production and then abandoned. It had been an excellent light tank that became a poor medium tank, incapable of replacing the M4 Medium Tank.

The United States had to transport overseas from domestic training areas tremendous quantities of troops and material. The following armour troops were fielded: 16 armoured divisions, 65 separate tank battalions, 28 mechanized cavalry squadrons, 48 infantry division reconnaissance troops, 4 airborne division recon-

aissance platoons and 68 tanks destroyer battalions. Some idea of the complexity of this movement problem can be gained from the fact that to move one armoured division by rail, 71 railway trains were needed, comprising a total of 475 Pullman cars, 1422 flat cars, 201 gondolas, 82 kitchen cars, 40 boxcars and 82 baggage cars. To move one armoured division by ship required an average of 45 troop and cargo ships exclusive of naval escort.

After the war, tank production ceased and plants were dismantled. The Stilwell Board, counterpart of the post-World War I Westervelt Board, recommended a five year research and development programme to create a tank family having simplified and standardized components. This was to make available rapid design and production in the event of another emergency. The Board also recommended Arctic tests because of the possibility that the region would be involved in a future war.

The world situation in 1948 demanded action; consequently a four year programme of rebuilding existing tanks began. But in 1949 the Chief of Army Field Forces said that none of the existing tanks was capable of fighting the Russian tanks. There was much loose reporting, pseudo-science and playing on hopes, fears and even credulity to encourage the public to believe that future wars would be push-button affairs and that the newly-created Air Force and the atomic bomb would quickly win all future wars with no inconvenience to the rest of the populace. And men like Dr Vannevar Bush, who had great influence at the Pentagon, predicted that guided missiles would make air attacks impossible and drive the tank from the battlefield.

Early in 1946 the Tank Destroyer Command, the Armored Command and the Cavalry had been merged into the Armored Cavalry. General Jacob Devers, Chief of A.G.F. and wartime Chief of the Armored Force, set up a Panel on Armor in 1949. This resulted in a plan to integrate armour throughout the army in a branch called Armor. The 1950 Reorganization Act carried this out and created Armor as 'a continuation of the cavalry' but without a chief. Key ordnance personnel familiar with design were shifted to other ordnance activities in order 'to make them well rounded'.

In June 1950, the secretary of the army told the graduating class of the U.S. Military Academy at West Point, New York, 'It may well be that tank warfare as we have known it will soon be obsolete'. Yet reality proved to be different. South Korea was invaded on 25 June 1950 and the M24 Light Tank, the Chaffee, was the only tank among American occupation forces in Japan because 'heavier tanks would have damaged Japanese roads and bridges'. North Korean tanks for a time had a field-day.

In spite of the Devers Board integration, two armoured divisions were formed during the Korean War, with five armoured cavalry regiments and twelve tank battalions as parts of infantry divisions. However, even after China entered the war, no armoured division was yet available. As to tanks, the Philbin Subcommittee of the Congress found what it called a deplorable situation. Its recommendations led to President Harry S. Truman ordering a new $500 million tank programme.

The army built the M47 out of existing components and design of the M48 was undertaken. It was rushed into production and in 1960 still was not considered battle-worthy without additional modifications. The army's excuse was that 'the state of the art' had not sufficiently progressed.

With the administration of President Eisenhower in 1953 came sweeping changes in the Defense Department, but no single high level officer with experience in armoured warfare was in any position of importance, and although armour had been a separate branch there had been no branch chief since branch chiefs were discontinued in 1942. This condition still exists today.

Since 1954 the number of armoured divisions has fluctuated. In November 1960, the Porter Hardy Subcommittee of the Armed Services Committee of the House of Representatives criticized the tank programme, but no definite programme was undertaken until Defense Secretary Robert S. McNamara later concluded a treaty with the Federal Republic of Germany to develop jointly a main battle tank, the MBT70.

In 1958 a nomenclature system for aircraft and missiles was adopted and then extended to tanks and other vehicles. Under this, any new project became XM followed by an Arabic numeral without duplication. If and when standardized, the X was dropped. The navy also used this system and also added to its previous L.V.T. and L.V.T.(A) designations L.V.W. for wheeled. L.V.H. for hydrofoil, L.V.T.(P) for personnel and L.V.T.(H) for Howitzer-equipped landing vehicles..

The United States exported over 18,000 tanks between 1949 and 1964. It is not known how this compares with Soviet tank exports, but British and French exports during the same period were about 14 and 3 per cent respectively of this amount.

In 1967 the United States Armor School and Armor Centre were functioning under one head for administrative purposes, but the various boards involving armour, engines, combat developments, maintenance, and human research each reported to other agencies located elsewhere. This resulted from the reorganization that placed responsibilities previously divided under separate services into a Materiel Command.

Vehicle testing thenceforth went through definite phases and stages. Assuming that eight prototypes of a vehicle were built, they might be tested as follows:

No. 1 to Aberdeen Proving Ground for initial cold starting tests, cooling tests and tests of braking, power, fuel consumption, speed, stability, mobility, human engineering factors, kit installation, obstacle crossing ability; after which it would be sent to the Airborne, Electronics and Special Welfare Board at Fort Bragg for loading and air and land transport tests.

No. 2 to Aberdeen Proving Ground for endurance and reliability tests.

Nos. 3 and 4 to Fort Greeley, Alaska, for year-round environmental tests.

No. 5 to Armor and Engineer Board Fort Knox for service tests, maintenance tools, manual preparation, man–machine compatibility, fuel and oil consumption, swimming tests, installation and kit installation.

No. 6 also undergoes such tests at Fort Knox and is then shipped to the Infantry Board at Fort Benning for tests.

No. 7 to the Artillery Board at Fort Sill if an SP, then to the General Equipment Test Activity for transportation tests, and then to Panama for tropical environmental tests.

No. 8 is sent to Yuma Proving Ground for cooling tests and tests involving vapour, dust, high altitude, desert, rock, etc.

If missiles are involved, one of the vehicles may go to White Sands Proving Ground, New Mexico, or to the Air Defense Board at Fort Bliss, Texas. If C.B.R. (chemical, bacteriological and radiological) protection is involved, a vehicle may also go to Dugway Proving Ground, Utah.

After the Materiel Command was established in 1962, responsibility for armour design and control was moved from the Ordnance-Tank Automotive Command at Detroit and given to the Weapons Command at Rock Island Arsenal, Illinois, for reasons still obscure. At the same time the Ordnance, Transportation, Signal, and Chemical Corps were broken up. The Materiel Command was set up in St Louis and a new Mobility Command had headquarters in Detroit.

Responsibility for design and testing of each major weapons system was placed in the hands of a Project Manager. Unfortunately, the previous system of having the Ordnance Corps develop and the using arm test and either accept or reject it was thus dropped. The new system was based on a computer-determined 'cost-effectiveness', and responsibility greatly subdivided. Project Managers were frequently changed. This was corrected in 1970, but only after millions of dollars had been wasted and responsibility so fragmented that it could not be pinned on anyone.

The MBT70 programme, curiously enough, was not project-managed by the Weapons Command but was directly under the Commanding General of the Army Materiel Command. Congress finally ordered abandonment of the MBT70 programme and allocated funds for a new tank design programme. At the same time a committee was established at Fort Knox to establish the military requirements and design specification for a new main battle tank. The committee reached conclusions at the end of 1972. The Mobility Command was dropped to become the Troop Support Command was re-established as a major subordinate unit of the Materiel Command.

In 1971, a practice long common in other countries was adopted. That is, prospective manufacturers were invited to submit prototype designs of some vehicles. Then, after evaluation, a final contract was to be awarded to two firms presenting the winning designs provided that their construction costs met the government-established 'should-cost' figure. The first contract under this system went to one rather than to two firms for development of the XM800 vehicle.

Another organizational change was made but one which received very little publicity. This was the creation of an Operational Test and Evaluation Agency, by definition 'separate and distinct from the developing agency', the Materiel Command. But, rather than using skilled technicians to perform acceptance testing, the OTEA will conduct its operational tests using actual troop units to subject vehicles to the use and abuse of the average soldier.

However, this may still not correct a problem reported by the Comptroller General to the Congress. In a report dated 17 July 1972 it was stated that, 'As many as seven major Army Commands (each with its own missions such as weapons, missiles, munitions, etc.) may be involved in the development and production of a tank'.

WORLD WAR I VEHICLES AND VARIATIONS

Shaffer Armoured Tractor, 1915, based on Fageol orchard tractor, spiked front wheels, conventional rear wheels, small cylindrical turret w/bevel face, 1 mg, 1½ tons, project only, 9' 10½" × 4' 6" × 7'.

Automatic Land Cruiser I, 1915, based on Automatic Machine Company 'Alligator', 19 bogie wheel chassis, bevelled prow, Driggs Schroeder 1pdr gun pedestal-mounted in bow, driver and commander on raised seats under centre cupola, overhung rear, project only, 23' 6" long.

Automatic Land Cruiser II, 1915, similar but rounded armour, centre front sponson, small side mg sponsons, 1pdr gun and 2 mg front, 2 mg rear, 6 three wheel bogie sets, project only.

Hamilton Tracklayer, 1917, same vehicle as British Newton Tractor, Buick version.

Victoria Tank (Hamilton Tank), 1917, commercially designed for US as result of experimental work done on Hamilton Tracklayer by A C Hamilton, bevelled sides over skirted tracks, vertical back, long glacis, small pyramidal cupola, not armed, chain drive to front sprockets, 2 large, 3 small bogie wheels.

CLB 75, 1917, C L Best agricultural tractor w/hull resembling Quonset hut, V-front and rear, wire-cutter front, large cylindrical turret w/conical roof at rear, sheet metal mock-up only w/simulated weapons, also in flat surface version.

Holt, 1917, very similar to above but much smaller, centre mounted flat top turret on Holt tractor, mock-up only.

Special 18 (Scat the Kaiser), 1917, Holt tractor w/o steering wheels, box hull, large pyramidal superstructure over rear two-thirds, mock-up only w/simulated weapons.

Special 18 Modified, very similar but raised front plate for driver and large rear-mounted dome top cylindrical turret, 20 mph, sheet metal mock-up w/simulated weapons.

HA36, 1917, tiny motorcycle-engine-powered one-man tank resembling World War I British heavy tanks, simulated weapons, Holt built.

Wickersham Land Torpedo, cable-controlled tiny demolition vehicle closely resembling WWII German SdKfz302, this appears to be the only such device actually built, but during WWI there were also patented a Villar and Talbot steam wheeled land torpedo, an H E Elrod 'Automobile projectile', and a G A Parker track-laying land torpedo as well as a Flettner wheel-and-track land torpedo.

Caterpillar G9, 1917, Holt tractor basis, faceted box hull, rear turret, resembled Special 18 Modified but larger and higher hull, small front mg turret added, tested by army.

Holt Gas-Electric, 1917, built as a tank, box hull, V-front w/75mm

pack howitzer low in front, side sponsons each w/Vickers mg, petrol-electric transmission, 10 bogie wheels in heavy track frame, rail for support instead of rollers, 25 tons, 16′ 6″ × 9′ 1″ × 7′ 9½″.

Navy No. 1, simulated tank on heavy truck, actually an armoured car, bevelled radiator armour, bevelled hull top, cupola front and rear.

Steam Tank, 1918, resembled British heavy tanks but 2 heavy pointed track guides for each front horn, F/T in front plate, 2 mg each side sponson, small box cupola in rear, small conical turret w/F/T added later above front cab, steam powered, 50 tons, 34′ 9″ × 12′ 6″ × 10′ 4½″.

Steam Wheel Tank, 1918, tricycle type, box hull on 2 eight-foot steam tractor wheels forward and triple small steering roller w/tail-piece rear, 75mm pack howitzer in nose, mg sponson left and right front corners of hull, steam driven, 23′ 3″ × 10′ 1″ × 9′ 10″.

359

Skeleton Tank, 1918, resembled British heavy tanks but track frames of pipes and standard plumbing connections, box hull supported between track frames, small cylindrical turret w/simulated armament, 9 tons, 25′ × 8′ 4½″ × 9′ 6″.

Ford Tank, mock-up, squat vehicle for 2 men, used commercially available parts, squat cupola like Renault FT, spoked agricultural tractor idlers, one unsprung support roller, 6 road wheels on frame.

Ford Tank, pilot, similar but 2 support rollers on leaf spring, 2 Ford Model T engines, double tailpiece, mg in ball mount in left front sponson, 3 tons, 13′ 8″ × 5′ 6″ × 5′ 3″.

360
Ford Tank, 1918, production version w/mg mount from 6 Ton Tank,

15,000 ordered, 15 completed, 13′ 8″ × 5′ 6″ × 5′ 3″.

Mark I (Ford 3-Man Tank), 1918, resembled 6 Ton Tank but suspension somewhat like Ford Tank, mg in ball mount in right front sponson, driver left front sponson, conical 8-sided turret w/37mm, large dome cover, tailpiece, 7½ tons, 16′ 6″ × 6′ 6″ × 7′ 9″.

6 Ton Tank (6 Ton Special Tractor was camouflage title), 1918, US copy of Renault FT17, modified gun mount, Marlin mg but Browning substituted in 1919, 37mm gun model also existed, 4 mph, 7½ tons, 15′ 7″ × 5′ 9″ × 7′ 6½″.

6 Ton Tank Modified, 1931, radio mast fitted to cupola cover.

Radio Tank (Wireless Tank), US 6 Ton Tank w/radio super-structure like Renault TSF.

6 Ton Artillery Tractor, armament removed and special small tailpiece of angle iron substituted to eliminate interference w/tail support wheels of 155mm GPF field-gun.

Smoke Tank, 1924, 37mm 6 Ton Tank fitted w/vertical sulphuric acid cylinder on each side of rear of hull for introduction of acid into exhaust pipe.

6 Ton A1, prototype, 1929, 6 Ton Tank (MG) w/rear of hull extended for substitution of Franklin 6 cylinder air-cooled engine baffled for cooling, radial slots in rear top, 7¼ tons, 17′ 3½″ × 7′ 9″ × 7′ 6½″.

361

6 Ton A1, 1930, rear of hull redesigned and lengthened w/new top deck louver arrangement, 6 mph, 17′ 3½″ × 7′ 9″ × 7′ 6½″.

362
6 Ton A1 (Radio), 1931, 1 radio tank modified to substitute

Franklin engine in lengthened rear end, superstructure slightly modified, buggy whip antenna mounted on cupola dome.

6 Ton Tank Modernized, 1929, Franklin engine, redesigned transmission, 3 bogie Christie suspension.

363

Mark VIII, 1919, same as British Mark VIII but Liberty instead of Rolls-Royce engine and Browning mgs instead of Hotchkiss, 1 mg mount either side of superstructure plated over, in 1925 box cupola in 1 vehicle was replaced by a stroboscope, in 1933, an internal and external cooled Liberty engine was tested, identified by protruding left side ventilator fan box, 34' 2" × 12' 6" (9' w/sponson withdrawn) × 10' 3".

WORLD WAR I AND IMMEDIATE POST WORLD WAR I SELF-PROPELLED GUNS

3" A/A Caterpillar, 1916, Holt built, first US track-laying SP, low flat bed open chassis.

8" Howitzer Caterpillar, 1917, rebuilt from 1916 model.

75mm Caterpillar Mount, 1917, 2½ ton artillery tractor w/M1916 75mm field piece and outriggers, driver right rear, solid track frames, rail support, 12' × 6' 4½" × 7' 6".

3" Caterpillar Mount (SS-I), open carriage, split track frame, 4 bogie wheels and 3 bogie wheels each side, 4 support rollers, 20' 8" × 10' × 9' 6".

SP Caterpillar Mount Mark I, 1918, British Mark VIII ½/8" gun, split track frame, gun mounted front in armoured recoil cover, crane centre, driver right rear, engine radiator left rear, 29 tons, 23' 8" (vehicle only) × 9' 10" × 9' (to top of crane).

SP Caterpillar Mount Mark II, 1918, similar but handrail around chassis, 155mm M1 Filloux, driver right centre, support roller on separate frame, 30½ tons, 21' 2" overall × 9' 10½" × 8'. .

SP Caterpillar Mount Mark III, 1918, similar but rear half exposed of total alternating large and small bogie wheels, 8 support rollers, 240mm Schneider howitzer, driver right front, radiator vertical in front of driver, 55¼ tons, 24' 9" overall × 9' 10" × 9' 5".

SP Caterpillar Mount Mark III M1, same w/radiator flat.

SP Caterpillar Mount Mark IV and IVa, petrol-electric, the second named was power unit, 35 tons each, gun unit resembled Mark I, 240mm Schneider gun, round base trail jack in rear, French St Chamond design, 29' 9" overall × 8' 6" × 13'.

SP Caterpillar Mount Mark V and Va, similar for 240mm Schneider howitzer, power unit only completed.

SP Caterpillar Mount Mark VI, 1920, 75mm gun M1920 on rear of 6 bogie wheel 4 support roller open chassis Caterpillar mount, auto-mobile type hood w/2 sets of side vertical louvers, horizontal radiator louvers, 12' 1" × 6' 11" × 5' 9½".

SP Caterpillar Mount Mark VI M1, same chassis w/3.3" howitzer M1919 in large 3-sided armoured shield w/double bevel front, 2 support rollers removed, 2 rear hydraulic spades, 12' 4" × 6' 11" × 7' 6".

SP Caterpillar Mount Mark VII, 1919, 75mm gun M1916 rear mounted on vehicle resembling 2½ ton Artillery tractor but w/overhanging wedge nose w/side louvers, 11' 3" × 5' 3" × 6' 11".

SP Caterpillar Mount Mark VII M1, same but w/3.3" M1919 howitzer modified, 11' 3" × 5' 3" × 6'.

SP Caterpillar Mount Mark VIII, 240mm Schneider M1918 howitzer, no other details available.

SP Caterpillar Mount Mark IX, 155mm gun M1920 rear mounted, rectangular hood w/double narrow horizontal louvers in sides, loop travel lock, heavy track frames, 6 support rollers, double hydraulic spades, 24 tons, 18' 1" (24' 1") × 9' 2" × 7' 8½".

SP Caterpillar Mount Mark IX M1, 1921, same w/8" howitzer M1920, became M1-E w/new engine in 1926, 18' 1" × 9' 2" × 7' 8½".

SP Caterpillar Mount Mark X (4.7" Gun Motor Carriage Model 1922), similar to Mark IX but single sets of horizontal hood louvers, 2 support rollers, 19' 7" overall × 7' 6" × 5' 3".

SP Caterpillar Mount Mark XI, resembled French 194mm SP of World War I, 240mm howitzer M1920, improved version of Mark III SP.

SP Caterpillar Mount Mark XII, similar w/194mm gun M1920 originally, later 8" gun M1920.

SP Caterpillar Mount Mark XIII, similar to Mark VII but smaller, 4.7" M1920 A/A/ gun.

SP Caterpillar Mount Mark XIV, 3"

M1920 A/A gun on open chassis, similar to Mark VI M1 w/o shield.

364

75mm Pack Howitzer on Holt T35 Chassis, 1927, tiny Caterpillar tractor w/armoured box hull undercut in rear, howitzer centre mounted, no support rollers, heavy track frames.

2½ Ton Artillery Tractor M1918, Armoured bonnet w/high laminated radiator box, driver rear and exposed, rigid suspension, 4 road wheels, 4 support rollers, Cadillac or Liberty engine, 10' 6" × 4' 10" × 5' 6".

5 Ton Artillery Tractor M1917 (Old Betsey), Armoured bonnet only, articulated rigid suspension, 2 two wheel bogies, 4 support rollers, driver rear and exposed. 11' 1½" × 5' 3" × 6' ½".

10 Ton Artillery Tractor, 1917, armoured engine, rigid suspension, 13' 6" × 7' × 8'.

10 Ton Artillery Tractor M1917, experimental, same w/shorter suspension but same dimensions.

Divisional Artillery Tractor M1920, resembled 2.5T M1918 tractor but armoured bonnet sloped downward to the front, leaf springs, 2 two wheel bogies, no support rollers, seats in rear for driver and 2 men, 3¼ tons, 10' 8" × 5' × 5' 7".

Corps Tractor M1921, armoured bonnet projecting beyond tracks, radiator armour w/large slots, leaf springs, 6 road wheels, 2 support rollers, driver centre and exposed, 9 tons, 14' 4½" × 7' 2" × 7' 1".

Army Tractor M1922E, long low recessed armoured bonnet, laterally flexible track and cable suspension influenced by British Medium D tank, 18 tons, 20' 6" × 8' 6" × 7' 6".

10 Ton Tractor With Crane, 1930, resembled M1917 5 Ton Artillery Tractor, made for US Mechanized Force as ARV, A-frame on bow, jib crane right side, no armour except bonnet.

CHRISTIE AND CHRISTIE TYPE VEHICLES

▼ 365
Christie Motor Carriage for 8″ Howitzer, 1919, Mark VI howitzer rear mounted on open carriage w/5 large bogie wheels and one centre high support roller same size, latter later replaced by much smaller roller and several track links removed, 17 tons, 16′ 5″ × 9′ 7″. × 6′ 7″.

Wheeled Caterpillar Christie for 155mm Gun (155mm Gun Motor Carriage Model of 1920), 155mm GPF M1918 facing rear on open chassis, convertible, 4 large bogie wheels, centre pair adjustable and raised when on wheels, individual vehicle variations, 22 tons, 19′ 8″ (18′ 8″ in travel position) × 9′ 8″ × 6′ 8″.

Wheeled Caterpillar Christie for 155mm Gun, 1921, same modified by raising hull slightly and reversing gun.

Christie Motor Carriage, 1920, 75mm M1920 gun on small carriage w/ large front and rear wheels, 1 small centre bogie wheel, 8 tons, 12′ × 7′ 6″ × 7′ 3½″.

Christie Motor Carriage, 1921, same w/105mm M1920 howitzer and additional small centre bogie wheel, 12′ × 7′ 6″ × 6′ 4″.

Wheeled Caterpillar Christie for 4.7″ A/A gun, 1923, long, low, open platform vehicle, driver rear, gun forward of centre facing forward, medium sized front and rear wheels, 2 slightly smaller centre bogie wheels, 22′ 8″ × 10′ ½″ × 8′ 7½″.

155mm Gun M1918 on Christie M1924 Mount, similar to Wheeled Caterpillar Christie for 155mm Gun M1921 but square bow and more substantial bogie wheels, later underwent several minor modifications, 19′ 8″ × 9′ 8″ × 6′ 8″.

Christie Medium Tank M1919, low chassis w/rounded bow, large cylindrical turret w/6pdr in large ball mantlet, large dome top cupola w/mg in ball mount, large road wheels, 1 small bogie wheel in centre, later bogie wheel pair scissors assembly w/support roller in centre, 18′ 2″ × 8′ 6″ × 9′.

Christie Medium Tank M1921, rebuilt M1919, centre wheel pair increased in size, hull like WWII German assault guns w/6pdr in large ball mount in front plate, small conical cupola, mg in right and left front sponsons over tracks, 14 tons, 18′ 2″ × 8′ 6″ × 7′ 1″.

Christie Amphibious Tank, 1922, barge-like open top hull, 3 evenly spaced bogie wheels, twin screws, steered by varying screw speeds, 6.5 tons.

▼ 366
Christie Amphibious Tank, 1923, rebuilt 1922 model, 2 closely spaced drive-chain connected bogie wheels in rear, 1 bogie wheel front, flat top box hull w/75mm M1897 gun in notched nose, top bevelled to sides.

Christie Amphibious Tank, rebuilt M1923, 4 evenly spaced bogie wheels, otherwise little change except wedge-shaped bow and driver centre, 16′ 8″ × 7′ × 7′ 6″.

Christie Amphibious Tank, 1924, second rebuilt M1923, higher hull covered over and faceted, bow gun in oval opening, originally w/2 snorkel towers, later removed.

Christie M1928, suspension in final form, 4 large disc bogie wheels plus sprocket and idler, wedge-shaped bow, no turret, simulated mg in bow, pedestal mounted mg right front, 8.6 tons, 17′ × 7′ × 6′.

Christie M1931 (T1 Combat Car), gear driven, 4 large bogie wheels, centre pair raised when on wheels, cylindrical turret w/cupola forward, 50 cal mg (T3 Medium Tank when chain driven and armed with 37mm gun), sharp V-type glacis, Liberty engine, 10½ tons, prototype of Russian BT series and Polish wheel and track tanks, 18′ 9″ × 7′ 4″ × 7′ 6″.

Combat Car T1E1, same w/minor modifications.

Combat Car T1E2, with Cummins diesel engine, modification not completed.

Combat Car T1E3, American La France engine, speed increased.

T3E1 Medium, engine changed.

▼ 367
Medium Tank T3E2 (American La France Tank), 1933, 4 bogie wheels, 2 rear near together, octagonal flat-sided pyramidal turret w/octagonal cupola, short 37mm gun in large ball mount, mg on either side of turret, mg right front glacis, clutch brake steering, 14.2 tons, 18′ 9″ × 8′ × 7′ 8″.

Medium Tank T3E3, 1936, many minor modifications including controlled differential steering applied to 5 existing T3E2 tanks.

Medium Tank M1934, similar to T3E1 Medium but mg at each corner of superstructure on which turret was mounted, could fire in all directions simultaneously, remote-controlled 37mm gun, faceted armour, project only.

Combat Car T2 (Armoured Car T5), 1931, armoured car type hull w/conical top turret, 1 large road wheel forward, 2 large road wheels rear, latter later skirted, radial engine, 50 cal and 30 cal mg coaxial, wheel or track vehicle as half track, later rear end raised 7 inches and watercooled engine installed, 14′ 11″ × 7′ 5″ × 6′ 10″.

Combat Car T2 Modified, front wheels removed, 14′ 10½″ × 7′ 5″ × 6′ 10″.

Combat Car T2E1, 1932, again modified, turret moved forward, front wheel bracket removed, 8 tons, 12′ 3″ × 6′ 6″ × 6′ 10″.

Combat Car T3, not built, term applied to T1E1 Light Tank.

▼ 368
Combat Car T4, Ordnance Department version of Combat Car T1, peripheral holes in front and rear road wheels, centre pair spoked, mg right glacis, faceted turret w/50 cal and 30 cal mg, 9.6 tons, 16′ 1″ (15′ 6″ on wheels) × 7′ 7″ × 6′ 7″.

Combat Car T4E1 (Combat Car T4 Modified) (T4–12 Ton), 1933, new turret w/50 cal and 30 cal mg became standard for later combat cars, 30 cal mg each side sponson, front armour reshaped, 16′ 1″ × 7′ 7″ × 6′ 7″.

Combat Car T4E2, slope-sided barbette box hull w/small cupola, long glacis w/louvers, engine front, 50 cal and 30 cal mg front, 15′ 10″ × 8′ 2½″ × 7′ 10″.

Combat Car T6, 1935, convertible type, project only.

ORD. NO. I2652
369

Combat Car T7, similar to Combat Car T4 but only 3 bogie wheels and final combat car type turret, 11 tons, 16′ 8″ × 8′ 7½″ × 8′ on wheels 8′ 1″ on tracks.

Medium Tank T4 (Convertible), same as Combat Car T4 but thicker armour, 16′ 1″ × 8′ 2″ × 7′ 4″ on tracks 7′ 1″ on wheels.

Medium Tank T4E1 (Medium Tank M1 (Convertible)), 1935, barbette hull w/1 cal 50 and 5 cal 30 mgs, 16′ 1″ × 8′ 2″ × 7′ 4″.

Christie M1932, similar to M1928, no turret, V-bow, 5 tons, duralumin instead of armour, simulated cannon in nose, pneumatic tyred bogie wheels, 22′ × 7′ × 5′ 8″.

Christie M1936, rebuilt M1932, hull cut off at second bogie wheel and 75mm M1897 gun in front plate, driver and commander had small dome cupolas near rear.

Christie Flying Tank, 1936, 3 bogie wheels, flat top hull sloping forward slightly, simulated cannon in nose, small dome cupola centre right, left cupola more forward, was intended to be carried under the belly of a bomber and released near the ground w/o the plane landing, 4 tons.

Christie M1937, similar to M1932 but wide bow, small conical cupola in glacis, centre of hull open, coil spring covers parallel and exposed above tracks, front idlers on bracketed stub shafts, not armoured, 6 tons, sold to Britain.

Christie M1938, modified M1937 type, hull cut off in front, simulated gun in bow, hull raised, angles of coil springs and covers not uniform, small swept-back cupola.

Christie High Speed Model T12, 1938, similar to M1938 but bow built up and rounded, no armament, rear of hull w/slight transverse raised portion, large engine breather protruded above rear deck, duralumin covered (not armour).

Bibb–Bigley–Reynolds (Bechold) Tank, airborne, commercially offered in 1940 but none built.

Bigley Gun Motor Carriage (Gun Motor Carriage T42), 1942, Christie M1938 w/tortoise shell superstructure of duralumin, later w/pyramidal superstructure and simulated 37mm gun and mg in glacis, 2 mg each side, 1 rear of cupola, still later all removed but simulated 37mm in nose.

COMMERCIAL TYPES AND VARIATIONS OTHER THAN CHRISTIE

370

Cunningham Scout (G2T1), 1933, Carden-Loyd type, driver left w/head cover, small mg right in turret w/front overhang, 2 bogie pairs w/2 pistons in horizontal hydraulic cylinders, 2 support rollers, US Patent application 671,529, 1 built, 7′ 4″ × 4′ 11″ × 5′ 4″.

371

Chemical Mortar Motor Carriage T2, Carden-Loyd type chassis w/open top hull, Vickers-Armstrongs 6-ton tank-type suspension w/spoked road wheels, 2 support rollers, mortar right front, 9′ 9½″ × 6′ 5½″ × 4′ 2″.

Disston, 1933, armoured box w/partial glacis beside hood portion, fitted over commercial Caterpillar tractor 35 or 40, mg left glacis, A/A gun rear.

Disston, 1934, similar but double glacis, mg left side, conical bevel-front turret w/37mm gun capable of A/A fire, later furnished w/track extension device for front idler, bringing tracks even w/nose, 10 tons total weight.

372

Marmon-Herrington CTL-1, 1935, resembled Russian Komsolometz tractor but continuous rubber track, 4 small disc bogies on large leaf springs, 1 support roller, 1 mg right glacis, 4 tons, 11′ × 6′ 4″ × 5′ 2½″.

CTL-1A, very similar but spoked bogies.

CTL-3, 1937, similar but 50 cal mg in centre front plate and 30 cal either side, shorter glacis, 4 slotted, spoked or peripheral hole bogie wheels, 1 support roller w/added short leaf spring, 10′ 9″ × 6′ 3″ × 5′ 5½″.

CTL-3A, 1938, similar but cradle brace added to suspension, front armour slightly bevelled to sides, centre 50 cal mount later closed over.

CTL-3M, suspension, track and sprocket similar to US M3 Light Tank, 2 bogie wheel pairs, 1 support roller, hull like CTL-3A.

CTL-6, 1939, similar but front plate faired away to either side, rear of hull higher, 2 bogie wheel pairs, volute springs, 3 mgs in front plate, short pitch Carden-Loyd type track.

CTM-3TBD, 1941, very similar but w/ pyramidal turret having rounded mantlet for two 50 cal mgs, 3 mgs in front plate as in CTL-6.

CTLS-4TAC (T14 Light Tank), similar suspension, small left hand turret w/30 cal mg, 8.4 tons, 11′ 6″ × 6′ 10″ × 6′ 11″.

CTLS-4TAY (T16 Light Tank), same but w/right hand turret, 11′ 6″ × 6′ 10″ × 6′ 11″.

CTMS-1TBI, 1942, same hull but w/large centre mounted pyramidal turret w/20mm gun in armoured mount, 13′ 9½″ × 7′ 8″ × 8′ ½″.

373

MTLS-1GI4 (Virgie), same w/large turret, twin 20mm guns in large mantlet, 30 cal mg in eyeball mount on right side of turret, A/A gun and bow mg, 16' 1" × 8' 8" × 9' 2½".

'T' NUMBERED LIGHT TANKS AND RELATED VEHICLES

T1 Chassis (G1T1), 1927, engine front, bow armour, open hull, 4 holes in track frame, 4 bogie pairs, 2 support rollers, link suspension w/o springs, skeleton tracks, 12' 6" × 5' 10½" × 5' 2".

Cargo Carrier T1, 1928, same w/open wood cargo body, 12' 11½" × 8' 5" × 5' 2".

75mm Self-Propelled Gun T1, pack howitzer on T1 Cargo Carrier, 10' 9" × 6' 1" × 6' 3".

4.2" Mortar Carriage T1, same w/chemical mortar, 13' 5" × 5' 10½" × 5' 4".

Cargo Carrier T1E1, improved, exposed road wheels, steel cargo body, 12' 10" × 8' 2" × 5' 2".

T1 Light Tank Prototype, G1T1 chassis, track frame w/o holes, mock-up wooden hull and turret w/short 37mm gun and coaxial mg, heavy grouser skeleton tracks, 12' 6" × 5' 10½" × 7' 1½".

T1E1 (G1T2) (M1 Light Tank) (T3 Combat Car), no front overhang, fuel tanks over tracks at rear, original track frames w/1 hole, later w/4 holes, 2 support rollers, 12' 8½" × 5' 10½" × 7' 1½".

T1E2 (G1T3), 1929, rebuilt T1E1, 3 support rollers, turret w/over-hanging top edge placed further forward, later w/long 37mm gun and top of engine compartment raised, 12' 10" × 6' 3" × 7' 7".

T1E3, 1930, T1E1, rebuilt, long 37mm gun, suspension converted to hydraulic, 4 support rollers, 12' 8½" × 5' 10½" × 7' 1½".

▼ 374

T1E4, 1932, rebuilt T1E1, hull reversed w/engine rear, two 4 bogie wheel sets w/bogie boxes for controlling side thrust and short pitch track, leaf springs, suspension copied from Vickers-Armstrongs 6 Ton Tank, 8.5 tons, 15' 5" × 7' 3" × 6' 7".

T1E5, 1932, rebuilt T1E1 adding Cleveland differential, 12' 8½" × 5' 10½" × 7' 1½".

T1E6, 1933, rebuilt T1E4, hull raised, box louvers on sides of engine compartment, American La France 12 cylinder 240 HP engine, 9.2 tons, 15' 5" × 7' 3" × 6' 7".

T2, 1934, chassis and suspension similar to T1E4 but higher rounded engine compartment for radial engine, bevel top edge cylindrical turret w/bustle, 50 cal and two 30 cal mgs, 2 support rollers, 13' 10½" × 7' 9½" × 6' 9".

T2E1 (M2A1), 1934, rebuilt T2, very similar but rubber block track and 2 volute spring bogie wheel pairs, 2 support rollers, 9.4 tons, 13' 5" × 7' 4½" × 7' 9".

T2E2 (M2A2), 1934, similar but twin turrets, 50 cal and 30 cal mgs in left, 30 cal in right turret, cupola added later to left turret, 8 tons, 13' 7" × 7' 10" × 7' 9".

T2E3, 1935, T2 chassis w/barbette superstructure.

▼ 375

T3, chassis similar to T2, originally w/volute spring suspension w/2 bogie pairs on wedge-shaped supports, 2 support rollers, later several versions of rubber torsion suspension, final suspension of horizontal arms w/centre rubber torsion centre each pair, wedge-shaped supports eliminated, mg sponson right glacis, driver set back on left, no turret, shutter louvers centre of glacis, Ford V-8 engine, rubber block track, 11' 3" × 6' 9½" × 4' 6".

T3E1, same as original T3 but w/Menasco air-cooled engine, cancelled as a tank to become Cross Country Carrier T5.

T3E2, 1936, T3 w/thicker armour, intended as National Guard tank, project suspended, 8' 9" × 8' × 7' 8".

T4, 1936, T3E2 w/Guiberson radial diesel engine, project suspended.

T5, design study of T6 chassis w/several types of turrets and armament variations.

T6, 1939, suspension on T3 type vehicle modified w/1 volute spring bogie wheel pair front, connected trailing idler and single rear road wheel, 2 support rollers, driver centre, two commercial automobile engines, resembled British Carden-Loyd Mark VI as built, turret was intended but never completed, 12' 5½" × 7' 11" × 5' 2½".

'T' NUMBERED COMBAT CARS

T1, T2, T4, see Christie types.

T3, see T1E1 under 'T' numbered light tanks.

T5, 1933, similar to T2E1 Light Tank, 2 turrets, mg right glacis, 2 volute spring bogie wheel pairs, 2 support rollers, rear idler support part of rear bogie support, 6.5 tons, 13' 4" × 7' 6" × 6' 8".

▼ 376

T5E1, same chassis w/large barbette hull recessed in rear centre, similar to light tank T2E3, 13' 4" × 8' 1" w/o armament (10' 7" w/armament) × 8' 1".

T5E2, T5 w/single turret, became M1 Combat Car, 13' 4" × 7' 4½" × 6' 9".

T5E3, 1936, original T5 modified for Guiberson radial engine, 13' 4" × 7' 4½" × 6' 9".

T5E4, 1938, T5 w/volute spring front bogie wheel pair, rubber torsion rear bogie pair, trailing idler, 1 front support, 2 rear support rollers.

T6, T7, see Christie types.

'M' NUMBERED COMBAT CARS

M1, 1936, see Combat Car T5E2, similar to T2E1 Light Tank, 2 volute bogie wheel pairs, 2 support rollers, 50 cal and two 30 cal mgs in cylindrical flat front turret offset to left, no lips on ports or peepslots, 13' 7" × 7' 10" × 7' 5".

M1E1, same w/flaps on peepslots, Guiberson engine, 13' 7" × 7' 10" × 7' 5".

M1E2, 1937, rear bogie pair and idler moved back 11", rear of hull reshaped for better access and to increase fuel capacity, became M1A1 Combat Car, 14' 7" × 7' 9" × 7' 5".

M1E3, suspension modified for wide continuous band rubber track, transmission changed, drive shaft lowered, 14' 7½" × 8' 2" × 7' 4½".

75mm Howitzer Motor Carriage T17, 1942, combat car M1E3 basis, project dropped.

M1A1, 1937, turret offset to right, wireless added, 9.75 tons.

M1A1E1, 1938(M1A1 w/Guiberson radial diesel engine, 14' 7" × 7' 9" × 7' 5".

Twin 20mm Gun Motor Carriage T17E1, 1942, twin A/A guns on M1 chassis, project only.

M2, 1940, M1A1 w/trailing idler, became M1A1 Light Tank, 14' 4" × 7' 9" × 7' 6".

'M' NUMBERED LIGHT TANKS AND RELATED VEHICLES BEFORE DUPLICATIONS WERE ELIMINATED

M1, see Light Tank T5E2.

M1A1, M1 Combat Car w/trailing idler, flat rear deck.

M1A2, reworked M1 Combat Car.

M2A1, see Light Tank T2E1 and M1E2 Combat Car.

M2A2, 1936, see Light Tank T2E2, 13' 7" × 7' 10" × 7' 9".

M2A2E1, same w/Guiberson diesel engine, 13' 7" × 7' 9" × 7' 8".

M2A2E2, 1937, two lower flat-sided turrets, 2 bogie wheel pairs on rail, rubber torsion suspension, box shaped engine compartment, 13' 9" × 8' 1½" × 6' 10½".

377

M2A2E3, 1938, same modified w/trailing idler, fluid drive and first tank w/gyro stabilizer, 12' 1" × 8' 1½" × 6' 10½".

M2A3, 1938, left hand turret octagonal, right cylindrical, 2 volute spring bogie wheel pairs, 2 support rollers, 14' 6½" × 7' 9" × 7' 5".

378

T3 Howitzer Motor Carriage, M2A3 Light Tank basis, w/left turret retained, 75mm pack howitzer in right of box hull, 13' 7" × 7' 10" × 7' 5".

M2A3E1, 1938, M2A3 w/Guiberson diesel radial engine.

M2A3E2, M2A3 w/Electro-Gear transmission replacing both previous transmission and differential.

M2A3E3, same as M2A3 but trailing idler, 10.75 tons, 14' 10" × 7' 9" × 7' 5".

M2A4, flat-sided octagonal turret w/5-sided cupola, flat rear end, 1 mg fixed in each side sponson, fired by driver, 37mm gun and 1 mg coaxial, 1 mg in glacis, trailing idler, 14' 7" × 8' 4" × 8' 2½"

M2A4 Modified, modified recoil mechanism, blast deflector.

M2A4 with Rear End of M3 Light Tank, modified engine compartment.

M2A4, late production, partly welded turret w/fewer peepslots.

M3, 1941, riveted, rear overhang, trailing idler, 37mm L/57 gun and 1 mg coaxial in octagonal bevel-forward turret w/6 sided cupola, sponson mgs, right glacis mg, both Continental and Guiberson engines used, welded turret substituted in 1942, sponson openings later sealed up, heavy peepslot covers in front plate, later cast and welded turret w/cylindrical cupola, cupola later eliminated partial skirts furnished for British use, 14' 10" × 7' 4" (7' 8" w/sandshields) × 8' 3" (w/o cupola 7' 6").

M3E1, 1941, Cummins diesel engine substituted, silencer on top, 8-sided welded turret w/cupola, trailing idler, rear end built out, 15' 6" × 8' 1" × 8' 2".

M3E2, 1941, welded turret, twin Cadillac engines and twin hydra-matic transmissions substituted.

M3E3, same power train as M3E2, cast turret, fuel tanks over tracks, prototype for M5 Light tank, 14' 2½" × 7' 4" × 7' 6½".

M3A1, 1942, same as late M3 but w/integrated fighting compartment, 14' 7" × 7' 4" × 7' 6½".

M3A1E1, M3A1 w/welded hull, cupola later added.

M3A1 Modified, 1943, M3A1 w/automatic 37mm gun.

4.5" Gun Motor Carriage T16, 1942, SP from Light Tanks M3 and T7 components, 3 bogie wheel pairs, volute springs partly skirted, open chassis, 19' 7" × 9' 1" × 7' 5".

4.5" Gun Motor Carriage T16E1, same w/minor alterations.

M3A2, 1942, welded hull and integrated fighting compartment, project dropped as a duplication and designation revoked.

379

M3A3, resembled M5 Light Tank but sponsons sloped inward, welded hull, cast turret w/bustle, partially skirted.

M3A3E1, 1943, M4A3 w/Spicer torque converter and W670 engine.

M3A3E2, 1943, same w/R950 engine.

380

75mm Howitzer Motor Carriage T18, 1941, massive rounded edge cast superstructure on M3 Light Tank chassis w/75mm pack howitzer in right front, 15.25 tons, 14' 10" × 7' 4" × 7' 3½".

75mm Howitzer Motor Carriage T41, wider version of 75mm Howitzer Motor Carriage T18, welded armour howitzer centre front, project dropped.

3" Gun Motor Carriage T20, 1942, A/A gun on low silhouette light tank, M3 chassis, project only.

75mm Gun Motor Carriage T29, 75mm T8 gun on M3 chassis, cancelled.

75mm Howitzer Motor Carriage T47, 1942, M3 Light Tank chassis w/overhanging slope-sided sponsons, 2 angle glacis, slope-sided faceted turret, later w/turret for M18, mock-up only.

3" Gun Motor Carriage T56, 1942, M3A3 chassis w/larger engine, gun rear mounted in shield continuing side hull bevel, 16 tons, 16' 11" × 8' 3" × 7' 9½".

3" Gun Motor Carriage T57, similar but w/o shield.

Mobile Maxson Turret, 1942, four cal 50 mgs on turretless M3 Light tank.

Mobile Maxson Turret, same on turretless M3A3 Light tank.

Command Tank, Field Modification, turret removed, box superstructure w/50 cal mg substituted.

Satan (CWS–POA), Canadian Ronson F/T w/shroud on M3A1 Light tank.

E5–R2 (M3) Flame Tank, M3A1 Light tank w/F/T.

E7–7 Flame Tank, F/T on M3A1 Light tank, periscope type mounted in assistant driver's position.

M1A1 Flame Tank, 1943, M3 Light tank, bow gun cut off so that it could be interchanged as desired w/F/T.

Mine Exploder T1, M3 Light tank, 3 small thick steel rollers on a dolly pushed in front of each track, the tank pulling 4 similar rollers on a centre yoke.

Light Mine Exploder T2, H–frame welded to the tank bow supporting by cables a heavy axle w/heavy sleeved arms to detonate mines.

EARLY MEDIUM TANKS AND MEDIUM TANK "T" NUMBERS THROUGH T6

Medium A, 1921, flat hull, front mounted bevel-sided turret w/cupola having overhanging cover, turret 6pdr in large round mantlet, cupola mg in similar smaller mount, covered track frames, flat steel track grousers, 23 tons, 21' 7" × 8' × 9' 6".

Medium M1922, similar but track frames higher in rear than in front influenced by British Medium D, partly closed track frames, cable suspension, later coil spring, 4 support rollers, flat wood grousers, tracks centre jointed, 25 tons, 25' 11" × 8' 10" × 11'.

Medium M1924, similar to Medium A but lighter, top of hull flush w/tracks, vertical front plate w/6pdr, smaller turret w/mg cupola, mock-up only, completed.

Medium T1, 1926, similar to Medium A, steel skeleton tracks, horizontal track frame louvers, 2 mud chutes, 22 tons, 21' 6" × 8' × 9' 4½".

Medium T1E1 (Fu Manchu), 1931, rebuilt T1, engine changed and ventilation improved.

T2 (G4T–1), 1930, generally resembled British Vickers Medium, 37mm gun and mg in right front plate, 47mm and 50 cal mg in faceted mantlet in bevel-sided turret w/cupola, engine front, box over left centre track, 6 bogie wheel pairs, 4 support rollers, large track frames, steel skeleton tracks, 16' × 8' × 9' 1".

T2 Modified, 1931, hull lowered, 30 cal mg only in front plate, 30 cal A/A mg added, fuel tank in box added on left rear behind original box, front plate mg mount later reduced in size, 16' × 8' × 8' 6".

T3, see Christie types.

T4, see Christie types.

T4E1, see Christie types.

T5 Phase I, 1937, box hull w/mg each corner, bevel front turret w/37mm gun and mg, 2 bow mg. rubber block track, 3 volute spring bogie wheel pairs, 2 support rollers, 15 tons, 17' 3" × 8' 2" × 8' 11½".

T5 Phase II, project only.

T5 Phase III (M2 Medium), 1939, similar to T5E1 but 1 long 37mm gun w/shield, in 1940 shield was replaced by cup mantlet, bow mgs moved from centre glacis to lower corners, 20 tons, 18' × 8' 7" × 9' 3".

M2 Pilot, 1938, octagonal welded turret bevelled front and rear, 37mm gun and mg, smaller but higher superstructure w/mg each corner, faceted glacis surmounted by driver's cowl, 3 support rollers, Continental radial engine, 17' 3" × 8' 2" × 8' 11½".

T5E1, 1938, same w/twin 37mm guns, splash plates for deflecting mg fire in rear over tracks, Guiberson radial diesel engine, 18' 0" × 8' 7" × 9' 3".

T5E2, front of hull modified to straight across, 75mm pack howitzer added right front, 2 mg centre front, left front and both rear corner mgs retained, small 6-sided

cupola w/rangefinder and mg, general design led to M3 Medium 18' × 8' 7" × 9' 3".

T6, 1941, cast hull w/side doors, 2 hinged-down cowls, 1 mg low in right glacis, 2 mg low in centre glacis, cast turret w/long 75mm gun and mg, M3 Medium tank cupola right top of turret, mock-up only.

T6, 1941, originally short M2 75mm L/31 gun w/counterweight, later M3 L/40 gun installed and wedge-shaped front end added experimentally, no cupola prototype of M4A1 Medium, 18' 6½" × 8' 8" × 9' 7½".

MEDIUM TANK "M" NUMBERS BEFORE DUPLICATIONS WERE ELIMINATED.

M1, see Medium Tank T4E1 under Christie types.

M2, see Medium Tank T5 Phase III.

M2E1 (M2 Shop Pilot) (M2 Medium Experimental), 1939, strengthened suspension, Guiberson diesel radial engine, later new octagonal turret was substituted.

M2A1, 1939, new turret w/inside peepslot covers, bullet splash rails across glacis, later production w/armoured recoil mechanism cover and outside hinged peepslot covers, 18' × 8' 7" × 9' 3".

E2 Flame-thrower Tank, M2A1 w/long flame gun replacing 37mm in same mount.

M2 with British Radio Turret, 1941, mock-up turret of design later to be incorporated in British production order Grant (M3 British) tanks.

M3 Pilot, close pitched riveted hull, 75mm M2 L/31 gun in right front sponson, cast bevel front turret w/37mm L/57 gun and mg, high dummy cupola, prominent 3-piece bolted final drive gear housing, sharp glacis w/2 bow mgs, 3 volute spring bogie wheel pairs, 3 support rollers in centres of bogie support frames.

M3, lower cupola w/mg, Wright engine, later w/long M3 75mm gun riveted hull, side doors eliminated in late production, 18' 6½" × 8' 11½" × 10' 3".

M3 British (Grant), same w/squat cast British wireless turret, no cupola.

M3E1, M3 w/Ford liquid-cooled engine.

M3A1, cast hull w/side doors which were later eliminated, see also Shop Tractor T10 below, 18' 6" × 8' 11½" × 10' 3".

M3A1E1, 1942, M3 w/3 Lycoming 6-cylinder engines, identified by small rounded plate on rear deck.

M3A2, 1941, M3 w/welded hull and cast turret, 18′ 6″ × 8′ 11½″ × 10′ 3″.

M3A3, welded hull, cast turret, 2 diesel engines, counterweight on M2 gun for experimental stabilizer, 18′ 6″ × 8′ 11½″ × 10′ 3″.

M3A4, 1941, M3 w/riveted hull lengthened for installation of 5 Chrysler passenger car engines in common crankcase, 33.75 tons, 19′ 8″ × 8′ 11½″ × 10′ 3″.

M3A4 with Trailing Idler, 1942, experimental trailing idler hinged to single rear bogie wheel. **383**

M3A4 with Experimental Suspension, original horizontal volute spring suspension (HVSS) w/3 support rollers offset to rear of each bogie bracket. **384**

M3A5, 1942, stabilizer counterweight on gun, twin GMC diesel engines, 32.5 tons, 18′ 6″ × 8′ 11½″ × 10′ 3″.

M3A5E1, M3A5 w/twin hydramatic transmission, 31 tons.

M3A5E2, M3A5 w/single hydramatic transmission.

155mm Gun Motor Carriage T6 (M12), 1942, M3 Medium tank chassis w/M1918 A1 155 mm L/38 gun, wide trail spade, later production on M4 Medium tank chassis, 21′ 11½″ × 8′ 8″ × 7′ 11″.

3″ Gun Motor Carriage T24, 1941, resembled M7 Howitzer Motor Carriage but octagonal crew compartment, 18′ 7½″ × 8′ 11½″ × 8′ 7″.

105mm Howitzer Motor Carriage T25, M3 Medium tank chassis, not completed.

75mm Gun Motor Carriage T26, M3 Medium tank chassis not completed.

105mm Howitzer Motor Carriage T32, hull same height all around, front armour later heightened and ring mount added, becoming prototype for M7 Howitzer Motor Carriage, 18′ 8″ × 8′ 6″ × 7′ 4½″.

385

40mm Gun Motor Carriage T36, driver in raised position in front plate, huge cast turret low in front, high in rear, gun in high angle mount in front, 18′ 6″ × 8′ × 12′ 3½″.

3″ Gun Motor Carriage T40 (M9), 1942, M1918 A/A gun in hull almost identical to that of T32 Howitzer Motor Carriage, 26.5 tons, 18′ 8″ × 8′ 11½″ × 7′ 8″.

25pdr Gun Motor Carriage T51, 1942, British gun in vehicle similar to Canadian Sexton, pulpit overhang on right side, 18′ 8″ × 8′ 6″ × 7′ 4½″.

E3 Flame-thrower Tank, 1942, 75mm gun sponson sealed up, F/T in turret in place of 37mm.

E6/R3 (M3–4) Flame-thrower Tank, periscope-type F/T mounted top front of hull in Medium M3A5.

E7 (M3), Navy Mark I F/T experimentally mounted on M3 Medium.

Shop Tractor T10 (Leaflet Tank) (Cassock Tank) (CDL Equipment), American version of British CDL Tank, shield added to 75 mm gun, new CDL turret w/o dummy gun as in British model, pilot model on M3A1, production models on M3.

Cargo Carrier T14 (M30), 1942,, armoured ammunition carrier for M12 Gun Motor Carriage, mg in ring mount centre rear, truck bows over rear portion.

Heavy Tractor T16, modified turret-less M3 w/truck bows and tarpaulin.

Prime Mover T1, turret removed and pintle added for towing 240mm field howitzer.

Tank Recovery Vehicle T2 (M31), 1942, crane on tank turret, stowage boxes on rear deck, dummy 75mm gun w/access doors, square box over 75mm sponson, converted M3,

M31B1 based on M3A3, M31B2 based on M3A5 Mediums, 1 converted to bridge-layer in Italy, 18′ 6″ × 8′ 11½″ × 10′ 3″.

M3 with Spigot Mortar Attachment, anti-mine device, experimental.

M3 Cargo Carrier, see M4 Medium Tank series.

Mine Exploder T1, 4 flat discs on high frame caster pushed in front of each tank, low 4 disc yoke assembly pulled in centre rear, front casters later guided by cables from kingpins.

HEAVY TANK 'T' NUMBERS BEFORE ADOPTION OF CONSECUTIVE NUMBERING SYSTEM

T1, 1940, cast slope-sided hull, cast slope-sided turret w/3″ and 37mm guns coaxial, 30 cal mg in cupola, dual 50 cal mg in front plate, dual 30 cal mg in bow, 4 bogie wheel pairs, skirted, hydramatic transmission, 57 tons, 23′ 1″ × 10′ 3″ × 9′ 11″ (10′ 2½″ top of cupola).

T1E1 (M6A2), (Fu Manchu), 1942, modified T1, one 30 cal bow gun, electric transmission, 62 tons, 23′ 9″ × 10′ 3″ × 9′ 11″.

T1E1 Experimental (M6E1), T26 Medium tank turret w/90mm T7 gun substituted on M6.

T1E2 (M6), 1941, cast turret w/rear mg on rotor mount, originally w/o cupola, M3 Medium tank cupola added later, torque converter, 60 tons.

T1E3 (M6A1), 1942, welded hull, cast turret, disc brakes.

'T' NUMBERS AFTER ADOPTION OF CONSECUTIVE NUMBERING SYSTEM INCLUDING NUMBER IN THE PIPELINE

T5 Tank Recovery Vehicle, remodelled from Mine Exploder T1E1, see M4 Medium Tank series, 19′ 4″ × 8′ 7″ × 9′ 8″.

T5E1 Tank Recovery Vehicle, same, modified.

T6 High Speed Wrecker, 1955, M103 tank basis, 7 road wheels, 6 support rollers, front mounted crane, rear cab, unarmoured.

T6E1 High Speed Wrecker, 34′ 11″ (overall) × 12′ 2″ × 13′ 5″.

T6 Gun Motor Carriage, see M3 Medium Tank series.

T6 Tank Recovery Vehicle, see under M41 series.

386
T7 Light Tank, 1942, resembled Light Tank M3A3 but shaped cast hull, mg right front, 37mm gun in cast bevel-front turret, trailing idler, boxed-in volute springs, 2 bogie wheel pairs, 3 support rollers, hydramatic transmission, engine and final drive on rails for easy removal. (*above left*)

T7E1 Light Tank, same w/Livermore transmission.

T7E2 Light Tank, 1941, similar but lower, 3 mg in glacis but later removed, 57mm gun in cast turret having bustle, 2 spread bogie wheel pairs, angled volute springs, 20 tons. (*above right*)

T7E3 Light Tank, similar to T7 but twin Hercules engines and Detroit automatic transmission.

T7E4 Light Tank, 1942, similar to T7 but Wright radial engine and hydramatic transmission.

T8, designation not used.

T9 Airborne Tank, designation originally applied to Bigley-Christie w/57mm gun which was never completed, designation withdrawn.

T9 Light Tank, 1942, miniature T7 Light Tank but welded hull, airborne, 37mm gun and mg in cast turret having bustle, 1 mg right glacis, differential bulge centre of glacis, 2 bogie wheel pairs and trailing idler, 2 support rollers, short pitch steel tracks, 7¾ tons.

T9E1 Pilot Light Tank, 1942, bogies on rail, 8 tons, 12' 1½" × 7' 2½" × 6'.

T9E1 (M22 Light Tank), driver's cowl moved forward, glacis mg eliminated, bogie pairs connected by rods.

T9E2, experimental SP, turret removed from T9E1 and 81mm breech-loading mortar in special turret installed, 12' 1½" × 7' 2½" × 6'.

T9E2 Modified, minor changes, wider track.

T9 Utility Carrier, see M24 series.

Light Tractor T18, 1942, T9E1 production model w/turret removed and pintle added, 12' 1½" × 7'. 2½" × 3'.

T10 Light Tank, amphibious, project cancelled.

T10 Shop Tractor, see M3 Medium Tank series.

T10E1 Shop Tractor, see M4 Medium Tank series.

T11, designation not used.

387
T12, recovery vehicles, see M26 Medium Tank series.

T13 Light Tank, tiny 2-man tank w/20mm gun, project on Allis Chalmers tractor.

T13 Medium Tank, 1945, M4A1 Medium Tank w/M26 tank turret and guns, misapplied title.

T13 Utility Vehicle, see M24 series.

T14 Light Tank, 1942, see Commercial CTLS-4TAC, designation applied to undeliverable Netherlands East Indies order to Marmon-Herrington which was taken over.

T14 Assault Tank, 1943, British designed, American built, 3 bogie wheel pairs, cast hull w/recessed bow mg, cast turret w/75mm L/40 gun, hinged armour skirts, 47 tons, only 2 built, 20' 4" (21') × 10' 3" × 9' 1".

T14 Cargo Carrier, see Miscellaneous Vehicles.

T14 Mine Resistant Vehicle, see M4 Medium Tank series.

T14 Recovery Vehicle, see M4 Medium Tank series.

T15, T15E1 and T15E2 Mine Resistant Vehicles, see under M4 Medium Tank series.

T15E3 Mine Resistant Vehicle, see T26.

T16 Light Tank, see commercial CTLS-4 TAY.

T16 Armoured Utility Vehicle, see M18.

T16 and T16E1 Gun Mortar Carriages, see M3 Light Tank series.

T17 Command Post Vehicle, see M18.

T17 Howitzer Motor Carriage, originally a study on the mounting of a 75mm or 105mm howitzer on an M3 Light Tank chassis, lack of space caused a restudy on mounting the 105mm howitzer on the M1E3 Combat Car because of its low power tunnel.

T17E1 Twin 20mm Gun Motor Carriage, see 'M' numbered Combat Cars.

T18 Light Tractor, see T9E1 Light Tank.

T18 Howitzer Motor Carriage, see M3 Light Tank series.

T18 and T18E1 Personnel Carrier, see M41.

T20 Medium Tank, 1943, low flat welded hull, cast turret w/76mm L/55 gun, mg right glacis, driver centre, early M3A4 Medium Tank horizontal volute spring suspension, 3 support rollers, Ford engine, torquematic transmission, 31½ tons, 18' 11" (24' 6") × 10' 3" × 8'.

T20E1 Medium Tank, same but w/75mm automatic cannon, not built.

T20E2 Medium Tank, same but w/3" M7 gun, not built.

T20E3 Medium Tank, same hull but torsion bar suspension, 6 bogie wheels, 3 support rollers, originally, later 5, same turret as on final M4 Medium Tank turret w/76mm L/55 gun, torque converter, rubber block tracks, 33.75 tons, 1 built, proposal to standardize as M27B1 denied, 18' 11" (24' 6") × 10' 7" × 8' 1".

T20 Gun Motor Carriage, see M3 Light Tank series.

T21 Light Tank, 1943, lightened T20E3 chassis, 20 tons, Armored Force 'ideal' tank, not completed.

T22 Medium Tank, same chassis and suspension as T20, final type M4 Medium Tank turret w/76mm l/55 gun, M4 transmission, 2 built, 20' (24' 5") × 10' 7" × 8'.

388
T22E1, T20 chassis but massive cast turret w/75mm l/40 M1 automatic cannon, split hatch covers left side of turret, crew of 3, M4 transmission, 31¾ tons, 20' (21' 2") × 10' 7" × 7' 11".

T22E2, same w/3" M7 gun, not built.

T22 Cargo Carrier, see M4 Medium Tank series.

T23 Medium Tank, T20 originally w/slope-sided welded turret w/experimental mantlet, later w/76mm L/55 gun in late M4 Medium tank turret, petrol-electric transmission, 250 produced, 19' 9" (24' 9½") × 10' 3" × 8' 1" (to top of cupola).

T23E1, same but w/75mm automatic cannon, not built.

T23E2, same but w/3″ M7 gun, not built.

T23E3, 1944, 76mm M1A1 gun, torsion bar suspension, 6 bogie wheels, front one separated from the others, 5 support rollers, petrol-electric transmission, 35 tons, 1 built, proposal to standardize as M27 denied, 20′ 3″ (25′ 6″) × 10′ 8″ × 8′ 4″ (to top of cupola).

T23E4, T23E3 w/M4A3 E8 HVSS and late M4 Medium Tank turret w/76mm gun, several contemplated versions of this were cancelled because they were considered too wide, 19′ 9″ (25′ 8″) × 11′ 3″ × 8′ 2″ (to top of cupola).

90mm Gun Motor Carriage, lightweight open T23 chassis w/petrol-electric transmission,.90mm A/A guns w/o shield on trunnions and turntable, project only

155mm Gun Motor Carriage T79, T20 chassis w/T23 petrol-electric transmission, project only.

155mm Gun Motor Carriage, T79, same w/heavier gun, project only.

T79E1, same w/shield, project only.

8″ Howitzer Motor Carriage T80, same as for 8″ howitzer, project only.

T24 Light Tank (M24) (Chaffee) (Panther Pup), 1943, squat hull, squat turret w/bustle, 75mm L/39 gun and mg coaxial, bow mg, 5 bogie wheels, torsion bar suspension, partial skirting, 2 support rollers forward, 1 rear, octagonal access plate centre of glacis, left rear vision cupola added later, experimentally w/heavy grouser rubber track, also w/23″ offset track, hydramatic transmission, 16′ 4″ (18′) × 9′ 8″ × 7′ 3″ w/cupola.

T24E1 Light Tank, original 75mm gun w/German Pak 40 muzzle brake, torque converter, rounded overhanging rear deck w/larger louvers, 16′ 4″ (18′) × 9′ 4″ × 7′ 3″.

T24 Gun Motor Carriage, see M3 Medium series.

T25 Heavy Tank (T25 Medium Tank), T23 hull w/massive turret having bustle, 90mm gun in massive mantlet, cupola on right, HVSS, 24″ track, 41.8 tons, 2 made, 19′ 9″ (26′) × 11′ 3″ × 9′ (to top of cupola).

T25E1, 1943, T23E3 chassis, torsion bar suspension, 6 bogie wheels, 5 support rollers, same turret as T25, 90mm T7 L/53 gun, torque converter, 40 built, 20′ 8″ (26′ 11½″) × 10′ 7″ × 9′ 1½″.

389

T25E1 Modified, same turret w/large cylindrical ears for range-finder, torquematic transmission, 38 tons.

T25E1 with T26E1 Turret as in T26E1 but modified for 105mm gun w/muzzle brake, design study only.

T25 Gun Motor Carriage, see M3 medium.

T26E3, (M26), (General Pershing), similar but larger bustle, 90mm gun w/muzzle brake, torque converter, later production had angled instead of rounded driver bulge, 20′ 9″ (28′ 4″) × 11′ 4½″ × 9′ 1½″.

T26E3 With Experimental Twin Machine Gun Mount, twin 50 cal mgs on pedestal on turret top, remote-controlled.

T26E4 (T26E1–1), (Long Tom), (Super Pershing), pilot vehicle shipped to Europe and further modified by adding angled supplementary armour over nose.

T26 Heavy Tank (T26 Medium Tank), similar to T25E but petrol-electric transmission, 43 tons, 22′ (26′ 4″) × 11′ 4″ × 9′ 1½″.

T26E1, T26 w/torque converter, 20′ 9″ (27′ 6″) × 11′ 4″ × 9′ 1½″.

T26E1 Modified (T26E1–1), same w/T15E1 L/73 gun, outside coil spring equilibrator, added bustle counter-weight, renumbered T126E4.

T26E2, (M45), massive turret w/bustle 105mm howitzer, 6 bogie wheels, 5 support rollers, torsion bars, torque converter, 46 tons, 20′ 9″ (21′ 4½″) × 11′ 4″ × 9′ 2½″.

T26E4, 1945, last production, enclosed equilibrator springs, later production eliminated outside springs, new travel lock to raise muzzle because of tube length, 20′ 9″ (33′ 10″) × 11′ 4½″ × 9′ 1½″ over cupola.

T26E5, T26E3 w/90mm M3 gun torque converter and 3 speed planetary transmission, 51 tons, 20′ 9″ (28′ 4″) × 12′ 4″ × 9′ 1½″.

T26 Gun Motor Carriage, see M3 Medium series.

Mine Resistant Vehicle T15E3, T26E1 w/strengthened belly and suspension components.

T27, see 81mm Mortar Carrier under M5.

390

T28, 1946, heavy tank w/M26 components, resembled German assault guns, 97.2 tons, 8 bogie wheels, double tracks, outside set w/partial skirting removable for rail travel and could be towed by tank, cast hull, huge mantlet in nose w/105mm T5E1 L/67 gun w/muzzle brake, two 50 cal mgs, vision cupola left front and right centre, ring mg mount right centre, later changed to T95 Gun Motor Carriage, 24′ 7″ (36′ 4″) × 13′ 11″ (over crane) × 8′ 8″ (9′ 4″ overall).

T29, 1946, 105mm T5E2 L/67 w/and w/o muzzle brake, gun in rectangular mantlet, coaxial 50 cal mg, 30 cal bow gun, 68 tons, 8 bogie wheels, 7 support rollers, torsion bars, cast turret w/bustle, vision cupola rear, 24′ 2″ (37′ 11″) × 12′ 5″ × 10′ 7″.

T29E1, 1947, changes involving Allison V–12 engine installation.

T29E2 Heavy, T29 w/MIT combination hydraulic power transverse and elevating mechanism w/computing sight.

T29E3, turret modified for range-finder, large box-like range-finder ears in centre sides of turret, original gun w/o muzzle brake.

T29 Gun Motor Carriage, see M3 Light Tank.

T29 Mortar Carriage, see M5 Light Tank.

T30 Heavy, 1947, similar to T29E3 but larger turret w/rear centre cupola, 155mm L/41 gun w/muzzle brake and power rammer, 2 cal 50 mgs, 1 cal 30 mg, 8 bogie wheels, torsion bars, 7 support rollers, 67 tons, large yoke travel lock in rear, round hinged pistol ports in turret sides, 24′ 2½″ (34′ 10½″) × 12′ 6″ × 10′ 7″.

391

T30E1, same gun w/automatic rammer-ejector.

T30 Cargo Carrier, see M4 Medium Tank series.

T31 Demolition Tank, see Rocket Launcher T94 under M4 Medium tank series.

T31 Cargo Carrier, rear box hull on T84 Howitzer Motor Carriage chassis, high ring mount right front, 21′ × 11′ 2″ × 8′ 10″.

T32 Heavy, similar to T30, 90mm L/73 gun w/muzzle brake, round hinged pistol port in left bustle only, cupola on turret, 7 bogie wheels, 6 support rollers, 60 tons, 23′ 2½″ (35′ 6½″) × 12′ 4″ × 9′ 3″.

T32E1, 1946, 90mm T15E2 gun, 7 bogie wheels, 6 support rollers, transmission changes, welded bow w/o bow mg.

T32 Howitzer Motor Carriage, see M3 Medium tanks.

T33 Flame-thrower Tank, 1945 and 1951, special modified turret on M4A3E8 Medium, wedge shaped mantlet w/75mm M6 L/39 gun from M24 Light tank and separate curved mantlet w/parallel E20–20 F/T tube on right, small F/T in turret hatch, see also E20–20 under M4 Medium tank series.

T34 Paddy Vehicle, 1945, light amphibious cargo carrier, modified from T39 Utility Vehicle, M5 Light tank power train, folding rudder in rear, winch centre rear, covered engine compartment skirted, 19′ 5½″ × 8′ 3″ × 7′ 7″ w/o cab, 9′ 8″ overall.

T34 Heavy Tank, 1946, variation of T30, 120mm L/62 gun w/muzzle brake, 2 cal 50 mgs coaxial, 1 cal 30 bow mg, 70½ tons, bore evacuator added in 1949, 24′ 2½″ (37′ 8″) × 12′ 5″ × 10′ 6″.

T35 Flame-tank, M26 tank chassis, squat 12-sided turret w/Canadian Iroquois F/T, vision cupola on left of hull.

T35 and T35E1 Gun Motor Carriages, see M4 series.

T36, see 40mm Gun Motor Carriage T36 under M3 Medium tank series.

T36 Mortar Motor Carriage, see 155mm Mortar Motor Carriage T96 under M37.

T37 Phase I, 1949, chassis and hull similar to T24 Light tank, welded cylindrical turret w/bustle, 76mm T94 gun w/muzzle brake, range-finder and lead computer, 30 cal mg on remote-controlled horizontal pivot mount on each side of bustle, 24 tons, 18′ 1″ (23′ 11″) × 10′ 3″ × 8′ 6″.

T37 Phase II (T41), 1949, automatic lead computer, range-finder, welded turret w/larger mantlet, gun stabilized in elevation and azimuth, 26 tons, 18′ 1″ × 10′ 7″ × 8′ 11½″.

T37 Phase III, 76mm T91 automatic cannon.

T38 Mortar Motor Carrier, see 4.2″ mortar on M37 Gun Motor Carriage chassis.

T39 Engineer Armoured Vehicle, 1954, M46 Medium tank w/modified turret and British 6½″ demolition gun, large square door left side of turret, bulldozer, kingpost crane centre front, small crane and winch in armoured cab on rear deck.

T39E1, rear cab eliminated, rear crane strengthened, front boom added.

T39E2 Engineer Armoured Vehicle (M102), 1955, extendible tripod crane in front, turret cupola added, M47 Medium tank chassis, 165mm T156 gun, 27′ 11″ × 12′ 2″ × 10′ 11″.

T39 Utility vehicle, 1945, see M18.

T39 Light Tractor, 3 road wheels plus trailing idler, very small sprocket, open top, no armour, sometimes w/centre ring mount and mg.

T40 Medium Tank (M26E2) (M46) (Patton), 1949, remodelled M26 w/new engine and transmission, 48½ tons, 20′ 9″ (27′ 11″) × 11′ 4″ × 9′ 1″ to top of cupola.

T40 Gun Motor Carriage, M3 Medium series.

T41 Gun Motor Carriage, see M3 Light tank.

T41, see T37 Phase II light tank.

T41E1, cast turret, much elongated bustle (counterweight), T91E3 90mm gun w/ bore evacuator, new turret traversing system, 18′ 4″ (20′ 5″) × 10′ 8½″ × 9′ 4″·overall.

T41E1 with Fender Kits, remote-controlled 30 cal mg in box on each fender front.

T41E2 Light Tank, (M41A1), cast streamlined turret, cupola moved to right side, smaller range-finder ears moved back slightly, 18′ 4″ (26′ 5″) × 10′ 6″ × 9′ 4″.

T41 Howitzer Motor Carriage, see M3 Light tank.

T41 and T41E1 Utility Vehicles, see M18.

T42 Medium, 1949, new turret on T40 Medium and change in frontal armour, torsion bars, 5 bogie wheels, 3 support rollers, range-finder with small ears front of turret, stabilizer, 38 tons, 18′ 5″ (25′ 10½″) × 11′ 7½″ × 8′ 11½″.

T42 with Fender Kits, same w/remote-controlled 30 cal mg on front fender each side.

T43 Heavy, 1949, larger version of M48 Medium, large turret w/large overhanging bustle sloping upward, stabilized 120mm gun w/muzzle brake and 2 cal 50 mgs coaxial, range-finder, rounded bow, no bow mg, 60 tons, 23′ 6″ (37′ 2″) × 12′ 2″ × 10′ 7½″.

T43E1 Heavy (M103), various modifications, gun w/bore evacuator, 63 tons.

T43 E2, see M103A1.

T46 and T46E1, see M76.

T47 Howitzer Motor Carriage, see M3 Light.

T48 Prototype, 7 road wheels, 6 support rollers, dome turret w/right rear cupola.

T48 Medium (M48), 1951, rounded bow, T42 chassis w/new turret w/cut down bustle, centre side rectangular ears, cupola right centre, ventilator rear left of bustle, 90mm T139 gun, 6 bogie wheels, 5 support rollers, torsion bars, 49 tons.

T48 with Launcher Kit, 1953, six fanned-out smoke launcher sets on 4 sides of turret.

T48E2, new cupola and T-head muzzle brake, see M48A2.

▼ 396
T49 Light tank, 1951, 90mm low power smooth bore gun on T41 Light tank chassis.

T49 Gun Motor Carriage, see M18, one vehicle w/57mm gun, the other became T67 w/75mm gun, 17′ 10½″ × 8′ 10″ × 7′.

T50 Light Recovery Vehicle, T41 Light tank chassis, extendible front mounted boom, raised cupola in centre, remote-controlled mg cupola in rear.

▼ 397
T51 Heavy Recovery Vehicle (M51), M48 Medium chassis, cab front, heavy centre mounted crane, 7 bogie wheels, 4 support rollers, standard tank cupola later added centre front, 60 tons.

T51 Gun Motor Carriage, see M3 Medium series.

T52, see T52 SP in M4 Medium tank series.

T53 and T53E1, see T53 SP in M4 Medium tank series.

T54, medium tank, 1951, T48 chassis, 105mm gun in T48 type turret w/early low cupola as used late in WWII.

T54E1, 1954, T48 chassis, 105mm gun in oscillating turret like French AMX50, 6 bogie wheels, 5 support rollers.

▼ 398
T54E2, 1956, 105mm gun in non-oscillating long nose long bustle turret w/mg cupola, 6 bogie wheels, 5 support rollers.

▼ 399
T55 Tracked Infantry Utility Vehicle, 1952, small 5-man carrier, 3 bogies and trailing idler on rail, sloped-in hull, round hatch left glacis, driver prone, 6 tons, 12′ 3″ × 7′ 11″ × 5′ 5½″.

T56 Tracked Infantry Utility Vehicle, similar, 4 bogie wheels and trailing idler, 2 support rollers, carried 10 men.

T56 Gun Motor Carriage, see M3 Light tank.

T57 Heavy Tank, 1952, 110mm gun in bulbous turret on outside gimbals, 7 bogie wheels, 6 support rollers T32 Heavy tank basis.

T57 Gun Motor Carriage, see M3 Light tank.

T58 Heavy Tank, 1954, T43 Heavy tank chassis, 155mm gun w/muzzle brake in oscillating turret, 7 bogie wheels, 6 support rollers, 60 tons.

T58E1, 1954, same w/155mm gun in non-oscillating turret.

T59 Armoured Personnel Carrier (M59), predecessor of T113, 5 bogie wheels, 18′ 5″ × 10′ 8½″ × 7′ 4″.

T62 Medium Recovery Vehicle, ARV on M48 Medium tank chassis.

T64 Mortar Carrier (M84), 1956, see 4.2″ Mortar on M75.

T64 and T64E1 Howitzer Motor Carriage, see under M24.

T65 Flame Tank, M39 Armored Utility Vehicle w/Canadian Iroquois F/T in protruding right front sponson, small dome cupola centre.

T65 Gun Motor Carriage, see under M5.

T66 Flame Tank (Mechanized Flame-thrower T66), 1950, E25–30 F/T substituted for 90mm gun in M47 Medium tank.

T67 Gun Motor Carriage, see T49 Gun Motor Carriage, 17′ 10½″ (22′) × 8′ 10″ × 7′.

T67 Flame Tank (M67), F/T substituted for 90mm in M48 Medium tank.

T68 Flame Tank, turretless M4A3E8 Medium tank, small vision cupola in place of turret, Canadian Iroquois F/T in right front plate.

T69 Medium Tank, 1952, 90mm gun in oscillating ball-type w/o cupola on outside trunnions, T42 Medium tank chassis.

T70, see M18 Gun Motor Carriage, 17′ 10½″ × 9′ 2″ × 8′ 10″.

▼ 400
T71 Light Tank (25 Ton Tank), 76mm gun in oscillating turret mounted on outside gimbals, standard cupola, M41 components, bevelled and faired hull, mock-up only, 15′ 7″ (23′ 6″) × 9′ 4″ × 8′ (8′ 5″).

T71 and T71E1 Gun Motor Carriages, see M4 Medium.

T72 Gun Motor Carriage, see M4 Medium tank series.

T73 Armoured Personnel Carrier, see M41 Light tank series.

T73 Gun Motor Carriage, M3 Light Tanks.

T74 Medium Recovery Vehicle (M74), 1952, M4A3E8 Medium tank basis, resembled M32A1 Recovery Vehicle, high rear travel lock for holding A-frame, front platform ramp on cable, 26′ 1″ (27′ 5″) × 10′ 2″ × 10′ 3″.

T75, T76, T77 and T77E1, see M24.

T77 Heavy Tank, 110mm gun, see also T77 Gun Motor Carriage under M24.

T78 Gun Motor Carriage, see M24 Light tank series.

T79 Armoured Infantry Vehicle, Stubby glacis, driver cowl left, commander vision cupola centre of hull, oval access plate lower bow, horizontal louvers on sides near front, 5 bogie wheels, 3 asymmetrical support rollers.

T79 Flat Track Vehicle, experimental, 4 bogie wheel and trailing idler flat track suspension, smaller louvers but front, rear and sides.

▼ 401
T79 and T79E1 Gun Motor Carriages, see T23 Medium tank series.

T80, projected SP on T23 Medium tank chassis, see T23 Medium tank series.

T81 Mortar Carrier, see M5 Light tank series.

T81 Combination Motor Carriage, see M24.

T82 Howitzer Motor Carriage, see M5A1 Light tank series.

T83, see M40.

T84, see 8″ Howitzer Motor Carriage under M46.

T85 and T85E1 Multiple Gun Motor Carriage, see M5.

T86 and T86E1 Gun Motor Carriage, see M18.

T87 and T87E1 Gun Motor Carriage, see M18.

▼ 402

T88 Medium Assault Recovery Vehicle (M88), M48A2 components, 6 bogie wheels, 3 support rollers, raised box hull rear flat, 2 driver cowls, mg cupola, A-frame hinged outside of cowls, 55 tons, 27′ 1½″ × 11′ 3″ × 10′ 3″.

T88 Howitzer Motor Carriage, see M18.

T89, see M46E1.

T90 Gun Motor Carriage, see M4 series.

T91, details not known.

T92 (Ultra Light Tank), 1952, airborne, T185 76mm gun in cleft turret, 50 cal mg right, 30 cal mg left side of turret, 3 bogie wheels, 2 support rollers, 18 tons, pilot had shorter hull and simpler vision devices, 15′ 9″ (20′ 8″) × 10′ 4″ × 7′.

T92 Howitzer Motor Carriage, see also M26 Medium tank series.

T93, see M26 Medium tank series.

T94 Mortar Motor Carriage, see M4 Medium tank series.

T95 Medium Tank, 1956, 90mm smoothbore gun w/bore evacuator at muzzle in squat turret w/mg cupola, commander's ranging unit IR light in right hand turret blisters, large bustle, 5 large road wheels w/peripheral holes, 41 tons.

T95E1, same as T95 but M48E2 turret w/mg cupola and range-finder ears, disc road wheels, later w/T95E3 suspension, 21′ × 10′ 6″ × 7′ 10½″.

T95E2, same as T95E1 but T54E2 turret w/105mm gun, IR equipped, 22′ 7½″ × 10′ 4″ × 9′ 6″.

T95 E3, (T95 with Friction Hydro-pneumatic Suspension System), 1960, T95E2 w/controllable track system for obstacle crossing, weapon elevation and vehicle concealment, 5 road wheels, no support rollers, normal bow.

T95E4, 1961, T95 w/Solar gas turbine, 1100 HP.

T95E5, mock-up only, T54E2 turret w/105mm gun.

T95E6, 1958, mock-up only w/T54E2 turret.

T95 with Controlled Suspension, 1966, 90mm gun w/o bore evacuator in M60 turret w/o cupola, 5 road wheels, 2 support rollers, rounded bow faired in on each side behind final drive, considered test rig only.

T95 With Variable Height Hydro-pneumatic Suspension, 1967, Shillelagh in M60 A1E1 turret mock-up, 6 road wheels, 3 support rollers, 2 bevel bow w/cut in each side behind final drive, test rig only.

T96 Medium Tank, 105mm gun, project only.

T96 Mortar Carriage, see M37.

T97 155mm Gun Motor Carriage (M53), M41 Light tank chassis, 1 bogie wheel added, 3 unevenly spaced support rollers for front half of track, trailing idler bogie wheel, large rear cab w/155mm T80 gun, wide trail spade, 48 tons, 22′ 8″ w/o spade (33′ 6″ overall) × 11′ 8″ × 11′ 8″.

T98 105mm Howitzer Motor Carriage, 1945, M41 Light tank chassis, 105mm T96E1 L/22.5 howitzer in large rotating box cab bevelled forward, 18′ 10″ × 10′ 4″ × 11′ 2″.

T98E1 Howitzer Motor Carriage (M52), improved ventilation, 18′ 6″ × 10′ 4″ × 11′ 2″.

T99 Howitzer Motor Carriage, 155mm Howitzer on M41 chassis, resembled T97, production vehicles w/105mm howitzer.

T99E1 modified 17′ (20′ ½″) × 10′ 3½″ × 10′ 10″.

T99 Austerity Mount, extreme rear mounted 155mm howitzer on M41 chassis w/o superstructure or shield, airborne concept.

(-----) 75 mm A/A gun on M41 chassis, no armour above track line.

▼ 403

T100 Gun Motor Carriage (Stinger), quad 60 cal guns w/radar disc outside mounted on welded turret, M41 chassis.

T101 (SPAT) (M56) (Scorpion), 1956, 90mm T125 Gun Motor Carriage, muzzle brake, several shield types, basic M76 tractor chassis, 4 pneumatic bogie wheels, rubber band tracks w/steel cross grousers, one vehicle modified 1958 for GM turbine, 14′ 6″ (20′ 2″) × 8′ 2″ × 7′ 2½″.

▼ 404

T106 Gun Motor Carriage, 1950, modified M29C (Weasel) Cargo Carrier w/105mm recoilless rifle on centre mounted pedestal, later rifle was front mounted on 4 post mount, 12′ 3″ w/gun rear × 5′ 1″ × 6′ 2½″.

T108, see M55.

T110 Heavy Tank, 120mm gun, in fixed streamlined turret covering rear half of vehicle, gun mounted midships w/quick stop mantlet and automatic loader, commander at rear top w/standard mg cupola.

T113 Armoured Personnel Carrier, 1957, aluminium armour, 8 tons, slightly lower than M59 APC, 4 bogie wheels and trailing idler, driver left, commander's cupola centre front.

T113E1, same w/o trailing idler.

T113E2, 1958, improved, w/diesel engine, low vertical bow, w/trim vane and longer glacis, M113 prototype.

T114, Armoured Personnel Carrier, 1957, smaller than T113 w/longer glacis, low wide turret faired away in front, 50 cal mg, 5¼ tons, later w/large conical turret.

T116, T116E1, cargo carrier, 15′ 5½″ 7′ 1½″ × 5′ 4″.

405

T117 Armoured Personnel Carrier, 1957, (T117 Full Tracked Personnel Carrier), same as T113 but steel instead of aluminium armour, 8 tons.

406

T118 Engineer Tank (Combat Engineer Vehicle), 1960, turret mounted A-frame, cupola on turret, hoist and dozer blade, T95 tank chassis, 26½ tons.

T118E1, same improved.

T118E2 Combat Engineer Vehicle, 1960, similar but on M60A1 tank chassis.

T119 Crane (Unarmoured Wrecker), 1955, flat hull, centre mounted girder crane, 4 bogie wheels and trailing idler, rear hydraulic spade, 12 perforations along hull top, crane rear mounted in production vehicle, 20' 10" (22' 5") × 10' 4" × 9' 1".

T120 Crane, 1955, similar but crane cab mounted in rear, 12 perforations along hull top.

T120E1 Light Recovery Vehicle (M578), 1961, remote-controlled mg above cab.

T141 Twin 40mm Gun Motor Carriage, M41 Light tank chassis, similar to M19 Gun.

T141E1 Gun Motor Carriage (M42) (Duster), improved version.

T149, M113 w/SS11 rear mounted.

T162, T99E1 SP w/175mm gun.

T164 Self-Propelled Mount, two 105mm recoilless rifles over each track on common trunnion, T62 Light Carrier chassis, 4 pneumatic bogie wheels, light track.

T165 Self-Propelled Mount, same chassis w/four 105mm recoilless rifles parallel in centre, and 1 on each side below this level.

T165E1, improved.

T165 Modified, quad 50 cal mg mount in place of recoilless rifles.

T166 Gun Motor Carriage (M50), 1952, outgrowth of T165, louvers in right front glacis, 5½ tons.

T166 Modified, 14 rocket projectors on each side mounted on common trunnion.

T166 Modified, T166 w/top mounted 105mm recoilless rifle.

T166 Modified, three 105mm recoilless rifles parallel and 1 below over each track on common trunnion.

T185 Light Tank, 18 tons, 76mm gun and 30 cal mg coaxial in a cleft turret.

T194 Howitzer Motor Carriage, 1952, resembled T98 but open top, 20' 1" × 12' 9" × 9' 6".

T195 Howitzer Carriage, 1956,, amphibious, aluminium armour, 105mm howitzer w/bore evacuator, M113 components, 7 bogie wheels, no support rollers, partly skirted, 19 tons, originally intended for 110mm howitzer, 18' 7" × 10' 4" × 8' 6".

T195 Modified, missile projector.

T195E1, T195, w/diesel engine, 20' ½" × 10' 10" × 9' 6½".

T196, T195 w/155mm howitzer w/muzzle brake, 20½ tons, 18' 7½" × 10' 2" × 8' 6".

T196E1, T196 w/diesel engine, see M109.

T235 Gun Carriage, 1958, chassis interchangeable w/T236 and T245, 175mm gun, open chassis, wide trail spade, 4 bogies and trailing idler, 31 tons, 29' 10" (36' 8" travel position), 37' 4" firing position) × 10' 4" × 9' 1".

T236 Howitzer Carriage, 8" howitzer, 28¾ tons, 24' 1" × 10' 4" × 9' 1".

T245, almost identical to T235 but w/155mm gun, 29' 10" overall × 10' 11" × 9' 1¾.

407

T249 Missile Vehicle (Vigilante B), 5 bogie wheels, components from M113, Vulcan gun in large turret w/radar.

T256, 8" howitzer, almost identical to T236.

T257 Mortar Carriage, 81mm mortar on T113.

T257E1, 81mm mortar on T113E1.

T257E2, 81mm mortar on T113E2.

'M' NUMBERED AND RELATED VEHICLES AFTER ADOPTION OF CONSECUTIVE NUMBERING SYSTEM

M4 Medium Tank, 1942, T6 w/welded hull, no side door, cast turret w/o bustle, small square cast pistol ports in turret sides, split hatch covers top right of turret, M3 75mm L/40 gun, 16" tracks, 79 track shoes, support rollers offset to rear, bow mg right glacis, 3 piece front end, later V-type front end cast glacis, appliqué armour later added over cowls and on hull sides, 31.5 tons, turret peepslots later eliminated and pattern improved, 18' 6½" × 8' 8" 8' 11".

M4 (76mm Wet), 1943, 34 tons, long gun in original turret, wet ammunition stowage, 18' 3" × 8' 6½" × 9' 6½".

M4 with Hedgerow Removal Prongs (Culin Device), 1944, two or more long sharpened angle irons welded to final drive housing, variations.

M4 (105), 1943, cast front end, flat glacis, no cowls, mg right glacis, 105mm L/25 howitzer, 34 tons, later w/HVSS, 20' 3" × 8' 9" × 9' 8".

M4E1, 1943, misnamed, M4A4 hull w/modified rear deck covers to accommodate D200A diesel engine, a modified Wright Cyclone, on M4 chassis, 19' 5" × 8' 8" × 8' 11".

M4E1, 1942, misnamed, M4A1 w/experimental T1 76mm gun, 30¼ tons, 18' 6½" (23') × 8' 6½" × 9' 6½".

M4E2, 1943, early HVSS and 24" steel track, 19' 5" × 8' 8" × 8' 11".

M4E3, M4 w/Chrysler V–12 A65 engine.

M4E4, torsion bar suspension, 5 bogie wheels, 24" centre guide track, 19' 5" × 9' 8" × 8' 11".

M4E5 (M4A3 (105)), 1944, misnamed, 105mm T8 howitzer in original turret, cast front end, cast armour, cowls jutting out, see M4A3(105).

408

M4E6, welded hull, cast front end w/cast glacis, new turret w/bustle and 76mm L/55 gun, wet ammunition stowage, 19' 4" × 8' 7" × 9' 5".

M4 with Experimental Suspension, similar to M4E6 but w/same HVSS as tested on M3A4 Medium.

M4E7, 1943, misnamed, M4A1 cast hull, 75mm gun, Ford engine.

M4E8, cast front end, original turret w/new flat wide mantlet and 76mm gun, Ford engine, HVSS, 23" steel tracks.

M4E9, 1944, 23" steel tracks w/additional 4' ½" added to each track by means of extended end connectors.

M4A1, 1942, successor to T6 Medium tank, original production w/cast hull, no side doors but 3 bow mgs as in T6, 2 centre fixed mgs later eliminated, drop-down cowls, 3 piece front end, later round cast and then V-type cast, later some w/appliqué hull or turret armour or both, cast turret, later side turret peepslots were eliminated, M2 75mm gun and coaxial mg, later improved turret w/wide mantlet and M3 gun, finally 76mm w/o muzzle brake and then w/muzzle brake, support rollers above bogie brackets, 79 track shoes, late production w/HVSS, 20' 4" × 9' 9" × 9' 2".

M4A1 with Hedgerow Removal Prongs, same as corresponding M4, variations existed.

M4A1 (76mm Gun), similar to M4E1 w/76mm w/o muzzle brake, standard 75mm turret w/built-out bustle counterweight, turret ordered into production and then cancelled, 20' 2" (24' 6") × 9' 10" × 9' 11".

M4A1 (76mm Wet), long 76mm gun in turret w/bustle, wide mantlet, vision cupola on right, split hatch cover on left, turret ports added, 20' 2" (24' 6") × 9' 10" × 9' 10".

M4A1 (76mm Wet) HVSS, 1944, gun w/muzzle brake, new type HVSS.

M4A1E1, 1942, NDRC experimental tank w/aluminium foil insulation and air-conditioning equipment.

M4A1E2, 1942, NDRC experimental IR device for driving and observation as well as sighting, vehicle painted w/IR reflecting paint, had recording odograph.

M4A1E3, 1943, M4A1 w/torque converter.

M4A1E4, designation not used.

M4A1E5, new continental radial C-4 engine w/cooling modifications which later became standardized changes.

M4A1E8, 1944, M4A1 (76mm Wet) HVSS pilot.

M4A1E9, 1944, 23" track w/4½" spaced-out end connectors.

M4A1 (76mm M1), experimental modification for new gun.

▼ 409
M4A1 with Half Track Suspension (Centipede), 1943, 2 half track suspension units, 3 support rollers.

M4A2, same as M4 but w/twin GMC diesel engines, went through modifications similar to M4A1, early suspension w/return roller above bogie brackets and later offset to rear of brackets, 18' 6½" × 8' 8" × 8' 11".

M4A2 (76mm Wet) HVSS, long 76mm gun w/muzzle brake, turret w/vision cupola on right, split hatch cover on left, flat glacis, mg right front, cast front end.

M4A2E1, M4A2 w/special GMC V-8-184 diesel.

M4A2E2, no information available.

M4A2E3, no information available.

▼ 410
M4A2E4, torsion bar suspension, 6 bogie wheels, 3 support rollers, 24" centre guide steel track.

M4A2E9, 24" steel track w/4½" spaced-out end connectors.

M4A3, same as M4 but w/Ford V-8 liquid-cooled engine, went through modifications similar to M4A1 but none had 3 piece front end or 3 bow mgs, some w/M3 gun in early turret and cast bow were modified in Japan during Korean War to mount the 76mm, 20' 7" × 9' 10" × 9' 2".

M4A3 (75mm Wet), wet ammunition stowage, 19' 7" (25' 4") × 9' 10" × 9' 9½".

M4A3 with Wooden Sides, 1944, used by USMC on Iwo Jima to prevent adherence of Japanese magnetic mines.

M4A3 (76mm M1A1C) (M1A2), modified in Great Britain, turret rebalanced w/large steel plate welded to bustle.

M4A3 (76mm Wet), exterior same as M4A2 (76mm Wet), w/ or w/o muzzle brake.

▼ 411
M4A3 (105), 1943, erroneously called M4E1, similar to M4 (105), later w/new turret, heavier mantlet, vision cupola on right and 2 oval hatches on left, still later w/HVSS, 20' 5½" × 9' 10" × 9' 2".

M4A3 (105), w/T121 twin 50 cal mg mount on top of turret.

M4A3E1, 1943, appliqué armour vehicle w/Spicer torque converter.

M4A3E2 (Assault Tank) (Jumbo) (Cobra King), 1943, intended for breaching Siegfried Line, wide tracks w/extended end connectors, completely rounded front end, thick armour added, mantlet thickened, later type turret w/75mm M3 gun, wet ammunition stowage, some later w/76mm substituted in the field.

M4A3E3, M4A3 w/torquematic transmission.

M4A3E8, M4A3 w/HVSS, 75mm M2 gun in original turret, later M3 gun in late turret, finally 76mm w/quick change tube, wet ammunition stowage, 5 support rollers.

M4A3E8, w/remote-controlled 50 cal mg, remote-controlled gun in box on left turret side.

M4A3E8, original vehicles modified in Japan during Korean War to mount 76mm in original turret.

M4A3E8 with Shillelagh, 1955, experimental installation of Shillelagh.

M4A3E9, 1944, 37" wide track w/4½" extended end connectors.

M4A3 w/32½" grousers, similar.

M4A4, lengthened M4 type hull to accommodate 5 Chrysler passenger automobile type engines w/common crankcase, 83 instead of 79 track shoes, 75mm M3 gun, 3 piece front end, 20' 2" × 8' 7" × 9' 9".

412

M4A4 with Allis-Chalmers Suspension,
suspension, similar to that on M6
High Speed Tractor, 3 support
rollers.

413

M4A4 with Horizontal Suspension,
same suspension as tested on M3A4
Medium tank, not M4A3E8 type.

M4A4E1, 105mm howitzer in original
type turret, heavy mantlet, cast
cowls, 34½″ track.

M4A5, US designation for Canadian
Ram I and Ram II.

M4A6, M4A4 welded hull, V-type
front end, glacis, cast turret,
RD1820. Caterpillar-Wright diesel
engine, 75mm gun, 83 track shoes,
21′ 2″ × 8′ 7″ × 10′ 3″.

3″ Gun Motor Carriage T35, 1942,
M4A2 chassis, welded flat top hull,
squat partly open top turret
bevelled inward top and bottom,
3″ M7 gun, 30 tons, 18′ 9″ × 8′ 5″
× 8′ 9″.

3″ Gun Motor Carriage T35E1,
similar, hull sloped in all around,
bevelled armour covering final
drive, sloped in turret, twin GMC
diesel engines, pilot of M10, 18′ 8″
× 10′ × 8′ 1½″.

414

Multiple Gun Motor Carriage T52, M4
chassis, Bofors 40mm gun in centre
of horiontally pivoted barrel turret,

50 cal mg either side of barrel, all
remote-controlled.

90mm Gun Motor Carriage T53,
open M4 chassis, rear mounted
90mm A/A gun, rear of hull
w/drop sides, various types of
shields tested, final being semi-
circular, 20′ 3″ × 8′ 7″ × 9′ 2″
w/o shield.

415

90mm Gun Motor Carriage T53E1,
similar but gun centre mounted,
folding outrigger braces on front
and rear bogie frames, various
types of shields, final one being an
angled box, 19′ 8½″ (24′) × 11′ ½″
× 10′ 7″ w/original shield.

90mm Gun Motor Carriage T71, M10
w/welded faceted turret, large
wedge-shaped bustle counterweight,
heavy curved mantlet, round
cupola left rear of turret, 18′ 8″
(24′ 6″) × 10′ × 8′ 1½″.

90mm Gun Motor Carriage T71E1
(M35), same but M10A1 chassis.

76mm Gun Motor Carriage T72,
1943, 76mm in open top turret
w/small bustle, later final type M4
tank turret was substituted, 18′ 8″
× 10′ × 8′ 5½″.

Tarantula, T72 w/mine flail made of
a cut-down auto frame, engine and
3 drums with chains on either side
of differential field fix.

155mm Gun Motor Carriage T83
(M40) (Big Shot), rear-mounted
M1A1 155mm gun on M4A3E8
w/cast front end, resembled Gun
Motor Carriage M6, trail spade and
ramp combined, 42 tons, 20′ 7″
(29′ 9″) × 10′ 4″ × 8′ 9½″
(10′ 9″ overall).

8″ Howitzer Motor Carriage T83,
same w/8″ howitzer.

155mm Mortar Motor Carriage T90,
1944, 155mm breech loading
mortar L/10 in M4 tank turret,
19′ 4″ × 8′ 7″ × 8′ 7″.

10″ Mortar Motor Carriage T94,
1945, M40 chassis w/250mm T5E3
mortar, mock-up only completed.

Rocket Launcher T34 (Calliope),
60 unit 4.6″ rocket projector on
frame above tank turret, 2 bottom
rows 12 tubes each, could be
jettisoned, also used on M4s other
than M4A1.

Rocket Launcher T34E1, similar on

M4A1, 2 bottom rows 14 tubes
each.

Rocket Launcher T34E2, same but
square tubes.

Rocket Launcher T39, 20 7.2″
rockets, square tubes in solid
frame.

Rocket Launcher T72, similar to T34
but 60 short tube 4.6″ rockets.

416

Rocket Launcher T40 (M17)
(Whizbang), 1943, M4A1 (US) or
M4A4 (British), large 20 tube box
type 7.2″ rockets close to turret
top.

Rocket Launcher T40 (Short),
similar but short tubes.

Rocket Launcher T73, similar to T39
but 10 square tubes in box on
M4A1, 7.2″ rockets.

Rocket Launcher T76, one 7½″ tube
in place of 75mm gun in M4A1 tank.

Rocket Launcher T76E1, one long
7½″ rocket tube in place of 76mm
gun on M4A3E8 tank.

Rocket Launcher T94 (T31
Demolition Tank), massive cast
turret w/7.2″ tube and loader built
out on each side of main turret,
75mm M3 gun tube used for F/T
in centre front of turret, M4A3E8
chassis, all weapons remote-
controlled.

Rocket Launcher T99, 1945, 22
rockets in 2 open lattice box
frames on each side of M4A3
turret on common trunnion, also
on M26 tank.

Rocket Launcher T105, 1 very long
7.2″ box projector in place of
75mm on M4A1.

E4–5 (E4R2–5R1) (E4R3–5R1)
(M3–4–3), F/T in place of bow mg
on M4A2 tank.

E4R4 5–6RC, 1942, periscope type
F/T out of bow mg opening
w/small guard rails in glacis of
M4A2 tank.

POA Flame-thrower (Pearl Harbor
Flame-thrower), Navy Mark I F/T
inside old 105mm howitzer tube
w/breech cut away, coaxial mg
retained.

POA–CWS75–H1, M4, M4A1 and
M4A3 w/75mm gun tube as

modified above, when used by USMC hull sides were covered w/detachable wooden sides to prevent adhesion of Japanese magnetic mines and w/screen baskets over turret hatches.

POA–CWS75–H2, modification of above, gun tubes restored and flame-gun tube mounted parallel and to right of gun tube.

E6R1 (E6–R3) (M3–4) periscope type F/T above assistant driver in M4A1 and M4A3 tanks.

E12R2, turret periscope type F/T in M4A1 Medium tanks.

E12–7R1 (M5–4), M4A1 Medium tank, early turret w/F/T in dummy 75mm tube, and small flexible F/T top rear.

M3–4–3 Flame-thrower Tank, bow F/T replacing bow mg in M4A1, M4A2 and M4A3 Medium tanks.

(- - - - -) M4A1 Medium tank, early turret w/F/T in parallel tube and small flexible F/T top rear, experimental.

E13–13, M4A1 76mm (Wet), gun replaced by F/T in dummy 75mm gun tube.

E13R1–13R2, M4A1 late turret w/gun replaced by F/T in dummy 75mm gun tube, also experimentally w/small projection at rear of bustle w/flexible additional F/T.

E19–19, M4A3 76mm (Wet) w/F/T in blister on left side of mantlet, prototype only.

E20–20 (T33), 1945, M4A3E2 w/E20 F/T on mantlet right, 75mm gun from M24 Light tank, also periscope type F/T on turret top, see also T33, 22′ 8″ × 9′ 4″ × 9′ 5½″.

Crocodile, British F/T w/trailer for M4, modified in Europe, flame-gun in armoured box beside assistant driver's hatch.

B1 Mechanized Flame Gun, F/T replacing bow gun in M4 series tanks.

B2 Mechanized Flame Gun, F/T added to bow gun in M4 series tanks.

E18 Mechanized Flame Gun, 1945, bow type F/T.

Skink (Scorpion) M4A3 Medium Tank w/multiple E–1 liquid phosphorus anti-personnel dischargers on sides and front.

Mine Exploder T1E1 (Earthworm), 1943, 6 large flat roller discs in 3 units in tricycle arrangement guided by cables and A–frame pushed by M4, 31′ 5″ × 12′ 4″ × 9′ 8″ to 33′ 4″.

Mine Exploder T1E2, 1943, still larger 7 discs w/peripheral holes per unit, 19′ 1″ (28′ 2″) × 11′ 3″ × 8′ 6″.

▼ 417
Mine Exploder T1E3 (M1) (Aunt Jemima), 1943, 2 units of 5 ten-foot discs w/4 large oval holes, chain and gear driven, back plate welded on as snubber for receiving assisting push from another M4A1 tank.

Mine Exploder M1A1, units changed to 4 solid discs w/internal and external chain drive off sprockets.

Mine Exploder T1E4, large curved wishbone boom braced to tank sides, 16 serrated edge cast armour discs on a dolly, each disc individually rubber torsion sprung, later the 2 outer and 8 inner discs were smooth edged, 19′ 4″ (28′ 1½″) × 10′ 10″ × 9′ 9½″.

Mine Exploder T1E5, 2 units of 6 serrated discs each, both units free to move vertically, supported on large centre frame, chain and gear driven, 30′ 6″ × 11′ 3″ × 9′ 8″.

Mine Exploder T1E6, almost identical to T1E3 but serrated edge discs.

Mine Exploder T2, flail type, same as British Sherman Crab I.

Mine Exploder T3 (Scorpion), same as British Sherman Scorpion but w/US-built hydraulic lift.

Mine Exploder T3E1, rebuilt T3 changed from flail to sand-filled roller on longer arms, 27′ 6″ to front of rotor × 12′ 4½″ × 9′ 10″.

Mine Exploder T4 (Crab), British Sherman Crab.

Mine Exploder T5, V-shaped plough fork w/hydraulic dozer controls.

Mine Excavator T5E1, 1943, M1 bull-dozer blade w/fork fingers added.

Mine Excavator T5E2 (Potato Digger), similar to T5E1 but w/V-shaped centre armour shield protecting hydraulic mechanism behind blade, 27′ 8″ × 12′ 4″ × 9′ 8″.

▼ 418
Mine Excavator T5E3, same w/side deflecting ploughs, 26′ 1″ × 10′ 10″ w/wings folded, 14′ w/wings extended × 14′.

Mine Excavator T6E1, similar to T5E3, top of plough curved forward.

Mine Excavator MB4–20, M1A1 Bulldozer w/variations.

▼ 419
Mine Exploder T8, pivoted frame holding 3 spring plungers geared to sprockets, 29′ 2″ × 12′ 5″ × 9′ 10″.

Mine Exploder T8E1 (Johnnie Walker), improved model w/geared lifter on right glacis.

Mine Exploder T9 (Steam Roller), 1943, 6 foot cast steel studded roller 10′ wide on frame towed behind tank, 36′ 11″ extended to 45′ 7″ × 12′ × 9′ 10″.

Mine Exploder T9E1, same roller placed on long rotatable pipe in pivot welded to front end, 18′ 6½″ extendable to 30′ 6″ × 11′ 9″ × 9′ 8″.

Mine Exploder T10 (Tricycle), M4 tank hull and turret mounted on 2 wide 8′ tyred wheels in front and very wide 6′ wheels forming a rear roller, NDRC designed, 28′ 6″ × 15′ × 20′ 1″.

Mine Exploder T11 (M4A4 with Spigot Mortar Attachment), 1945, 6 spigot mortars fanned horizontally across glacis top on elevatable frame, supporting brackets welded to glacis.

▼ 420
Mine Exploder T12, turret removed and 25 fanned-out spigot mortars vertically mounted in turret well and 5 spigot mortars on glacis.

Mine Exploder, M4A3 w/flail improvised by USMC in the field from dozer parts and tow cables.

NDRC Rota Flail, 2 solid girders welded to tank sides supporting large roller w/extending fingers to which heavy chains were fastened.

Mine Resistant Vehicle T14, M4 w/added belly armour and strengthened track and suspension.

Mine Resistant Vehicle T15, 1944, raised M4A1 hull w/o turret but w/cupola, on strengthened suspension w/steel bogies, special heavy sprockets, very heavy tracks.

Mine Resistant Vehicle T15E1, same w/bogie wheels strengthened.

Mine Resistant Vehicle T15E2, improved version.

Snake Tank, 1943, M4 w/flat snake, mine exploding explosive charge pushed forward by means of ratchet and feed fingers on snake.

Snake Tank, jointed pipe-type snake pulled behind tank.

Snake Tank, 1954, snake w/wedge cross section, operated like 1943 version.

Bridging Tank, 1944, field modification in Italy on rebuilt M4 tank, long double track bridge supported by small front A–frame for dropping in place, small rear frame for lifting and chocking in position for pick-up.

M4 with Searchlight, field modification, turret removed and searchlight mounted in centre of hull.

E–turret, redesign on M4 chassis of Shop Tractor T10 on M3 chassis.

Shop Tractor T10E1, experimental CDL w/wide special cast turret on M4A1 chassis and hull, also called E-Vehicle Special Stowage.

Concertina Wire-layer, 1952, M4A3E8 w/triple belt concertina wire-layer mounted on front glacis in heavy cast pivot.

M4A3E8 CDL, 1951, 75mm gun w/searchlight, intended as mass conversion for use in Korea but dropped.

Doozit, 1943, wooden platform on M1 dozer blade to carry explosives for breaching walls, modified in Great Britain.

Recovery Vehicle T14, crane on turret, welded hull w/side doors, see M32, 17′ 5½″ × 8′ 9½″ × 9′ vehicle only.

Cargo Carrier T22, companion vehicle for 240mm Howitzer Motor Carriage, large rear cargo box, 50 cal mg ring mount on 3 supports right front.

Cargo Carrier T30 (Tiny), very similar but HVSS and 2 vision cupolas front of hull.

Cargo Carrier M3, similar to T22 but ring mount was in rear.

M5 Light Tank, see Light tank M3E3.

M5A1 Light Tank, same as M5 but w/turret bustle, some later w/curved top side stowage box in right side of turret, 15′ 2½″ × 7′ 4″ × 7′ 6½″.

M5A1E1, 1943, M5A1 w/T73 mount and automatic 37mm gun, 13′ 10½″ × 7′ 10½″ × 7′ 6½″.

81mm Mortar Carrier T27, M5A1 w/o turret, 16′ 5″ × 7′ 6″ × 7′ 4″.

4.2″ Mortar Carrier T29, M5A1 w/o turret, 16′ 5″ × 7′ 6½″ ×.7′ 4″.

4.2″ Mortar Carrier T81, M5A1 w/o turret.

75mm Howitzer Motor Carriage T47, 1942, miniature of T32 Howitzer Motor Carriage, open top, pack howitzer, 16.25 tons, later w/turret from M8 and covered hull.

155mm Howitzer Motor Carriage T64, see M24.

Twin 40mm Gun Motor Carriage T65, M5A1 chassis w/added bogie wheel pair, guns rear mounted in cylindrical open top turret w/curved partial shields, predecessor of T64E1 Gun Motor Carriage on M24 Light tank chassis, 18′ 2″ × 9′ 1″ × 6′ 4″.

105mm Howitzer Motor Carriage T82 (Little Joe), 1944, M5A1 chassis, miniature M7 Howitzer Motor Carriage.

Multiple Gun Motor Carriage T85, 1944, four 20mm Oerlikon guns rear mounted in open cylinder on

large cylindrical superstructure, M5 chassis w/1 extra bogie wheel pair, partly skirted, 18′ 9″ × 9′ 5″ × 7′ 3″.

Multiple Gun Motor Carriage T85E1, 1944, same chassis w/new revolving cylindrical platform rear mounted.

Experimental A/A vehicle, twin cal 30 mg on turretless M5.

105mm Pack Howitzer on M5A1, 1943, experimental, miniature M7 type w/o pulpit, howitzer centre front, sometimes erroneously identified as T47 Howitzer Motor Carriage.

Navy Mark 17 Mount on M5A1, twin cal 30 A/A on turretless M5A1.

155mm M1 Howitzer on lengthened M5 chassis, improved trail spade.

Reconnaissance Vehicle "B", 1944, turretless M5 w/mg on ring mount right front.

Reconnaissance Vehicle T8, same w/minor changes.

Reconnaissance Vehicle T8E1, similar w/large flat vision cupola in centre w/mg mounted above.

Reconnaissance Vehicle T8E1 Modified, twin cal 30 mg instead of single.

Command Tank, turret replaced in the field by a box superstructure on M5A1 chassis.

Experimental Twin 50 cal A/A on M5A1, similar, w/large A/A ring mount.

Q Tank, M5A1 w/prototype F/T in place of 37mm gun.

E5 R2 (M3) Flame Tank, periscope type F/T on M5A1.

E7–7 Flame Tank (E7–M5A1), 1943, short F/T and mg in M5A1 turret, complete turret was interchangeable w/normal turret.

E8 (M5A1) Flame Tank, similar w/special small turret.

E9–9 Flame Tank, bow mg removed from M5A1, F/T mounted low on glacis, normal turret armament retained, w/large wheeled fuel trailer.

M5A1 with Hedgerow Device (Rhino), sharpened angle irons welded to bow.

Mine Exploder for M5A1 Light Tank, low steerable pushed carriage w/auxiliary wheels to control jump leading each track and a trailer in rear between the tracks supporting 20 armour plate discs, built in the field by 6616 Mine Clearing Company.

M6 Heavy Tank, see T1E2 Heavy tank.

M6E1 Heavy Tank, see T1E1 Heavy tank.

M6A1 Heavy Tank, 1942, see T1E3 Heavy tank.

M6A2 Heavy Tank, see T1E1 Heavy tank.

M6A2E1, 1945, massive turret w/large bustle, 105mm gun w/ muzzle brake, M6A2 chassis.

M7 Light Tank, originally T7 Light tank, later M7 Medium tank, production version of medium T7, weight increased from 20 to 27 tons because of thicker armour and 75mm gun, dropped after 27 were made, 17′ (17′ 7″) × 9′ 2″ × 7′ 4″.

M7 Howitzer Motor Carriage, 1942, 105mm L/25 howitzer, pulpit replaced ring mount on T32, low rear side armour, later higher, see also T32 under M3 Medium Tank, 19′ 9″ × 9′ 8½″ × 8′ 4″ to top of pulpit.

M7 Howitzer Motor Carriage Modified, 1943, experimental modification w/hinged side armour, M3 Medium Tank chassis, forerunner of M7B1.

M7B1 Howitzer Motor Carriage, 1944, 105mm howitzer, M4 chassis, based on above, higher pulpit,

20′ 7½″ × 9′ 5½″ × 8′ 6″ to top of pulpit.

M7B1 Modified, British 10″ mortar substituted for 105mm howitzer, fired napalm or phosphorus projectiles.

M7B2, High Pulpit, right side gun shield to top of pulpit.

M8 Howitzer Motor Carriage, 75mm pack howitzer in M18 SP type turret on M5A1 Light tank chassis, 16′ 6″ × 7′ 7″ × 7′ 6½″.

M8 Motor Carriage with 75mm Tank Gun, experimental installation of M3 tank gun by Armored Force Board, sometimes incorrectly called M8A1.

M9 Gun Motor Carriage, see 3″ Gun Motor Carriage T40 under M3 Medium tank series.

M10 Gun Motor Carriage (Wolverine), production T35E1, 3″ L/53 gun, modified bow, GMC diesel engine, 30.5 tons, 19′ 7″ w/gun × 10′ × 8′ 1½″.

M10A1 Gun Motor Carriage, Ford engine, turret later remodelled to be more open at rear, counterweight bustle added, armour bosses eliminated in 1943.

M10 Modified, 90mm T7 gun substituted experimentally.

M10 Modified, roof and square auxiliary cupola w/horizontal peepslots added to top of turret.

M12, see Gun Motor Carriage T6 under M3 Medium tank.

M13–16, SPs other than full tracklaying.

M17 Rocket Launcher, see T40 Rocket Launcher under M4 Medium tank.

M18 Gun Motor Carriage (T70), welded turret w/76mm M1 L/55 gun used by Tank Destroyer Force, 37.5 tons, 5 bogie wheels and 4 support rollers, helical springs, outgrowth of T67 Gun Motor Carriage which had 5 bogie wheels and 4 support rollers, bevelled-in cylindrical open top turret w/75mm M3 gun on T49 Gun Motor Carriage, which had a chassis resembling M24 Light tank, 5 bogies on helical springs, 2 support rollers, welded hull on turret w/bustle, mg right of sharply angled glacis, 57mm gun, 1 support roller later added in rear, 16 tons, 17′ 10″ (21′ 10″) × 9′ 5″ × 7′ 9″ (8′ 5″ to top of turret mg).

75mm M3 Gun in M18, experimental.

M18 Modified, 1944, 6 flat hinged fold-up sides w/cover forming a large asymmetrical cupola.

M18 with M36 Turret, 90mm gun, experimental.

Armored Utility Vehicle T16 (M44), 1945, resembled later M59 APC, 22.5 tons, 6 bogie wheels, 4 support rollers, small right and left front hatches, 6-sided commander's cupola front centre.

Armored Utility Vehicle T39, based on M18.

Armored Utility Vehicle T41 (M39), 1943, 5 bogie wheels, 4 support rollers, open top converted M18, 35.5 tons, 17′ 4″ × 9′ ½″ × 6′ 4″ (7′ 6″ to top of mg).

Armored Mortar Carrier, M39 w/81mm mortar.

Armored Utility Vehicle T41E1 (M44E1), 1945, similar to T16 Armored Utility Vehicle, 6 bogie wheels, 4 support rollers, rear top hatch front hinged instead of side hinged as in M44, top of hull raised 10″, 21′ 4″ × 10′ × 7′ 2″ (9′ 4″ to top of mg).

Command Post Vehicle T17 (TACP) (Tactical Air Control Party vehicle), M44E1.

Esch Device (Pilot T86 Gun Motor Carriage), M18 w/built-on boat hull and skirts, twin rudders, track propulsion, 29′ 3″ × 10′ 2″ × 9′ 7″.

76mm Gun Motor Carriage (Amphibian) T86, Esch Device w/a section of hull from sponsons upward removed and replaced w/a new and larger watertight hull, 4 vertical scuppers front sides of hull, 2 folding rudders, no screws.

T86 Modified, third steering position added just forward of turret, front hull corners bevelled and cut down for addition of vision blocks, no scuppers.

T86E1, 1944, built-up rear top of turret, improved boat-shaped hull, twin screws in tunnel beneath vehicle, 3 vertical scuppers.

T86E1 Modified, modified hull, skirts lowered forming deeper screw tunnel, later smaller tunnel and 1 screw.

105mm Howitzer Motor Carriage (Amphibian) T87, 1945, ½ ton lighter than T86E1, hull shortened, rear top of turret built up, 2 scuppers, 27′ 1″ × 10′ 2″ × 9′ 7″.

T87E1, one road wheel added, turret moved forward, NDRC design study only.

105mm Howitzer Motor Carriage T88, 1944, M18 w/T8 howitzer substituted for 76mm gun, 17′ 9″ × 9′ 5″ × 8′ 5″.

B15T Carrier, M18 components, 5 bogies, LVT tracks, low flat hull, 16 tons.

M18 Modified, floats added to M18, false bow and stern.

M19 Twin 40mm Gun Motor Carriage (T65E1), M24 Light tank chassis, improved T65 w/higher side shields, 18 tons, 20′ 1″ × 9′ 10″ × 9′ 10″.

M19A1 (T65E2), minor modifications including higher gun mount.

M19A1 Modified, 1952, field modification in Korea, 50 cal mg bow-mounted for sniper protection.

M19A1 with 75mm Automatic A/A gun, official modification but no T number.

M22 Light Tank, see T9E1 Light tank.

M24 Light Tank, see T24 Light tank, 16′ 4½″ (18′) × 9′ 9″ × 8′ 1½″ to top of cupola, 9′ 1″ overall.

155mm Howitzer Motor Carriage T64, 1942, M24 Light tank hull, w/M5 Light tank suspension w/1 extra bogie wheel pair, open top, no shield, double rear trail spade, 19½ tons, resembled Gun Motor

Carriage T65, 19′ 7″ × 9′ 11″ × 7′ 5″.

155mm Howitzer Motor Carriage T64E1 (M41), 1944, M24 chassis, partial side armour w/hand rails at rear, otherwise like T64, top bows and tarpaulin, 21½ tons, 19′ 2″ × 9′ 10″ × 8′ 1½″.

105mm Howitzer Motor Carriage T76 (M37), resembled M7 Howitzer Motor Carriage but on M24 Light tank chassis, circular 50 cal mg pulpit, bow top, 23 tons, later experimentally fitted w/4.2″ recoil less mortar or 75mm recoilless rifle on pulpit top, 17′ 4″ (18′ 1″) × 9′ 11″ × 7′ 11″ (8′ 0″ overall).

Multiple Gun Motor Carriage T77, 1943, six 50 cal A/A mgs in shaped welded turret w/bustle, left and right rear cupola, bow mg, 16′ 6½″ × 9′ 11″ × 6′ 7½″.

Multiple Gun Motor Carriage T77E1, same w/cupola openings covered w/clear plastic bubbles protected by rod grills.

90mm Gun Motor Carriage T78, M24 chassis, project only.

Combination Gun Motor Carriage T81, 1944, 40mm Bofors and two 50 cal mgs on T65E1 Gun Motor Carriage chassis.

155mm Mortar Motor Carriage T96, 1945, originally planned for T16 Armored Utility Vehicle as 155mm Mortar Motor Carriage T96, but changed to M37 chassis.

Quad 75mm Rifles on M19 Self-propelled Carriage, 1945, 4 recoil-less rifles rear mounted, partial vertical side shields, 17′ 11″ × 9′ 4″ × 8′ 3½″.

75mm Self-Propelled Mount, 1947, 75mm T18 automatic A/A gun on open M24 chassis.

M24 Light Tank with T122 Mount, large cupola w/remote-controlled twin 50 cal mg on top of turret.

Rocket Launcher T45, 10 rocket launcher frame on each side of M24 Light tank turret.

M24 Light Tank with German 12-Ton Prime Mover Suspension, 1946, experimental adaptation of German half-track suspension to light tank.

M24 with Searchlight, 1950, equipped w/standard 18″ commercial light.

Armored Utility Vehicle T9 (T9 Utility Carrier), 1944, M5 and M24 Light tank components, 4 bogie wheels, large trailing idler, 2 support rollers, hull like M5 but high centre cab and rear cargo box, 9½ tons, 16′ 1″ × 8′ 1″ × 6′.

Armored Utility Vehicle T13, 1943, cab front, M24 chassis, 15.5 tons, forerunner of T16 (M44), 18′ 1″ × 9′ 9″ × 8′ 4″.

M26 (General Pershing), see T26E3 Heavy tank, variations in driver cowl in glacis.

M26E1, 1945, 90mm T54 gun w/muzzle brake, torque converter-planetary transmission (cross-drive), 24 volt electrical system, 47 tons, 20′ 9″ (31′ 4″ gun reversed) × 11′ 5″ × 9′ 1″ to top of cupola.

M26E2, see T40 Medium tank and M46 Medium tank.

M26 with T121 Machine Gun Mount, 1946, remote-controlled dual 50 cal mg in cupola on turret.

T12 Armored Recovery Vehicle, M26 basis, modified turret w/large bustle, turret mounted extensible girder boom, front fork spade, 21′ 11″ vehicle (24′ 10″ travel position) × 12′ 4″ × 11′ 2″.

M29C (Weasel), 1941, light amphibious tender designed by NDRC.

M29C Carrier with 37mm Gun, 1945, 37mm gun on T32 tripod mounted on right top, 3 tons, 16′ (19′ 2″) × 5′ 7½″ × 5′ 11″.

M29C with 75mm Recoilless Rifle, 1945, gun originally rear mounted on pedestal, later centre mounted, experimental, predecessor of T106.

M29C with 105mm Recoilless Rifle, 1956, gun centre mounted on pedestal, experimental, 17′ 4″ × 5′ 10″ × 7′.

M29 Wire Layer.

M30, see Cargo Carrier T14 under M3 Medium tank series.

M31, see Tank Recovery Vehicle T2 under M3 Medium tank series, 24′ 6″ × 10′ × 10′ 4″.

M32 Recovery Vehicle, see T14 Recovery Vehicle under M4 Medium tank series.

M32B1, M4A1 Tank chassis w/crane and A-frame hinged to hull front, welded turret like that on full track Prime Mover M34 but flatsided, 16½″ tracks, some w/mortar on glacis.

M32B3, M4A3 w/16½″ track. 26′ 10″ × 8′ 11″ × 9′ 9″ vehicle.

M32A1, M4 HVSS w/23¾″ track.

M32A1B1, M4A1 HVSS w/23¾″ track.

M32A1B3, M4A3 HVSS w/23¾″ track, 26′ 10″ (32′ 2″) × 8′ 11″ × 10′ 3″ to 21′ 2″.

M33 Prime Mover, converted from M31 Tank Recovery Vehicle, turret removed, winches retained, ring-mounted mg above 75mm gun sponson.

M34 Full Track Prime Mover, converted from M32B1 Recovery Vehicle, turret removed, winches retained, later rounded special turret w/open hatch in front and split hatch on bustle.

M35 Prime Mover, M10 Gun Motor Carriage w/turret removed and pintles added front and rear.

M36 Gun Motor Carriage, M10A1 chassis w/heavy turret and 90mm L/53 gun, 32 tons, see T71E1, 19′ 7″ (24′ 6″) × 10′ × 10′ 5½″.

M36B1 (Jackson) (Can Opener), M36 turret on M4A3 Medium tank, 20′ 7″ (24′ 6½″) × 8′ 8½″ × 8′ ½″.

M36B2, M10 chassis, sloped-in turret cover, 21′ 10½″ (24′ 6″) × 10′ × 9′ 2″.

M37 Howitzer Motor Carriage (105mm Light Self-Propelled Howitzer), see T76 under M24 Light tank series, 18′ × 9′ 10″ × 7′ 11″ (8′ 8″ over A/A gun).

4.2″ Mortar Carrier T35, M37 chassis.

M39 Armored Utility Vehicle, see T41 under M18 Gun Motor Carriage series, 17′ 10″ × 9′ 5″ × 6′ 5½″.

M40 Gun Motor Carriage, see T83 under M4 Medium tank series.

M40 with Added Armor, square cab added.

M41 Howitzer Motor Carriage, see 155mm Howitzer Motor Carriage T64E1 under M24 Light tank series.

M41 Light Tank (Full Tracked 76mm Combat Tank) (Walker Bulldog), see T41, first tank built around its power plant, stabilized in elevation and azimuth, 76mm gun, automatic loader, selector, indexer, rammer, catches empty case to reinsert in proper rack, range-finder, long bustle, remote-controlled mgs on turret sides later removed, some w/jettison fuel tanks, 25.5 tons, Lycoming or Continental engine, 23′ 1″ (26′ 11½″) × 10′ 5″ × 8′ (10′ 1″).

M41A1, see T41E2, seen in Vietnam w/pintle mounted mg and shield atop turret.

M41A2, M41A3, minor improvements, including new turret traversing system and fuel injection engine.

Light Recovery Vehicle T6, M41 chassis type A-frame.

T6E1, similar w/mortar mounted on glacis.

Armored Personnel Carrier T18 (Armored Utility Vehicle T18 (Armored Infantry Vehicle), 1949, used M41 components, 5 bogie wheels, 3 unevenly spaced support rollers, high box hull, bevelled top side, double bevel glacis, originally low cupola left front, higher cupola right, later centre and 2 remote-controlled mg boxes on sides.

Armored Personnel Carrier T18E1, 1949, cupola left, centre front vision cupola w/50 cal mg, 21 tons, later small centre dome cupola w/1 mg.

Armored Personnel Carrier T18E2, 1951, T122 cupola added as on M24 Light tank.

T18E1 Modified (M75), new remote-controlled turrets both sides of hull.

Armored Personnel Carrier T73, resembled T18E1 but lower, horizontal louvers in sides.

M41 with Shillelagh, 1958, special squat turret w/152mm combination missile and projectile gun.

M42 40mm Self-Propelled Anti-Aircraft Artillery, (Duster), see T141E1 Gun Motor Carriage, 19′ 1″ (20′ 10″) × 10′ 7″ × 9′ 4″.

M42 Modified, Ford-Sperry A/A fire control system, radar dish right front of turret.

M42A1, improved version of M42, 25 tons, 19′ 1″ (20′ 10″) × 10′ 7″ × 9′ 4½″.

M42A2, same w/levelling device added.

M42 Flame Tank, M5/4 flame-gun in M4 tank in dummy 75mm gun tube.

M42B1 (Flame Tank M5/4), 1945, F/T in dummy 75mm gun tube on M4A1 Medium tank.

M42B2 (Flame Tank M5/4), 1945, F/T in M4A2 Medium Tank.

M42B3 Flame Tank (Flame Tank M5/4), 1945, M4A3 Medium tank w/long F/T in place of 75mm gun, bogie frames connected by rail below support rollers.

M43 Howitzer Motor Carriage, rear-mounted 8″ L/26 howitzer on M4A3 Medium tank chassis, 24′ 1″ × 10′ 4″ × 10′ 10″.

M43B3, M46 tank w/special turret and long F/T.

M44 Howitzer Motor Carriage, (155mm Medium Self-Propelled Howitzer), 1954, M41 chassis, 155mm howitzer nose mounted in open top box hull, tarpaulin bows, louvers in glacis, 6 bogie wheels including idler, 4 support rollers, see also M44 and M44A1 Armored Utility Vehicles under M18 Gun Motor Carriage series, 20′ 2½″ × 10′ 7½″ × 9′ 10″ (10′ 2½″).

M44A1, same w/diesel engine, 20′ 2″ × 10′ 7″ × 10′ 2½″.

M44 Tractor with Experimental Cupola Mount, standard unarmoured tractor w/small armour cupola replacing mg ring mount.

M45 Heavy Tank (M45 Medium Tank), see T26E2, 1 experimental vehicle w/F/T on right front fender, w/fuel trailer.

XM45 E1, experimental armoured refuelling vehicle for M132 Flame-thrower vehicle, has 50 cal mg.

M46 Medium Tank (M26E2) (Patton), 1949, remodelled w/new

engine and transmission, 48.5 tons, see T40, 20' 4" (27' 11") × 11' 4" 9' 1" to top of cupola.

M46E1 (M46A1) Medium Tank, T42 turret w/sloping sides, rounded small bustle w/bustle box substituted, other modifications.

M46E1 with Fender Kits, 30 cal remote mg kit at front of each fender.

8" Howitzer Motor Carriage T84, 1944, T26E1 chassis, 8" M1 howitzer, no shield, large U-shaped travel lock, double trail spade, 22' 9" × 11' 2½" × 10' 5".

8" Howitzer Motor Carriage T89, 1944, modified M26 chassis, rear mounted howitzer, hull resembled T83 (M40), 24' 1" × 10' 4" × 10' 10".

Howitzer Motor Carriage T92, 1944, 240mm howitzer M1 rear mounted on modified M26 chassis, open top 3-sided shield, 2 vision domes forward, large trail spade, 20' 9" (31' 10") × 11' 1" × 10' 6".

Gun Motor Carriage T93, same as T92 but w/8" Gun M1, 23' 9" (37' 3") × 11' 1" × 11' 11".

Rocket Launcher T99/M26, 1945, two 11 rocket launcher frames on each side of M26 turret on common trunnion.

Flame Tank E24–29 (Prototype Non-Integral Flame-thrower), standard M46 tank w/F/T on left glacis, fuel towed in squat 2 wheel trailer.

Flame Tank, M46 chassis, high barbette hull having sharp glacis, small turret w/F/T, project only.

M46 with 18" Commercial Searchlight, 1952, standard equipment for all tanks in Korea.

Moritzer, 1956, M46 chassis w/rear mounted special 115mm mortar.

M47, M46 w/T42 turret and change in frontal armour on hull, chassis and armament variations, 3 support rollers, 48½ tons, 20' 10½" (27' 9½") × 11' 6" × 9' 9¼".

M48 Medium Tank (Full Tracked 90mm Combat Tank), see T48, elliptical turret and hull, early type commander's cupola, exposed A/A gun, double personnel heater exhaust pipe from left of driver's hatch out over left fender, 22' (27' 8½") × 12' 4" × 10' 7½".

M48 Phase III, M48 Tank w/M47 fire control equipment.

M48C, M48 of mild steel, letter 'C' for condemned embossed into right front of hull.

M48C with Fender Kits, experimental 30 cal mg remote-controlled on front of each fender.

M48 A1, M1 cupola, gun stabilized in both elevation and azimuth, larger driver's hatch, 22' 6" (28' 7½") × 10' 11" × 10' 3½".

M48E1, first w/British 105mm gun, no cupola but ventilator on left rear of turret.

M48A1E1, M48A1 w/British 105mm. .

M48A1E2, M48A1 w/90mm gun M41 and M60 turret components, diesel engine, No. 2 and No. 4 track support rollers and rear track tension idler wheel removed and replaced by M48A2 type front compensating idler spindle and arm, single personnel heater exhaust pipe from right of driver's hatch out over right fender.

M48E2, prototype of M48A2.

M48A2, 1956, fuel injection engine, I/R equipment, 50.75 tons, larger driver's hatch, louvered doors and raised rear deck for better cooling, No. 2 and No. 4 support rollers removed except in USMC version, 22' 6" (28' 6") × 10' 11½" × 10' 2".

M48A2C, improved fire-control equipment, resembles M48A2 except for turret like M60s and small idler tension wheel located between drive sprocket and rear road wheel replaced by front compensating idler spindle and arm.

M48A2E1, 1959, M48A2 w/multi-fuel engine.

M48A3, 1960, production version of M48A1E2, No. 2 and No. 4 support rollers reinstalled when used in Vietnam, 50 cal mg sometimes removed from top of cupola and mounted in front of commander's or loader's hatch, top of dozer blade sometimes welded to bow similar to Culin device of WWII, 22' 7" (28' 6") × 11' 11" × 10' 3".

M48A4, 1965, M60 turret w/105mm gun on M48E3 chassis, M19 cupola, 22' 6½" (30' 6") × 11' 11" × 10' 3" (11' 3" w/riser).

M48A2 with SS10, five SS10 missiles on each side of 90mm gun.

M48 with 18" Commercial Searchlight, 1957, electrically operated shutters to prevent before and after glow, several varieties.

M48 with Navy Signal Light, 1961, light on top of turret, improvised by NYNG.

M48 with Xenon I/R Light, 1962, light mounted above gun and moves with it.

M48 with Shillelagh, squat cast turret, right centre cupola, rotatable hatch w/3 extendable periscopes, left rear side extendable range-finder, ventilator rear right top.

M48 with Expendable Roller Mine Clearing Device (M48 with Light Mine Clearing Roller), 1957, small rollers supported in front of each track.

M48 with AGT–1500 Gas Turbine, rear deck raised, turret replaced by cab for test purposes.

High Herman (Tank Mounted Heavy Mine Clearing Roller), mine roller similar to T1E4 in M4 Tank series but 25 plain and serrated discs on dolly across entire vehicle front.

Larrapin' Lou, 1952 (Tank Mounted Light Mine Clearing Roller), 2 units of 6 serrated discs each on heavy double carriage or A-frame.

M48 with Heavy Mine Clearing Device, 2 interconnected casters of 6 discs each supported on heavy booms.

M48 Series Tankdozer w/M8 or M8A1 Dozer.

AVLB (Armoured Vehicle Launching Bridge), scissors-type bridging device on M26 tank chassis, 36' 3" × 13' 2" × 12' 7½".

AVL Unit Rig and Equipment Model (M48A2 AVLB) (M48A2 Tank Chassis Transporting Launcher), scissors-type launcher for 40, 60 or 63 foot bridge.

AVLB, similar to M60A1 chassis.

Assault Bridge, collapsible Ark type bridge improvised by occupation forces in Germany.

M50 Gun Motor Carriage (Ontos), see T166 Gun Motor Carriage, commander's hand rail and mg mount added later, 12' 6½" w/weapons × 8' 6" × 7'.

M50A1, 1965, improved engine and tracks, I/R sighting.

M51 Tank Recovery Vehicle (Full Tracked Heavy Recovery Vehicle) see T51, 33' 3" × 11' 11" × 10' 9".

M52 Gun Motor Carriage (105mm Light Self-Propelled Howitzer), M41 Light tank chassis, see T98E1, 19' ½" w/gun × 10' 4" × 10' 10".

M52A1, Improved, 19' × 10' 4" × 10' 10".

M53 Gun Motor Carriage (155mm Self-Propelled Field Artillery Gun), 155mm T80 gun on modified M48 chassis, 7 bogie wheels including trailing idler, 3 evenly spaced support rollers, see T97, 25' 11" (33' 6") × 11' 9" × 11' 8" to top of hull.

M54, same chassis and cab w/105mm howitzer.

M55 8" Heavy Self-Propelled Howitzer 1952, same chassis and cab w/8" howitzer, resembled M53, 23' 5" (25' 11½") × 11' 1" × 11' 4½" to top of hull, 12' 2" overall.

M56 Gun Motor Carriage (90mm Self-Propelled Anti-Tank Gun), (Scorpion), see T101, 14′ 11½″ (20′ 2″) × 8′ 5½″ × 6′ 9″.

M56 Modified, 1958, 106mm recoilless rifle in place of 90mm gun.

M56 with M45 Quad 50 Mount, 1955, experimental w/four 50 cal mgs.

Scorpion Dart, basic chassis w/Dart missile.

Scorpion Mortar Carrier, 81mm or 4.2″ mortar or 106mm recoilless rifle.

Scorpion Personnel Carrier, covered, hull sloped in all around, centre cupolas, skirted.

M59 Armored Troop Carrier (T59) (Full Tracked Armored Personnel Carrier), 1955, larger but similar to M113 of which it was predecessor, trim vane on bow, 5 bogie wheels, 3 asymmetrically placed support rollers, small vision cupola centre right, remote-controlled 50 cal mg, 20 tons, 17′ 11″ × 10′ 8½″ × 8′ 2″.

M59A1, tank mg cupola on right, driver's cupola centre, some w/wide trim vane, some w/recoilless rifle added, 17′ 11″ × 10′ 8½″ × 9′ 7″.

M59 with Flat Track Suspension, 1958, 4 large bogie wheels, no support rollers.

XM60, M48 w/hemispherical turret, test model.

M60 Interim Tank, see M48A3, 22′ 9½″ (28′ 6½″) × 11′ 1½″ × 10′ 8″.

M60E1, new long nose turret w/British 105mm gun.

436

M60E2, driver and driver controls in turret, much larger and longer cupola on turret, left side remote-controlled 20mm gun, Shillelagh main armament.

437

M60A1 Full-Tracked 105mm Combat Tank, improved M60E1, turret w/large rear overhang and long

nose, stabilizer added in 1968, cutting bar from dozer blade tip frequently welded across front in Vietnam to cut brush, 22′ 9″ (30′ 6″) × 10′ 11″ × 10′ 6″.

M60A1E1 Full Tracked 152mm Combat Tank (M60A2) (M66), 1965, M60 chassis, Shillelagh in new turret w/low cupola each side, higher centre cupola, Zenon I/R light, 22′ 11½″ (24′) × 10′ 11″ × 10′ 8″.

M60A1E2 (M60A2), M60A1 chassis, stabilized Shillelagh gun-launcher and stabilized commander's position, higher version, 22′ 11″ (24′ ½″) × 10′ 11″ × 10′ 8″.

M60A2 Experimental, 1970, same vehicle w/remote-controlled 20mm gun mounted on right side of turret.

M60A1E3, 1969, M60A1E2 w/British 105mm gun because of problems w/Shillelagh.

M60A3, 3 phased modifications 1972–75 to existing M60A1s to include replaceable rubber-track pads, wider track, laser RF and solid state computer, tube over bar suspension w/rotary shock absorber, new 900 HP engine, thermal gun wrap, new 4 speed hydrostatic transmission w/new planetary final drive, and elimination of commander's cupola.

M60A1E4, 1970, depression limit bar across glacis, remote-controlled A/A mg right side of cupola, remote-controlled 20mm gun right side of turret, experimental prototype.

AVLB (Armoured Vehicle Launched Bridge), 60 foot scissors bridge on M60A1 tank chassis, 36′ 7″ × 13′ 2″ × 13′ 1″.

M66, see M60A1E1.

M67 Flame-thrower Tank, production T67, M48A1 w/F/T, 22′ 10½″ (27′) × 10′ 11″ × 10′ 1½″.

M67A1 Full-Tracked Flame-thrower Tank, 1961, M48A2 w/F/T substituted for 90mm gun, 50 cal tank cupola added, 22′ 6½″ (26′ 8½″) × 10′ 11″ × 10′ 10½″.

M67A2 Full-Tracked Flame-thrower Combat Tank, M48A3 tank converted to F/T, conversion involved reducing 5 support rollers to 3 but USMC conversion retained 5, 22′ 6½″ (26′ 9″) × 11′ 11″ × 10′ 3″.

M70, reserved for MBT70 German-American tank.

M74 Recovery Vehicle, 1952, see T74.

M75 Armored Infantry Vehicle (Full-Tracked Armored Personnel Carrier), see T18E1 modified, 17′ ½″ × 9′ 4″ × 9′ ½″ (10′ 8″ to top of cupola).

4.2″ Mortar Carrier T64, M75 chassis.

M84 Tracked 107mm Self-Propelled Mortar, 4.2″ mortar on M59 APC, 18′ 5″ × 10′ 8½″ × 7′ 10″.

M85 Cargo Carrier (T85), see XM274.

M88 Full-Tracked Medium Recovery Vehicle, see Medium Assault Vehicle T88, seen in Vietnam w/mg and shield, 27′ 1″ × 11′ 3″ × 9′ 7″ to top of cupola.

M88 (PI), 1972, product improved M88 w/new diesel engine and transmission and other improvements, similar to those made on M60A3 tank, later called M88E1.

M102 Armored Engineer Vehicle, see T39E2.

M103 Full-Tracked 120mm Combat Tank, see T43E1 Heavy Tank, 22′ 11″ (37′ 1½″) × 11′ 11″ × 10′ 6″.

M103A1 (T43E2), same w/improved fire control and turret basket.

M103A1E1 experimental M60 fire control and M60 engine and transmission.

438

M104 (XM104) (Scout 'n' Shoot), 1961, airborne 105mm howitzer carriage, rear mounted short howitzer, very small vehicle, 4 bogies, 2.5 tons, several variations, 1st test vehicle 12′ 9″ × 5′ 3″ × 5′ 4″; 2nd test vehicle 12′ 6″ × 5′ 9″ × 5′ 4″ w/o roll-over frames. production vehicles 9′ 11″ (13′ 4″) × 8′ 5″ × 5′ 10″.

M106 Tracked 107mm Self-Propelled Mortar (XM106), 4.2″ mortar on M113, large baseplate carried on left rear, 16′ 2″ × 9′ 5″ × 8′ 2½″ to top of mg.

M106A1, improved model, diesel engine.

M107 175mm Self-Propelled Field Artillery Gun, very long gun, see T235, late production gun tubes had a bell shaped muzzle, 18′ 2″ (41′ 10″) × 10′ 4″ × 9′ 2½″.

M107 (Mod) (M107E1), improved engine cooling, improved hydraulic and electrical lines, traverse, recoil spades and rammer-loader.

M108 Light Self-Propelled Howitzer, see T195E1, skirts later removed, same door changes as on M109, 20′ ½″ × 10′ 9½″ × 10′ 9″.

M109 Medium Self-Propelled Howitzer, 1962, see T196E1, first production had double rear doors, later single rear door, power shift transmission, 20′ ½″ (21′ 8″) × 12′ 1″ × 12′ 1½″.

M109E1 (M109A1), same w/new 8-foot longer gun, 20′ ½″ (29′ 8″) × 12′ 1″ × 12′ ½″.

M109G, same as M109 but horizontal sliding howitzer breech, made for Switzerland.

M110 8″ Heavy Self-Propelled Howitzer, 1961, see T236, 21′ (24′ 6½″), × 10′ 4″ × 9′ 8″.

M110 (Mod) (M110E1), same improvements as M107 (Mod).

M110E2, longer tube 8″ howitzer.

M113 Armored Infantry Vehicle (Full-Tracked Armored Personnel Carrier), see T113E2, amphibious, 15′ 11″ × 8′ 10″ × 7′ 2½″ (to top of cupola 8′ 2″).

M113E1, same w/GE gas turbine.

M113E2, same w/diesel engine.

M113A1, 1962, new diesel engine, increased radius of operation, numerous modifications in field in South Vietnam including additional weapon placement, belly armour, searchlights, etc., rounded commander's turret is US modification, as M113A2, M113A3 or ACAV (Armored Cavalry Assault Vehicle) w/angular welded turret is either early US or Vietnam field modification, vehicles seen in Vietnam w/conical turret mounted on riser and another w/57mm RR in place of forward turret, also w/forward mg w/shield and two armoured helicopter seats at top rear.

M113 with 20mm HS 820, German universal turret and radar w/Hispano Suiza 20mm gun.

M113 with Knapprich HS 30 Turret, experimental.

M113 with Weapons Ports (Porcupine), 1965, infantry school modifications, later production type w/gravity swinging covers and bullet-proof glass on sides and rear, see also XM734.

M113 with M61 Vulcan (20mm M61A1/M113A1), electrically operated Gatling gun centre mounted, see XM741, also later w/7.62mm Vulcan mini-gun, 15′ 11½″ × 8′ 9½″ × 8′ 8″.

M113A1/Vulcan A, 1965, weapon front mounted, probably M732.

M113A1/HS 820/665, triple Hispano Suiza gun, w/partial shield.

M113 with SS11, 1960, rear of hull built up slightly, projector rear top, according to German press another version in 1965 had missiles mounted right centre on a turn-table, see T149.

M113, w/XM175 high velocity grenade launcher in pot-belly open-top turret.

AN/MPS30 Ground Service Radar, utilizes T257E1 Mortar Carrier chassis.

T257 Mortar Carrier, M113 chassis.

T257 (M125) Mortar Carrier, improved.

T257E2 (M125A1), diesel engine.

▼ 439

TOW (Tube Launched Optically Tracked Wire Guided), supersonic missile rear-mounted on M113.

M113 With Scissors-type Bridge, front mounted bridge 33′ span.

M113 With Vehicle Launched Bridge, very light 30′ scissors bridge rear-mounted on modified chassis.

M113 With Recovery Kit, hydraulic crane left side, winch inside, bracing jack either side of rear, became XM806.

M113 With Waterjet Propulsion Kit, experimental development by Aerojet-General Corporation for US Limited Warfare Laboratory.

M113 Fitters Vehicle, ARV, 15′ 11½″ × 8′ 7½″ × 10′ 8″.

M113C+R Prototype, smaller version of M113, driver cupola left, remote controlled 20mm gun right, M114 commander's vision cupola centre w/conical dome cover, long glacis, 15′ 1″ × 7′ 11″ × 6′ 11″ to top of mg.

M113C+R, 1965, same as sold to the Netherlands, driver left front, radio operator and mg right front, commander's cupola and heavy mg centre middle.

M113C+R, 1969, same as sold to Canada, driver left, radio operator left centre, commander's cupola and heavy mg, centre right.

M113 with Dart (T149SP), 1957, Dart A/T missile.

M113 with Integrated Command Station (M113 with Stoner Turret)

(M113 Armored Assault Vehicle), 1966, 25mm in completely enclosed one-man cupola w/panoramic vision.

M113 with Bulldozer Kit, light dozer w/double hydraulic controls.

M113/Grasshopper, 1972, test rig for releasing self-imbedding anti-vehicle mines which have sensors that distinguish vehicle types, experimental.

M113A1–P1, product improved, similar to XM765.

M113 (A1FV) (20mm), similar but only 2 ports, also w/25mm gun, 17′ 7″ × 8′ 10″ × 8′ 9″.

M113 A/A, modified to mount twin 40mm mount from M42, 18′ 10″ × 8′ 10″ × 10′ 1″.

Land Sparrow, Raytheon A/A missile system w/separate fire-control vehicle.

M114 Reconnaissance Vehicle Prototype, 1961, similar to M113 but long glacis, flared front conical rear turret later changed to flat dome w/mg, 4 bogie wheels, no support rollers, amphibious, first few vehicles had almost symmetrical hulls raised in the centre and large square door in rear.

M114 Armored Command and Reconnaissance Carrier, 1962, modified turret forming vision cupola w/split hatch covers, round rear exit door, 14′ 8″ × 7′ 8″ × 7′ 1″.

M114A1 Full-Tracked Carrier Command and Reconnaissance Vehicle (M114A1 C+R), side skirts eliminated, 14′ 8″ × 7′ 8″ × 7′ 1″.

M114A1/HS 820 (M114A2), 1956, 20mm gun in modified cupola.

M114 with Keller Turret, 1963, remote-controlled 20mm gun on right top.

M114 with HS 820 (M114A1E1) (Carrier C+R M114A1 with 20mm Gun HS 820), 1965.

M114A1 with TRW 25mm Cannon (M114 with Stoner Turret), centre mounted rear pivoted long gun.

M114A1, 1968 version w/sloping sides and swinging loop-hole covers, remote-controlled HS120 gun.

M114A1E1, M114A1 w/remote-controlled 20 mm gun.

M114A1 (PI), 1973, product improved w/new engine and transmission, front sprockets moved forward, new torsion bars and shock absorber, 8 pilots built.

M116, same as M113 but steel instead of aluminium armour.

M116, w/Davy Crockett.

M125 Full-Tracked Self-Propelled 81mm mortar, see T257E2.

M125A1, improved, w/diesel engine, 15' 11½" × 8' 10" × 6'.

M132 Flame-thrower Vehicle, M113 w/F/T and mg in special dome turret in centre front of vehicle, w/and w/o skirts, minigun sometimes added in Vietnam, 15' 11½" × 8' 9½" × 7' 11½".

M132A1, same on M113A1 chassis, 15' 11½" × 8' 10" × 6'.

XM138, unarmoured 155mm howitzer on M109 chassis.

M162, see M113A1/HS820/665.

M163, M113 w/Vulcan gun.

XM166, M42 mount on XM548 cargo carrier chassis.

XM179, 155mm howitzer on armoured M110 chassis.

XM274 Cargo Carrier (T85) (M85), M41 Light tank chassis, resembled Cargo Carrier T44, 5 bogie wheels, 3 asymmetrically placed support rollers.

XM474, hybrid radar carrier on M113 chassis, open box w/folding radar screen, 18' ½" × 8' 4" × 4' 11".

XM474E1 and E2 Guided Missile Support Carrier (Pershing) missile carriers used in conjunction w/supplementary vehicles, 18' ½" × 8' 4" × 6' 1".

XM501 E1, E2 and E3, guided missile loader-transporter for Hawk missiles.

XM546 (Mauler), 12 round missile launcher and radar screen in folding assembly on modified XM551, 20' 8" × 9' 2" × 9' (w/radar folded).

XM546E1 Full-Tracked Armored Guided Missile Equipment Carrier, improved.

XM548 and XM548E1, unarmoured cargo carrier w/twin HS820 centre mounted guns, ammunition carrier w/hoist, same chassis also as light unarmoured recovery vehicle w/mg and shield on ring mount in Vietnam, basically M113 w/o armour, 19' 4" × 8' 9½" × 6' 2" w/o cab, 8' 9" w/cab.

M548 With Welder Kit, field fix for use in Vietnam.

AN/MPQ-4A, radar on M548.

XM549, armoured Gama Goat.

Sam-D, rear mounted 6 rocket projector on MS48 chassis, several team vehicles include radar vehicle.

XM551 Armored Airborne Reconnaissance Vehicle (AR/AAV) (Airborne Assault Vehicle) (Sheridan) (M551), 1962,

squat turret resembling that on M41 with Shillelagh, stabilizer, aluminium hull, driver has centre rotating cowl, rear square and overhung, trim vane and buoyant bogie wheels later eliminated and all around screen of DD type provided 5 bogie wheels, no support rollers, hydrojet propulsion in water, 16½ tons, seen in Vietnam w/mg and shield atop turret and belly armour added, xenon light added in Vietnam, 20' 8" × 9' 2" × 9' 8" to top of mg.

M551 Medium AVLB, experimental 60' bridging device, project only, 33' 11" × 11' 2" × 11' 1".

M551 Armored Engineer Vehicle, project only, 29' 2" × 9' 2" × 8' 4" to top of cupola.

M551 w/Laser Range-finder, high cupola w/RF and heavy mg mounted above it.

M551 w/XM103E7 105mm, gun w/concentric recoil mechanism.

M551 w/76mm gun, gun as on M41 Light tank.

Light Weight Interim MBT, battle tank based on XM551, project only, 21' × 9' 2" × 8'.

155mm Self-Propelled Mount, based on M551, project only, 21' × 9' 2" × 6' 9".

Recovery Vehicle (M551 Basis), project only 21' 8" × 9' 2" × 9' 7" to top of cupola.

M551 plans contemplated accompanying vehicles of the following types, all of which remained projects only: Mauler; MICV65, bevel-sided hull, remote-controlled 20mm; forward area air defence vehicle, 20mm weapons system, similar in appearance to M551 but Vulcan gun; A/A Rapid Fire 30mm Weapons System, same chassis as above but twin 30mm in Oerlikon-

type turret; airborne crane, resembled T119; combat engineer vehicle, dozer blade, modified turret w/hinged extendible crane; 155mm SP, rear mounted gun, crew of 4 carried along left side of hull, large trail spade; and cargo carrier.

XM571 Articulated Cargo Carrier (Gama Goat), unarmoured.

XM571E1 Articulated Armored Utility Carrier, 1 mg, hinged side armour on Gama Goat.

XM577 Light Tracked Command Post Carrier, 1962, M113 basic chassis w/raised roof, box superstructure in rear, seen in Vietnam w/mg and shield roof mounted.

XM577A1 (M577A1), same w/diesel engine, 15' 11½" × 8' 10" × 8' 1" to top of hull.

M578 Full Tracked Light Armored Recovery Vehicle, production version of T120E1, same chassis as M107 SP, 19' 5½" (21' 1") × 10' 4" × 9' 10".

XM579 Fitters vehicle, ARV, 15' 11½" × 8' 7" × 10' 8".

M667 (Missile B) (Lance) (Tactically Loaded Guided Missile Equipment Launcher-Transporter), 1964, modified XM548E1 Cargo Carrier chassis, 21' 6½" × 8' 9½" × 6' 6" w/o cab 8' 8" w/cab, see also XM752.

XM667E1, amphibious capability added, 21' 4" × 8' 10" × 8' 7".

XM688 and XM688E1, 1967, loader transporter for Lance missile.

XM696 Light Unarmored Full Tracked Recovery Vehicle, XM548 chassis, hydraulic jackknife crane in left centre, 21' 11" × 9' × 9' 6".

▼ 444

XM701 Personnel Carrier
(MICV–65), 1965, large carrier,
4 bogie wheels, trailing idler,
faceted hull, sloped-in sides,
undercut rear, squat centre turret
w/20mm gun and mg, long glacis,
components from M107, M110 and
M578, variations between prototypes in bow configuration and bow
scuppers or skirts, differing
prototypes 19′ 4″ to 20′ 5″ ×
9′ 2″ to 10′ 4″ × 9′ 4″.

XM713 MICV, 1973, experimental
FMC vehicle.

XM723 (MICV–70) (Austere MICV,
mechanized infantry combat
vehicle).

**XM727 Guided Missile Equipment
Carrier** (Self-Propelled Hawk),
Triple Hawk missile projector on
XM548 chassis.

**XM728 Full Tracked 165mm Gun
Combat Engineer Vehicle** (CEV),
production vehicle of T118E2 on
M60A1 Medium tank chassis,
28′ 4″ × 12′ 2″ × 10′ 6″.

▼ 445

**XM729 Full Tracked Lightweight
Airborne Counterinsurgency
Combat Vehicle** (Assault Vehicle),
modified M116 APC w/small dome
vision cupola w/1 mg and 40mm
automatic grenade launcher, 16′ 4″
× 6′ 6½″ × 6′ 5″.

**XM729E1 Remote Area Counter-
insurgency Vehicle,** based on light
tank concept, GE power train as in
M113E1, cupola eliminated,
six firing ports similar to XM701,
w/M551 suspension, broad wheels
w/centre space, squat turret, 20 or
30mm and 1mg, 24′ 2″ × 10′ 4″
× 9′ 1″.

**M730 Self-Propelled Guided Missile
Equipment Carrier** (Chaparral), 4
Sidewinder Heat-Seeking missiles
on hydraulic launcher, modified
M548 chassis.

M732, see M113A1/Vulcan A.

**XM733 Remote Area Counter-
insurgency Vehicle,** 1966, modified
M116 APC w/added armour,
81mm mortar and 3 mgs.

XM733E1, same w/small gunner's
cupola w/1 mg and 40mm grenade
launcher.

▼ 446

**XM734 Full Tracked Armoured
Fighting Vehicle** (MICV), M113A1
w/relocated fuel tanks, 4 firing
ports in hull upper, 2 in rear, and
cupola w/twin mg, upper portion of
hull containing ports.

**XM741 Carrier With M163 20mm
Gun System,** hull sides and bow
vane filled w/expanded polystyrene
for flotation.

XM742, ARV version of XM803,
project only.

XM743 AVLB version of XM803,
project only.

XM745, Combat Engineer Vehicle
version of XM803, project only.

XM752, improved XM688.

XM754 Self-Propelled Launcher,
Hawk missile launcher on M113
type chassis, see XM727.

XM759 Marginal Terrain Vehicle,
unarmoured vehicle using air-roll
principle and resembling Japanese
swamp crossing vehicle of WWII.

XM759E1, same w/GE power train.

XM765 (MICV), similar to M113 (PI),
w/remote 50 cal gun, upper portion
of hull bevelled w/10 ports, trim
vane of trapezoidal cross section,
steel appliqué added to front and
sides, a Food Machinery Company
further variation exists w/5 ports
called Product Improved M113A1
or M113 (A1), see M113 (PI),
20′ 5″ × 10′ 4″ × 8′ 4″.

**XM800 Armored Reconnaissance
Scout Vehicle** (ARSV), 1970
project, FMC version hull
resembled British Scorpion, turret
resembled British Fox, 4 road
wheels, prototypes both wheeled
and tracked types.

MBT70, 1967, test rigs of several
conformations, 6 bogies and
trailing idler, controllable
suspension, very low hull, wide
tracks, very large turret ring but
no turret, raised engine compartment, 25′ × 11′ 6″ × 6′ 6″
to 7′ 6″.

MBT70, 1967, prototype w/turret
mounting Shillelagh, 25′ × 11′ 6″
× 6′ 6″ to 7′ 6″.

XM803, Austere MBT70 w/Con-
tinental engine HP reduced to 1250
and variable suspension system
simplified, 50 cal mg substituted
for 20mm gun and relocated to top
of commonder's periscope, ballistic
skirts added.

**XM806 Light Armored Full
Tracked Recovery Vehicle,** see
M113 w/recovery kit.

XM806A1, production version
w/diesel engine.

XM815, designation assigned in 1972
for new MBT planned to be in
volume production by 1980,
changed later to XM1.

LVT AND RELATED VEHICLES

Alligator Navy Model (Amphibious
Tractor T33), 1940 outgrowth of
Roebling 1935 and subsequent
experimental commercial
amphibians, 3 scuppers fore and
aft, 2 centre scuppers in track
frame, curved front cab,
unarmoured, 20′ × 9′ 10″ × 8′.

FMC Experimental LVT (Landing
Vehicle Tracked), similar but low
flat cabin extending from bow to
amidships, forerunner of LVT2,
unarmoured.

▼ 447

Borg–Warner 'A' Vehicle, 1942,
design not adopted but led to
LVT3, Light tank turret w/37mm,
2 bow mgs, 11 tons, also M3 w/o
superstructure or turret, horizontally
fluted duralumin track frames,
later flat metal, 5 rhomboid shaped
track frame openings, rear ramp,
unarmoured except for turret, 23′
× 11′ × 8′ 11″.

Borg–Warner 15T Carrier (Rex II),
resembled LVT1) but M18
suspension w/extra wide scoop
tracks, carried 50 men plus crew.

LVT1, 1941, 8.75 tons, sharp glacis,
faceted front cab, unarmoured,
production models by various
manufacturers showed variations,
21′ 6″ × 9′ 10″ × 8′ 1½″.

LVT2 (LVT Mark II) (Water
Buffalo), (Amphibious Tractor T34),
individual variations, lower cab,
2 visible support rollers, 12 tons,
some vehicles w/curved shields,
Continental engine, 26′ 2″ × 10′ 8″
× 8′ 2½″.

Beachmaster, resembled LVT1 with two dual hollow wheels each side for propulsion in water.

LVT–R, recovery vehicle on LVT2, A–frame mounted at rear.

LVT3 (Bushmaster), 1943, similar to LVT–2 but Cadillac engines and twin hydramatic transmissions, 19 tons, armour could be bolted on.

LVT3 Light Weight, stripped-down version, experimental, 24' 2″ × 11' 4″ × 8' 6½″.

T11, 1942, LVT3 w/Borg-Warner undercarriage, rear mg in bevel front box shield.

CA&E Light Weight, similar to T11, 27' 9″ × 10' 8″ × 8' 4″.

LVT3 Universal Carrier, 1947, prototype for LVT3C, covered hull, louvers in upper hull, underwent several modifications, some in stripped-down version.

LVT3C, 1950, covered over LVT3, vision cupola added, armour attachable, 19 tons, some later w/small mg turret in place of cupola, 25' 1½″ × 11' 2½″ × 10' 1½″.

LVT4, similar to LVT3 but w/rear ramp, various versions, some w/small partial mg cupolas in front, some modified to carry 105mm howitzer field carriage, square bevel bow, some w/lower portion of track frame removed and called LVT4 Light Weight, 26' 2″ × 10' 8″ × 8' 2½″.

LVT4 Rocket Carrier, 7.2″ T54 rocket projector, mounted amidships.

LVTZ, LVT earlier models used as cargo carriers only.

LVT(A)1, built-up armoured superstructure, long glacis, 37mm gun in welded slope sided turret w/bustle, later w/M3 Light tank turret, mg w/shield on either side behind turret, 19 tons, 26' 1″ × 10' 8″ × 8' 1″.

LVT(A)1 w/M24 Light Tank Turret, 21 tons, 26' × 10' 10½″ × 11' 3½″.

LVT(A)2 (LVT Armoured Vehicle Mark II), army specifications, similar to LVT2 but armoured, some w/improvised mg half turrets, some w/bevel-front box shields.

LVT(A)4, LVT(A)1 w/M8 Howitzer Motor Carriage turret, some w/supplementary mg mounts, some w/cylindrical cupola and 50 cal mg w/shield, 26' 2″ × 10' 8″ × 10' 2½″.

LVT(A)4 Modified, long glacis w/rounded nose, later supplementary armoured box cupola added to top of turret.

LVT(A)5, LVT(A)4 w/stabilizer and power turret, 40 tons, mg in flat front superstructure.

LVT(A)5 Modified, 1951, higher boat type hull, rounded barge bow, new tracks, 8 bogie wheels, LVT(A)5 turret, bow mg, 20 tons.

LVT Carpet Layer, LVT(A)2 w/side girders supporting extension of heavy planks strung together and carried on rails as a bridge to be dropped at one end and backed away from, paying out carpet.

LVT Prototype A Gun Carrier, 1950, boat hull similar to LVT(A)5 modified 1951, M18 Gun Motor Carriage turret w/105mm howitzer, 9 bogie wheels exposed, otherwise skirted, 37.5 tons, 27' 2″ (31' 6″) × 11' 1″ × 9' 7″.

LVT B15T, large cargo carrier, 25' × 11' 4″ × 9'.

Machine Shop LVT, repair vehicle.

PX–3 (Beulah), 1950, M59 APC type chassis, sloped-in hull, corner peepslots, rear side peepslots, 6 bogie wheels partly skirted, boat-like bow, 30' × 10' 11″ × 10' 2½″.

LVTPX–1, 1952, 'Wooden Shoe' bow, high sides, covered top, 2 small square side cupolas, 2 centre front vision cupolas, 7 bogie wheels partly skirted, hollow grouser tracks, 30 tons, 29' 2″ × 11' 6″ × 8' 3″.

LVT(P)5 Tracked Personnel Landing Vehicle (Model 5 Armored Amphibian Assault Personnel and Cargo Carrier), 1951, 40 tons, large rectangular box hull w/rounded edges, front ramp, 9 bogie wheels, later w/dome mg cupola, individual manufacturer differences, 29' 8″ × 11' 8½″ × 10' ½″ to top of cupola.

LVT(H)6, 1951 (LVTX–4) (LVT(A)6), similar to LVT(P)5 but w/squat slope sided turret w/bustle, 105mm howitzer, 29' 8″ × 11' 8½″ × 11' 11″.

LVT(H)6A1, M18 Gun Motor Carriage turret substituted, 43.3 tons, 29' 8″ × 11' 8½″ × 10' 3″.

LVTAA–XI (Twin Forty), similar, with M19 Gun Motor Carriage twin Bofors turret, 42.9 tons, 29' 8″ × 11' 8½″ × 11' 3″.

LVT–CRX–1, command vehicle, LVT(P)5 w/radio, desks, etc., 36 tons, 29' 8″ × 11' 8½″ × 8' 7½″.

LVT(P)5 (CMD), same as command vehicle, 36 tons.

LVT(P)5A1 Tracked Command Landing Vehicle, minor changes including small square cupola at rear, 40.75 tons.

LVT(P)6, similar to LVT(P)5 but 8 bogie wheels instead of 9, 20' 4″ × 10' 9″ × 8' 6″.

LVTRX–1 (Retriever), 1954, crane and A–frame on kingpin support on LVT(P)5, recovery vehicle.

LVTR–1, 1954, improved w/collapsible crane and kingpin, 41 tons, 31' 9″ × 11' 8½″ × 10' 9″ plus boom.

LVT R1A1, improved version.

LVT(P)5 Bulldozer, dozer could be dropped by means of explosive pins.

LVT EX–1 (Engineer Vehicle) (Amphibious Potato Digger), 1955, mine rake on LVT(P)5, 47 tons, 39' 7" × 15' 2" × 9' 1".

LVT E–1, 1959, combination mine rake and snake on late LVT(P)5, line charge discharger on roof, 47 tons, 39' 9" × 12' 8½" × 10' 8½".

LVT(PX)2, (LVT(P)6), 1952, many T59E1 APC components, resembled M59, small mg dome cupola right front, vision cupola left front, later w/V-nose, 21' 8" × 10' 8" × 8'.

▼ 454

LVT(HX)4, 1953, LVT(PX)2 chassis w/octagonal slope sided turret w/bustle, 105mm howitzer, 20.5 tons, 21' 8" × 10' 8" × 10' 8½".

LVT(HX)4 Modified, M19 twin Bofors turret substituted.

LVT AAX–2, same w/M42 Gun Motor Carriage A/A turret.

LVTUX–1 (Lightweight Barge Type Carrier), 1951, low flat LVT, leading idler and 10 bogie wheels, light cab forward, not armed, high box ramp w/jet nozzle, 27 tons, 36' 2" × 12' 2" × 8' 7" w/ramp extended.

LVT UX–2 (Goliath), 1957, 88 tons, 8 bogie wheels, round bow ramp, raised bow, 2 small vision cupolas forward, 2 pivoted retractable screws rear, double tracks, 44' 6" × 21' × 13' 6".

LCA (Landing Craft Assault), 1962, 7 bogie wheels, large catamaran hull overhanging front and rear, cab and ramp front, hinged retractable screws rear, 56' 9" × 21' × 14' 2".

LVTPX–10, modified LVT(P)5 w/indented bow ramp, tubular snorkels on rear deck, 29' 8" × 11' 8" × 8' 7½"

LVTPX–11, to replace LVT(P)5.

LVTPX–12, 1966, 6 bogie wheels, hull like MICV–65 (XM701), snub nose, gable type cupola w/20mm or 30mm gun and mg on right front, similar driver cupola on left front, twin hydrojets, 24 tons, 26' × 10' 6" × 10' 4".

LVTP–7 (Super Hog), 1970, production version of LVTPX–12, 50 cal mg substituted, ducted screws w/thrust deflectors.

LVTCX–7, 1971, command version.

LVTRX–7, ARV version.

LVTEX–7, engineering vehicle version.

▼ 455

76mm Gun Motor Carriage LVT(Aluminium Hull), 8 bogie wheels, partial skirting, 2 screws in high boxes at rear of tracks, M18 Gun Motor Carriage turret w/76mm gun, sloped-in super-structure, curved and straight glacis.

E14–7R2 LVT(A)1, 1944, F/T mounted in place of 37mm gun.

E7–LVT4 (Navy Mark I F/T), 1944, open LVT, F/T w/small square shield in centre front.

E7–LVT(A)4 (E14–7R2), Ronson F/T in turret in place of 75mm howitzer.

LVT–1 with T45 rocket launcher, twin 10 rocket launchers at rear.

LVT(A)2 (Landing Support), Corps of Engineers vehicle, two 3-row 4.5" rocket launchers centre, three 50 cal mg front and front sides, 20mm gun rear.

▼ 456

LVT(A)5 with T45 rocket launcher, rear mounted, remote controlled.

LVT(A)4 with T54 rocket launcher, 20 square tubes 7.2" launcher in solid frame mounted in centre, side armour built up to support and protect mechanism.

LVT3 with T89 rocket launcher, 10 tube 7.2" box launcher, similar to above.

LVT(A)4 with T90 rocket launcher, similar.

LVT Special Portable Ramp, 1944, ARK type bridge-layer, designed for access to coral cliffs on Tinian beach.

Salamander, amphibious demolition vehicle, 26' × 11' × 3'.

WADING AND FLOTATION DEVICES

Various wading devices were used during and after World War II. They included:
  Rectangular metal box stacks;
  Similar stacks with curved-over tops;
  Oil drums with or without pipe snorkels;
  Curved pipe snorkels;
  High cylindrical commander's snorkel and pipe stacks;
  Flotation devices including British designed and American built D.D. tanks;
as well as:
  Collapsible swimming floats;
  Flotation air bags, one of which was the T12 Flotation Device;
  Borg Device, large front and rear floats;
  ♯4 Device, very large sectional front and rear floats;
  Ritchie T6 (B B Device), 12 welded steel tanks attached all around by pins detached by explosive charges;
  Ritchie T7 (M18), front and rear floats;
  M19 Swimming Device, similar, improved;
  M20 Swimming Device, streamlined front and rear floats (with M24 Light tank, 41' 6" × 9' 10" × 8' 1½");
  T26 Device, details unknown.

▼ 457

T28 Swimming Device, low all around rounded boat hull;

Hall Device, collapsible side pontoons inflated by tank engine exhaust gas, screws driven off rear idler;

Engineer Pontoon Device, two pontoons w/outboard motors;

Yagow Device, like D.D.

Blankenship Device, detachable inflatable bags;

T15 Device, huge barge-like all around wooden frame, 2 screws and rudders;

Chrysler Armored Marsh Screw Amphibian, 1966, double Archimedes screw-propelled, operates in water, muck or snow;

RUC (River Utility Craft), 1970, larger Navy version w/hull resembling modern German APC, 20' 2" × 14' × 11' 6".

MISCELLANEOUS VEHICLES 1920 TO PRESENT

Jagger Sea Turtle, 1927, track-laying amphibious torpedo, project only.

Mortar Carriage T4, pre-World War II designation applied to 81mm mortar on any full track-layer.

Track Development Chassis T1 (Cunningham One-Man Tank) (G2T–1), 1928, box hull w/small cupola, Ford engine front, sloping glacis, 2 large wheels w/simulated spokes w/short pitch track, 1 mg, 8′ 7″ × 4′ 9″ × 5′ 1½″.

Track Development Chassis T2 (Cunningham Carrier), (G3T–1), flat top, engine front, raised cab rear w/small half pyramidal driver's cowl centre, heavy track frame, 2 leaf spring bogie pairs, 2 support rollers, no armament, 5 tons, 9′ 10″ × 6′ 1″ × 4′ 6½″.

75mm Howitzer Motor Carriage T1, 1931, 75mm pack howitzer on Track Development Chassis T2, 6 tons, 10′ 9″ × 6′ 1″ × 6′ 3″.

E-1 Flame Tank, 1939, Cunningham T2 w/front built up, 2 fuel tanks on rear deck, nitrogen tanks over tracks.

Baker Tank, 1942, NDRC designed 4 wheel vehicle w/the ability to jump obstacles of 47 foot breadth at 40 mph, intended as a tank destroyer, 5 tons, same name applied also to an 8 × 8 vehicle weighing twice as much, portion of suspension only completed.

Turtle Series, 1942, a generic name applied to the above as well as to medium and heavy track-laying vehicles designed by NDRC.

Turtle IVI-C, 33 tons, conventional in appearance, crew of 4, various armament combinations in centre dome-shaped turret, one 75mm gun, two 37mm guns or four 50 cal mg plus 2 driver's mgs and 2 commander's mgs, armour cast in units, 8 bogie wheels, skirted suspension, mock-ups only, 18′ 7″ × 9′ 1″ × 7′.

Turtle IVI-D, similar but guns mounted in turret top and gunner moving in elevation and azimuth with it, mock-up only.

Turtle IVI-AA, same basic chassis but squat driver and commander turret in front, one cast pyramidal turret centre, 1 rear each w/octuple pom-pom, mock-up only.

T1 Gun Motor Carriage (M5), 1941, 3″ A/A M6 w/large shield on Cletrac MG-2 Tractor, 4 bogie wheels, 2 support rollers, trailing idler, rubber track, trail spade, large travel lock, 15′ 1″ × 8′ 3″ × 6′ 2″.

T9 Howitzer Motor Carriage, 1942, 105mm howitzer on Cletrac MG-2 chassis, not completed.

T2 Heavy Tractor, 1941, resembled M10 w/o turret, early HVSS w/3 two-wheel bogies, 18′ 10½″ × 8′ 2″ × 7′.

T14 Cargo Carrier, 19′ 10½″ × 8′ 10″ × 9′ 11″.

T16 Universal Carrier, see Great Britain, Carriers.

T16E1 Universal Carrier, same.

Christie Airborne Tank, design study in competition w/T9 Light tank, small German StuG type w/37mm gun, 5 small bogie wheels, long coil springs, 2 upper track rollers.

Airborne tank, GM design study in competition w/T9 Light tank, no details available.

Armored Tractor T2, 1942, 3 volute spring bogie wheel pairs on skeleton frames, support rollers on same brackets, sloped-in cargo body over tracks, cab front, louvers in glacis.

Armored Cabs M1–M7, several varieties of slip-over armour to protect bulldozer vehicles and operators, various sizes for commercial dozers.

Bulldozers, various designs fitted to Light and Medium tanks w/ and w/o turrets, and to other vehicles.

UET (Universal Engineering Tractor), 3 bogie wheels and trailing idler w/dozer and earthmover device, also used as troop carrier, 20′ 6″ × 7′ 10″ dozer wings folded, 10′ 6″ w/dozer wings extended × 7′ 10″.

Mine Exploder T13 (Beezie) (Beetle) Cargo Carrier T15 armoured w/high rear cab, pushing Centipede 2 leading, 3 following, A/M rollers on outriggers.

T46 Amphibious Carrier (Other) with Quad 50 cal mount, 1950, experimental A/A mount improved at Fort Bliss.

A6E1 (M76), improved cargo carrier.

Thiokol Swamp Spryte, 1969, thin armour shell over M76 chassis, mg right front, XM175 high velocity automatic grenade launcher mounted behind forward cab.

ABC (All Purpose Ballastable Crawler), 1959, M113 type chassis with dozer for dropping ballast.

Atomic Powered Tank, M107 suspension, cast egg-shaped bow w/2 mg cupolas, T95 turret w/mg cupola on high, narrow cast hull.

Millman/Convair Steam Tank, 1964, commercial proposal by General Dynamics Corporation, 3′ scale model demonstrated and rejected.

MACV, see XM800.

MICV70, projected APC to replace M113, same as XM723.

115mm SP, composite NATO project.

Air Cushion Vehicle (ACV), experimental unarmoured air cushion vehicle mounting several

mgs, 3 types of such vehicles were purchased in 1968, all called SK5, 2 were called AACV or Assault Air Cushion Vehicles armed with 2 light and 1 heavy mg and one grenade launcher, the third, a TACV, or Transport Air Cushion Vehicle was similarly armed but also would accommodate 12 or more combat ready troops, 38′ 10″ × 23′ 9″ × 15′ 11″.

Transphibian (The Monster) (Tree Eater), huge tricycle for crushing vegetation in Vietnam.

Rome Plow, large semi-armoured bulldozer w/C-shaped dozer blade and tree splitting spike.

Viking Sweeper, experimental field fix in Vietnam, rectangular steel frame set on 96 fifty pound steel wheels attached 17 feet in front of dozer blade mounted on semi-armoured 290M tractor.

Scorpion/Continental-Teledyne, 1971, British Scorpion Reconnaissance Tank w/Continental diesel engine, automatic transmission and new turret for Bushmaster gun.

Railroad Track Destroyer, pilot vehicle, M48 chassis w/hull removed and device for picking up and breaking ties and rails installed.

Railroad Track Destroyer, improved model on M103 chassis, sloping covered superstructure for picking up rails and ties, notching the rails w/50 cal, AP bullets and breaking rails into segments and ties into pieces by forcing ties across and rails around round bending blocks.

YUGOSLAVIA

Yugoslavian tank units were organized around a heterogeneous collection of armour, mostly French, in the period after World War I when the country came into existence. Czech turretless tankettes were purchased, and a few units had received them before Germany overran Yugoslavia in 1941.

After guerrilla troops were organized they formed several small armour units, some of which were trained by the British in North Africa. Later, others were organised in Italy and equipped with American Light tanks, a number of which they subsequently modified into self-propelled guns.

After World War II, Yugoslavia was equipped with Russian vehicles and also produced the Russian T34 locally but with a dome turret similar to the one on the Russian Stalin tank. Yugoslavia later received a considerable amount of American armour. Still more recently, armoured personnel carriers of Yugoslav design have been manufactured there.

458
T34, Russian T34 w/front corners of hull bevelled and Yugoslav dome-type turret resembling that on Stalin III but w/bustle and partly outset cupola at left rear, 100mm

gun, experimental, only a few modified.

459
(- - - - -), 1945, American M3A3 Light tank chassis, turret removed,

Russian 76.2mm gun and shield from German SdKfz139 mounted in place of original turret.

M–590 (M65), 1965, APC resembling American M113, two-angled glacis w/square doors and flush cupolas, 5 smoke mortars each side of hull at rear, front corners and top sides of hull bevelled, 20mm gun remote-controlled right front.

T32SId, Czech designed and possibly built in Czechoslovakia, 47mm gun and 1 mg in box hull w/large low cupola, LT35 (S2a) suspension.

(- - - - -), 1973, scissors-type bridge-layer.

Bibliography

AFV (series), re-titled 'AFV/Weapons' from No. 18, Various authors, Edited by Duncan Crow, Profile Publications Ltd., Windsor, 1969–1975.

AFV Data Book, R. P. Hunnicutt, Privately published, San Mateo, 1965.

AFV Recognition, Parts I–II, The War Office, London, 1942–1943.

AFV Recognition, Parts 1 and 2, USAAF, Washington, 1944.

Airmen or Noahs, Rear Admiral Murray F. Sueter, Sir Isaac Pitman & Sons, Ltd., London, 1928.

An Album of the Armored Forces, Israeli Armoured Force, Tel Aviv, 1966.

Alternate Automobile Power Systems, Alexander Bloch, Automotive Industries, Philadelphia, 1968.

American Tanks and Tank Destroyers, Elizabeth Mallett Conger, Henry Holt and Company, New York, 1944.

American AFVS of World War II— And After, Edited by Duncan Crow, Profile Publications Ltd., Windsor, 1972.

Amphibian Vehicles, FMFM 9–2, U.S. Marine Corps, U.S. Government Printing Office, Washington, 1964.

Anti-Tank Tactics, The War Office, London, 1953.

Anzio After Battle Report, Armored School Library, Fort Knox.

L'Arme Blindée Dans La Guerre, General J. Boucher, Payot, Paris, 1953.

L'Armement de la France 1936– 1939, Robert Jacomet, Les Editions Lajeunnesse, Paris, 1945.

Armored Vehicles From Their Conception to the Present Times, George Bradford, The Miniature AFV Collectors Association, Preston, Ontario.

Armor on the Eastern Front, Uwe Feist and W. J. Spielberger, Aero Publishing Co., Fallbrook, California, 1968.

Armor in the Western Desert, Uwe Feist and W. J. Spielberger, Aero Publishing Co., Fallbrook, California, 1968.

Armour, Richard M. Ogorkiewicz, Stevens & Sons Ltd., London, 1960.

Armoured Crusader: Major General Sir Percy Hobart, Major Kenneth Macksey, Hutchinson, London, 1967.

Armoured Fighting Vehicles, Vickers-Armstrongs Ltd., London, 1945.

Armoured Fighting Vehicles of World War One, Edited by Duncan Crow, Profile Publications Ltd., Windsor, 1970.

Armoured Vehicles and Armour, R. M. Ogorkiewicz, U.S. Army Research Office (Durham), 1961.

Army Historical Series, Stalingrad to Berlin: The German Defeat in the East, Earl F. Ziemke, U.S. Government Printing Office, 1968.

L'Artillerie D'Assaut de 1916 a 1918, Lt. Col. Lafitte, Librairie Charles-Lavauzelle, Paris, 1919.

The Assault on Pelelieu, Major Frank D. Hough, USMC Historical Division, U.S. Marine Corps, Washington, 1950.

Atomic Weapons in Land Combat, Colonel G. C. Reinhardt and Lt. Col. W. R. Kintner, Military Service Publishing Co., Harrisburg, 1954.

Automobile Steam Engines and Other External Combustion Engines, Committee on Commerce and Public Works, 90th Congress, 2nd Session, Government Printing Office, Washington, 1968.

Automotive Historical Records, Vols. I–IV, Aberdeen Proving Ground, 1944.

The Black Beret, Charles Graves, Hutchinson & Co., Ltd., London.

Bellona Military Vehicle Prints (Series) Various authors, Bellona Publications Ltd., Bracknell, 1964 onwards.

Bericht: Erfahrungen Mit Panzerwagen, Major Bornschlegel,

German General Staff, 1921, Translated by Ray M. Weiss and Captain Robert J. Icks, 1935.

Biennial Report of Chief of Staff 1943–1945 to the Secretary of War, United States News, Washington, 1945.

Os Blindado Attraves Dos Seculos, Coronel J. V. Portella F. Alves, Biblioteca do Exercito-Editoro, Rio de Janeiro, 1964.

Blitzkrieg, Major F. O. Miksche, Faber and Faber Ltd., London, 1941.

Blitzkrieg: Armies on Wheels, Brigadier General S. L. A. Marshall, The Infantry Journal, Washington, 1943.

Bofors, A.–B. Bofors, Bofors, 1958.

The Boiler Plate War, John Foley, Walker and Company, New York, 1963.

Brazen Chariots, Major Robert Crisp, Ballantine Books, New York, 1961.

A Brief History of the Royal Tank Corps, F. E. Woolnough, Gale & Polden, Aldershot, 1923.

British AFV's, Official Album File 54/1/1617, The War Office, London, 1944.

British and American Tanks of World War II, Chris Ellis and Peter Chamberlain, Arms & Armour Press, London, 1969.

British and Commonwealth AFVs, 1940–46, Edited by Duncan Crow, Profile Publications Ltd., Windsor, 1971.

British and Commonwealth Armoured Formations 1919–1946, Duncan Crow, Profile Publications Ltd., Windsor, 1972.

British Armoured Fighting Vehicles 1919–40, Edited by Duncan Crow, Profile Publications Ltd., Windsor, 1970.

British Army Vehicles and Equipment Parts I–II, R. E. Smith, Ian Allan, Shepperton, 1964.

British Military Vehicles, FVRDE, Chertsey, 1954–1966.

British Tanks and Fighting Vehicles 1914–1945. B. T. White, Ian

Allan Ltd., London, 1970.

Canada's Soldiers 1604–1954, George F. G. Stanley and Harold M. Jackson, The Macmillan Company of Canada Ltd., Toronto, 1954.

Combat Equipment Technical Intelligence Bulletin (CETIB) TB/381–1, Department of the Army, Washington, 1958.

Carden-Loyd Light Amphibious Tank, Vickers-Armstrongs Ltd., London, 1931.

Carden-Loyd Light Armoured Vehicle, Vickers-Armstrongs Ltd., London, 1931.

I Carri Armati Nel Combattimento, Istituto Poligrafico Della Stato, Roma, 1931.

Il Carro da Combattimento, S. Ten. cpl. a. cor. Guido Giannettini, Tipografia Regionale, Roma, 1965.

Carros de Combate, Enrique García Albors, Sebastian Rodriguez, Toledo, 1934.

Catalogue of Enemy Ordnance Material, Office Chief of Ordnance, Washington, 1944.

Les Chars D'Assaut, Commandant F. J. Deygas, Charles-Lavauzelle & Cie., Paris, 1937.

Le Char D'Assaut, Captain L. Dutil, Berger-Levrault, Nancy, 1920.

Les Chars D'Assaut et le Materiél a Chenille, L. A. Legros, Imprimerie Chaix, Paris, 1921.

Chieftain, Battle Tank of the '70's, War Department and the Central Office of Information, London, 1963.

Christie Military Vehicles, Michael Rosen, privately published, San Leandro, 1965.

Combat Tanks, G. B. Jarrett, IPD Publishing Company, New York, 1968.

Contribution to Victory, The Associated Equipment Company Ltd., Adams Brothers & Shardlow Ltd., London, 1946.

Contribution to Victory, Frank Rowlinson, Metropolitan-Vickers Electrical Co., Ltd., Manchester, 1947.

Corazzati Italiani 1939–45, Benedetto Pafi, Cesare Falessi and Goffredo Fiore, D'Anna Editore, Roma, 1968.

Crew Drill for Medium Tanks, HMSO, London, 1930.

Czolgi-Wczoraj Dzis I Jutro, Lieut. L. Furs-Zyrkiewicz, Warszawskie Zakaldy Graficyne, Warszawa, 1937.

D & P Test Facilities & Capabilities, Aberdeen Proving Ground, 1960.

Le Defaut de L'Armure, Colonel Georges Ferré, Charles-Lavauzelle et Cie., Paris, 1948.

The Desert Rats, Major General G. L. Verney, Hutchinson Ltd., London, 1954.

Design and Development of Fighting Vehicles, R. M. Ogorkiewicz, Macdonald, London, 1968.

Design Record, Canadian Developed Military Vehicles, World War II, Vols II & III, Department of Munitions and Supply, Ottawa, 1950.

Die Deutsche Panzertruppe 1939–1945, H. Scheibert and C. Wagenir, Podzun-Verlag, Bad Nauheim, 1966.

Development of the Agricultural Tractor in the United States, Parts I and II, R. B. Gray and W. R. Humphries, American Society of Agricultural Engineers, St. Joseph, Michigan, 1956.

Development of Cromwell Series, Ministry of Supply, London, 1944.

Development of Gas Turbine Power Plants for Traction Purposes in Germany, Bright, Institute of Mechanical Engineering, London, 1946.

Die Deutschen Geschuetze 1939–1945, Dr. Jur. F. M. von Senger und Etterlin, J. F. Lehmanns Verlag, Muenchen, 1960.

Die Deutschen Kampfwagen Im Weltkriege, Major· Ernst Volckheim, Verlag E. S. Mittler & Sohn, Berlin, 1937.

· *Die Deutschen Panzer 1926–1945*, Z. Auflage, Dr. Jur. F. M. von Senger und Etterlin, J. F. Lehmanns Verlag, Muenchen, 1965.

Development of New Series German Tanks, R. Kaufman, Dept. of Commerce No. PB 16717, Washington, 1945.

Dynamic Defense, Captain B. H. Liddell Hart, Faber & Faber Ltd., London, 1940.

The Eighth Army, Sept. 1941 to Jan. 1943, HMSO, London.

89 Million Miles of Testing in 20 Years, General Motors Proving Ground, Milford, 1944.

Elements of Ordnance, Colonel Thomas J. Hayes, John Wiley & Sons, Inc., New York, 1938.

Employment of Armored Units, Armored Force, Fort Knox, 1942.

Engines of War, The Mechanized Army in Action, Adam and Charles Black, London, 1942.

The Evolution of the Tank, Rear Admiral Sir Murray Sueter, Hutchinson & Co., London, 1937.

Export of Surplus War Material, Report to Parliament by Secretary of State for Foreign Affairs and the Minister of Defence, HMSO, London, 1956.

Exposición de Material de Guerra Tomada al Enemigo, Ministerio de Asientos Exteriores No. 3, San Sebastian, 1938.

Eye Witness, Sir Ernest D. Swinton, Hodder and Stoughton Ltd., London, 1932.

50 Famous Tanks, George Bradford and Len Morgan, Arco Publishing Company, Inc., New York, 1967.

Fighting Tanks, Edited by C. Murray Wilson, Seeley Service & Co., Ltd., London, 1929.

Fighting Tanks Since 1916, Major Ralph E. Jones, Captain George H. Rarey and 1st Lieut. Robert J. Icks, National Service Publishing Company, Washington, 1933.

Fighting Vehicles of the Red Army, B. Perrett, Ian Allan Ltd., London, 1969.

Fighting Vehicles and Weapons of the Modern British Army, Stevenson Pugh, Macdonald, London, 1962.

The First Battle of the Tanks, J. H. Everest, Arthur H. Stockwell, Ltd., London, 1942.

Ford at War, Hilary St. George Saunders, Harrison and Soris Ltd., London, 1946.

Forging the Thunderbolt, Mildred Hanson Gillie, Military Service Publishing Co., Harrisburg, 1947.

Fremde Heere, Die Armeen Der NATO-Staaten, Dr. Friedrich Wiener, Verlag Carl Ueberreuter, Wien, 1966. (Vols. 1 and 2.)

Fremde Heere, Der Warschauer Pakt, Dr. Friedrich Wiener, Verlag Carl Ueberreuter, Wien, 1965. (Vols. 1, 2 and 3.)

Fremde Heere, Die Armeen Der Neutralen und Blockfreien Staaten Europus, 1. Auflage, Dr. Frederich Wiener, Verlag Carl Ueberreuter, Wien, 1968.

Fresh Target, Middle East Hq. British Army, 1943.

Die Gegenschlag, Dr. Jur. F. M. von Senger und Etterlin, Kurt Vowinckel Verlag, Neckar, Gemuend, 1959.

German AFVs of World War II, Edited by Duncan Crow, Profile Publications Ltd., Windsor, 1973.

German Defence Tactics Against Russian Break-Through, Department of the Army, Pamphlet 20-233, 1951.

(The) German Panzers from Mark I to Mark V 'Panther', Aero Publishers, Inc., Fallbrook, California, 1966.

German Tanks, 1914–1918. Heinz J. Nowarra, Arco Publishing Co., New York, 1968.

German Tanks and Armoured Vehicles, B. T. White, Ian Allan, Shepperton, 1966.

German Vehicles, Reports of Examination (Various titles), Department of Tank Design, Ministry of Supply, London, 1942–1944.

German Tank Development, C10S Report FF 1215, 24 Nov. 1944, Department of Commerce, Washington.

German Tank Maintenance in World War II, Department of the Army Pamphlet 20-202, 1954.

(The) German Tank in World War II, Ordnance Museum, Aberdeen Proving Ground, 1962.

Die Gespenster-Division, Alfred Tschimpke, Verlag Frz. Eher Nachf., Muenchen, 1940.

The Ground Self-Defence Force, Tokyo, 1958.

Grundlagen Des Schiessens Aus Dem Panzer, W. I. Nikulen, Deutsches Militaer-Verlag (East) Berlin, 1961.

Guarding the United States and Its Outposts, Stetson Conn, Rose C. Engelman and Byron Fairchild, United States Army in World War II, Government Printing Office, Washington, 1964.

La Guerre Des Blindés, Major Eddy Bauer, Librairie Payot, Lausanne, 1947.

Handbuch Fuer Schuetzenpanzer, Bundesministerium Fuer Landes Verteidigung, Wien, 1964.

Handbook of the Mark VIII Tank, Technical Regulation 1325-B, Government Printing Office, Washington, 1934.

Handbook of Motor Vehicles Used by the United States Armed Forces, Timken-Detroit Axle Company, Detroit, 1946.

Handbook of Ordnance Material ST 9-159, U.S. Army Ordnance Center and School, Aberdeen Proving Ground, 1964.

Handbook of German Military Forces, TM-E 30-451, U.S. War Department, Washington, 1945.

Handbook on the Soviet Army, Department of the Army Pamphlet 30-50-1, Government Printing Office, Washington, 1958.

Handbook on Japanese Military Forces, TM-E 30-480, U.S. War Department, Washington, 1944.

Handbuch Fuer Panzerbesatzungen–Panzerschiessen, Deutscher Militaerverlag, (East) Berlin, 1966.

Hearings Before Committee on Armed Services, U.S. House of Representatives, U.S. Government Printing Office, various years.

Heigls Taschenbuch Der Tanks Teil I–II, O. H. Hacker, Robert J. Icks, Otto Merker und G. P. Von Zezschwitz, Teil III, G. P. Von Zezschwitz, 1938, J. F. Lehmanns Verlag, Muenchen, 1935.

Histoire de L'Armée Motorisée, André Duvignac, Imprimerie Nationale, Paris, 1947.

History of German Tank Development, Robert Schilling, Department of Commerce, Washington, 1945.

History of the Development of Tank Design at the Skoda Works, L. B. Magruder, CIOS Target 18/93, Department of Commerce, Washington, 1945.

Historical Monograph APG Museum 1919–1960, Karl F. Kempf, Aberdeen Proving Ground, 1960.

History of the German General Staff, Walter Goerlitz, Praeger, New York, 1953.

History and Role of Armor, U.S. Army Armor School, Fort Knox, 1959.

History of LVTs, Board for Development of Landing Vehicles Tracked. Captain E. E. Roth, Detroit, 1945.

History of the Second World War, British War Production, M. M. Postan, HMSO and Longmans Green & Co., London, 1952.

History of the Second World War, Design and Development of Weapons, M. M. Postan, D. Hay, J. D. Scott, HMSO and Longmans Green & Co., London, 1964.

History of U.S. Armor, Publication No. 1 (Second Edition), The Patton Museum Society, Ft. Knox, 1968.

Hobo's Funnies: The 79th Armoured Division, Major-General Nigel W. Duncan, Profile, 1971.

How Russia Makes War, Raymond L. Garthoff, George Allen & Unwin, Ltd., London, 1954.

Identification Handbook Soviet and Satellite Ordnance Equipment, 5th Edition, HQ USAEUR, 1963.

Illustrated Record of German Weapons, Section III AFVs and Section IV, The War Office, London, 1946.

Interrogation of Herr Stiele Von Heydekamp, German Tank & Engine Program Report No. 153, June 28, 1945, Office of the Publication Board, Department of Commerce, Washington.

In the Wake of the Tank, Lt. Col. G. Le Q. Martel, Sifton Praed & Co., Ltd., 1935.

Istruzione Sul Carro Armati Mod. 1921 E Mod. 1930, Istituto Poligrafico Della Stato, Roma, 1931.

Japanese Automotive Diesel Engines, Japan Ordnance Association, Tokyo, 1964.

Japanese Tanks and Fighting Vehicles Vol 1, Revised edition, Lt. Gen. Tomio Hara and Akira Takeuchi, Shuppan Kyodo Sha, Tokyo, 1969.

Japanese Tanks and Armoured Vehicles Vol 2, Lt. Gen. Tomio Hara and Denji Eimori, Shuppan Kyodo Sha, Tokyo, 1961.

Japanese Tanks and Anti-Tank Warfare (Special Series 34) No. PB 19536, Department of Commerce, Washington, 1945.

Kampfpanzer 1916–1966, Dr. Jur. F. M. von Senger und Etterlin, J. F. Lehmanns Verlag, Muenchen, 1966.

Kampfschule Der Panzertruppen–Schiessen Bei Nacht Mit MG und Gewehr, H Div 298/20a, OHL, 1944.

Kampfwagen An Die Front, General W. Nehring, Verlag Johannes Detke, Leipzig, 1934.

Der Kampfwagenkrieg, General Ludwig Ritter von Eimannsberger, J. F. Lehmanns Verlag, Muenchen, 1934.

Kampfwagen Panther, Rheinmetall-Borsig, 1943.

Das Kleine Panzerbuch, Dr. Jur. F. M. von Senger und Etterlin, J. F. Lehmanns Verlag, Muenchen, 1964.

Kleine Panzerkunde, Gerhard Borchort, Kurt Erhart, Siegfried Modrach, Manfred Otto, Deutscher Militaer verlag (East) Berlin 1967.

Korea 1950, Office of the Chief of Military History, Government Printing Office, Washington, 1952.

Land Mines, Engineer School Special Text St. 5-32-2, Fort Belvoir, 1954.

Leyte Campaign, After Battle Reports, Armored School Library, Fort Knox.

The Liberty Engineer 1915–1942, Vol 1 No. 3. National Air and Space Museum, Smithsonian Institution, Washington, 1968.

The Liddell Hart Memoirs, Vols I and II, Sir Basil Liddell Hart.

Life in a Tank, Richard Haigh, Houghton Mifflin Company, Boston, 1918.

Light Fighting Unit 'Even', Societé Hotchkiss-Rive, Paris, 1963.

Light Tank M5A1 Drawings in Miniature, Office Chief of Ordnance, Detroit, 1945.

The Line, Pressed Steel Car Company, Hammond, 1946.

The Lorraine Campaign, H. M. Cole, U.S. Army in World War II, Government Printing Office, Washington, 1950.

Machine Age Armies, John Wheldon, Abelard-Schuman, London, 1968.

Machine Warfare, Major General J. F. C. Fuller, Hutchinson, London, 1942.

Mechanization, Vickers-Armstrongs Ltd., London, 1931.

The Mechanization of War, Victor Wallace Germains, Sifton Praed, London, 1926.

Mechanized Flamethrower Operations in World War II — Chemical Corps Historical Studies No. 5, Historical Office, Office of the Chief of the Chemical Corps, Washington, 1951.

Medium Tank M3 Technical Manual 9-750, Government Printing Office, Washington, 1941.

Medium Tank M4A1 and M4A3 Drawings in Miniature, Office Chief of Ordnance, Detroit, 1945.

Military Heritage of America, Col. R. E. DuPuy and Col. T. N. DuPuy, McGraw Hill and Co., 1958.

Military Vehicles, C. B. Colby, Coward-McCann, Inc., New York, 1956.

Merchants of Death, Engelbrecht and Hanighen, Dodd, Mead & Co., New York, 1934.

Military Improvisation During the Russian Campaign, Department of the Army Pamphlet 20-201, 1951.

Mine Exploder Mission to European Theater of Operations, Office Chief of Ordnance, Washington, 1944.

Mit den Panzern in Ost und West, General Oberst Guderian, Volk und Reich Verlag, Berlin, 1942.

Moderno Armamento de la Infanteria, de Narro, De Rodriguez, Toledo, 1935.

Moderne Artillerie (2 Volumes) Fred Vos, Alkenreeks, Alkman, 1968.

Motorizacion y Mechanizacion de Ejercito, E. G. Albors, De Rodriguez, Toledo, 1935.

NDRC Final Report, National Defence Research Council, Washington, 1947.

Nephadsereguenk, Zrinyi Katonai Kiado, Budapest, 1965.

Normandy to the Baltic, Viscount Montgomery of Alamain, Houghton Mifflin, Boston, 1948.

New Notes on the Red Army No. 1, The War Office, London, 1944.

North American Supply, H. Duncan Hall, HMSO, London, 1955.

OCOD Production Summaries, Office Chief of Ordnance, Detroit, 1945.

An Outspoken Soldier, Lt. Gen. Sir Giffard Le Q. Martel, Sifton Praed, London, 1949.

On Future Warfare, Colonel J. F. C. Fuller, Sifton Praed & Co., Ltd., London, 1928.

'Operations of Encircled Forces — German Experience in Russia', Department of the Army Pamphlet 20-234, 1952.

Operations of the 301st Battalion T.C., Major R. I. Sasse, 305th Brigade Tank Corps, AEF, France, 1918.

Operation Victory, General de Guingand, Charles Scribner, New York, 1947.

(The) Ordnance Department: Planning Munitions for War, United States Army in World War II, Constance McLaughlin Green, Harry C. Thomson and Peter C. Roots, Government Printing Office, Washington, 1955.

(The) Ordnance Department: Procurement and Supply, United States Army in World War II, Harry C. Thomson and Lida Mayo, Government Printing Office, Washington, 1960.

(The) Ordnance Department: On Beachhead and Battlefront, Lido Mayo, Government Printing Office, Washington, 1968.

Ordnance Spare Parts in Mechanized Warfare, Ordnance Department, Detroit, 1944.

'Ordnance Vehicle Characteristics Manual', Office Chief of Ordnance, Detroit, 1944.

Our Armoured Forces, Lt. Gen. Sir Giffard Le Q. Martel, Faber and Faber, Ltd., London, 1946.

Outline of Combat Vehicle Production, Tokyo Motor Vehicle Works, Mitsubishi Nippon Heavy Industries, Ltd., Tokyo, 1961.

Over My Shoulder, Sir Ernest D. Swinton, Hodder and Stoughton Ltd., London, 1951.

Pancelos Csatak, Nagy Gabor, Zrynyi Katonai Kiado, Budapest, 1966.

Panther, Uwe Feist and W. J. Spielberger, Feist Publishing Co., Buena Vista, California, 1968.

Pantservoertuigen 1, Fred Vos, Alkenreeks, Alkman, 1963.

Pantservoertuigen 2, Fred Vos, Alkenreeks, Alkman, 1965.

Panzer, Dr. Jur. F. M. von Senger und Etterlin, Athenaeum-Verlag, Bonn, 1958.

Der Panzer, A. S. Antonow, B. A. Artamonov, B. M. Korobkow, and E. I. Magidowitsch, Verlag Des Ministeriums fuer Nationale Verteidigung (East) Berlin, 1959.

Panzer Am Balkan, Wilfred Von Oven und Juergen Hahn-Butry, Wilhelm Limpert-Verlag, Berlin, 1941.

Panzer Battles 1939–1945, Maj. Gen. F. W. Von Mellenthin, Cassell & Company, Ltd., London, 1955.

Panzer Der NATO, Siegfried Modrach, Deutsche Militaer Verlag (East) Berlin, 1962.

Panzer Gestern und Heute, Ing-Oberst W. D. Mostawenko, Deutsche Militaer-Verlag, (East) Berlin, 1961.

Panzer Division, The Mailed Fist, Major K. J. Macksey, Ballantine Books Inc., New York, 1968.

Die Panzergrenadiere, Dr. Jur. F. M. von Senger und Etterlin, J. F. Lehmanns Verlag, Muenchen, 1961.

Panzer Im Gefecht, N. Korolkow, Deutscher Militaer-Verlag, (East) Berlin, 1962.

Panzerkampfwagen Buch, Hauptman Kurt Kaufman, Verlag Offene Worte, Berlin, 1940.

Die Panzerkampfwagen Unserer Gegner, Oberst Esser, Automobilcentrale Zeitschrift, Stuttgart, 1946.

Panzerkennblaetter Serie I–IX, Dr. Fritz Wiener und Herbert Hahn, Friedrich Schirmer, Burgdorf / Hannover, 1958–1965.

Panzerleader, General Heinz Guderian, Translated by Constantine Fitzgibbon, Michael Joseph, London, 1952.

Die Panzer Lehr-Division, Franz Kurowski, Podzin-Verlag, Bad Nauheim, 1964.

Das Panzer Merk-Buch, Schultze-Deycke, Verlag Offene Worte, Berlin, 1937.

Die Panzertruppen Der USA-Armee, Eberhard Arnold, Verlag des Ministerium Fuer Nationale Verteidigung, (East) Berlin, 1960.

Panzertypen Aus Dem 2 Weltkrieg (1939–1945), Bundesministerium Fuer Landes Verteidigung, Wien, 1962.

Panzer und Motor, General Walther Nehring, L. Voggenreuter Verlag, Potsdam, 1936.

Patton and His Third Army, Brig. Gen. Brenton G. Wallace, Military Service Publishing Co., Harrisburg, 1946.

Photographs for Recognition Training, Armored Vehicles, Training Aids Division, U.S. Army Air Force, New York, 1943.

Pictorial History of Tanks to 1945, Chris Ellis and Peter Chamberlain, Arms and Armour Press, London, 1973.

'Preliminary Survey of German AFV Plants', GBI/Tech/39U/SRI Headquarters SHEAF, May, 1945.

Program of the Exhibition of German & Other Vehicles and Equipment at Chobham Lane, Chertsey, Ministry of Supply F. V. Division, 1946.

Pulk Pancerny (History of the 1st Armoured Regiment) 1944–45, The Saint Catherine Press Ltd., Bruges, 1945.

Rabotchie Kristiyanskaya Krasnaya Armiya, Moskva, 1934.

Ramie Pancerne (The Armoured Arm) of the 2nd Polish Corps, Raferat Hult, Rome, 1946.

The Red Army Today, Ely, Military Service Publishing Company, Harrisburg, 1949.

The Remaking of Modern Armies, Captain B. H. Liddell Hart, John Murray, London, 1927.

Renault, Saint-Loup, The Bodley Head, London, 1957.

Report on the Interrogation of Dipl.-Ing. Ernest Kniepkamp, W. J. Simmons, Target No. 181, BIOS, London, 1945.

Reports on German Armour (Various titles of individual German Vehicles), Military College of Science, School of Tank Technology, Chertsey, ca 1942–44.

'Research, Investigation and Experimentation in the Field of Amphibian Vehicles,' Quarterly Report No. 6, 1955, and Final Report 1957. Ingersoll-Kalamazoo Division, Borg-Warner Corporation, Kalamazoo.

Review of Development and Procurement of New Combat and Tactical Vehicles by the Department of the Army, Report to the Congress of the United States by the Comptroller General of the United States, U.S. General Accounting Office, Washington, 1960.

Revolutionary New Power Plant, The Small Gas Turbine, Hill, Boeing Airplane Co., Seattle, 1950.

The Rommel Papers, Edited by Captain B. H. Liddell Hart, Collins, London, 1953.

Die Roten Panzer, I. G. Andronikow and W. D. Mostawenko, edited by Dr. Jur. F. M. von Senger und Etterlin, J. F. Lehmanns Verlag, Muenchen, 1963.

The Royal Armoured Corps, Captain J. R. W. Murland, Methuen & Co., Ltd., London, 1943.

The Royal Armoured Corps, Frank Owen and H. W. Atkins, The War Office, London, 1945.

'Royal Armoured Corps, Part 7: Tank Hunting and Destruction Pamphlet No. 42', The War Office, London, 1940.

'Russian Combat Methods in World War II, Department of the Army Pamphlet 20-230', 1950.

Russian Tanks 1900–1970, John Milsom, Arms and Armour Press, London, 1970.

Russian Tanks 1915–1968, John M. Broroton and Uwe Forst. Forst Publications, Berkeley 1970.

San Pietro After Battle Report, Armored School Library, Fort Knox.

Die Schweren Franzoesischen Tanks, Die Italienischen Tanks, Haupt.-Ing. Fritz Heigl, Verlag R. Eisenschmidt, Berlin, 1925.

Semana de Las Fuerzas Armadas, Ministerio de la Defensa, Caracas, 1952.

The Sherman, Peter Chamberlain and Chris Ellis, Arms and Armour Press, London, 1968.

Six Ton Tank M1917 Technical Regulation 1325-A, Government Printing Office, Washington, 1934.

A Shipbuilder's Yarn, Sir Eustace H. W. Tennyson D'Encourt, Hutchinson & Co., Ltd., London, 1960.

A Short History of the Royal Tank Corps, Gale & Polden, Ltd., Aldershot, 1930.

The Sinai Campaign, 1956, Major Edgar O'Ballance, Faber and Faber, London, 1959.

Sketch Book O.R. & D., Aberdeen Proving Ground, 1945.

The Six Day War, Randolph and Winston Churchill, Heinemann, London, 1967.

Some Aspects of Mechanization, Colonel Lt. Rowan-Robinson, Wm. Clowes and Sons, Ltd., London, 1928.

Sonderpanzer, Uwe Feist and W. J. Spielberger, Aero Publishing Co., Fullbrook, 1968.

Springboks in Armour, Harry Klein, MacDonald, London, 1965.

A Soldier's Story, General Omar

Bradley, Henry Holt, New York, 1951.

Soviet Arms and Soviet Power, General Augustin Guillaume, Infantry Journal Press, 1949.

The Soviet Army, Edited by Captain B. H. Liddell Hart, Weidenfeld and Nicholson, London, 1956.

Soviet Combat Tanks, 1939-1945, Chris Ellis and Peter Chamberlain, Almark, 1970.

Sowiecka Bron Pancerna, 2 Warszawka Dywizja, Panuna Wlochy, Grudzien, 1943.

Stabilized Optical Sight for German Tank Guns, Item No. 9 and 18, File XXXII CIOS, 1945, Department of Commerce, Washington.

Storia Della Motorizzazione Militare Italiana, Generale Angelo Pugnani, Stabilimento Poligrafico Roggero & Tortia, Torino, 1951.

The Story of the Churchill Tank, Vauxhall Motors, Luton, 1946.

The Strategy of Indirect Approach, Captain B. H. Liddell Hart, Faber and Faber, London, 1946.

The Story of 79th Armoured Division October 1942 — June 1945, Privately printed, 1945.

The Story of U.S. Tanks and Self-Propelled Artillery, The Ordnance Museum, Aberdeen Proving Ground, 1960.

Sturm-Artillerie, G. Tornau und F. Kurowski, Maximilian-Verlag, Herford, 1965.

Sturmartillerie, Uwe Feist and Walter Spielberger (Two Volumes), Aero Publishers, Inc., Fallbrook, California, 1967.

The Swedish Army, Anders Grafstroem Hoersta Foerlag A.-B. and Bailey Bros. & Swinfine Ltd., London, 1954.

Swift Sword, Brigadier General S. L. A. Marshall, American Heritage, 1967.

Tactical Problems for Armor Units, Colonel Paul A. Disney, Military Service Publishing Company, Harrisburg, 1952.

Tank, Arch Whitehouse, Doubleday & Co., Inc., Garden City, 1960.

Tank and Armoured Car Training Vol II War, HMSO, London, 1927.

The Tank Corps, Major Clough and A. Williams-Ellis, George H. Doran Company, New York, 1919.

Tank Data, Ordnance School Aberdeen Proving Ground, 1960.

Tank, Infantry, Mark III* Instruction Book, Vickers-Armstrongs Ltd.

The Tank, Its Birth and Development, Wm. Foster & Co., Lincoln, 1919.

The Tank, Douglas Orgill, Heinemann, London, 1970.

Tanks, A. H. Franks, Sir Isaac Pitman & Sons, Ltd., London, 1943.

Tanks, Major Kenneth Macksay and John H. Batchelor, Macdonald, London, 1970.

Tanks, Colonel Shunzo Inoma, War Office, Tokyo, 1944.

The Tanks, Captain B. H. Liddell Hart, Vols 1–2, Cassell, London, 1959.

Tanks 1914–1918, The Log Book of A Pioneer, Sir Albert G. Stern,

Hodder and Stoughton, London, 1919.

Tanks Advance, Gordon Beckles, Cassell and Co., Ltd., 1942.

Tanks and Other Armoured Fighting Vehicles, B. T. White, Blandford Press, London, 1970.

Tank Employment FMFM 9–1, HQ USMC, Washington, D.C., 1965.

Tanks in the East, Colin Kerr, Oxford University Press, Melbourne, 1945.

Tanks are Mighty Fine Things, Wesley W. Stout, Chrysler Corporation, Detroit, 1946.

Tanks in the Great War 1914–1918, Brevet Colonel J. F. C. Fuller, E. P. Dutton & Co., New York, 1920.

Tanks and Armored Vehicles, Lt. Col. Robert J. Icks, Duell, Sloan and Pierce, New York, 1945.

Tanks and How to Draw Them, 'Cuneo', The Studio, London, 1943.

Tanks in Battle, Colonel H. C. B. Rogers, Seeley Service & Co., London, 1965.

Tanks in the Next War, Major E. W. Sheppard, Geoffrey Bles, London, 1938.

Tanks, MMG's and Ordnance, A. H. and A. W. Reed, 3rd Division (New Zealand Historical Committee), Dunedin, 1947.

'Tank Museum Guides', Royal Armoured Corps Centre, Bovington, 1950 onwards.

Tanks and Other Military Track-Laying Vehicles, Co-operative Bibliography No. 1, Douglas W. Bryant, Library of Congress, Washington, 1941.

Tank 'S', A.B. Bofors, Bofors, 1965.

Tanks and Tank-Folk, Eric Kennington, Country Life, Ltd., London, 1945.

Tanks of the Croat Armies, Eurico Po., Intyrama, Rome, 1969.

Tank Training Vols I and II Training, HMSO, London, 1930–1936.

The Tank User, Technical Note 2–62, Human Engineering Laboratories, Aberdeen Proving Ground, 1962.

Tank Warfare, J. R. Lester, George Allen & Unwin, Ltd., London, 1943.

Tank Warfare, F. Mitchell, Thomas Nelson and Sons, Ltd., London, 1919.

Tarawa, Captain James R. Slocum, Historical Section, HQ USMC, Washington, 1947.

Target, Middle East HQ, British Army, 1942.

Taschenbuch Der Tanks, Maior F. Heigl, J. F. Lehmanns Verlag, Muenchen, 1926, 1927, 1930.

Taschenbuch Der Panzer 1943–1960, Dr. Jur. F. M. von Senger und Etterlin, J. F. Lehmanns Verlag, Muenchen, 1960.

Technische Lehrbuch ueber Kettenfahrzeugen und Kettenfahrschule, Ing. Ulrich Wacker, Verlag E. S. Mittler & Sohn, Frankfort/Main, 1959.

Technische Mitteilungun uber Kampfwagen, W. Dorffler, Eisenschmidt, Berlin, Heft 1 1922 and Heft 2, 1926.

Die Technische Loopban, H. J. Van

Doorne, Van Doorne's Automobielfabriek N.V., Eindhoven, 1954.

10 Years Before Pearl Harbor, Marmon-Herrington Co., Inc., Indianapolis, 1944.

Testing for War, General Motors Proving Ground, Milford, 1944.

Thoughts on War, Captain B. H. Liddell Hart, Faber and Faber, London, 1954.

Tiger Fibel, D656/27, OKH, 1943.

Tracks for Fighting Vehicles, E. W. E. Micklethwait, School of Tank Technology, Chertsey, 1944.

The Tiger Tanks, Heinz J. Nowarra, Uwe Feist and Edward T. Maloney, Aero Publishers, Inc., Fallbrook, California, 1966.

The Truth About Our Tanks, Ivor Halstead, Lindsay Drummond, Ltd., London, 1942.

Umlcené Zbrane, Nase Vojsko, Praha, 1966.

U.S. Armor—Cavalry, Duncan Crow, Profile Publications, Windsor, 1973.

U.S. Army Air Defense Digest, U.S. Army Air Defense School, Fort Bliss, Texas, 1967.

The United States Marines, Lynn Montross, Rinehart & Company, Inc., New York, 1959.

Unsere Neue Panzertruppe, Major Ernst Volckheim, Verlag Bernard & Graefe, Berlin, 1938.

U.S. Marine Operations in Korea 1950–1953, Vols 1–3, Lynn Montross and Captain Nicholas A. Canzona, U.S. Marine Corps Historical Branch, Washington, 1954.

The U.S. Marines and Amphibious War, Peter A. Isely and Philip A. Crowl, Princeton University Press, Princeton, 1951.

U.S. Tanks, Colonels Robert J. Icks and G. B. Jarrett, Arco Publishing Company, New York, 1968.

U.S. Vehicle Production in World War II, Office Chief of Ordnance, Detroit, 1945.

Vehicle Engineering Data Vols 1–3, Aberdeen Proving Ground, 1920–1939.

Vehicles of War, Metropolitan Cammell Carriage & Wagon Co., Ltd., Birmingham, 1945.

Verlorene Siege, Feldmarschall Erich von Manstein, Athenaeum Verlag, Bonn, 1955.

Vorlaeufiges Merkblatt fuer der Beckaempfung der Engl., Infanterie Pz Kpfw Mk. IV, D226–6, OKH, 1942.

Walker Bulldog, Its Design and Production, Edward N. Cole and Harold G. Warner, Detroit Section Society of Automotive Engineers, 1951.

The War, 1967. Zeev Anner, Joseph Alkoni and Alex Gal, Otpaz Ltd., Tel Aviv, 1967.

War As I Knew It, Lt. Gen. George S. Patton, Jr., Annotated by Colonel Paul D. Harkness, Houghton Mifflin Company, Boston, 1947.

War Diary of the English Electric Company, Ltd., March 1938—August 1945.

'Warfare in the Far North', Department of the Army Pamphlet,

20–292, 1951.

Wartime Tank Production, Select Committee, Parliament, HMSO, London, 1946.

The Water Buffalo, Vols 1–2, Food Machinery Corporation, 1945.

'Weapons and Equipment Recognition Guide Southeast Asia', D. A. Pamphlet 381–10, January, 1966.

Wir Stossen Mit Panzern Zum Meer, E. E. Christopher, Steiniger-Verlag, Berlin, 1940.

With Rommel in the Desert, H. W. Schmidt, George G. Harrap & Co., Ltd., London, 1951.

With the Tanks of the 1st Polish Armoured Division, K. Jamar, H. L. Smit & Zn, Hengelo, 1946.

The World's Armoured Fighting Vehicles, Dr. Jur. F. M. von Senger und Etterlin, Translated by R. M. Ogorkiewicz, MacDonald, London, 1962.

Woerterbuch Der Kraftfahrt, H. Georges und R. Schnaubel, Verlag von Quelle & Meyer, Leipzig, 1938.

World War II Campaigns, Department of Military Art and Engineering, United States Military Academy, West Point, 1947–1951.

Worthington Park Outdoor Tank Museum, Royal Canadian Armoured Corps, Camp Borden, 1963.

Worthy, Larry Worthington, The MacMillan Company of Canada, Ltd., Toronto, 1961.

Wozy Bojowe 1914–1964, Janusz Magnuski, Wydawictwo Ministerswa Obrony Naradowy, Warszawa, 1964.

Zwalczanie Samochodow Pancernych, Major Furs-Zyrkiewicz, Wojskowy Instytut Naukowo-Wydadanicyz, Warszawa, 1932.

RECENT PUBLICATIONS

Acquisition of Major Weapons Systems, Report B-163058 to the Congress, The Comptroller General of the United States, 17 July 1972.

A.F.V.s of the World, Vol. 3, British and Commonwealth A.F.V.s 1940–1946, Edited by Duncan Crow, Profile Publications Ltd., Windsor, 1971.

A.F.V.s 1919–1940, British Armoured Fighting Vehicle, Vol. 2, Edited by Duncan Crow, Profile Publications Ltd., Windsor, 1970.

Armour Camouflage and Markings, North Africa 1940–1943, Vol. 1, George R. Bradford, published by the author, Preston, Ontario, 1971.

Armour Camouflage and Markings, North Africa 1940–1945, George R. Bradford, published by the author, Preston, Ontario, 1971.

Armoured Fighting Vehicles of World War I, Vol. 1, edited by Duncan Crow, Profile Publicatlons Ltd., Windsor, 1970.

Armoured Fighting Vehicles of the World, Christopher Foss, Ian Allan, Shepperton, 1971.

Armoured Fighting Vehicles of the World, Christopher Foss, Ian Allan, London, 1971.

Armoured Fighting Vehicles of the World, American A.F.V.s of World War II, Vol. 4, edited by Duncan Crow, Profile Publications Ltd., Windsor, 1972.

Atlante Mondiale dri Nazzi Corazzati, Nicola Pignati, Ermauno Albertilli, Editore, Parma, 1972.

The Battle for North Africa, John Strawson, Charles Scribner Sons, New York, 1969.

The Blitzkrieg Era and the German General Staff 1865–1941, Larry H. Addington, Rutgers University Press, New Brunswick, 1971.

British and American Tanks of World War II, Chris Ellis and Peter Chamberlain, Arms & Armour Press Ltd., London, 1969.

British Armoured Fighting Vehicles 1919–1940, edited by Duncan Crow, Profile Publishing Co. Ltd., Windsor, 1971.

British and Commonwealth Armoured Formations 1919–1945, Profile Book No. 3, Duncan Crow, Profile Publishing Co. Ltd., Windsor, 1971.

Call to Arms, The Memoirs of General Sir Harold Pyman, C.B.E., Leo Cooper, London, 1971.

The Churchill Tank, Chris Ellis and Peter Chamberlain, Arms & Armour Press Ltd., London, 1971.

Famous Tank Battles, Colonel Robert J. Icks, Doubleday & Co. Inc., New York, 1972.

Fighting Vehicles of the Red Army, B. Perrett, Ian Allan Ltd., London, 1969.

History of the Second World War, Sir Basil Liddell Hart, C. P. Putnams Sons, New York, 1970.

History of the Second World War, B. H. Liddell Hart, G. P. Putnams Sons, New York, 1970.

Hitler's Last Offensive, Peter Elstob, Macmillan Company, New York, 1972.

Japanese Tanks and Fighting Vehicles, Vol. 1, revised edition, 1969.

Japanese Tanks, The Graphic Quarterly, Tokyo, 1971.

Japanese Tanks, The Koku-fan, Tokyo, October 1968.

Kampfpanza Leopard, Raimund Knicht, J. F. Lehmanns Verlag, Munich 1972. (English version.)

The M4 Sherman, The Koku-fan, November 1971, Tokyo.

Modern Armour Support Vehicles, Profile Book No. 1, Robert J. Icks, Profile Publications Ltd., Windsor, 1971.

Modern U.S. Armoured Support Vehicles, Colonel Robert J. Icks, Profile Book No. 1, Profile Publications, Windsor, 1971.

The Observer's Fighting Vehicles Directory World War II, B. H. Vanderveen, Frederick Warner & Co. Ltd., London, 1969.

The Observer's Fighting Vehicle Directory World War II, revised edition, 1972.

The Observer's Military Vehicle Directory, May 1945, B. H.

Vanderveen, Frederick Warner & Co. Ltd., London, 1972.

Panzer in Russland, Horst Scheibert and Ulrich Elfrath, Podzum-Verlag, Horkeim, 1971.

The Patton Papers 1885–1940, edited by Martin Blumenson, Houghton Mifflin Company, Boston, 1972.

Pershing: A History of the Medium Tank T20 Series, R. P. Hunnicutt, Feist Publications, Berkeley, 1971.

Pictorial History of Tanks of the World 1915–1945, Peter Chamberlain and Chris Ellis, Arms & Armour Press Ltd., London, 1972.

Portrait of Power, G. B. Jarrett and Robert J. Icks, Vermount Publications, Wickenburg, Arizona, 1971.

Portrait of Power, Colonels G. B. Jarrett and Robert J. Icks, Vermount Publications, Forest Grove, Oregon, 1972.

'Profiles in Armour' (as title for 'Armour in Profile', now reissued in 'A.F.V./Weapons Profiles').

Russian Army Tanks, The Koku-fan, Tokyo, February 1970.

Russian Tanks 1900–1970, John Mitsom, Arms & Armour Press Ltd., London, 1970.

Russian Tanks 1915–1968, John M. Brereton and Uwe Feist, Feist Publications, Berkeley, 1970.

Sixty Days That Shook the West & The Fall of France, Jacques Benoit-Mechin, G. P. Putnams Sons, New York, 1963.

Soviet Combat Tanks 1939–1945, Chris Ellis and Peter Chamberlain, Almark Publications, London, 1970.

Suomalaiset Panssarivaunujoukot 1919–1969, P. Kantakoski, Arnn A. Kaust, 1969.

79th Armoured Division: Hobo's Funnies, N. W. Duncan, Profile Book No. 3, Profile Publications Ltd., Windsor, 1972.

The Tank, Douglas Orgill, Heinemann, London, 1970.

Tank, Kenneth Macksey and John H. Batchelor, Macdonald, London, 1970.

Tanks and Other Armoured Fighting Vehicles 1900–1918, B. T. White, Blandford Press, London, 1970.

Tanks and Other A.F.V.s of the Blitzkrieg Period 1939–1941, B. T. White, Blandford Press, London, 1972.

The Tanks of Tammuz, Shabbai Teveth, The Viking Press, New York, 1969.

Tank Warfare, Kenneth Macksey, Stein & Day, New York, 1971.

Techniques of Anti-Tank Warfare, FM23-3, Department of the Army, Washington, 1966.

To Lose a Battle, Alistair Horne, Little Brown & Co., Boston, 1969.

U.S. Armoured-Cavalry, A Short History 1917–1967, Duncan Crow, Profile Book No. 4, Profile Publications Ltd., Windsor, 1973.

West of Alamein, Colonel G. B. Jarrett, Sentinel Book, Northridge, California, 1971.

The World Tanks Annual 1971, The Koku-fan, Tokyo, May 1971.

Glossary

A.P.C., Armoured Personnel Carrier, see PERSONNEL CARRIER.

A.R.V., Armoured Recovery Vehicle, a vehicle for salvaging a disabled combat vehicle.

A.V.R.E., Armoured Vehicle, Royal Engineers, a vehicle equipped for demolition and other engineering uses.

ACCORDION WIRE, coiled spring wire used today in preference to barbed wire because of its ease of handling.

ADAPTER, in ammunition, usually a threaded bushing which adapts a fuze to the body of a shell.

AIMING, the action of pointing a weapon by sighting.

ALLOY, a mixture of two or more metals.

AMATOL, a high explosive mixture of ammonium nitrate and trinitrotuluene.

AMMONAL, a high explosive of trinitrotoluene, ammonium nitrate and flake aluminium that produces a brighter flash than other high explosives and therefore facilitates observation.

AMMONIUM PICRATE, a high explosive made of picric acid and hot water solution of ammonia, relatively insensitive to shock and friction.

AMMUNITION, see ROUND.

AMTRAC, see L.V.T.

ANGLE OF ELEVATION, the angle between the horizontal and the axis of the bore when a gun is elevated.

ANGLE OF SIGHT, the angle made by the line of sight and the horizontal.

ANTENNA, that part of a wireless that emits or intercepts wireless ether waves.

ARMING OF FUSE, the release through set-back (centrifugal force) of the fuse which permits it to function on impact of the projectile.

ARMOUR, a general word referring to the whole field of armoured vehicles; with reference to the vehicles themselves, the term refers to the protective covering which may be either plate or cast armour. Either kind in turn may be face hardened or homogeneous. That is, it may be harder on the surface or it may be of the same consistency throughout.

ARMOUR BASIS, a combination of thickness and angle of obliquity which makes armour of a given thickness the equivalent of thicker armour at an angle of ninety degrees.

ARMOUR PIERCING, that quality of a projectile that permits it to penetrate armour rather than shattering on impact.

AUTOFRETTAGE, see COLD WORKED GUN.

AUTOMATIC GUN OR WEAPON, a gun or weapon that loads, fires, extracts, ejects and reloads, continuing the cycle so long as the firing mechanism is 'on' and the feed mechanism supplies live ammunition. May be of the blowback, recoil or gas operated type.

AUXILIARY GENERATOR, a separate petrol-operated electric generator used in armoured vehicles to recharge batteries and sometimes designed also to supply heat for the crew in cold weather.

AZIMUTH, the angle of measurement of rotation of a tank turret.

BARV, Beach Armoured Recovery Vehicle, a salvage vehicle designed for operation in conditions of surf or amphibious operations.

BALL MOUNT, a spherical machinegun mount in the turret or hull of an armoured vehicle which permits flexible fire in several directions.

BALLISTICS, the science that deals with the behaviour of a projectile, subdivided into interior ballistics (within the GUN), exterior (outside the GUN) and terminal (at the target).

BALLISTIC CAP, a cap on the nose of a projectile that improves its penetration and also increases the BITTING ANGLE.

BARBETTE, a type of SUPER-STRUCTURE, a box-like hull in which the weapons are mounted.

BARREL, the tubular structure of a GUN as distinguished from the breech ring and BREECH MECHANISM.

BASKET (TURRET), a framework which is suspended from the interior of a tank turret to carry the gun crew with the TURRET as it rotates.

BITING ANGLE, the angle beyond which a projectile will ricochet.

BLACKOUT LIGHT, a light for vehicles that is coloured or shaded in such a way that it is not visible except from directly ahead.

BLOWBACK, the simplest system for actuating a low power, small calibre AUTOMATIC GUN. The inertia of the BREECH, the resistance of its operating spring and related moving parts form the basis for keeping the CARTRIDGE CASE seated in the CHAMBER for the short time necessary for safety, but it provides no means for positively locking the BREECH in firing position.

BOGIE, the supporting and converging units of a track-laying vehicle consisting of two arms pivoting on an axle and mounting wheels which ride on and distribute the sprung weight of a vehicle along its track; sometimes corrupted to mean each wheel in a suspension system.

BOOSTER, a sensitive high explosive in a metal container screwed into the ADAPTER and extending into the main explosive charge of the projectile for the purpose of insuring complete DETONATION of the main charge.

BORE, the inside of a CANNON BARREL, TUBE or LINER.

BORE SAFE, a term applied to FUSES which are not armed until the projectile has passed out a safe distance beyond the muzzle of a GUN.

BORE EVACUATOR, a device which utilizes the vacuum produced behind a projectile being fired forcibly to draw out the powder gases from the TUBE of a GUN and to discharge them outside the TURRET.

BOURRELET, the accurately-machined surface about one-sixth calibre width in the rear of the OGIVE of a shell which centres the forward part of the shell in the BORE and provides a guide for the travel of the projectile in the BORE.

BOW, the front end of an armoured vehicle.

BOW VANE, a flat hinged piece on the BOW of an amphibious or SNORKEL equipped vehicle to aid in stability when in the water.

BOW WAVE, the characteristic wave produced by the movement of water past the structure of a ship or an amphibious vehicle BOW.

BREECH, the rear end of a GUN.

BREECH MECHANISM, a mechanical device mounted in a Breech ring and used for closing the rear end of a GUN after loading so that it can be fired. It usually is of the Slotted Screw type, Eccentric or Nordenfelt type, Sliding Wedge type or Drop Block type. If of the SEMI-AUTOMATIC type, the mechanism opens after RECOIL ready to accept the next ROUND.

BURSTER, similar to BOOSTER but used with chemical shells and having just sufficient force to release the chemicals without excessive dispersion.

BUSHING, (RUBBER) an annular cylinder of rubber (like a series of doughnuts) bonded to a metal shaft and inserted in a metal housing which permits the shaft to rotate slightly but to return to its original position, used in the connecting links of tank tracks as contrasted with such tracks using a dry pin type of track.

CALIBRE, a term used to designate the diameter of the BORE of a GUN in inches, millimeters or centimeters and also to indicate the length of the BORE of a CANNON, usually stated as, for example, L/25 or 25 times the diameter of the BORE. This measurement differs by country. In the U.S. it is measured from the inside face of the seated breechblock to the MUZZLE. In Germany, it is measured from the muzzle to the rear face of the BREECH.

CANNELURE, the groove produced in the rotating bands of a shell by the RIFLING of the GUN.

CANISTER, an artillery projectile consisting of small lead or steel balls or flechettes in a light metal container that breaks upon leaving the muzzle to produce a shotgun effect.

CANNON, a TUBE, in U.S. usage, of calibres above .60″ diameter with a recess at the BREECH end called a CHAMBER to seat a projectile and a breech ring containing a BREECH MECHANISM which provides a means of expanding gases and a guide for the projectile propelled thereby. Also see GUN, HOWITZER and MORTAR.

CANT, lateral displacement from a horizontal position.

CARGO CARRIER, a self-propelled vehicle to carry supplies and capable of cross-country operation.

CARTRIDGE, a ROUND of small arms ammunition sometimes incorrectly called a SHELL. Also sometimes applied to complete ROUNDS for CANNON.

CARTRIDGE CASE, the container for the propellant charge in fixed or semi-fixed ammunition, sometimes incorrectly called a SHELL.

CASTER, a swivelled wheel sometimes used with mine exploder devices.

CASE, shortened from CARTRIDGE CASE.

CENTRIFUGAL CAST CANNON, pouring of molten metal into a chill mold which is rotated at high speed so that centrifugal force will cause the metal to take the shape of the mould before solidifying, a process that eliminates the need for forging.

CHAMBER, the part of a CANNON in which the ROUND is placed.

CHAR, the French word for TANK.

CHASE, that part of a CANNON in front of the TRUNNION band or CRADLE.

CHASSIS, the portion of a vehicle that makes it mobile to distinguish it from the portion used for fighting or other purposes.

CHEMICAL AGENT, a substance in the form of GAS, SMOKE or INCENDIARY that produces a toxic effect, a screening smoke or a burning action.

CLINOMETER, an instrument for measuring vertical angle and used in INDIRECT FIRE.

COAXIAL, the mounting of two weapons in the same mount.

COLD WORKED GUN, a process in gun manufacturing of subjecting a TUBE of interior diameter less than the CALIBRE desired to an interior hydraulic pressure in order to enlarge it permanently. The outside diameter is enlarged slightly but returns to the original dimension while the interior remains enlarged.

COLLIMETER, a sighting device for direct fire that comprises a lens and a translucent cross which cannot be seen unless the collimeter axis appears to coincide with the target when viewed over or to the side of the device.

COMBAT CAR, another name for a light TANK.

COMBAT VEHICLE, as distinguished from a transport or soft skin vehicle.

COMPENSATING IDLER, an IDLER wheel adjustable for track tension.

COMPLETE ROUND, consists of a projectile with ROTATING BAND, explosive filler, FUSE, ADAPTER and BOOSTER or BURSTER with a metallic or plastic CARTRIDGE CASE containing a PRIMER and propelling charge or separate PRIMER and cartridge bag.

CONCENTRIC RECOIL SYSTEM, see RECOIL SYSTEM.

CONVERTIBLE, a combat vehicle that can operate on either wheels or TRACKS.

CONTROL ROD, part of the linkage needed for operating brakes, clutch, accelerator, etc.

CORDITE, a DOUBLE BASE propellant powder composed of nitroglycerine, gun cotton and mineral jelly made into paste by the addition of acetone and pressed out like spaghetti or vermicelli.

COUNTER RECOIL MECHANISM, a device for returning a GUN to the firing or 'IN BATTERY' position after completing the RECOIL. The mechanism is usually called a RECUPERATOR.

CRADLE, the non-recoiling part of a GUN MOUNT that permits elevation of the gun about the TRUNNIONS and houses the RECOIL SYSTEM and guides it in recoil.

CUPOLA, a small turret-like protuberance above a HULL or TURRET used for vision or ventilation.

DECK, the floor of an armoured vehicle; sometimes incorrectly applied to the top of the SUPERSTRUCTURE.

DEFLECTION, the algebraic sum of the DEVIATION due to DRIFT, due to the direction and force component of the wind acting on the projectile during flight and the magnitude and direction of lateral JUMP.

DE MARRE COEFFICIENT or Factor K, part of a projectile penetration of armour formula which permits comparison of plates of the same type but of varying thicknesses, using ammunition of the same type. Other things being equal, the penetration of a projectile in armour depends on the striking angle, being greatest at NORMAL IMPACT. Up to an angle of twenty degrees from normal, penetration is but little affected. Beyond an angle of forty-five degrees, RICOCHETS usually result except that the higher the velocity, the better the chance of penetration. The depth of penetration is roughly proportional to the cosine of the angle of impact, measuring from the normal.

DETONATION, the chemical reaction incident to the almost instantaneous decomposition of a high explosive.

DEVIATION, the distance of a point of impact or the centre of impact of a series of shots from the centre of a target.

DIRECT FIRE, firing a weapon when the target is visible.

DISPERSION, the pattern of hits of a group of ROUNDS fired from the same weapon under identical external conditions.

DOUBLE BASE POWDER, a powder containing nitrocellulose and another principal explosive agent; such powders have an objectionable feature in that they cause a brilliant MUZZLE FLASH.

DRIFT, the component part of DEFLECTION not due to wind. Departure of a projectile from the plane of fire due to rotation of the projectile and resistance of the air; to the right or left depending on whether RIFLING is right or left handed.

ELEVATING MECHANISM, a mechanical device located between the tipping part and the fixed part of a GUN MOUNT which permits the rotation of the GUN on its TRUNNIONS in a vertical plane.

END CONNECTOR, a strip which connects and retains the ends of two adjacent TRACK PINS.

ENGRAVING, the groove produced in a ROTATING BAND or BOURRELET after passage of a projectile through the rifled BORE of a CANNON.

EPISCOPE, a pivoted or ball-mounted PERISCOPE.

EQUILABRATOR, SPRINGS or pneumatic action to permit TRUNNIONS to be placed considerably to the rear of the centre of mass of tipping parts thus equalizing and thereby overcoming muzzle heaviness when elevating the gun and firing at high elevations.

EROSION, BORE, wearing away of the metal ahead of the powder chamber from the high temperatures due to firing, causing eventual inability to rotate the projectile.

EXPLOSIVE D, see AMMONIUM PICRATE.

EXTENDED END CONNECTOR, an END CONNECTOR with either a transverse extension to provide additional TRACK width or a vertical extension to reduce TRACK throwing.

FACE HARDENED, armour plate, the surface of which has been given greater hardness than the body.

FIRE CONTROL, the procedure of obtaining firing data and applying them to a GUN so that the TRAJECTORY of the projectile will hit the desired target.

FIRING JACK, also called outrigger; an adjustable brace for firing at a halt from certain self-propelled mounts.

FIXED AMMUNITION, complete ROUND loaded into a CANNON as a unit.

FLARE, a pyrotechnic for illuminating terrain at night.

FLAREBACK, ignition of residue

powder or of an ammunition bag from burning powder residue.

FLASH HIDER, or FLASH ELIMINATOR, an attachment to the muzzle of a gun so that its position will not be revealed when firing at night.

FORCING CONE, the short, tapered portion of a gun tube BORE beginning at the origin of the RIFLING which forces the ROTATING BAND of a projectile into the RIFLING.

FRAGMENTATION, the shattering into many irregular pieces of a projectile from the explosion of the bursting charge.

FREE BOARD, in an amphibious vehicle, the height of the HULL remaining above the waterline.

FUSE, DELAY and INSTANTANEOUS, a mechanism attached to a projectile for the purpose of detonating it on impact or a moment thereafter or after a definite time in flight.

GAS OPERATED, a term applied to an AUTOMATIC WEAPON that utilizes a small portion of the powder gases in the BARREL to actuate a piston which, in turn actuates subsequent operation.

GROUSER, a device for increasing the traction of a tank TRACK.

GUN, a term used in connection with artillery, meaning a CANNON of over 25 CALIBRES in length.

GUN MOTOR CARRIAGE, a self-propelled GUN.

GUN MOUNT, the mechanism which supports the tipping parts of a GUN and provides a means of elevating (and in some cases traversing) the CANNON.

HANGFIRE, an abnormal delay between the instant of impact of a firing pin on a PRIMER and the explosion of a propelling charge.

HOLLOW CHARGE, projectiles with shaped or hollow charges are known as HEAT, high explosive, anti-tank. A cavity, copper-lined or with a small metal core acts somewhat as a concave lens by concentrating or focusing the force of explosion against the lining or core to achieve a velocity of some 27,000 ft/sec. The hole produced in target armour decreases in diameter with the depth of penetration and the metal jet itself gradually is reduced in effectiveness. Penetration also is reduced when the projectile is used in a rifled weapon. Therefore the projectile must be spin-stabilized by one means or another to be effective.

HOMOGENEOUS ARMOUR, having the same chemical and physical characteristics throughout.

HOP, the displacement of any mobile GUN CARRIAGE or MOUNT with respect to the ground caused by the shock of firing, after the projectile has left the bore.

HORSEPOWER (HP), a measurement of power, usually further identified as Brake, Indicated or Delivered, there being a drop from the horsepower developed and which can be utilized at the drive SPROCKETS. Ratings differ between English and Metric systems.

HOWITZER, a CANNON of medium length (12 to 20 calibres long) generally mounted so as to be capable of high angle fire. Propelling charges usually are specially designed to permit ZONE FIRE.

HOWITZER MOTOR CARRIAGE, a self-propelled HOWITZER.

HULL, portion of a combat vehicle that houses the crew and operating equipment and the armament if there is no revolving turret.

HYDROPNEUMATIC, a combination of hydraulic RECOIL brake, a COUNTER RECOIL buffer and a pneumatic COUNTER RECOIL MECHANISM.

HYDROSPRING, a combination of hydraulic RECOIL brake, a hydraulic COUNTER RECOIL buffer and a spring COUNTER RECOIL MECHANISM.

IDLER, the undriven guide wheel carrying a tank TRACK, the driven wheel being the SPROCKET.

IN BATTERY, the position of a GUN in its recoil mounting after having completed the cycle of RECOIL and COUNTER RECOIL and again is in a position to fire.

INCENDIARY, a chemical agent that generates sufficient heat to cause the ignition of any combustible substance with which it comes in contact.

INDIRECT FIRE, a means of firing mathematically when a target cannot be seen from the gun position by the use of an aiming stake or a prominent terrain feature· which can be seen by both the gunner and observer.

JACKET, a cylindrical steel forging concentric with and shrunk to the TUBE of a GUN for strength and usually extending from the BREECH to a point beyond the vertical plane of the axis of the trunnions.

JET, see ROD.

JET PUMP, a water pump used instead of SCREWS in an amphibious COMBAT VEHICLE.

JETTISON TANK, a disposable container for fuel which can be released mechanically from the inside of a vehicle.

JUMP, the angle of the displacement through the axis of the GUN moves in any mobile gun carriage or mount with respect to the ground before the projectile has left the bore and which is due to the play of the mating parts.

KIT, individual crew equipment.

KIT, WATERPROOFING, a collection of materials necessary to waterproof a vehicle for deep-water fording.

LVT, Landing Vehicle, Tracked, a light amphibious vehicle propelled in water by the motion of its tracks.

LAND, the raised portion of the RIFLING in a CANNON.

LAYING, the action of pointing a GUN in elevation and traverse without the use of a sight but often used to mean including the use of a sight.

LEAD ANGLE, a distance between the target and point of aim to compensate for the movement of the target after firing.

LEAD AZIDE, a standard detonating explosive, replacing fulminate of mercury as less sensitive to shock.

LEAP, the tendency of an armoured vehicle to continue to move forward after the suspension has stopped.

LIFTING EYE, sometimes called lug, a metal loop welded to a HULL and used for towing or lifting.

LINER, a rifled and chambered lining for a TUBE intended for replacement when eroded without disturbing the RECOIL MOUNT.

LIP, any protrusion on a metal surface but usually a smooth raised portion on the surface of armour intended to divert a projectile from the opening the lip protects.

LOUVER, a slatted opening designed to permit ventilation while deflecting small arms projectiles.

LUNETTE, the ring assembly on a towed GUN or trailer that engages the PINTLE or hook on a PRIME MOVER doing the towing.

MANTLET, an armoured protrusion for protecting the trunnions of the GUN in the TURRET of an armoured vehicle.

MATERIEL, a French word covering the gamut of ordnance.

MIL, a unit of measurement in sighting a GUN and comprising 1/6400 of a circle. In practice, the arc which subtends a MIL at the centre of a circle is equal in length to 1/1000 of the radius.

MINE, an explosive device usually planted in the ground which detonates when a weight is applied. May be anti-personnel (A/P) or anti-tank (A/T).

MOBILITY, the ability of a vehicle to move, usually subdivided into STRATEGIC MOBILITY, the ability to move rapidly over long distance, and TACTICAL MOBILITY, the ability to be agile under conditions of combat.

MONOBLOC, one piece construction of a gun TUBE.

MORTAR, a short weapon of 6 to 15 calibres in length of low velocity fire at high angles. May be smooth BORE or rifled (see RIFLING).

MUDGUARD, a covering over tank

TRACKS.

MUDGUARD KIT, a remote-controlled machine-gun operated by a tank driver and located over a MUDGUARD.

MUZZLE BRAKE, an attachment screwed to the muzzle of a GUN that deflects the expanding powder gases laterally or backward by means of baffles or slots, thus reducing the load on carriage or mount.

MUZZLE FLASH, the observable incandescent gas at the muzzle of a GUN when fired.

OBSCURATION, the reduction in visibility of a target from the gunner's position produced by muzzle blast when firing, due to smoke, dust or snow.

OBTURATION, the sealing of the BREECH of a GUN to prevent the escape of powder gas to the rear.

OGIVE, the front conical or curved portion of a projectile.

PEEP SLOT, an opening in an armour HULL or TURRET that provides limited vision for a crew member.

PERISCOPE, an optical device using mirrors or prisms by means of which a viewer's eyes are below the actual line of sight.

PERSONNEL CARRIER, an automotive vehicle designed to carry infantry.

PETARD, a large explosive charge discharged from a low velocity projector.

PIECE, a term applied to any explosive fired weapon.

PILOT, the first manufactured full-scale model of a combat vehicle.

PINTLE, the hook to engage the LUNETTE of a trailed load. Also a mechanical pivot or stand on which a machine-gun is mounted.

PITCH, the distance between TRACK PINS in referring to a vehicle TRACK. With reference to vehicles as a whole, a bucking movement caused by improper or inadequate springing. When applied to a SPROCKET, it is the distance between corresponding points of adjoining teeth.

POWER TRAIN, the engine and associated gears and drive shafts for delivering motion to the wheels or TRACKS of a vehicle. See TRANSMISSION.

PRIMER, a device fitted to the base of a CARTRIDGE CASE which ignites the powder charge to fire a projectile. May be percussion, friction, electric, ignition or a combination of these.

PRIME MOVER, a vehicle intended to tow heavy loads.

PROTOTYPE, a specimen vehicle built for the purpose of testing a vehicle design.

QUADRANT, GUNNER'S, a device with spirit level and angle measurement used to lay a GUN accurately in indirect fire.

RACE, the track on which a tank

TURRET rotates.

RANGEFINDER, an optical device or laser to measure the distance from GUN to target.

READY ROUND, a ROUND located near the GUN for rapid access.

RECOIL OPERATED, a term applied to an AUTOMATIC GUN in which the GUN barrel recoils to the rear under the pressure of the powder gases. The movement in recoil unlocks the barrel and actuates the related mechanism. The BREECH block is locked positively during firing and remains locked to the barrel and recoils with it until the gas pressure has dropped to safe limits.

RECOIL SYSTEM, the recoil system for a CANNON comprises a recoil brake mechanism for dissipating the energy of recoil; a COUNTER RECOIL mechanism for returning the gun to BATTERY; and a COUNTER RECOIL buffer mechanism for easing the gun into BATTERY with a minimum of shock: the entire system involves the use of an oil filled cylinder, a perforated piston which allows the oil to pass from one side to the other and which by being connected to the gun acts as a recoil brake. Compression of a SPRING on recoil effects COUNTER RECOIL. The COUNTER RECOIL buffer is an additional small oil-filled cylinder and buffer rod which engages near the end of return travel the small orifice which permits oil to be pushed out slowly, increasing resistance in the last few inches to enter BATTERY gently. In a CONCENTRIC RECOIL SYSTEM the recoil brake mechanism, spring and buffer are grouped around one piston.

RECUPERATOR, a RECOIL SYSTEM in which compressed air or nitrogen is used instead of a HELICAL SPRING. Nitrogen is usually used because it prevents corrosion of the interior of the cylinder.

REMOTE CONTROL, a means of firing a weapon or controlling a vehicle or some part of it from elsewhere than the normal control position.

RETICULE, sometimes called graticule. Engraving on an element of the optical system of a gun SIGHT which permits a gunner to estimate range, speed and type of projectile.

RICOCHET, a glancing rebound of a projectile from an impact point.

RIFLING, the spiral grooves in the BORE of a GUN which impart accuracy and stability to the projectile in flight. They may be either right hand or left hand.

RIPPLE FIRE, successive fire by separate CANNON in a unit or the separate TUBES of a rocket projector.

ROAD WHEEL, one of the wheels in contact with the TRACK

which supports a tracked vehicle.

ROCKWELL, a measure of hardness of steel.

ROD, a term applied to a jet of fuel ejected from a flame-thrower.

ROLL, a swinging lateral movement of the HULL of a vehicle moving at an angle of ninety degrees to such movement.

ROTATING BAND, a raised band of soft metal near the base of a projectile for the purpose of being ENGRAVED by the RIFLING in order to impart rotation to the projectile.

ROUND, all the ammunition components necessary to fire a weapon once.

RUNNING GEAR, the suspension of an automotive vehicle.

SALVO FIRE, unit fire by CANNON for the firing of all TUBES of a rocket projector at once.

SCREEN, a fabric enclosure which can be raised around a combat vehicle in order to permit it to be floated.

SCREW, a marine propeller as used on an amphibious vehicle. A shrouded SCREW, is one which is enclosed in an open ended cylinder also called a Kort nozzle; when capable of being used to pivot for steering and with the cylinder split into two parts, it is called a Sheldon jet glow rudder.

SEMI-AUTOMATIC, a GUN which is similar to an AUTOMATIC GUN except that the trigger must be pulled for each round fired.

SEMI-FIXED, complete ROUNDS of ammunition in which provision is made by increments or ZONE charges for adjusting the propelling charge to the ZONE to be fired and which, like FIXED ammunition, are loaded into the CANNON as a unit.

SEPARATE LOADING AMMUNITION, that which requires the loading of a projectile, the propelling charge and the PRIMER, in that order.

SEPARATED AMMUNITION, similar to SEMI-FIXED but the projectile is never assembled to the CASE as with SEMI-FIXED.

SHAPED CHARGE, see HOLLOW CHARGE.

SHELL, a hollow projectile which may contain a high explosive, a chemical, an inert filler or no filler at all.

SHOT, a solid projectile or one which contains only a small bursting charge.

SHRAPNEL, technically a hollow shell containing lead balls and a bursting charge to discharge the ball from the shell which acts as a short shotgun. Popularly applied to fragments from high explosive or mortar shells.

SIGHT, an optical device employed to lay a GUN accurately for firing at a specific target.

SLEIGH, that part of a RECOIL SYSTEM which recoils with a CANNON and guides it in recoil.

SLIP RING, a rotor with wiping

contacts that permits the carrying of electric current from the HULL into the TURRET of a combat vehicle.

SMOKE, a chemical agent which when released from its container spreads through the atmosphere in the form of liquid or solid particles producing an obscuring fog.

SNORKEL (or in German, from which it derives, Schnorkel) comprising a breather pipe which enables a combat vehicle to operate when submerged.

SPALL, a fragment of metal detached on the outside of armour plate and caused by the impact of a projectile. When it occurs on the inside it is called BACK SPALL.

SPLASH RAIL, see LIP.

SPONSON, a projection mounting a weapon and located on a combat vehicle HULL.

SPRING, the mechanical cushioning device used in the SUSPENSION of a vehicle. Among these are:
  BEVELLING WASHER, also called disc spring, a series of dished discs which act in combined bending and direct stress and which is used in compression.
  CONE SPRING, one form of HELICAL SPRING wound on a tapered mandrel and used in compression.
  DOUBLE CONE SPRING, one which comprises two similar CONE SPRINGS joined at the small ends. Used in compression.
  ELLIPTICAL SPRING, a LEAF SPRING either full or semi (half).
  LEAF SPRING, a SPRING made of flat or slightly curved plates or leaves of regularly varying length superimposed on one another. Used in compression.
  HELICAL SPRING, also called coil spring. A bar or wire coiled in the general form of a helix and used in compression, extension or torsion.
  RUBBER TORSION, a suspension system of rubber bonded to steel which permits movement through the deformation of the rubber torsionally under dynamic load.
  RING SPRING, a series of metal or rubber rings of alternately larger and smaller diameters which bear against one another along wedge-shaped or conical forces.
  TORSILASTIC, see RUBBER TORSION.
  TORSION BAR, a bar anchored at one end and attached to an axle supporting a ROAD WHEEL at the other end and acting as a SPRING by the twist produced by the motion of the axle.
  VOLUTE, a conical SPRING made from a flat bar so wound that each coil partially overlaps the next adjacent coil. Used in compression.

SPROCKET, a toothed wheel which engages a TRACK and is driven by the source of power.

SPUD, see GROUSER.

SQUAT, the inertial tendency of the HULL of a track-laying vehicle to remain stationary as the chassis begins a forward movement.

STEERING, a means of interrupting the transmission of power between engine and TRACK so that by slowing or stopping one TRACK or the other, the vehicle is made to change direction. This is done by means of clutch-brake where one TRACK is stopped completely; geared when disengaging one clutch engages another having a different speed ratio; differential, which has a brake for each TRACK and used an automobile-type differential; and the controlled differential, which permits one TRACK to be braked while the other is speeded up while power continues to both TRACKS. This last sometimes is called the Cletrac, an abbreviation of the Cleveland Tractor Company which patented the device.
Steering of a track-laying vehicle in modern practice has become combined mechanically with the TRANSMISSION.

STRATEGIC MOBILITY, the characteristic of MATERIEL which permits it to be moved great distances in a short period of time as opposed to TACTICAL MOBILITY.

SUPERSTRUCTURE, the upper portion of a combat vehicle HULL.

SUPPORT ROLLER, also called Return Roller and Jockey Wheel. An upper track roller to support and guide a tank TRACK to the SPROCKET and IDLER.

SUSPENSION, a device for supporting a vehicle by means of WHEELS or by TRACKS which, in turn, support ROLLERS. A suspension may be rigid (without SPRINGS), link in which the BOGIES are interconnected and without SPRINGS. Compensating, in which the motion from one BOGIE is compensated by a counter motion through springing with the adjoining BOGIE or by a countermotion transmitted to a BOGIE on the opposite side. Spring, the general system of absorbing road shocks by SPRING action.

SWAY, the tendency of the HULL of a vehicle to continue to move in the original direction as the TRACKS begin to make a turn.

TACTICAL MOBILITY, the characteristic of MATERIEL to be moved about quickly on the battlefield.

TAKEOFF, POWER, a stub axle from the main TRANSMISSION which can be used for power purposes other than moving the vehicle.

TANK, an armoured vehicle designed to advance against an enemy while protected from enemy fire.

TETRYL, a highly explosive coal tar derivative compound used as a BOOSTER charge.

THERMITE (THERMIT), an incendiary agent composed of aluminium flakes and powdered iron or chrome oxide. When ignited the aluminium combines violently with the oxide, producing an intense heat which melts the container and releases its molten contents.

TNT, trinitrotoluene, also called Trition, Trotyp, Trinol, Tritolo, a high explosive relatively insensitive to blows or friction, when ignited by flame it burns without exploding.

TORQUE, a twisting motion. As applied to an internal combustion engine, the persistence of twist of the crankshaft as differentiated from HORSEPOWER.

TOWING SHACKLE, a bolted U-pin welded to a vehicle HULL and used when required to fasten a cable in order to tow a vehicle.

TRACK, the element that supports a track-laying vehicle which is guided by the IDLER, SPROCKET, TRACK SUPPORT ROLLERS and which carries lugs on its inner face which are called guides. Depending on whether the guides are single or double, the TRACK is a double-guide or a single-guide respectively.

TRACK ASSEMBLY, the components of a TRACK which may include TRACK PINS, detachable rubber blocks or pads, END CONNECTORS, etc.

TRACK CENTRE, the median line of a TANK TRACK. Vehicle width sometimes is expressed in the distance between right and left TRACK CENTRES.

TRACK FRAME, the complete assembly of TRACKS, BOGIES and rollers on one side of a track-laying vehicle.

TRACK PAD, a detachable rubber block used to protect commercial highways from being chewed up by tank tracks which skid when making turns in steering.

TRACK PIN, the element connecting link between track plates. It may be 'dry' or a simple pin or it may be 'sealed' involving rubber washers, or 'floating' involving rubber rings. See also BUSHING (RUBBER).

TRAIL SPADE, a plate with sharpened point and angled to the rear to penetrate the earth as a brace for a field gun, a large SELF-PROPELLED GUN or an ARV.

TRAJECTORY, the curve in space traced by the centre of gravity through the air of the fired projectile.

TRANSMISSION, a mechanical system for changing speed or power ratio between an engine and the DRIVE SPROCKETS. It involves a system of gears which can be shifted to provide differing ratios is order to utilize engine power efficiency. A Gear Box type shifts manually. An automatic transmission shifts by means of inertial or hydraulic action. A torque converter comprises a multi-step oil turbine with a fluid coupling which is capable of exerting TORQUE when needed. The Torqmatic type combines an automatic transmission with a torque converter which provides torque multiplication in the several speed ranges of the automatic transmission. A Cross Drive is a form of this last which combines with a controlled differential which speeds up one track as the other is slowed and which adjusts itself to speed and load. Related are the double differential and triple differential types.

TRILITE, a high explosive of Trinitrophenol and Dinitrophenol.

TRIM, in an amphibious vehicle, its position when in water.

TRIMVANE, see BOW VANE.

TUBE, the BARREL of a GUN or a rocket projector.

TURRET, a revolving armour assembly mounting the main armament.

TURRET RACE, the ring with bearings on which the TURRET RING rests and is rotated.

TURRET RING, the toothed ring fastened to the TURRET intermediate between the TURRET and the RACE by means of which the TURRET is rotated.

VESICANT, a chemical agent which can cause inflamation, burns and tissue destruction internally and externally.

VISION SLOT or SLIT, an opening in HULL or TURRET through which a crew member may have a limited view of the outside terrain.

WHEEL-CUM-TRACK, a combat vehicle equipped with both wheels and TRACKS and mechanically capable of changing from one to the other.

WINDSCREEN, a steel or aluminium cap placed on the nose of a projectile to reduce head resistance when in flight.

YAW, in simple terms, the angle of a projectile in its TRAJECTORY as compared with a direct line from gun to target.

ZONE, the area in which MORTAR or HOWITZER projectiles will fall when a particular size of powder charge is used and the elevation of the piece is varied from minimum to maximum.

Index